International Series in Pure and Applied Mathematics
William Ted Martin, *Consulting Editor*

LOGIC FOR MATHEMATICIANS

International Series in Pure and Applied Mathematics

William Ted Martin, *Consulting Editor*

Ahlfors · Complex Analysis

Golomb & Shanks · Elements of Ordinary Differential Equations

Lass · Vector and Tensor Analysis

Leighton · An Introduction to the Theory of Differential Equations

Nehari · Conformal Mapping

Rosser · Logic for Mathematicians

Sneddon · Fourier Transforms

Stoll · Linear Algebra

Weinstock · Calculus of Variations

LOGIC FOR MATHEMATICIANS

J. Barkley Rosser
Professor of Mathematics
Cornell University

New York Toronto London
McGRAW-HILL BOOK COMPANY, INC.
1953

LOGIC FOR MATHEMATICIANS

Library of Congress Catalog Card Number: 51-12640

To Annetta

PREFACE

The present text is just what its title claims, namely, a text on logic written for the mathematician. The text starts from first principles, not presupposing any previous specific knowledge of formal logic, and tries to cover thoroughly all logical questions which are of interest to a practicing mathematician.

We use symbolic logic in the present text, because we do not know how otherwise to attain the desired precision. Any reader of the text must perforce become a competent operator in symbolic logic. However, for us this is only a means to an end, and not an end in itself. Indeed, to mitigate the difficulties of learning and operating the symbolic logic, we have introduced some novelties. These may be of interest to students of logic, but introduction of logical novelties is not any part of the aim of this text. We seek to convey to mathematicians a precise knowledge of the logical principles which they use in their daily mathematics, and to do so as quickly as possible. In this respect, we feel that the present text is unique.

Modern logic has become a large and diversified field of study, with many well-developed branches. Many of these branches have little value to the mathematician as a tool for mathematical reasoning. A text on such a branch of logic, however excellent, would be of little interest to a reader who is primarily a mathematician. Contrariwise, certain topics of great value as tools for mathematical reasoning have little interest for students of logic, and are almost never treated in books on logic. Thus it happens that among the many books on logic, none is completely suitable for the mathematician.

One of the most suitable is the epoch-making "Principia Mathematica" of Whitehead and Russell. The subject matter in "Principia Mathematica" was admirably chosen for the needs of mathematicians, and we have followed this text closely with regard to subject matter. We have omitted a few topics which seem to be little used nowadays, and instead have included treatments of such new developments as Zorn's lemma. We have improved on the symbolic machinery of "Principia Mathematica," which is out of date and extremely unwieldy. By using techniques invented since its writing, we have succeeded in condensing most of "Principia Mathematica's" three large volumes into the present text.

Since familiar logical principles often look very strange in the garb of symbolic logic, we have included a large number of pertinent examples of ordinary mathematical reasoning handled by symbolic means. This should help the reader to apply the principles of this text to his own problems in mathematical reasoning.

Although the present text is complete and does not presuppose any previous acquaintance with logic, it is written for the mathematician with some maturity. For one thing, the illustrative examples are chosen from a variety of fields of mathematics, and their point will be lost on the mathematically immature.

By including numerous exercises, we have tried to make this text suitable for classroom instruction, and have used it this way ourselves. With a teacher to help, less maturity is needed on the part of the reader than if he is reading it alone. However, even with a teacher to help, it is recommended that the student should have had some mathematics beyond the calculus, preferably a course in which some attention was paid to careful mathematical reasoning. Let us recall that this text attempts to treat all logical principles which are useful in modern mathematics, and unless the reader has some acquaintance with the mathematical fields in which the principles are to be used, he will find a study of the principles alone rather sterile. It is in the hope of counteracting such sterility that we have included so many illustrations of reasoning from standard mathematical texts.

We are vastly indebted to the many logicians with whom we have been associated in the past twenty years as well as to the many others whose writings we have read. This debt is only partially indicated by the titles in our bibliography. Almost equally important for the present text have been the many suggestions from mathematicians who are not primarily logicians, but who have been kind enough to tell us of logical questions which they would like to see answered. We hope that they will find them answered in the present text.

Those theorems, or parts of theorems, or corollaries, which are referred to at least five times in later sections are marked with a ★. Those of particular importance are marked with a ★★.

At the end of the present text there is a bibliography arranged alphabetically according to the names of the authors. References to items having a single author are made by giving the author's name and the date of the item, as "Hardy, 1947." In the one case where this is ambiguous, we use "Zermelo, 1908, first paper" and "Zermelo, 1908, second paper." References to items having two authors are made by giving the names of the authors, as "Hardy and Wright."

J. BARKLEY ROSSER

ITHACA, N.Y.
September, 1952

CONTENTS

GLOSSARY OF SPECIAL LOGICAL SYMBOLS

We list here only symbols peculiar to logic. The number opposite each symbol is the page on which it is defined or explained. Standard mathematical symbols are not listed except insofar as they are defined in terms of logical symbols.

$\alpha \bigwedge \beta$	356
$\mathrm{Nc}(\alpha)$	371
NC	372
$\leq_c$	375
$\geq_c$	375
$<_c$	375
$>_c$	375
$m \leq n \leq p$	375
$m \leq n < p$	375
$m = n < p$	375
$\times_c$	378
$\bigwedge_c$	381
n^m	381
Fin	417
Infin	417
$m - n$	426
$Q(m \div n)$	426
$R(m \div n)$	426
$\sum_{x=m}^{n} f(x)$	426
$n!$	427
$\binom{n}{m}$	427
Den	430
Count	430
$\aleph_0$	430
PI	444
NTBX	444
c	444
$\aleph$	444
$P\ \mathrm{smor}_R\ Q$	456
smor	456
$+_s$	458
$\times_s$	459
sr	461
$p(x,P)$	462
$\mathrm{No}(P)$	470
NO	470
$<_0$	471
$>_0$	471
$\leq_0$	471
$\geq_0$	471
0_0	475
1_0	475
$+_0$	475
$\times_0$	475
ω	477
$\mathrm{Card}(\phi)$	477
Ω	479
ω_0	479
ω_1	479
$\aleph_1$	479
ω_2	481
$\mathrm{stCan}(\alpha)$	486
ND	493
$\mathrm{AxC}(n)$	493
AxC	493
$\mathrm{Ub}(\beta,R)$	493
$\mathrm{Sup}(\beta,R)$	493
$\mathrm{Max}(\beta,R)$	493
$Z_1(n)$	493
Z_1	493
$Z_2(n)$	494
Z_2	494
$Z_3(n)$	494
Z_3	494
$Z_4(n)$	494
Z_4	494
FC	494
$Z_5(n)$	494
Z_5	494
$Z_6(n)$	495
Z_6	495
$Z_7(n)$	495
Z_7	495
$Z_8(n)$	509
$Z_9(n)$	509
$\gimel$	519

CHAPTER I

WHAT IS SYMBOLIC LOGIC?

1. A Hypothetical Interview. We wish to record an imaginary interview between a modern mathematician and one of past times. Our mathematician of the past will be Descartes, but we should like to leave our modern mathematician anonymous; in the classic tradition of mathematics, we shall refer to him as Professor X. We imagine Professor X equipped with a time-traveling machine, so that he can go back to chosen points in time and interview various famous mathematicians of the past. Professor X elects to go back to a time just after the invention of coordinate geometry by Descartes and to have an interview with Descartes about his new invention. Professor X takes with him a gift of several reams of coordinate paper, together with a supply of mechanical pencils and erasers, which so impress Descartes that he is very cordial. They discourse on many matters, of which we shall record only their discussion of continuous curves.

They define a curve as continuous if it can be drawn without lifting the pencil from the paper. Descartes, fascinated with his pencils and paper, draws a large number of curves and classifies them into continuous and discontinuous. Fortified with his knowledge of early twentieth century mathematics, Professor X is able to suggest many interesting curves and even manages to trick Descartes at first with some special curves like

$$y = \frac{\sin x}{x},$$

which is not defined at $x = 0$ and so has a gap there which makes it discontinuous. However, Descartes, being a clever mathematician, soon catches on to all Professor X's tricks and can quickly and unerringly classify even the most complicated curves as continuous or discontinuous.

Needless to say, Professor X is familiar with the modern precise definition of continuity:

(1) A function f is continuous at $x = a$ if $f(a)$ is defined and unique, and if for each positive ε there is a positive δ such that whenever $|x - a| < \delta$ it follows that $|f(x) - f(a)| < \varepsilon$.

(2) A function f is continuous if it is continuous at $x = a$ for each value of a.

Professor X decides to acquaint Descartes with this definition with the intention of persuading him to adopt it in place of the vague intuitive idea of tracing a curve without lifting the pencil from the paper. He decides further that he cannot argue in favor of his precise ε-δ definition on the basis that it is more useful for deciding whether a curve (or function) is continuous. Already, with his vague definition of continuity, Descartes can decide which curves are continuous and can do so quickly and correctly. As a matter of fact, Professor X realizes that he himself usually decides whether a function is continuous by visualizing if its graph can be drawn with a continuous pencil stroke and only uses the ε-δ definition of continuity to prove the conclusion which he has reached by visualizing the graph. Clearly then, the value of the ε-δ definition lies mainly in proving things about continuity and only slightly in deciding things about continuity. Professor X reflects that the situation is quite analogous to that in early twentieth century mathematical circles where, if one has a difficult mathematical problem, one is apt to proceed quite intuitively, interchanging limits of integration, differentiating under the integral sign, etc., in hopes of guessing an answer. Only after one has guessed an answer, and wishes to verify it beyond doubt, does one bring in the precise definitions, the ε's and δ's, and the other powerful machinery of modern mathematics. For getting answers, it is better to use intuitive arguments, even rather vague ones. For proving answers, only rigid, formal arguments can be trusted.

Professor X thinks of an analogous situation which he can present to Descartes. For the Egyptian originators of geometry, geometric concepts were quite vague. A straight line was a stretched string; parallel lines were wagon tracks; etc. This vagueness did not prevent the Egyptians from discovering many useful geometric theorems but made it quite impossible for them to prove them. However, the Greeks introduced the precise ideas of abstract straight lines, etc., and were thus enabled to devise proofs of geometric theorems. The great increase of geometric knowledge with the Greeks makes it hard to believe that the increased precision was not also of value in discovering geometric theorems as well as proving them.

Actually, Professor X found Descartes very agreeable to his suggestions and quite willing to replace his vague idea of continuity by a precise one. However, Descartes raised one difficulty which Professor X had not foreseen. Descartes put it as follows.

"I have here an important concept which I call continuity. At present my notion of it is rather vague, not sufficiently vague that I cannot decide which curves are continuous, but too vague to permit of careful proofs. You are proposing a precise definition of this same notion. However, since my definition is too vague to be the basis for a careful proof, how are we going to verify that my vague definition and your precise definition are definitions of the same thing?"

If by "verify" Descartes meant "prove," it obviously could not be done, since his definition was too vague for proof. If by "verify" Descartes meant "decide," then it might be done, since his definition was not too vague for purposes of coming to decisions. Actually, Descartes and Professor X did finally decide that the two definitions were equivalent, and they arrived at the decision as follows. Descartes had drawn a large number of curves and classified them into continuous and discontinuous, using his vague definition of continuity. He and Professor X checked through all these curves and classified them into continuous and discontinuous using the ε-δ definition of continuity. Both definitions gave the same classification. As these were all the interesting curves that either of them had been able to think of, the evidence seemed "conclusive" that the two definitions were equivalent.

2. The Role of Symbolic Logic. When Professor X returned to the present, he related these matters to us. We said that we were reminded of the situation with respect to symbolic logic. Professor X suggested that, as he knew nothing about symbolic logic, the connection could hardly be apparent to him, and he asked if we could explain without getting too complicated. We replied as follows.

Suppose Professor X wishes to prove that from assumption A he can deduce conclusion Z. How does he proceed? The most straightforward way is to observe that B is a logical consequence of A, then C is a logical consequence of B, and so on until he comes to Z. For this, it is required not only that Professor X be able to discover the sequence of statements $B, C, \ldots$, but that he be able to decide that each is a logical consequence of the preceding. One thing that symbolic logic does is give a precise definition of when one statement is a logical consequence of another statement. To get the connection with Descartes, we set up an analogy as follows. A step of Professor X's proof (such as deducing B from A, or C from B, etc.) is to correspond to one of Descartes's curves. Deciding whether the step is logically correct or not is to correspond to deciding whether the curve is continuous or not. To continue the analogy, we note that Professor X is quite skillful at deciding when a step is logically correct, just as Descartes was quite skillful at deciding when a curve is continuous. Moreover, Professor X bases his decisions on a rather vague intuitive notion of logical correctness, just as Descartes based his decisions on a rather vague intuitive notion of continuity. Furthermore, the vague intuitive notion of logical correctness is adequate for deciding about the correctness of a logical step, just as the vague intuitive notion of continuity was adequate for deciding about the continuity of a curve. If one wishes to *prove* the correctness of a logical step, a precise definition of logical correctness will be needed, just as a precise definition of continuity was needed before

Descartes could prove a curve to be continuous. Finally, symbolic logic furnishes a precise definition of logical correctness and so is analogous to the ε-δ definition of continuity, which furnishes a precise definition of continuity.

"Why do you think my notion of logical correctness is rather vague and intuitive?" asked Professor X. "I admit that I very seldom justify the logic involved in my proofs, but that doesn't prove that I can't. After all, I took two years of good stiff courses in logic under the chairman of the philosophy department back in '27–'29."

Our reply was that classical logic was quite inadequate for mathematical reasoning, being particularly weak in treating functions, use of infinite classes, and other matters of great importance in mathematics. As a matter of fact, the first treatment of logic adequate for use in modern mathematics was the famous "Principia Mathematica" of Whitehead and Russell (see Whitehead and Russell).

Professor X admitted that his two years of logic had been of very little use in mathematics. He further admitted that he had no notion how to give a precise definition of logical correctness. Nevertheless, he had always been able to tell which proofs were valid and which were not. What would he gain by learning a precise definition of logical correctness?

We countered by referring him back to his interview with Descartes. What would he have said if Descartes had answered in similar fashion that he had been getting along very well with a vague definition of continuity and had no need of a precise definition?

This seemed to satisfy Professor X. However, he had one further question to ask.

"I should like to ask the same question that Descartes asked. You are proposing to give a precise definition of logical correctness which is to be the same as my vague intuitive feeling for logical correctness. How do you intend to show that they are the same?"

This is not merely Professor X's question. It should be the question of every reader of the present text.

Actually, not all mathematicians have exactly the same notion of logical correctness. Mathematics is a living, growing subject, and mathematicians do not all work in the same branch of mathematics. Often mathematicians in one branch of mathematics make constant use of some logical principle which is regarded with distrust by mathematicians in other branches. The axiom of choice, to which we shall devote a chapter of discussion, is such a principle.

However, there is a sort of "common denominator" of notions of logical correctness, and we claim to give a symbolic logic which is a precise definition of logical correctness which agrees with this "common denominator."

Our symbolic logic is accordingly incomplete. In the case of a principle like the axiom of choice, which is in dispute among mathematicians, our symbolic logic deliberately fails to classify it as either correct or incorrect, leaving the individual reader free to make whichever decision pleases him most. However, we do attempt to convince the reader that logical principles which are judged correct by the great majority of mathematicians are classified as correct by our symbolic logic and that principles which are judged incorrect by the great majority of mathematicians are classified as incorrect by our symbolic logic.

Our procedure for doing this has already been foreshadowed in the interview between Descartes and Professor X. Just as they decided to accept the equivalence of the intuitive and precise definitions of continuity because these definitions agreed in a large number of cases, even so a reader might be convinced that our symbolic logic agrees with his intuitive notions of logical correctness if he is shown that they agree in a large number of cases. Accordingly, we shall give a large number and wide variety of illustrations of mathematical reasoning and show how to classify each as correct or incorrect on the basis of our symbolic logic. We have tried to choose our illustrations from well-known sources, so that there would be no doubt about the general opinion of mathematicians as to the correctness or incorrectness of the reasoning in our illustrations. With the general opinion on the correctness agreeing with our symbolic logic in a wide variety of cases, we feel that most readers will be convinced.

For the benefit of any professional skeptics, we admit here and now that certainly no number of illustrations could ever suffice to carry absolute conviction.

The symbolic logic which we present is a modernized version of that presented in the "Principia Mathematica" of Whitehead and Russell. We have altered the form of the system somewhat, using a greatly simplified version of the theory of types due to Quine (see Quine, 1937). Minor details have been adjusted to bring them into line with common mathematical usage. Simplifications and improvements of the proofs have been adopted from numerous sources. We have not attempted to list these sources, since in the present text we are not concerned with the genesis of the logic but with its applications. Persons interested in the connections of this symbolic logic with others may consult such works as Hilbert and Bernays; Church, 1944; Quine, 1951; and Hilbert and Ackermann.

3. General Nature of Symbolic Logic. The aim in constructing our symbolic logic is that it shall serve as a precise criterion for determining whether or not a given instance of mathematical reasoning is correct. The symbolic logic which we shall present is primarily intended to be a tool in mathematical reasoning. Of course, many of the logical principles involved have general application outside of mathematics, but there are many fields of human endeavor in which these principles are of little value. Politics, salesmanship, ethics, and many such fields have little or no use for the sort of logic used in mathematics, and for these our symbolic logic would be quite useless. In engineering and science, particularly those branches of science which make extensive use of mathematics, the symbolic logic might be of considerable value. However, it would be fairly inadequate for the logical needs of even the most mathematical sciences. For one thing, no adequate symbolic treatment of the relationship involving cause and effect has yet been devised. However, if one is satisfied to restrict attention to purely mathematical reasoning, several quite satisfactory symbolic logics are available. We present one such in the present text.

The components of mathematical reasoning are mathematical statements. So, in building a symbolic logic, we must start with a precise definition of what a mathematical statement is. Intuitively, we can say that it is merely a declarative sentence dealing exclusively with mathematical and logical matters. Needless to say, it need not be true. "3 is a prime" and "6 is a prime" are both mathematical statements, the first true, and the second false.

Because all existing languages are full of words with multiple or ambiguous meanings, it was found necessary to construct a complete new language in order to be able to give a precise definition of "mathematical statement." This language is called symbolic logic. In order to aid the reader in learning this new language, we shall introduce him to it gradually over several chapters. Our discussions will be rather general and descriptive at first, becoming more and more exact. Correspondingly our notion of a mathematical statement will at first be merely the vague notion of a declarative sentence but will gradually be sharpened. Finally in Chapter IX we shall have developed our symbolic logic sufficiently to be able to give a precise definition of a mathematical statement.

We shall drop the "mathematical" and henceforth refer to a mathematical statement merely as a "statement."

Once a precise definition of "statement" has been given (see Chapter IX), one can give a precise definition of "valid statement" and of "demonstration." A demonstration shall be a sequence of statements such that each statement is either already known to be valid or is an assumption or is derived from previous statements of the sequence in a specified fashion. The analogy with the usual form of mathematical demonstration is quite intentional. Certain statements, designated as "axioms," are taken to be valid, and then any other statement is called "valid" if it is the final statement in a demonstration that involves no assumptions, that is, that proceeds from axioms alone.

Our definitions of "axiom" and "demonstration" will be carefully and intentionally framed so that they depend only on the forms of the statements involved, and not in the least on the meanings. Thus the decision as to whether a statement is an axiom or whether a sequence of statements is a demonstration depends not on intelligence, but on clerical skill. One could build a machine which would be quite capable of making these decisions correctly. That is, one could build a machine which would check the logical correctness of any given proof of a mathematical theorem. That the check is mechanical does not mean that it requires no intelligence at all. There are many machines of a sufficient complexity that at least a low order of intelligence is required to match their performance. In the present case, the ability to perform simple arithmetical computations is enough to check axioms and demonstrations, as was shown by Gödel (see Gödel, 1931), who put the definitions into an arithmetical form. Thus, a person with simple arithmetical skills can check the proofs of the most difficult mathematical demonstrations, provided that the proofs are first expressed in symbolic logic. This is due to the fact that, in symbolic logic, demonstrations depend only on the forms of statements, and not at all on their meanings.

This does not mean that it is now any easier to discover a proof for a difficult theorem. This still requires the same high order of mathematical talent as before. However, once the proof is discovered, and stated in symbolic logic, it can be checked by a moron.

This complete lack of any reference to the meanings of statements in symbolic logic indicates that there is no need for them to have meanings. This allows us to introduce formulas whenever they are useful without reference to whether they are meaningful. In fact, there is a type of formula about whose meaning (if any) there is great disagreement. It happens to be a useful type of formula, and we use it frequently, not being the least bit inconvenienced by its possible lack of meaning (see Chapter VIII).

This lack of reference to meanings also enables us to evade quite a number of difficult philosophical questions. This situation is quite in line with current mathematical practice. Consider the positive integers, which are at the basis of most of mathematics. Mathematicians do not care in the least what the meanings of the positive integers are, or even if they have meanings. For the mathematician, it suffices to know what operations he is permitted to perform on the positive integers. Once this information is available, any information as to the meanings of the integers is wholly irrelevant for mathematical purposes. The same applies to real numbers, imaginary numbers, functions, or any other of the paraphernalia of mathematics.

The matter was well expressed by Lewis Carroll, long-time mathematical lecturer of Christ Church, who upon being asked to contribute to a philosophical symposium responded:

> "And what mean all these mysteries to me
> Whose life is full of indices and surds?
> $x^2 + 7x + 53$
> $= \frac{11}{3}$."

We shall not make any use of the familiar term "proposition." This is because the word "proposition" refers to the meanings of statements, and we intend to ignore the meanings (if any) of our statements. However, we shall here say a word about propositions and the problems connected with them just to show how useful it is not to have to consider these problems.

A proposition is the meaning of a statement, and one says that the statement expresses the proposition. One difficulty that arises immediately is that of deciding when two different statements express the same proposition. Sometimes it is easy. Thus "three is a prime" and "Drei ist eine Primzahl" certainly express the same proposition. However, what about "Three is a prime" and "Three is greater than unity and is not divisible by any positive integers except itself and unity"? Do they express the same proposition or equivalent propositions?

Any attempt to be precise and pay attention to meanings would involve us with such problems as the above, which are really quite irrelevant for mathematics. For mathematics, it is the form that must be considered, and the meaning can be dispensed with. Our symbolic logic will accord with this doctrine.

Actually, although one carefully builds the symbolic logic so that it can be used without reference to meaning, this does not mean that we can ignore meaning in devising our logic. We recall that our symbolic logic is intended to give a precise definition of an intuitive notion of logical correctness. So the mechanical operations of our symbolic logic, though devoid of meaning, must nevertheless manage to parallel closely the intuitive thought processes based on meaning. Clearly, then, careful attention is paid to meaning and intuitive thought processes in inventing the symbolic logic.

Now that the symbolic logic has been invented, we could present it to the reader merely as a mechanical system, without reference to the motivation which underlies it. Certainly it is intended to be used in this way. Nonetheless, the reader will find it easier to learn, remember, and use the symbolic logic if we explain to him the underlying thought processes. Consequently much of our discussion in the earlier chapters will be quite intuitive in character and not particularly precise. Gradually, as our symbolic logic crystallizes out of the intuitive background, we shall become more precise, though we shall never lose sight of our intuitive background completely even after we have finally completely defined our symbolic logic and are proceeding quite mechanically.

4. Advantages and Disadvantages of a Symbolic Logic. We have already mentioned some advantages of a symbolic logic over a simple intuitive notion of logical correctness, namely, its greater precision and its lack of reference to meanings; because of the lack of reference to meanings, many difficult philosophical problems can be evaded and mechanical checks of proofs are possible.

A symbolic logic is a formal system and as such has the advantage of objectivity which is inherent in any formal system. This can be illustrated by a reference to the origins of geometry. To the Egyptians, a straight line was a stretched string. Now two stretched strings are much alike, but not completely so, and thus one person's idea of a straight line would not coincide exactly with another person's idea. As an extreme instance, one man may be dealing with a fine silk cord, and the second man with a towrope. In this case, their "straight lines" would be quite appreciably different. Then came the Greeks, who replaced the stretched string by an abstract idea of a straight line which was defined by purely formal axioms. From that time on, the straight line has meant the same thing to all who accepted the Greeks' definition. Analogously, by means of symbolic logic we replace a person's intuitive ideas, subjectively conceived and full of personal psychological overtones, by abstract formal ideas which can be the same for all persons.

A symbolic logic uses symbols and so has the advantages arising from the use of symbols, in particular, greater ease in handling complex manipulations. This is so familiar to mathematicians that an instance is probably unnecessary. We cite one anyhow for completeness. Consider the simple problem: "Mary is now three times as old as Jane. In ten years Mary will be twice as old as Jane. How old are Mary and Jane now?" Algebraically this is almost trivial. We take the symbols M and J to stand for the present ages of Mary and Jane, getting

$$M = 3J,$$

$$M + 10 = 2(J + 10).$$

Subtraction gives $J = 10$, whence we get $M = 30$. The point is that, though this is very simple when handled by symbols, it is not particularly easy if one tries to handle it intuitively. Certainly one can get the answer by words alone, but it is so awkward to do so that variants of the above problem are actually given as simple puzzles for those not accustomed to the use of algebraic technique.

It is interesting to note that the algebraic procedure outlined above does not differ greatly from the intuitive procedure that one might use to solve the problem verbally. In other words, use of symbolic manipulations does not necessarily give one any technique for solving the problem which was not already present in the intuitive case; it merely makes the existing techniques more flexible, more effective, and more apparent. This is characteristic of the use of symbols.

When one gives a precise definition of a concept, then there arises the possibility of generalizing or varying the concept by slight alterations in the definition. Thus, as long as the early Egyptians were thinking of parallel lines as wagon tracks, there was no possibility of getting non-Euclidean geometries in which parallel lines behave in quite unfamiliar fashions. However, after the Greeks had defined parallel lines as straight lines which never meet, and Euclid had defined geometry (we call it Euclidean geometry nowadays) by specifying that parallel lines should behave essentially like wagon tracks, then one could generalize to non-Euclidean geometries by specifying other behaviors for parallel lines. Similarly, by going from the simple intuitive concept of continuity to the precise ε-δ definition, one can then introduce many variations of continuity, such as absolute continuity, semicontinuity, and upper and lower semicontinuity.

An analogous situation has already arisen in connection with symbolic logic. There are now several different systems of symbolic logic available which differ in various details. We have chosen that one which seems to us most nearly in accord with the intuitive notion of logical correctness as conceived by most mathematicians.

Thus our choice of a system of symbolic logic is arbitrary. This is a disadvantage in that later study may show our choice to have been a poor one. It is also an advantage in that if we ever become dissatisfied with our choice, we can readily change it.

The main disadvantage of a system of symbolic logic is that it is a formal system divorced from intuition. Intuition arises from experience, and so may be expected to have some foundation in fact. However, a formal system is merely a model devised by human minds to represent some facts perceived intuitively. As such, it is bound to be artificial. In some cases, the artificiality is quite clear. Thus electrical engineers are taught a system for computing currents and voltages in rotating electrical machinery by representing them as complex numbers of the form $a + bi$, $i = \sqrt{-1}$ (see Glasgow, 1936). As there is nothing imaginary about the currents and voltages, this is clearly an artificial representation. Nevertheless, its advantages outweigh its obvious artificiality.

Probably the only time that the artificiality of a formal system does any harm is when the users of the system ignore or overlook the fact that it is artificial. Thus, for two thousand years it was supposed that the physical universe was actually a Euclidean three-dimensional space. This inhibited men's thinking tremendously and was a great misfortune. Nowadays, astronomical measurements have made it seem quite likely that the universe is non-Euclidean. Though this demonstrates the artificiality of Euclidean geometry, nonetheless Euclidean geometry is still extremely useful, as useful in fact as it ever was. Thus artificiality is not a serious disadvantage if one does not lose sight of the artificiality.

From the point of view of the nonmathematician, who finds it difficult to work with symbols, use of symbols is a disadvantage. We intend the present text for mathematicians, to whom the use of symbols is quite congenial, and so make no apology for the use of symbols.

We mentioned the possibility of mechanical checking of proofs as an advantage. It is not wholly an advantage. If a person has little clerical skill, he is liable to make mistakes in his mechanical checking, and so find it of little value. On the other hand, if one relies exclusively on intuition, there is danger of overlooking some detail which appears insignificant but isn't. The truth is that the average person cannot rely exclusively on either intuition or mechanical checking. For the average person, mechanical checking is a valuable adjunct to intuition, but in doing the mechanical checking he must continually refer back to his intuition to catch clerical errors.

We summarize the above points. Although we think that the average mathematician will find that a study of symbolic logic is very helpful in carrying out mathematical reasoning, we do not recommend that he should completely abandon his intuitive methods of reasoning for exclusively formal methods. Rather, he should consider the formal methods as a supplement to his intuitive methods to provide mechanical checks of critical points, and to provide the assistance of symbolic operations in complex situations, and to increase his precision and generality. He should not forget that his intuition is the final authority, so that, in case of an irreconcilable conflict between his intuition and some system of symbolic logic, he should abandon the symbolic logic. He can try other systems of symbolic logic, and perhaps find one more to his liking, but it would be difficult to change his intuition.

CHAPTER II

THE STATEMENT CALCULUS

1. Statement Functions. As indicated in the previous chapter, we shall not proceed at once to a precise definition of a statement. We have told the reader that essentially a statement is a declarative sentence (not necessarily true) which deals exclusively with mathematical and logical matters. We shall gradually make this idea precise, but in the present chapter we shall confine our attention to certain of the very simplest ways of building statements, by use of the so-called "statement functions."

We derive all the statement functions from two basic ones, "&" and "$\sim$". Consider two statements, "P" and "Q", of symbolic logic which are translations of the English sentences "A" and "B". Then "$(P\&Q)$" is the statement which is a translation of "A and B" and "$\sim P$" is the statement which is a translation of the negation of the sentence "A". If "A" happens to be a simple sentence, the negation would most usually be formed by inserting a "not" into "A" at the grammatically proper place. Thus "&" is the translation of "and", and, allowing for the difference of sentence structure, "$\sim$" is the translation of "not". Hence we usually refer to "&" and "$\sim$" as "and" and "not", and usually read "$(P\&Q)$" and "$\sim P$" as "P and Q" and "not P", respectively. However, when we wish to be very careful we refer to "&" and "$\sim$" by their correct names "ampersand" and "curl" or "twiddle".

To illustrate, let "P" and "Q" be translations of "It is raining now" and "It is not cloudy now". Then "$(P\&Q)$" is a translation of "It is raining now and it is not cloudy now", and "$\sim P$" and "$\sim Q$" are translations of "It is not raining now" and "It is cloudy now". Finally "$\sim(P\&Q)$" is a translation of "Either it is not raining now or else it is cloudy now or else it is both cloudy and not raining now" or of "It is not now both raining and not cloudy" or of some such negation of "It is raining now and it is not cloudy now".

"$(P\&Q)$" has properties analogous to the product of two numbers in arithmetic or algebra. For this reason, it is called the logical product of "P" and "Q", which are called the factors, and is often written "$(P.Q)$" or simply "(PQ)". Also, one omits the parentheses whenever possible without ambiguity, so that it may also be written "$P\&Q$", "$P.Q$", or "PQ". To diminish the number of possible cases of ambiguity, we agree that whenever a "$\sim$" occurs it shall affect as little as possible of what follows it. This is expressed as follows.

Convention. Any given occurrence of "$\sim$" shall have as small a scope as possible.

As an illustration, consider "$\sim PQ$" (or either of the alternative forms "$\sim P.Q$" or "$\sim P\&Q$"). According to our convention, the "$\sim$" affects "P" but not "Q", and so we understand "$\sim PQ$" to mean "$(\sim P)Q$" (or "$(\sim P).Q$" or "$(\sim P)\&Q$"). Without our convention, there would be the possibility that "$\sim PQ$" might mean "$\sim(PQ)$".

The expression "$P\sim Q$" is unambiguous even without our convention, since it clearly can mean nothing but "$P\&(\sim Q)$".

By means of "&" and "$\sim$", we can translate many other English conjunctions besides "and" into symbolic logic. As before, let "P" and "Q" be statements of symbolic logic which are translations of the English sentences "A" and "B", and let us seek to find a translation for "Either A or B". First we should agree whether we interpret "Either A or B" in the exclusive sense of "Either A or B but not both" or in the inclusive sense of "Either A or B or both". According to each of the four best unabridged dictionaries, the exclusive use is the only correct use, and the inclusive use has no justification at all in correct English. Nonetheless, in mathematics the inclusive form of "or" is very commonly used, and in everyday language, it is often not clear which is intended. In legal documents one commonly finds the inclusive "or" expressed as "A and/or B".

In some languages, there are different words for the exclusive and inclusive "or". Thus in Latin, the word "aut" denotes an exclusive "or" so that "aut" means "or—but not both", whereas "vel" denotes an inclusive "or" so that "vel" means "and/or". We shall translate both the exclusive "or" and the inclusive "or" into symbolic logic.

We take first the inclusive "or". We are seeking the interpretation of "A and/or B" or the equivalent "Either A or B or both". This statement is equivalent to denying that "A" and "B" are simultaneously false, and we use this fact to carry out the translation. That "A" is false would be translated as "$\sim P$", and that "B" is false would be translated as "$\sim Q$". That both are false would be translated as "$(\sim P)\&(\sim Q)$", which we can simplify unambiguously to "$\sim P\sim Q$". The denial of this is then translated as "$\sim(\sim P\sim Q)$". So we conclude that the translation of "Either A or B or both" is "$\sim(\sim P\sim Q)$".

To translate "Either A or B but not both", it suffices to adjoin the additional statement "not both", which certainly would be translated "$\sim(PQ)$". So the translation of "Either A or B but not both" is "$(\sim(\sim P\sim Q))\&(\sim(PQ))$", which we can simplify unambiguously to "$\sim(\sim P\sim Q)\&\sim(PQ)$" or "$\sim(\sim P\sim Q)\sim(PQ)$".

Although the exclusive "or" is the grammatically correct one, being sanctioned by the leading unabridged dictionaries, nevertheless, the inclusive "or" is much more commonly used in mathematics. In fact, it is used so often that it becomes burdensome to write the three "$\sim$'s" and the two parentheses involved in "$\sim(\sim P \sim Q)$", so that we adopt a shorthand, and commonly write "$(P \vee Q)$" in place of "$\sim(\sim P \sim Q)$". Whenever no ambiguity will result, we simplify "$(P \vee Q)$" to "$P \vee Q$".

One can think of the "$\vee$" of "$P \vee Q$" as denoting the Latin word "vel". We shall commonly read "$\vee$" as "or".

Strictly speaking, the notation "$P \vee Q$" is not part of symbolic logic, and if one were being really careful one would always write "$\sim(\sim P \sim Q)$". However, it is very handy to write "$P \vee Q$" instead, and to agree that whenever "$P \vee Q$" appears it is really "$\sim(\sim P \sim Q)$" which occurs. Similar considerations apply to our omission of parentheses. Strictly speaking, it is not permissible to omit parentheses, and we omit them only with the understanding that in any precise formulation they would actually be present.

To put it another way, omission of parentheses and replacement of "$\sim(\sim P \& \sim Q)$" by "$P \vee Q$" are not part of our symbolic logic, but only a convenience which we permit ourselves in talking about it.

Our convention about the scope of "$\sim$" requires that "$\sim P \vee Q$" should mean "$(\sim P) \vee Q$" rather than "$\sim(P \vee Q)$". To remove the ambiguity in "$PQ \vee R$" and "$P \vee QR$", we make use of an algebraic analogy. For this, we call "$P \vee Q$" the logical sum of "P" and "Q", which are called the summands. Then the algebraic formula analogous to "$PQ \vee R$" would be "$xy + z$", since "PQ" is the logical product of "P" and "Q". As we always interpret "$xy + z$" to mean "$(xy) + z$" and never "$x(y + z)$", we shall correspondingly interpret "$PQ \vee R$" as "$(PQ) \vee R$" rather than "$P(Q \vee R)$". By the algebraic analogy, we likewise interpret "$P \vee QR$" as "$P \vee (QR)$".

Another compound sentence which occurs in mathematical reasoning with great frequency is "If A, then B." Many variants are in common use, the most common of which are:

"B is a necessary condition for A."

"A is a sufficient condition for B."

"B if A."

"A only if B."

"A implies B."

Some logicians insist that the terminology "A implies B" be reserved for quite a different purpose. This is not standard mathematical practice, and we follow the mathematical practice which takes "A implies B" and "If A, then B" as interchangeable.

We seek a translation for "If A, then B." We note that, whenever "If A, then B" is valid, then we cannot have both "A" true and "B" false. Conversely, whenever we cannot have both "A" true and "B" false, we can surely conclude that "If A, then B" (since if not "B", then we would have "A" true and "B" false). So we can translate "If A, then B" by translating "We cannot have both 'A' true and 'B' false." Clearly we translate ". . . both 'A' true and 'B' false" by "$P{\sim}Q$". So we translate "We cannot have both 'A' true and 'B' false" by "${\sim}(P{\sim}Q)$".

Conclusion. We translate "If A, then B" into "${\sim}(P{\sim}Q)$".

The shorthand for this is "$(P \supset Q)$" or "$P \supset Q$". We read this as "P implies Q". We refer to the statement "$P \supset Q$" as an implication, or conditional, and "P" as the hypothesis and "Q" as the conclusion.

There is no very good analogue for "$P \supset Q$" in algebra. Perhaps the best is "$x \geq y$". Poor though this analogy is, we use "$xy \geq z$" and "$x + y \geq z$" as an analogy for interpreting "$PQ \supset R$" and "$P\mathbf{v}Q \supset R$" as "$(PQ) \supset R$" and "$(P\mathbf{v}Q) \supset R$", respectively. Similarly for "$P \supset QR$" and "$P \supset Q\mathbf{v}R$".

Still another compound sentence of frequent occurrence is "A if and only if B," or its variant "A is a necessary and sufficient condition for B." Obviously this is to be translated as "$(P \supset Q)(Q \supset P)$".

The shorthand for this is "$(P \equiv Q)$" or "$P \equiv Q$". We read this as "P is equivalent to Q" or just "P equivalent Q". We refer to the statement "$P \equiv Q$" as an equivalence, or biconditional, and "P" as the left side and "Q" as the right side.

This may be likened to "$x = y$" in algebra. Accordingly, by analogy with "$xy = z$" and "$x + y = z$", we interpret "$PQ \equiv R$" and "$P\mathbf{v}Q \equiv R$" as "$(PQ) \equiv R$" and "$(P\mathbf{v}Q) \equiv R$", respectively. Similarly for "$P \equiv QR$" and "$P \equiv Q\mathbf{v}R$".

In algebra, "$(xy)z$", "$x(yz)$", and "xyz" all refer to the product of the three numbers "x", "y", and "z", and it is not usual to make any distinction between them. In deriving algebra from a set of axioms, it is sometimes necessary to pretend that there might be a distinction between "$(xy)z$" and "$x(yz)$", but this is done only for the purpose of allowing one to state and prove the theorem that no distinction need be made. The situation is quite analogous with the logical product. It is usually permissible to interpret "PQR" as either "$(PQ)R$" or "$P(QR)$" without prejudice. In the few cases where it is not, it is the custom to "associate to the left." That is, "PQR" is considered to be "$(PQ)R$", "$PQRS$" is considered to be "$((PQ)R)S$", etc.

In dealing with sums, whether algebraic or logical, exactly the same situation occurs. In algebra, we seldom need to distinguish between "$(x + y) + z$", "$x + (y + z)$", and "$x + y + z$". In logic, we seldom need to distinguish which of "$(P\mathbf{v}Q)\mathbf{v}R$" and "$P\mathbf{v}(Q\mathbf{v}R)$" is meant by "$P\mathbf{v}Q\mathbf{v}R$", and when we do, we associate to the left, interpreting "$P\mathbf{v}Q\mathbf{v}R$" as "$(P\mathbf{v}Q)\mathbf{v}R$".

When we come to such statements as "$P \supset Q \supset R$" the algebraic analogy conflicts with the rule of association to the left. In algebra "$x \geq y \geq z$" means "$x \geq y$ and $y \geq z$", so that we should expect to interpret "$P \supset Q \supset R$" as "$(P \supset Q)\&(Q \supset R)$". On the other hand, association to the left would give "$(P \supset Q) \supset R$", which is quite a different statement. Under the circumstances it might be just as well to consider "$P \supset Q \supset R$" as ambiguous, and to write explicitly whichever of "$(P \supset Q) \supset R$", "$P \supset (Q \supset R)$", or "$(P \supset Q)\&(Q \supset R)$" is intended.

In the case of "$P \equiv Q \equiv R$", the algebraic analogy again conflicts with the rule of association to the left. However, association to the left yields "$(P \equiv Q) \equiv R$", which is of limited usefulness, whereas, since "$x = y = z$" means "$x = y$ and $y = z$", the algebraic analogy yields "$(P \equiv Q)\&(Q \equiv R)$", which is quite useful. Accordingly, in this case we follow the algebraic analogy and interpret "$P \equiv Q \equiv R$" as "$(P \equiv Q)\&(Q \equiv R)$", "$P \equiv Q \equiv R \equiv S$" as "$(P \equiv Q)\&(Q \equiv R)\&(R \equiv S)$", etc.

The forms which might be shortened to "$P \supset Q \equiv R$" or "$P \equiv Q \supset R$" are of infrequent occurrence, so that it is not worth while to decide on an interpretation for "$P \supset Q \equiv R$" or "$P \equiv Q \supset R$". Instead, we must leave in enough parentheses to resolve any ambiguity.

The rule about the scope of "$\sim$" covers any interpretations involving "$\sim$".

One can define many other connectives, but the ones we have listed appear to be the ones which occur with sufficient frequency to make a special notation for them worth while.

The form "$\sim P$" defines a statement function or function of the statement variable "P" in the sense that, if one puts a statement in for "P", one gets another statement "$\sim P$". This is quite analogous to the way in which one defines a function of a real number. Thus "$-x$" defines a function of the real number "x" in the sense that, if one puts a real number in for "x", one gets another real number "$-x$". Likewise "PP" defines another statement function, which can be considered the analogue of the real function defined by "x^2".

One can also have statement functions of more than one variable. Thus "PQ" and "$P \vee QR$" define statement functions of two and three variables which are respectively analogous to the real functions defined by "xy" and "$x + yz$".

We should warn the reader of one place where "if" means "if and only if" and should be translated as "$\equiv$". This is in definitions. Thus on page 18 of Fort, 1930, we find:[1]

"*Definition* 9. The infinite series, $a_0, a_1, a_2, \ldots$, is said to converge if s_n approaches a limit when n becomes infinite."

[1] From "Infinite Series" by Tomlinson Fort, copyright 1930 by Clarendon Press, courtesy of Oxford University Press.

Here it is certain that Fort intends for "if" to be interpreted as "if and only if." However, in using "if" in this sense, Fort is only following standard usage, which decrees that an "if" used in this fashion in a definition invariably means "if and only if."

Occasionally, one finds a less ambiguous wording in a definition. Thus, Fort on page 19 states:[1]

"*Definition* 11. $\sum_{n=-\infty}^{\infty} a_n$ is said to converge when and only when $\sum_{n=0}^{\infty} a_n$ and $\sum_{n=-1}^{-\infty} a_n$ both converge . . . ."

However, in a large majority of cases, one will merely find "if" used in the sense of "if and only if" in definitions, and should translate such definitions into symbolic logic by use of "$\equiv$".

EXERCISES

II.1.1. Write two short essays (not more than five sentences apiece) concerning the use of "and" and "but" as conjunctions between complete statements, telling:

(a) The logical difference between "and" and "but".
(b) The psychological difference between "and" and "but".

II.1.2. If "P" and "Q" are translations for "$x^2 > 0$" and "$x > 0$", write a translation for "$x^2 > 0$ whenever $x > 0$".

II.1.3. If "P", "Q", and "R" are translations for "$x = y$", "$x/z = y/z$", and "$z = 0$", write a translation for "If $x = y$, then $x/z = y/z$ except when $z = 0$".

II.1.4. If "P" and "Q" are translations for "$(n - 1)! + 1$ is divisible by n" and "n is a prime", write a translation for "$(n - 1)! + 1$ is not divisible by n unless n is a prime".

II.1.5. Show that "$\sim(P \equiv Q)$" is the same statement as "$P{\sim}Q \vee Q{\sim}P$".

II.1.6. If "P" and "Q" are known to be true, what can one say about "PQ"? If "PQ" is known to be true, what can one say about "P" and "Q"? If "$P \supset Q$" and "$Q \supset P$" are known to be true, what can one say about "$P \equiv Q$"?

II.1.7. If "P" is known to be true, what can one say about "$\sim\sim P$"?

II.1.8. On the basis that "$R{\sim}R$" is a contradiction, show that "${\sim}P{\sim}Q(P \vee Q)$" and "$P{\sim}Q(P \supset Q)$" are contradictions.

II.1.9. If we are told that "$R \supset \sim\sim R$" is true for every statement "R", what can we infer about "${\sim}P{\sim}Q \supset \sim(P \vee Q)$", "$P{\sim}Q \supset \sim(P \supset Q)$", and "$(P \equiv Q) \supset \sim(P{\sim}Q \vee Q{\sim}P)$"?

II.1.10. Show that "${\sim}P \vee P$" is the same statement as "$\sim\sim P \supset P$".

II.1.11. If "P", "Q", "R", and "S" are translations for "p is a prime", "n is an integer which divides p", "$n = 1$", and "$n = p$", write a translation

[1] *Ibid.*

for "A necessary condition for p to be a prime is that, if n is an integer which divides p, then $n = 1$ or $n = p$".

II.1.12. If "P" and "Q" are translations of "C is on the perpendicular bisector of the line joining A and B" and "C is equidistant from A and B", write a translation of "C is equidistant from A and B if and only if it is on the perpendicular bisector of the line joining them".

II.1.13. If "P", "Q", and "R" are translations of "$a \leq b + c$", "$c > 0$", and "$a \leq b$", write a translation of "If $a \leq b + c$ whenever $c > 0$, then $a \leq b$".

II.1.14. If "P" and "Q" are translations of "Triangle ABC has two angles equal" and "Triangle ABC is isosceles", write a translation of "A triangle with two angles equal is isosceles".

II.1.15. If "P", "Q", "R", and "S" are translations of "Triangle ABC is congruent to triangle DEF", "$AB = DE$", "$BC = EF$", and "$CA = FD$", write a translation of "Two triangles are congruent if the three sides of the one are equal respectively to the three sides of the other".

II.1.16. If "P", "Q", and "R" are translations of "$f(n)$ is a polynomial with integral coefficients", "$f(n)$ is a constant", and "$f(n)$ is a prime for all n", write a translation of "No polynomial $f(n)$ with integral coefficients, other than a constant, can be prime for all n".

II.1.17. If "P", "Q", "R", "S", and "T" are translations of "p and q are distinct odd primes", "p is of the form $4n + 3$", "q is of the form $4n + 3$",

$$\text{“}\left(\frac{p}{q}\right) = \left(\frac{q}{p}\right)\text{”}$$

and

$$\text{“}\left(\frac{p}{q}\right) = -\left(\frac{q}{p}\right)\text{”},$$

write a translation of "If p and q are distinct odd primes, then

$$\left(\frac{p}{q}\right) = \left(\frac{q}{p}\right)$$

unless both p and q are of the form $4n + 3$, in which case

$$\left(\frac{p}{q}\right) = -\left(\frac{q}{p}\right)\text{”}.$$

II.1.18. If "P", "Q", "R", and "S" are translations of "AB is a chord of circle O", "CD is a chord of circle O", "$AB = CD$", and "AB and CD are equidistant from the center of circle O", write a translation of "In the same circle, if two chords are unequal, they are unequally distant from the center".

II.1.19. If "P" and "Q" are translations of "$\prod_{m=1}^{\infty} (1 + a_m)$ converges" and "As $n \to \infty$, $\prod_{m=1}^{n} (1 + a_m)$ tends to a limit other than zero", write a translation of "We say that $\prod_{m=1}^{\infty} (1 + a_m)$ converges if, as $n \to \infty$, $\prod_{m=1}^{n} (1 + a_m)$ tends to a limit other than zero".

II.1.20. If "P", "Q", "R", and "S" are translations of "$f(x) \equiv g(x)h(x)$", "r is a root of $f(x)$", "r is a root of $g(x)$", and "r is a root of $h(x)$", write a translation of "If $f(x) \equiv g(x)h(x)$, then any root of $f(x)$ is a root of $g(x)$ or $h(x)$".

II.1.21. If "P", "Q", and "R" are translations of "$\phi(x)$ is an increasing positive function of x", "$\sum_{n=1}^{\infty} \frac{1}{\phi(n)}$ is convergent", and "$\int_1^{\infty} \frac{dx}{\phi(x)}$ is convergent", write a translation of "If $\phi(x)$ is an increasing positive function of x for which $\sum_{n=1}^{\infty} \frac{1}{\phi(n)}$ is divergent, then $\int_1^{\infty} \frac{dx}{\phi(x)}$ is divergent. On the other hand, if $\sum_{n=1}^{\infty} \frac{1}{\phi(n)}$ is convergent, then $\int_1^{\infty} \frac{dx}{\phi(x)}$ is convergent".

II.1.22. If "P", "Q", and "R" are translations of "A is a right angle", "B is a right angle", and "$A = B$", write a translation of "Any two right angles are equal".

II.1.23. If "P", "Q", and "R" are translations of "α is a unity", "The norm of α is $+1$", and "The norm of α is -1", write a translation of "The norm of a unity is ± 1, and every number whose norm is ± 1 is a unity".

2. The Dot Notation. It will be noticed that, by our conventions for omission of parentheses, we have established a sort of hierarchy of symbols. "$\sim$" is weakest in the sense that we make the interpretations listed in the following table, where the formula on the right is the interpretation of that on the left:

$\sim PQ$ . . . . $(\sim P)Q$
$\sim P \vee Q$ . . . . $(\sim P) \vee Q$
$\sim P \supset Q$ . . . . $(\sim P) \supset Q$
$\sim P \equiv Q$ . . . . $(\sim P) \equiv Q$.

Thus "$\sim$" is weaker than each of "&", "v", "$\supset$", and "$\equiv$". The next weakest is "&", as is shown by the following interpretations:

$PQ \vee R$ . . . . $(PQ) \vee R$
$P \vee QR$ . . . . $P \vee (QR)$
$PQ \supset R$ . . . . $(PQ) \supset R$
$P \supset QR$ . . . . $P \supset (QR)$
$PQ \equiv R$ . . . . $(PQ) \equiv R$
$P \equiv QR$ . . . . $P \equiv (QR)$.

Next weakest is "v", as shown by the interpretations:

$P \vee Q \supset R$	$(P \vee Q) \supset R$
$P \supset Q \vee R$	$P \supset (Q \vee R)$
$P \vee Q \equiv R$	$(P \vee Q) \equiv R$
$P \equiv Q \vee R$	$P \equiv (Q \vee R)$.

The symbols "$\supset$" and "$\equiv$" are of equal strength, since "$P \supset Q \equiv R$" and "$P \equiv Q \supset R$" are ambiguous.

If we write "PQ" with an "&", it is still weaker than any symbol except "$\sim$", as shown by the interpretations:

$\sim P\&Q$	$(\sim P)\&Q$
$P\&Q \vee R$	$(P\&Q) \vee R$
$P \vee Q\&R$	$P \vee (Q\&R)$
$P\&Q \supset R$	$(P\&Q) \supset R$
$P \supset Q\&R$	$P \supset (Q\&R)$
$P\&Q \equiv R$	$(P\&Q) \equiv R$
$P \equiv Q\&R$	$P \equiv (Q\&R)$.

There will be occasions when a strong "&" would be useful, and for this reason, we agree that if we write "PQ" with a dot, "$P.Q$", it is then stronger than any other symbol. That is, we agree on the following interpretations:

$P.Q \vee R$	$P(Q \vee R)$
$P.Q \supset R$	$P(Q \supset R)$
$P.Q \equiv R$	$P(Q \equiv R)$
$P \vee Q.R$	$(P \vee Q)R$
$P \supset Q.R$	$(P \supset Q)R$
$P \equiv Q.R$	$(P \equiv Q)R$
$P.Q \equiv RS$	$P(Q \equiv (RS))$
$P.Q \equiv R.S$	$P(Q \equiv R)S$.

By association to the left, the last formula on the right would be interpreted as "$(P(Q \equiv R))S$".

The next stage in the dot notation is to think of the dot not as standing for a logical product, but as strengthening whatever symbol it stands by. In the cases above, it could be understood that the dot is standing by an implicit "&" and strengthening it. Now we allow the dot to stand by any symbol and strengthen it. As none of "v", "$\supset$", or "$\equiv$" can be implicit, the dot must stand on one side or the other, in which case it strengthens that side only. If we wish to strengthen both sides, we use two dots, one on each side. Thus we have the following interpretations, in which the right-hand column contains the interpretations, and the middle column contains an intermediate formula obtained by inserting the pair of parentheses indicated by the dot.

$P \supset Q \vee R \equiv S$	. . . .	Ambiguous
$P \supset .Q \vee R \equiv S$	. . . . $P \supset (Q \vee R \equiv S)$	$P \supset ((Q \vee R) \equiv S)$
$P \supset Q \vee R. \equiv S$	. . . . $(P \supset Q \vee R) \equiv S$	$(P \supset (Q \vee R)) \equiv S$
$P \supset Q. \vee R \equiv S$	. . . . $(P \supset Q) \vee R \equiv S$	$((P \supset Q) \vee R) \equiv S$
$P \supset Q \vee . R \equiv S$	. . . . $P \supset Q \vee (R \equiv S)$	$P \supset (Q \vee (R \equiv S))$
$P \supset Q. \vee . R \equiv S$	. . . . $(P \supset Q) \vee (R \equiv S)$ . . .	$(P \supset Q) \vee (R \equiv S)$

Note that, as we said above, a dot on one side of a symbol strengthens that side only. Thus, only in the last illustration, where the "v" is strengthened on each side, is the "v" the dominant symbol of the formula. On the other hand, a dot standing for "&" operates in both directions.

Any symbol strengthened by a dot is stronger on that side than any symbol not strengthened by a dot. If two symbols are each strengthened by a dot, then they have the same strength relative to each other as though no dot were present. Thus we have the interpretations:

$P.Q \vee R. \supset S$ . . . . . . $(P(Q \vee R)) \supset S$
$P \equiv .Q \supset R. \vee S$ . . . . $P \equiv ((Q \supset R) \vee S)$.

However, notice the interpretations:

$P.Q \equiv .R \vee S \supset T$ . . . $P(Q \equiv ((R \vee S) \supset T))$
$P.Q \equiv R. \vee S$ . . . . . . $(P(Q \equiv R)) \vee S$
$P.Q \equiv .R \supset S. \vee T$ . . . $P(Q \equiv ((R \supset S) \vee T))$.

In the first of the last three illustrations the dot on the right of the "≡" strengthens it on the right so that it is stronger than the "⊃". However, the "≡" is not strengthened on the left, and so the dot between "*P*" and "*Q*" is stronger. In the second, the dot on the left of "v" strengthens it and so it and the implicit "&" between the "*P*" and "*Q*" have the usual strength relative to each other. However, in the third, the dot on the left of the "v" strengthens it, but the "≡" with the dot on the right is even stronger, to the right. On the left the "≡" is not strengthened, and the dot between the "*P*" and "*Q*" is stronger.

A good way to treat such formulas is to replace each dot in succession by a pair of parentheses, starting with the strongest dot in the formula, and working down. The strongest dot is that next to the strongest symbol, of course. Thus, in the last formula considered, we could successively replace dots by pairs of parentheses as shown in the table below:

$P.Q \equiv .R \supset S. \vee T$
$P.Q \equiv (R \supset S. \vee T)$
$P.Q \equiv ((R \supset S) \vee T)$
$P(Q \equiv ((R \supset S) \vee T))$.

The dot next to the "$\equiv$", being strongest, is first replaced by a pair of parentheses, giving the second formula of the table. Then the dot next to the "$\mathbf{v}$" is replaced by the appropriate pair of parentheses, and finally the dot between the "P" and "Q".

Rather commonly, if there are two dots of equal strength, either they are quite independent of each other, or else the formula is ambiguous. Thus, in "$P \supset Q.\mathbf{v}.R \equiv S$", the dots of equal strength are quite independent, whereas in the formula "$P\mathbf{v}Q \supset .R \equiv P. \supset Q$" the two dots of equal strength conflict and the formula is ambiguous, since we would have to replace the dots by parentheses as follows: "$(P\mathbf{v}Q) \supset (R \equiv P) \supset Q$", and this is ambiguous. In other cases of conflict, the ambiguity is sometimes relieved by special rules. Thus, in "$P.Q \equiv R.S$", we must replace the dots by parentheses as follows: "$P(Q \equiv R)S$", but this is rendered unambiguous by the rule of association to the left. Likewise, in

$$P \supset (Q \supset R). \equiv .PQ \supset R. \equiv .Q \supset (P \supset R)$$

we have to replace the dots by parentheses as follows:

$$(P \supset (Q \supset R)) \equiv (PQ \supset R) \equiv (Q \supset (P \supset R)).$$

By the algebraic analogy, this is then interpreted as

$$((P \supset (Q \supset R)) \equiv (PQ \supset R))\&((PQ \supset R) \equiv (Q \supset (P \supset R))).$$

If we wish to strengthen a symbol very much, we will put a double dot, "$:$", or triple dot, "$.:$" or "$:.$", or even a quadruple dot, "$::$" next to the symbol. A symbol strengthened by a double dot is, on that side, stronger than any symbol with a single dot or with no dot. If two symbols are both strengthened by a double dot, then they have the same strength relative to each other as though no dots were present. Similar considerations apply to symbols strengthened by triple or quadruple dots. A symbol can have a different number of dots on the two sides of it, including the possibility of no dots at all on one side. We have the illustrations:

$$P:.Q \equiv .R \supset S:\mathbf{v}T \quad . \; . \; . \quad P((Q \equiv (R \supset S))\mathbf{v}T)$$
$$P:Q \equiv .R \supset S:\mathbf{v}T \quad . \; . \; . \; . \quad (P(Q \equiv (R \supset S)))\mathbf{v}T$$
$$P:Q \equiv :R \supset S:\mathbf{v}T \quad . \; . \; . \; . \quad P(Q \equiv ((R \supset S)\mathbf{v}T)).$$

The last of these is just a repetition with double dots of an illustration that was given earlier with single dots.

In replacing multiple dots by parentheses, it is advisable to start with the strongest.

We shall feel free to use more dots or parentheses than the minimum required to dispel ambiguity if we thereby make the statement easier to read. Thus, although the statement "$P(Q \equiv ((R \supset S)\mathbf{v}T))$" can be unambiguously rendered as "$P.Q \equiv .R \supset S.\mathbf{v}T$", it will be much easier to interpret if written as "$P{:}Q \equiv .R \supset S.\mathbf{v}T$". Here it is immediately obvious that the double dot dominates the formula, whereas in "$P.Q \equiv .R \supset S.\mathbf{v}T$" a careful analysis must be made before one finds out that the dot next to the "$\equiv$" controls the dot next to the "$\mathbf{v}$", thus accidentally leaving the dot between the "P" and "Q" in a dominant position.

It is this possibility of making the dominant symbol of a formula readily apparent by the use of many dots next to it that is the real advantage of the dot notation. If one always uses a minimum number of dots, this advantage is lost.

Like the use of abbreviations such as "$P\mathbf{v}Q$" and omission of parentheses, use of dots is not part of our symbolic logic, but only a convenience which we permit ourselves in talking about it.

EXERCISES

II.2.1. By using dots rewrite the following unambiguously without parentheses:

(a) $P{\sim}Q(P \supset Q)$.
(b) $(P \equiv Q) \equiv PQ\mathbf{v}{\sim}P{\sim}Q$.
(c) $(P \supset R)(Q \supset R) \supset ((P\mathbf{v}Q) \supset R)$.
(d) $(PQ)R \supset P(QR)$.
(e) $(P \supset (Q \supset R)) \equiv ((PQ) \supset R)$.
(f) $PQR \supset ((P \equiv Q) \equiv R)$.
(g) $(P \supset (Q \supset R)) \equiv (Q \supset (P \supset R))$.
(h) $P \supset (Q \equiv (P \equiv Q))$.
(i) $(P \supset Q) \supset ((P \supset (Q \supset R)) \supset (P \supset R))$.

II.2.2. Rewrite the following unambiguously without the use of dots:

(a) ${\sim}Q \supset {\sim}P. \equiv .P \supset Q$.
(b) $P \supset Q.{\sim}P \supset Q. \equiv Q$.
(c) $PQ\mathbf{v}R. \equiv .P\mathbf{v}R.Q\mathbf{v}R$.
(d) $P\mathbf{v}Q \equiv {:}P \supset Q. \supset Q$.
(e) $Q \equiv S. \supset {:}R \equiv T. \supset .QR \equiv ST$.
(f) $P \supset {:}Q \equiv {\sim}Q. \supset {\sim}P$.
(g) $P \supset .Q \equiv R{:} \equiv {:}P \supset Q. \equiv .P \supset R$.
(h) $Q \supset {\sim}R. \supset {:}P\mathbf{v}Q.R. \equiv PR$.

3. The Use of Truth-value Tables. Suppose we start with several distinct statements "P_1", "P_2", . . . , "P_n" and combine them by means of "$\sim$" and "&" to form a compound statement "Q", using each as often as desired. Then "Q" will be called a statement formula derived from

"P_1", "P_2", . . . , "P_n", or more simply just a statement formula. "P_1", "P_2", . . . , "P_n" will be called the components of "Q". Thus "$\sim P$" is a statement formula with the component "P", and "$P \vee Q$" (which is really "$\sim(\sim P \& \sim Q)$") is a statement formula with the components "P" and "Q", and so on.

In setting up the above definition of a statement formula, we have taken the first step toward a precise definition of "statement." We are still a long way from a complete or precise definition, but one part of the definition has now been adopted, namely, that, if "P" and "Q" are any statements, then "$\sim P$" and "$(P\&Q)$" are also statements.

The study of statement formulas, with especial reference to their truth or falsity, constitutes the statement calculus.

If one writes down a statement formula at random, such as "P" or "$P \vee Q$", it is likely that the truth or falsity of it will depend on the truth or falsity of its component statements "P", "Q", etc., and if one does not have information about the truth of the components, one cannot come to any decision as to the truth of the formula. However, there are some statement formulas whose truth or falsity does not depend upon the truth or falsity of their components. For instance, "$PQ \supset P$" is true no matter what statements "P" and "Q" are used in it, and "$P \sim P$" is false regardless of what "P" is.

A statement formula which is true no matter what statements are taken in it is said to be "universally valid."

We now present a simple scheme for identifying those statement formulas which are universally valid. This method depends on the principle that each statement is either true or false. So the truth value of a statement must be either T (for truth) or F (for falsehood). Now, if one knows the truth value of "P", one can immediately infer the truth value of "$\sim P$". If "P" is T, then "$\sim P$" is F, and if "P" is F, then "$\sim P$" is T. We can summarize this in a "truth-value table" for "$\sim$" as follows:

P	$\sim P$
T	F
F	T

In this table, we have listed under "P" the possible truth values which it can take, and under "$\sim P$" the corresponding truth values that it would take.

Correspondingly, if one knows the truth values of "P" and "Q", one can immediately infer the truth value of "PQ". We summarize the way of doing this in a truth-value table for "&":

P	Q	PQ
T	T	T
T	F	F
F	T	F
F	F	F

Under the pair "P", "Q" we have listed the four pairs of truth values which "P" and "Q" can take, and under "PQ" the corresponding truth values that it would take. We feel that these truth values are unequivocally determined by our agreement that "&" is to serve as the equivalent in symbolic logic of the English word "and", and hence that we need not explain the entries under "PQ".

By using the two truth-value tables above, one can compute a truth-value table for any statement formula, since it is defined in terms of "$\sim$" and "&". Thus let us construct a truth-value table for "$P \supset Q$". This is built up from "P" and "Q" by the following sequence of steps:

1. Put together "$\sim$" and "Q" to get "$\sim Q$".
2. Put together "P" and "$\sim Q$" to get "$P\sim Q$".
3. Put together "$\sim$" and "$P\sim Q$" to get "$\sim(P\sim Q)$".

If we start with any pair of truth values for "P" and "Q", we can get the truth value for "$P \supset Q$" by going through the same sequence of steps. We summarize these calculations in the following truth-value table for "$\supset$":

P	Q	$\sim Q$	$P\sim Q$	$P \supset Q$
T	T	F	F	T
T	F	T	T	F
F	T	F	F	T
F	F	T	F	T

Similarly we get the truth-value table for "**v**":

P	Q	$\sim P$	$\sim Q$	$\sim P\sim Q$	$P \vee Q$
T	T	F	F	F	T
T	F	F	T	F	T
F	T	T	F	F	T
F	F	T	T	T	F

Use of these tables can often shorten the labor of constructing tables for more complicated statement formulas. Thus we get the following truth-value table for "≡" by thinking of "$P \equiv Q$" as built up out of "$P \supset Q$" and "$Q \supset P$":

P	Q	$P \supset Q$	$Q \supset P$	$P \equiv Q$
T	T	T	T	T
T	F	F	T	F
F	T	T	F	F
F	F	T	T	T

The entries in the columns under "$P \supset Q$" and "$Q \supset P$" are written down directly by referring to the truth-value table for "$\supset$".

We consider it as completely obvious that a statement formula is universally valid if and only if it takes the truth value T for every combination of truth values of its components. As we can check whether the latter is the case by constructing a truth-value table for the statement formula, we now have a means of testing whether a statement formula is universally valid. Thus, to show that "$PQ \supset P$" is universally valid, we construct its truth-value table:

P	Q	PQ	$PQ \supset P$
T	T	T	T
T	F	F	T
F	T	F	T
F	F	F	T

Since only T's appear in the last column, "$PQ \supset P$" is universally valid.

If one has a statement formula based on three or more statements, construction of a truth-value table becomes a fairly extended enterprise. Thus, we wish to show that "$P \supset Q . \supset . \sim(QR) \supset \sim(RP)$" is universally valid. If we denote this by "S", we construct the following truth-value table:

P	Q	R	$P \supset Q$	QR	$\sim(QR)$	RP	$\sim(RP)$	$\sim(QR) \supset \sim(RP)$	S
T	T	T	T	T	F	T	F	T	T
T	T	F	T	F	T	F	T	T	T
T	F	T	F	F	T	T	F	F	T
T	F	F	F	F	T	F	T	T	T
F	T	T	T	T	F	F	T	T	T
F	T	F	T	F	T	F	T	T	T
F	F	T	T	F	T	F	T	T	T
F	F	F	T	F	T	F	T	T	T

To show that "$P \supset Q. \supset .\sim(QR) \supset \sim(RP)$" always takes the value T involves the inspection of eight cases. This suggests that perhaps we can proceed more quickly if we try to show that it could never take the value F; and indeed we can.

Suppose there is a set of truth values for "P", "Q", and "R" which makes "$P \supset Q. \supset .\sim(QR) \supset \sim(RP)$" take the value F. Inspection of the truth-value table for "$\supset$" discloses that this can happen only in case we have:

(a) The truth value T for "$P \supset Q$".
(b) The truth value F for "$\sim(QR) \supset \sim(RP)$".

From (b), by the truth-value table for "$\supset$", we see that we must have:

(c) The truth value T for "$\sim(QR)$".
(d) The truth value F for "$\sim(RP)$".

From (d), we see that we must have:

(e) The truth value T for "RP".

From this follows that we must have:

(f) The truth value T for "R".
(g) The truth value T for "P".

From (g) and (a), we see, by the truth-value table for "$\supset$", that we must have:

(h) The truth value T for "Q".

As (f) and (h) contradict (c), we conclude that "$P \supset Q. \supset .\sim(QR) \supset \sim(RP)$" never has the value F. As it must have either the value F or T in each case, it must take the value T in all cases.

We notice that the procedure of constructing a truth-value table for a statement formula is purely mechanical and depends entirely on the form of the statement and not in the least on the meaning of the statement. One could certainly build a machine to construct truth-value tables for statement formulas. Thus we can permit the use of truth-value tables as part of our symbolic logic.

The suggested short cut, which we just explained, of assuming a statement formula to have the value F and deriving a contradiction is not a purely mechanical process, though it does not depend in any way on the meaning of the statement. We may take the following point of view with respect to it. An intelligent person, faced with the prospect of constructing a fairly extensive truth-value table, might seek a line of reasoning whereby he could learn what would be the result of constructing the truth-value table without actually going to the trouble of constructing the table. Our suggested short cut is one such possible line of reasoning. We cannot accept such short cuts as part of our symbolic logic, because we are carefully restricting our symbolic logic to purely mechanical processes. If a person wishes to operate purely within the symbolic logic, he must actually construct a truth-value table in each case.

Nonetheless, the suggested short cut is a convenient way of reassuring oneself that, if one should construct the truth-value table, one would indeed always get the truth value T for the statement in question. Thus our short cut, though not part of the symbolic logic, gives us valuable information about the symbolic logic.

We distinguish sharply between operations within our symbolic logic, and reasoning about the symbolic logic. The method of truth-value tables, being purely mechanical, can be admitted as a procedure within our logic. Our short cut, being not purely mechanical, can be allowed only as a means outside the logic of getting information about the logic.

As we shall have many occasions in the future to prove things about our logic, we should perhaps indicate roughly now what we shall consider as acceptable methods of proof about our logic. We shall avoid all abstruse and complex methods of proof. Our reasoning must be constructive in the sense that, if we claim the existence of anything, we must explain explicitly how to construct it. We shall also avoid indirect reasoning. This means that we reject our short cut even as a means of reasoning about the symbolic logic, since our short cut is an indirect argument, depending on reductio ad absurdum.

Actually, we can rewrite our short cut as a direct argument as follows. We note first from the truth-value table for "$\supset$" that if "V" has the value T, then so does "$U \supset V$", regardless of the value of "U". Likewise, if "U" has the value F, then "$U \supset V$" has the value T regardless of the value of "V". Likewise, if "U" has the value F, then so do "UV" and "VU", regardless of the value of "V". Using these observations, we now proceed as follows. If "P" has the value F, then so does "RP". Hence "$\sim(RP)$" has the value T, whence we infer that "$\sim(QR) \supset \sim(RP)$" has the value T, whence we infer that "$P \supset Q. \supset .\sim(QR) \supset \sim(RP)$" has the value T. This disposes of the case when "P" has the value F. We now let "P" have the value T. If "R" has the value F, we can repeat the argument above. This leaves the case where "P" and "R" both have the value T. Under this, we have two cases, namely, "Q" has the value T and "Q" has the value F. In the latter case "$P \supset Q$" has the value F, and so "$P \supset Q. \supset .\sim(QR) \supset \sim(RP)$" has the value T. In the former case, "Q" and "R" each have the value T, so that "$\sim(QR)$" has the value F, so that "$\sim(QR) \supset \sim(RP)$" has the value T, and likewise "$P \supset Q. \supset . \sim(QR) \supset \sim(RP)$" has the value T.

This argument can be summarized in the following abridged truth-value table, in which again "S" denotes "$P \supset Q. \supset .\sim(QR) \supset \sim(RP)$".

P	Q	R	$P \supset Q$	QR	$\sim(QR)$	RP	$\sim(RP)$	$\sim(QR) \supset \sim(RP)$	S
F						F	T	T	T
T		F				F	T	T	T
T	T	T		T	F			T	T
T	F	T	F						T

Construction of such an abridged truth-value table is hardly a mechanical process and so cannot be admitted as part of our symbolic logic. However, it is a direct and simple argument and so can be admitted as a means of obtaining information about the symbolic logic.

The distinction between operations which we permit within the symbolic logic and reasoning which we permit about the symbolic logic will become clearer as we proceed. However, we state the crucial point again, that operations within the symbolic logic must be purely mechanical. When reasoning about the symbolic logic, we permit nonmechanical reasoning processes, but we permit only very simple and direct reasoning processes.

EXERCISES

II.3.1. Prove that the following are universally valid:

(a) $P \supset Q.Q \supset R. \supset .P \supset R.$
(b) $\sim Q \supset \sim P. \supset .P \supset Q.$
(c) $P \supset R.Q \supset R. \supset .P \vee Q \supset R.$
(d) $P \supset Q.\sim P \supset Q. \supset Q.$
(e) $\sim P \supset Q\sim Q. \supset P.$
(f) $P \supset Q\sim Q. \supset \sim P.$
(g) $\sim P \supset P. \supset P.$
(h) $P \supset \sim P. \supset \sim P.$
(i) $P\sim Q \supset R\sim R. \supset .P \supset Q.$
(j) $P\sim Q \supset Q. \supset .P \supset Q.$
(k) $P\sim Q \supset \sim P. \supset .P \supset Q.$
(l) $P \supset Q.\sim P \supset R. \supset Q \vee R.$
(m) $\sim P \supset Q. \supset P \vee Q.$
(n) $P \supset Q. \supset Q \vee \sim P.$
(o) $P \equiv Q. \supset .Q \equiv P.$
(p) $P \equiv Q.Q \equiv R. \supset .P \equiv R.$
(q) $P \vee \sim P.$

II.3.2. Prove that the following are universally valid:

(a) $P \supset PP.$
(b) $Q \equiv S. \supset .\sim Q \equiv \sim S.$

(c) $Q \equiv S. \supset :R \equiv T. \supset .QR \equiv ST.$
(d) $P \supset Q. \supset :.P \supset .Q \supset R: \supset .P \supset R.$
(e) $P \equiv \sim P. \supset Q\sim Q.$
(f) $P \supset :Q \equiv \sim Q. \supset \sim P.$
(g) $P \supset .\sim Q \supset \sim(P \supset Q).$
(h) $P\mathbf{v}Q \equiv :P \supset Q. \supset Q.$
(i) $Q \supset R. \supset :.P \supset .R \supset S: \supset :P \supset .Q \supset S.$
(j) $PQ \supset R. \equiv .P\sim R \supset \sim Q.$

II.3.3. Let "P_1", "P_2", . . . , "P_n", "R_1", "R_2", . . . , "R_n" be any statements; let "Q" be the logical product of "$\sim(P_iP_j)$" for every i and j with $1 \leq i < j \leq n$. Then for $1 \leq k \leq n$, show that "$QP_k \supset .R_1P_1\mathbf{v}R_2P_2\mathbf{v} \ldots \mathbf{v}R_nP_n \equiv R_k$" is universally valid.

II.3.4. Write six statement formulas which always take the value F, and prove that they do so.

II.3.5. Write a logical sum of several of "PQR", "$PQ\sim R$", "$P\sim QR$", "$P\sim Q\sim R$", "$\sim PQR$", "$\sim PQ\sim R$", "$\sim P\sim QR$", and "$\sim P\sim Q\sim R$" which will take the value T for the following sets of values of "P", "Q", and "R":

P	T	T	F	F	F
Q	T	F	T	F	F
R	T	T	T	T	F

and will take the value F for all other sets of values of "P", "Q", and "R".

II.3.6. Prove that "$PQ \equiv QP$" and "$P\mathbf{v}Q \equiv Q\mathbf{v}P$" are universally valid. Since these are analogous to "$xy = yx$" and "$x + y = y + x$", we express them by saying that "&" and "**v**" are commutative.

II.3.7. Prove that "$(PQ)R \equiv P(QR)$" and "$(P\mathbf{v}Q)\mathbf{v}R \equiv P\mathbf{v}(Q\mathbf{v}R)$" are universally valid. Since these are analogous to "$(xy)z = x(yz)$" and "$(x + y) + z = x + (y + z)$", we express them by saying that "&" and "**v**" are associative.

II.3.8. Prove that "$(P\mathbf{v}Q)R \equiv PR\mathbf{v}QR$" is universally valid. Since this is analogous to "$(x + y)z = xz + yz$", we express it by saying that "&" is distributive with respect to "**v**".

II.3.9. Prove that "$PQ\mathbf{v}R \equiv (P\mathbf{v}R)(Q\mathbf{v}R)$" is universally valid. This is quite unlike any familiar algebraic principle. We express it by saying that "**v**" is distributive with respect to "&".

4. Applications to Mathematical Reasoning. For this, we give meanings to our formulas of symbolic logic. These meanings constitute principles of reasoning. Some formulas state invalid principles of reasoning. Thus the meaning of "$P \supset Q. \supset .Q \supset P$" is that, if an implication is true, then its converse is also true, which is not so. Other formulas state valid principles of mathematical reasoning; in particular any statement formula which always takes the value T states a valid principle of mathematical reasoning. Any principle of this sort is likely to be rather elementary when considered as a theorem of mathematics. Deeper methods of proof are needed to establish any really difficult theorems. Nonetheless, universally valid statement formulas can be used to justify a number of quite useful principles of mathematical reasoning. Indeed, one value of the statement calculus is that in effect it is a reservoir of such useful principles of mathematical reasoning. Each statement formula listed in Ex. II.3.1 is a statement formula from which one can derive useful principles of mathematical reasoning. We now derive and illustrate these principles.

1. By a study of the truth-value table for "$\supset$" we can verify the following principle, known as "modus ponens":

If "P" and "$P \supset Q$" are both proved, then one is entitled to infer that "Q" is proved.

When use is made of the rule of modus ponens, "$P \supset Q$" is called the "major premise" and "P" is called the "minor premise".

Rather commonly, if one has "$P \supset Q$" proved, one proved it by assuming "P" and deducing "Q". In such a case, if one has "P" proved, then the deduction of "Q" from "P" would constitute a proof of "Q" and we do not need to use modus ponens (unless it is used in the deduction of "Q" from "P"). However, even if "$P \supset Q$" was proved by some other means, we can nonetheless infer "Q" by modus ponens if "P" is known true. An illustration of this would be the following. Suppose one has proved "$\sim Q \supset \sim P$". By Ex. II.3.1(b), we have also proved "$\sim Q \supset \sim P. \supset . P \supset Q$". So we use modus ponens with "$\sim Q \supset \sim P. \supset .P \supset Q$" as the major premise and "$\sim Q \supset \sim P$" as the minor premise and infer "$P \supset Q$". If now "P" were also provable, we could use modus ponens again to infer "Q".

An obvious generalization is that, if one has proved each of "P_1", "$P_1 \supset P_2$", "$P_2 \supset P_3$", . . . , "$P_{n-1} \supset P_n$", then one can infer "P_n". Practical use is made of this generalization in the so-called "analytic method of proof" in solving problems in elementary geometry. We quote a selected explanation of this method (Stone and Mallory, page 68):[1]

"The steps of an analysis may be expressed symbolically as follows: If A is to be proved, reason thus: A will be true if B can be proved true; B will be true if C can be proved true; C will follow if D can be proved true; but D is given true; hence begin by proving that C is true."

2. If "P" and "Q" are proved, we can infer "PQ". This important principle is used in constructing our truth-value table for "&".

[1] From "Modern Geometry" by John C. Stone and Virgil S. Mallory, copyright 1930, courtesy of Benj. H. Sanborn & Co.

An illustration of the use of this principle would come in proving two lines to be parallel in solid geometry. In solid geometry, the definition of parallel lines involves a logical product, to wit: Two lines are parallel if (a) they are coplanar, (b) they never meet. To prove two lines parallel one proves separately each of the two factors of the logical product, and then infers their logical product. For instance:

THEOREM. The intersections of two parallel planes by a third plane are parallel lines (see Fig. II.4.1).

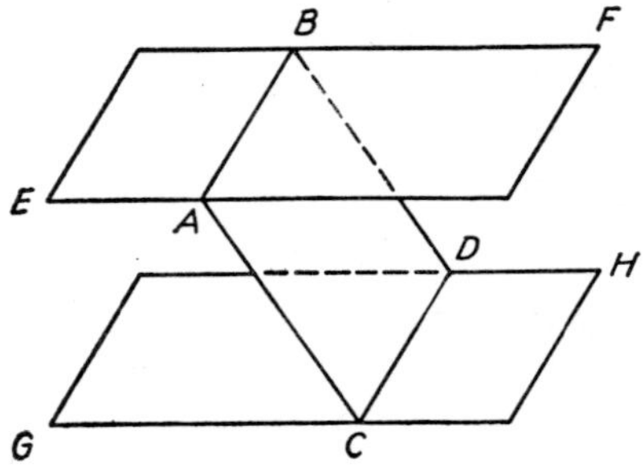

FIG. II.4.1.

Given: Parallel planes *EF* and *GH*, intersected in lines *AB* and *CD* by plane *ABCD*.

To prove: *AB* parallel to *CD*.

1. *AB* and *CD* are coplanar, since both lie in plane *ABCD*.
2. *AB* and *CD* never meet, for if they met, the point at which they meet would be a point at which planes *EF* and *GH* meet.
3. Therefore *AB* and *CD* are parallel.

Q.E.D.

Generalization to logical products of more than two factors is immediate. In general, if "P_1", "P_2", . . . , "P_n" are proved, we can infer "$P_1P_2 \cdots P_n$". As an instance of a proof of a logical product of four factors (which is proved by proving each of the four factors separately) we note Thm. 17 on page 145 of Birkhoff and MacLane:[1]

"THEOREM 17. The intersection $S \cap T$ of two subgroups S and T of a group G is a subgroup of G."

To prove this, one must prove that $S \cap T$ is a group, and the definition of a group G is the logical product of the following four statements:

(a) If x and y are in G, then xy is in G.
(b) If x, y, and z are in G, then $(xy)z = x(yz)$.

[1] From Birkhoff and MacLane, "A Survey of Modern Algebra," copyright 1941 by The Macmillan Company and used with their permission.

(c) There is a unit, e, in G such that for each x in G, $ex = x$.

(d) If e is a unit of G and x is in G, then there is an inverse x^{-1} in G such that $x^{-1}x = e$.

In the proof of their Thm. 17 given by Birkhoff and MacLane, (b) is taken as obvious, and they prove (d), (a), and (c).

In Thm. 179 on page 147 of Hardy and Wright, the conclusion is a logical product of five factors. It is proved by proving each factor separately.

3. The most fundamental way of proving "$P \supset Q$" is to assume the truth of "P" and then correctly deduce the truth of "Q". This is a very important principle, and in later chapters we shall give considerable attention to it. However, we have to pass over it for the moment, since it is beyond the scope of the statement calculus.

Nevertheless, the statement calculus furnishes a number of useful subsidiary methods of proving "$P \supset Q$". For instance, if we can find a statement "R" such that we can prove "$P \supset R$" and "$R \supset Q$", then by Ex. II.3.1(a), we can infer "$P \supset Q$". An obvious generalization is to infer "$P \supset Q$" from "$P \supset R_1$", "$R_1 \supset R_2$", . . . , "$R_{n-1} \supset R_n$", and "$R_n \supset Q$". A practical application of this will be noted under the methods of proving "$P \equiv Q$".

4. Another way of proving "$P \supset Q$" is to prove "$\sim Q \supset \sim P$" and make use of Ex. II.3.1(b). The proof of "$\sim Q \supset \sim P$" might be carried out in the fundamental way, namely, by assuming "$\sim Q$" and correctly deducing "$\sim P$". However, it is quite immaterial what method is used to prove "$\sim Q \supset \sim P$". If it is proved, then one can infer "$P \supset Q$".

This means of proving "$P \supset Q$" is widely used, and we quote several instances. The first is paraphrased from page 41 of Hardy and Wright.

THEOREM. If a is an integer and 2 divides a^2, then 2 divides a.

Proof. Assume 2 does not divide a. Then a has the form $2m + 1$. Hence a^2 is $4m^2 + 4m + 1$. Thus 2 does not divide a^2.

The next is quoted exactly from page 7 of Bôcher, 1907.[1]

"THEOREM 4. If the product of two or more polynomials is identically zero, at least one of the factors must be identically zero.

"For if none of them were identically zero, they would all have definite degrees, and therefore their product would, by Theorem 3, have a definite degree, and would therefore not vanish identically."

The next is taken from page 20 of Fort, 1930.[2]

"THEOREM 23. *Hypothesis*: $\sum_{n=0}^{\infty} a_n$ diverges. *Conclusion*: $\sum_{n=k}^{\infty} a_n$ diverges, k being any fixed integer."

[1] From Bôcher, "Introduction to Higher Algebra," copyright 1907 by The Macmillan Company and used with their permission.

[2] From Fort, *op. cit.*

The proof consists of assuming that $\sum_{n=k}^{\infty} a_n$ converges and deducing that $\sum_{n=0}^{\infty} a_n$ converges. The details are irrelevant for the present discussion, and we omit them.

Still other instances of proving "$P \supset Q$" by proving "$\sim Q \supset \sim P$" will appear incidentally in connection with the illustration of other principles.

We remark that the method of proving "$P \supset Q$" by proving "$\sim Q \supset \sim P$" could be used to advantage in many cases which are now handled by reductio ad absurdum. There is a method of proving "$P \supset Q$" by reductio ad absurdum that practically amounts to proving "$\sim Q \supset \sim P$", and one could usually simplify the proof by writing it as a proof of "$\sim Q \supset \sim P$". We shall cite some specific instances in connection with our discussion of reductio ad absurdum.

5. If one has an implication of the special form "$P \vee Q \supset R$" to prove, then special methods are available, to wit, if one can prove "$P \supset R$" and "$Q \supset R$", then by Ex. II.3.1(c) one can infer "$P \vee Q \supset R$".

The usual method of proving "$P \vee Q \supset R$" amounts to this. Thus the outline of a typical proof of "$P \vee Q \supset R$" might run in words somewhat as follows:

"*Given*: '$P \vee Q$'.

"*To prove*: 'R'.

"*Case* 1. 'P' is true. Then . . . (here a deduction of 'R' from 'P' is given).

"*Case* 2. 'Q' is true. Then . . . (here a deduction of 'R' from 'Q' is given).

"But since we are given that one of 'P' or 'Q' must be true, 'R' must follow. Q.E.D."

The reader will observe that "Case 1" comprises a proof of "$P \supset R$" and "Case 2" comprises a proof of "$Q \supset R$", and the proof would be shortened and simplified if one merely gave these proofs of "$P \supset R$" and "$Q \supset R$" and then cited Ex. II.3.1(c).

Another advantage in using Ex. II.3.1(c) instead of the verbal "proof by cases" cited above is the greater flexibility permitted by Ex. II.3.1(c). In the verbal form, one is committed to proving "$P \supset R$" by assuming "P" and deducing "R" as in "Case 1" and to proving "$Q \supset R$" by assuming "Q" and deducing "R" as in "Case 2". On the other hand, if one is using Ex. II.3.1(c), it suffices that each of "$P \supset R$" and "$Q \supset R$" be proved, and the method of proof is quite irrelevant. Thus, for instance, one might prove "$P \supset R$" by reductio ad absurdum and "$Q \supset R$" by proving "$\sim R \supset \sim Q$".

We illustrate the use of Ex. II.3.1(c) with the proof of a theorem from plane geometry. Suppose we have already proved: (a) If two sides of a triangle are equal, then the opposite angles are equal. (b) If two sides are unequal, then the opposite angles are unequal, and the angle opposite the greater side is the greater. We now wish to prove that, if two angles are unequal, then the opposite sides are unequal, and the side opposite the greater angle is the greater (see Fig. II.4.2). That is, in the notation of elementary geometry:

Given: Angle A greater than angle B.

To prove: Side a greater than side b.

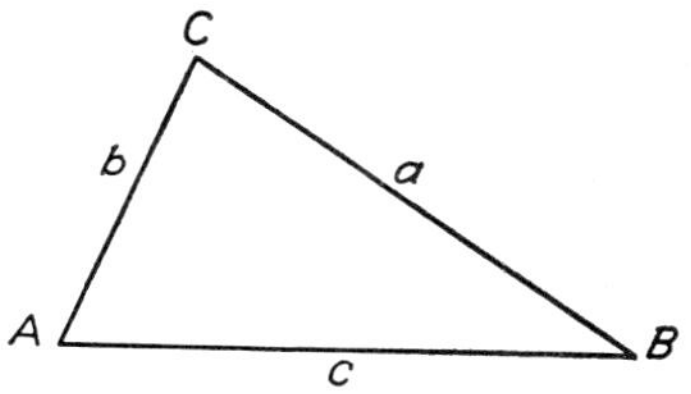

FIG. II.4.2.

By Ex. II.3.1(b), it suffices to prove "If a is not greater than b, then A is not greater than B". This is the same as "If a equals b or a is less than b, then A is not greater than B". So we now wish to prove "$P \vee Q \supset R$" where:

"P" is "a equals b".

"Q" is "a is less than b".

"R" is "A is not greater than B".

The proof proceeds by proving "$P \supset R$" and "$Q \supset R$". In fact our earlier proved result (a) gives "$P \supset R$" since if "P" then "a equals b" so that "A equals B" so that "A is not greater than B" so that "R", and our earlier proved result (b) gives "$Q \supset R$" since if "Q" then "a is less than b" so that "A is less than B" so that "A is not greater than B" so that "R". Then by Ex. II.3.1(c), the desired theorem follows.

We shall refer to the process of proving "$P \vee Q \supset R$" by proving each of "$P \supset R$" and "$Q \supset R$" as "proof by cases." We note the generalization that if "$P_1 \supset Q$", "$P_2 \supset Q$", . . . , "$P_n \supset Q$", then "$P_1 \vee P_2 \vee \cdots \vee P_n \supset Q$".

6. An interesting special case of the above is where we can prove "$P \supset Q$" and "$\sim P \supset Q$". Then by Ex. II.3.1(c), we get "$P \vee \sim P \supset Q$". However, we have "$P \vee \sim P$" by Ex. II.3.1(q), so that by modus ponens we get simply "Q". This process has been reduced to one step in Ex. II.3.1(d), which says that, from "$P \supset Q$" and "$\sim P \supset Q$", we get "Q". Use of this principle is also called "proof by cases."

An illustration of this is the proof given on pages 31 to 33 of Bôcher, 1907, of the theorem:[1]

"If D' is the adjoint of any determinant D, and M and M' are corresponding m-rowed minors of D and D' respectively, then M' is equal to the product of D^{m-1} by the algebraic complement of M."

The proof starts out:[1]

"We will prove this theorem first for the special case in which the minors M and M' lie at the upper left-hand corners of D and D' respectively."

When the proof has been completed for this case, we find the words:[1]

"Turning now to the case in which the minors M and M' do not lie at

[1] From Bôcher, *op. cit.*

the upper left-hand corners of D and D', . . ." and a proof is carried out for this case also.

7. Reductio ad absurdum. There are a number of minor variations of reductio ad absurdum, and we shall consider several of the more common. However, the prototype of all reductio ad absurdum proofs is the following. We wish to prove "P", and we do so by assuming the negation "$\sim P$" and deriving a contradiction. This being absurd, we reject the possibility "$\sim P$" and conclude "P".

A contradiction is any statement of the form "$Q \sim Q$". If we can derive a contradiction from "$\sim P$", this means we can prove "$\sim P \supset Q \sim Q$". Then by Ex. II.3.1(e), we infer "P".

It is not necessary that both "Q" and "$\sim Q$" be deduced from "$\sim P$" in order that we deduce a contradiction from "$\sim P$". The common situation with regard to reductio ad absurdum is that "Q" will be known true ahead of time. Then assuming "$\sim P$" we deduce "$\sim Q$". Combining this with the known result "Q" gives our contradiction "$Q \sim Q$", and we infer "P". As an illustration of this we note a portion of the proof of Thm. 3 on page 52 of Bôcher, 1907. Bôcher has assumed that a set of solutions of a system of homogeneous linear equations of rank r in n variables forms a fundamental system and is trying to conclude that they are $n - r$ in number. So he assumes that they are not $n - r$ in number and succeeds in contradicting a previously proved result (Thm. 1 on page 50 of Bôcher, 1907, to be precise).

In the situation where "Q" is known ahead of time and one proves "P" by reductio ad absurdum by assuming "$\sim P$" and deducing "$\sim Q$", an alternative proof is available, as follows. Assume "$\sim P$" and deduce "$\sim Q$". This proves "$\sim P \supset \sim Q$" from which follows "$Q \supset P$". However, "Q" is known, so that we infer "P" by modus ponens.

In an extremely rare form of reductio ad absurdum, one can deduce "P" from "$\sim P$". In this case, Ex. II.3.1(g) tells us that we can infer "P".

8. Proof of "$\sim P$" by reductio ad absurdum. This is a minor variation of the preceding. We assume "P" and deduce a contradiction "$Q \sim Q$". Then by Ex. II.3.1(f), we infer "$\sim P$". We quote the following illustration from page 46 of Hardy and Wright.[1]

"THEOREM 47. e is irrational.

"If $e = m/n$ and $k \geq n$, then $n|k!$, and

$$k!\left(e - 1 - \frac{1}{1!} - \frac{1}{2!} - \cdots - \frac{1}{k!}\right)$$

is an integer. But it is equal to

$$\frac{1}{k+1} + \frac{1}{(k+1)(k+2)} + \frac{1}{(k+1)(k+2)(k+3)} + \cdots,$$

[1] From "An Introduction to the Theory of Numbers" by G. H. Hardy and E. M. Wright, copyright 1938 by Clarendon Press, courtesy of Oxford University Press.

which is positive and less than

$$\frac{1}{(k+1)} + \frac{1}{(k+1)^2} + \frac{1}{(k+1)^3} + \cdots = \frac{1}{k};$$

and this is a contradiction."

As in the preceding type of reductio ad absurdum, we may have "Q" a known result and deduce "$\sim Q$" from "P". There is also the very rare form in which we deduce "$\sim P$" from "P". By Ex. II.3.1(h), we can infer "$\sim P$" in such a case.

As "$P \vee Q$" is "$\sim(\sim P \sim Q)$" a proof of "$P \vee Q$" by reductio ad absurdum would be a special case of a proof of "$\sim U$" by reductio ad absurdum.

9. Proof of "$P \supset Q$" by reductio ad absurdum. One can approach this in two different ways which come to the same thing. Since "$P \supset Q$" is "$\sim(P \sim Q)$", one can assume "$P \sim Q$" and try to deduce a contradiction. Alternatively, one can assume "P" with the intention of deducing "Q" and then elect to deduce "Q" by reductio ad absurdum. For this, one assumes "$\sim Q$" and seeks to derive a contradiction. The net result in this case is that one has "P" and "$\sim Q$" assumed and is trying to derive a contradiction. In one approach we have "$P \sim Q$" assumed; in the other we have "P" and "$\sim Q$" assumed. The difference is insignificant. So we characterize a proof of "$P \supset Q$" by reductio ad absurdum as a proof in which one assumes "$P \sim Q$" and tries to derive a contradiction "$R \sim R$". If one succeeds, then by Ex. II.3.1(i), one can infer "$P \supset Q$". We quote the following illustration from Altshiller-Court, 1925, pages 65 to 66 (see Fig.II.4.3).[1]

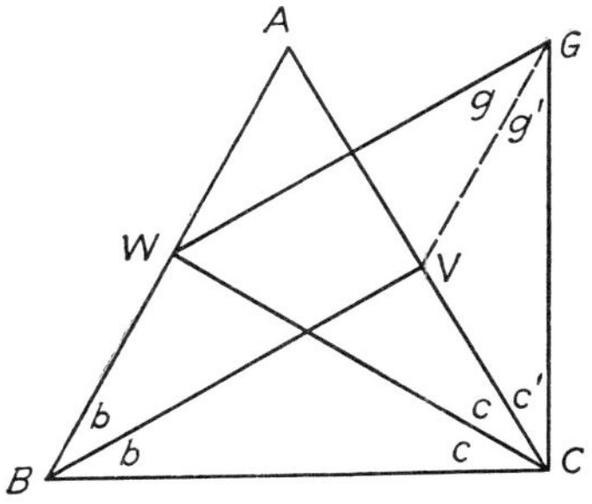

FIG. II.4.3.

"THEOREM. If two internal bisectors of a triangle are equal, the triangle is isosceles.

"Let bisector BV equal bisector CW. If the triangle is not isosceles, then one angle, say B, is larger than the other, C, and from the two triangles BVC and BCW, in which $BV = CW$, $BC = BC$, and angle B is greater than angle C, we have CV greater than BW. Now through V and W draw parallels to BA and BV respectively. From the parallelogram $BVGW$ we have $BV = WG = CW$. Hence the triangle GWC is isosceles, and $\angle(g + g') = \angle(c + c')$. But $\angle g = \angle b$. Hence $\angle(b + g') = \angle(c + c')$ and therefore g' is smaller than c'. Thus in the triangle GVC, we have CV smaller than GV, but $GV = BW$. Hence CV is smaller than BW. Conse-

[1] From "College Geometry" by N. Altshiller-Court, copyright 1925 by Johnson Publishing Co., courtesy of Barnes & Noble, Inc.

quently, the assumption of the inequality of the angles B, C leads to two contradictory results. Hence $B = C$, and the triangle is isosceles."

10. Proof of "$P \supset Q$" by reductio ad absurdum. We note a special case in which from "$P{\sim}Q$" one can derive "Q". Since one can also derive "${\sim}Q$" from "$P{\sim}Q$", the necessary contradiction is forthcoming, and we have a proof of "$P \supset Q$" by reductio ad absurdum. Alternatively, one may simply apply Ex. II.3.1(j). An illustration is afforded by the following proof.

"If $a \leq b + c$ whenever $c > 0$, then $a \leq b$.

"*Proof.* Assume that $a \leq b + c$ whenever $c > 0$, and also assume $a > b$. Then $(a - b)/2 > 0$. Take this to be c. Then

$$a \leq b + \frac{a-b}{2},$$

$$2a \leq 2b + a - b,$$

$$a \leq b."$$

11. Proof of "$P \supset Q$" by reductio ad absurdum. Another special case is that in which from "$P{\sim}Q$" one can derive "${\sim}P$". One can also derive "P" from "$P{\sim}Q$" and so get "$P \supset Q$" by reductio ad absurdum, or one may simply apply Ex. II.3.1(k). An illustration of this type of proof is the following (see Fig. II.4.4 and Fig. II.4.5).

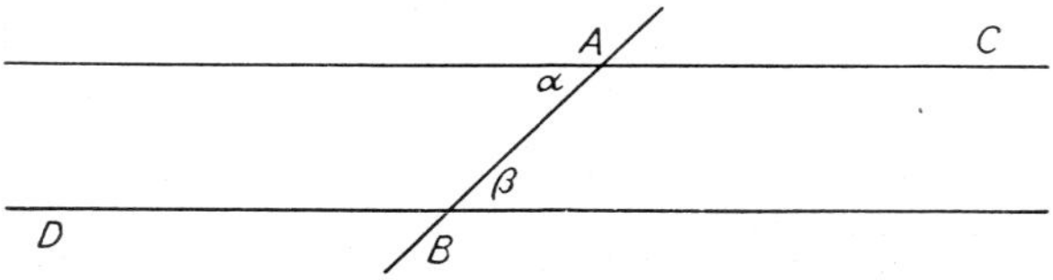

FIG. II.4.4.

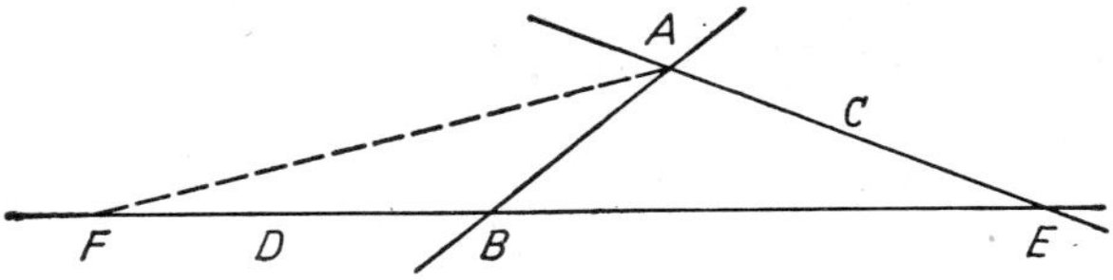

FIG. II.4.5.

"If two lines in a plane are cut by a transversal and alternate interior angles are equal, then the lines are parallel.

"*Given*: $\alpha = \beta$.

"*To prove*: AC parallel to BD.

"Suppose they are not parallel, so that AC and BD meet, say at E. Lay off BF equal to AE. Then triangles ABE and BAF are congruent (two sides and the included angle equal). Thus $\beta = \angle BAF$ which is less than α. So $\beta \neq \alpha$."

Strictly speaking, this proof is not complete, being only one case of a proof by cases. The other case, when AC meets BD on the other side of B, can easily be carried out in an analogous fashion.

In many of the cases where one assumes "$P{\sim}Q$" and deduces "${\sim}P$", no use is made of "P" in the deduction. In other words, "${\sim}P$" is deduced from "${\sim}Q$" alone. In such cases we have our choice of an alternative method of proof, namely, not to bother assuming "P", but merely to write out the deduction of "${\sim}P$" from "${\sim}Q$". This constitutes a legitimate proof of "${\sim}Q \supset {\sim}P$", from which we get "$P \supset Q$" immediately (see above, or refer to Ex. II.3.1(b)).

This alternative method seems more elegant to us than the reductio ad absurdum proof, but as both are quite valid it is certainly a matter of taste which one uses.

An illustration of a proof of "$P \supset Q$" by reductio ad absurdum in which one assumes "$P{\sim}Q$" and deduces "${\sim}P$" but makes no use of "P" in the deduction is to be found in the proof of Satz 1 on page 3 of Landau, 1930. On page 2, Landau has assumed Axiom 4, to wit:[1]

"Aus $x' = y'$ folgt $x = y$."

That is,

$$"x' = y' \supset x = y."$$

Then by Ex. II.3.1(b), one has immediately

$$"x \neq y \supset x' \neq y'."$$

However, Landau chooses to prove this by reductio ad absurdum. We quote:[1]

"*Satz* 1: Aus $x \neq y$ folgt $x' \neq y'$.

"*Beweis*: Sonst wäre $x' = y'$, also nach axiom 4, $x = y$."

12. Proofs of "$P \vee Q$". These are fairly uncommon, and no particular method is widely used. Ex. II.3.1(l), (m), (n), give three principles which could furnish proofs of "$P \vee Q$". The first is a special case of "proof by cases" which we mentioned earlier. We now illustrate each of Ex. II.3.1(l), (m), and (n) in the order named.

First illustration.

"If each a_n is positive, then either $\sum_{n=0}^{\infty} a_n$ converges or else it diverges to $+\infty$.

[1] From "Grundlagen der Analysis" by Edmund Landau, quoted by special license from the Department of Justice, Office of Alien Property.

"*Proof*. If $\sum_{n=0}^{N} a_n$ is bounded, then $\sum_{n=0}^{N} a_n$ is a bounded, monotone sequence and has a limit. Hence $\sum_{n=0}^{\infty} a_n$ converges. If $\sum_{n=0}^{N} a_n$ is unbounded, then one readily concludes that $\sum_{n=0}^{\infty} a_n$ diverges to $+\infty$."

For a slight variation of this, see Hardy, 1947, page 137.

Second illustration.

"If a is a least upper bound of E, then either a is in E or a is a limit point of E.

"*Proof.* Let a not be in E. Since a is a least upper bound of E, for every $\varepsilon > 0$ there is an x in E with $a - \varepsilon < x \leq a$. Since a is not in E, x must be different from a. So by definition, a is a limit point of E."

Third illustration.

This is taken from the proof of Thm. 45, page 41 of Hardy and Wright.[1]

"THEOREM 45. If x is a root of an equation

$$x^m + c_1 x^{m-1} + \cdots + c_m = 0,$$

with integral coefficients of which the first is unity, then x is either integral or irrational.

"If $x = a/b$, where $(a,b) = 1$, then

$$a^m + c_1 a^{m-1} b + \cdots + c_m b^m = 0.$$

Hence $b|a^m$. So if b has any prime factor p, it must divide a also, contradicting $(a,b) = 1$. So b has no prime factors, and so $b = 1$, $x = a$."

Note that the proof that b has no prime factors proceeds by reductio ad absurdum.

13. Proof of "$P \equiv Q$". Since "$P \equiv Q$" is "$(P \supset Q)(Q \supset P)$", it suffices to prove the two implications "$P \supset Q$" and "$Q \supset P$". In view of the multiplicity of ways of proving "$P \supset Q$", there is an even greater multiplicity of ways of proving "$P \equiv Q$".

The most obvious and direct way is to assume "P" and deduce "Q", thus proving "$P \supset Q$", and then assume "Q" and deduce "P", thus proving "$Q \supset P$". A common alternative is to assume "P" and deduce "Q", and then assume "$\sim P$" and deduce "$\sim Q$". This latter proves "$\sim P \supset \sim Q$", from which "$Q \supset P$" follows. However, many other possibilities present themselves. Thus, to cite one of the possibilities, one might prove both "$P \supset Q$" and "$Q \supset P$" by reductio ad absurdum.

We illustrate the three possibilities which we have specifically mentioned. In Bôcher, 1907, page 36, we find the theorem:[2]

[1] From Hardy and Wright, *op. cit.*

[2] From Bôcher, *op. cit.*

"A necessary and sufficient condition for the linear dependence of the m sets

$$x_1^{[i]}, x_2^{[i]}, \ldots, x_n^{[i]} \qquad (i = 1, 2, \ldots, m)$$

of n constants each, when $m \leq n$, is that all the m-rowed determinants of the matrix

$$\begin{Vmatrix} x_1' & x_2' & \cdots & x_n' \\ x_1'' & x_2'' & \cdots & x_n'' \\ \cdots & \cdots & \cdots & \cdots \\ \cdots & \cdots & \cdots & \cdots \\ x_1^{[m]} & x_2^{[m]} & \cdots & x_n^{[m]} \end{Vmatrix}$$

should vanish."

To prove necessity, Bôcher assumes that the m sets of constants are linearly dependent, and shows that all the m-rowed determinants vanish. To prove sufficiency, Bôcher assumes that all m-rowed determinants vanish and shows that the m sets of constants are linearly dependent.

This is then a clear-cut instance of proving "$P \equiv Q$" by assuming "P" and deducing "Q", and by assuming "Q" and deducing "P".

We turn now to an illustration of the proof of "$P \equiv Q$" by assuming "P" and deducing "Q", and by assuming "$\sim P$" and deducing "$\sim Q$".

Consider the discussion on page 74 of Wentworth and Smith[1] of how to "prove that a certain line or group of lines is the locus of a point that fulfills a given condition . . . ." Their instructions are that one should prove two things:[1]

"1. That any point in the supposed locus satisfies the condition.

"2. That any point outside the supposed locus does not satisfy the given condition."

Let "P" be a translation of "the point A is in the supposed locus" and let "Q" be a translation of "the point A satisfies the given condition". Then part 1 of Wentworth and Smith's instructions says that we should prove "$P \supset Q$" and part 2 says that we should prove "$\sim P \supset \sim Q$".

From these two, one can certainly infer "$P \equiv Q$". However, "$P \equiv Q$" says that being on the supposed locus is equivalent to satisfying the given condition, and so the supposed locus must indeed be the correct one, as we wished to prove.

This is illustrated in the following proof, which we condense from page 75 of Wentworth and Smith.[1]

[1] From "Plane and Solid Geometry" by George Wentworth and D. E. Smith, copyright 1913, courtesy of Ginn & Company.

THEOREM. The locus of a point equidistant from the extremities of a given line is the perpendicular bisector of that line (see Fig. II.4.6).

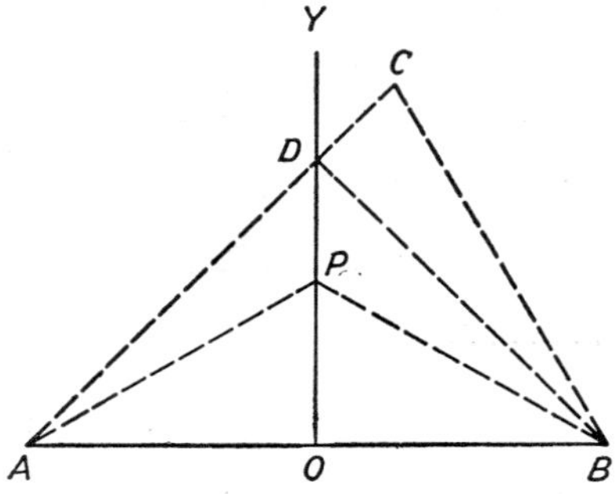

FIG. II.4.6.

Given: YO, the perpendicular bisector of the line AB.

To prove: That YO is the locus of a point equidistant from A and B.

Proof. Let P be any point in YO, and C any point not in YO. Draw the lines PA, PB, CA, and CB. Since $AO = BO$ and OP is common to both, the right triangles AOP and BOP have two sides and the included angle equal, and hence are congruent. So $PA = PB$. Let CA cut YO at D, and draw DB. Then, as above, $DA = DB$. So

$$CA = CD + DB > CB$$

since the straight line CB is the shortest distance between the two points C and B. So $CA \neq CB$. Therefore, YO is the required locus.

We now cite a proof of "$P \equiv Q$" in which one proves each of "$P \supset Q$" and "$Q \supset P$" by reductio ad absurdum.

On page 152 of Bôcher, 1907, we find the theorem:[1]

"A necessary and sufficient condition that a real quadratic form be definite is that it vanish at no real points except its vertices and the point $(0, 0, \ldots, 0)$."

In proving this, both "$P \supset Q$" and "$Q \supset P$" are proved by reductio ad absurdum. The details are sufficiently complicated that it is pointless to reproduce them. It happens that both these proofs by reductio ad absurdum are of the sort discussed earlier where one assumes "P" and "$\sim Q$" and deduces "$\sim P$" by use of "$\sim Q$" only. Thus with slight rewriting, this proof could be thrown into the form where one proves "$P \equiv Q$" by assuming "$\sim Q$" and deducing "$\sim P$", and assuming "$\sim P$" and deducing "$\sim Q$".

14. A situation which sometimes arises is where three or more statements are to be proved mutual necessary and sufficient conditions for each other.

[1] From Bôcher, *op. cit.*

Say there are four statements, "P", "Q", "R", and "S", and we wish to prove the six equivalences "$P \equiv Q$", "$P \equiv R$", "$P \equiv S$", "$Q \equiv R$", "$Q \equiv S$", and "$R \equiv S$". This means that we have twelve implications to prove. However it will suffice to prove a complete "cycle" of them, say "$P \supset Q$", "$Q \supset R$", "$R \supset S$", and "$S \supset P$", since the other eight can be deduced from these four by repeated use of the principle that, if "$P \supset Q$" and "$Q \supset R$" are proved, then "$P \supset R$" is proved. By choosing "P", "Q", "R", and "S" in a judicious order, one can often arrange it so that none of the implications of the cycle "$P \supset Q$", "$Q \supset R$", "$R \supset S$", and "$S \supset P$" is very difficult to prove.

For an illustration, we turn to pages 10 to 11 of Stone, 1932. We quote:[1]

"THEOREM 1.9. The five following assertions concerning the orthonormal set $\{\phi_n\}$ are equivalent:

"(1) $\{\phi_n\}$ is complete;

"(2) $(f,\phi_n) = 0$ for every n implies $f = 0$;

"(3) the closed linear manifold determined by $\{\phi_n\}$ is $\mathfrak{H}$;

"(4) for every f in $\mathfrak{H}$,

$$f = \sum_{\alpha=1}^{\infty} a_\alpha \phi_\alpha, \qquad a_n = (f,\phi_n);$$

"(5) for every pair f, g in $\mathfrak{H}$, the Parseval identity

$$(f,g) = \sum_{\alpha=1}^{\infty} a_\alpha \bar{b}_\alpha, \qquad a_n = (f,\phi_n), \qquad b_n = (g,\phi_n)$$

is true.

"We shall show that the following inferences are possible:

$$1 \to 2 \to 3 \to 4 \to 5 \to 1,$$

each arrow being directed from hypothesis to conclusion. The equivalence of the five assertions is then obvious."

Stone then proceeds with the proofs of the five implications, the details of which do not concern us here.

Another illustration, in which "$P \equiv Q \equiv R$" is proved by proving each of "$P \supset Q$", "$Q \supset R$", and "$R \supset P$" is to be found in the proof of the theorem on page 28 of Halmos, 1942. Another illustration with an unusual twist to it appears in Boas and Pollard.

15. In dealing with equivalences, one takes it for granted that, if "$P \equiv Q$", then "$Q \equiv P$". This follows from Ex. II.3.1(o). Another principle which is sometimes used is that, if "$P \equiv Q$" and "$Q \equiv R$", then

[1] From "Linear Transformations in Hilbert Space and Their Application to Analysis" by Marshall H. Stone, published 1932 by the American Mathematical Society, quoted by permission.

"$P \equiv R$". This follows from Ex. II.3.1(p). It is illustrated on page 3 of Bôcher, 1907, by the proof of:[1]

"THEOREM 5. A necessary and sufficient condition that two polynomials in x be identically equal is that they have the same coefficients."

Bôcher says that the proof follows from the two statements:[1]

"THEOREM 4. A necessary and sufficient condition that a polynomial in x vanish identically is that all its coefficients be zero."

". . . two polynomials in x are identically equal when and only when their difference vanishes identically, . . ."

16. One often hears mentioned the converse of a statement. However, the notion of the converse of a statement is not clearly defined in general. When the statement is a simple one of the form "$P \supset Q$", there is essential agreement as to what the converse is. Some people say that it is "$Q \supset P$" while others say that it is "$\sim P \supset \sim Q$", but since each of these follows from the other, there is no appreciable distinction between them. So we may say that, if we have a simple statement of the form "$P \supset Q$", then its converse is whichever of "$Q \supset P$" or "$\sim P \supset \sim Q$" is convenient to deal with.

THE CONVERSE OF A TRUE THEOREM IS NOT NECESSARILY TRUE!

Or necessarily false either, for that matter.

Another thing to note is that, if two statements are equivalent, it is not necessarily true that their converses are equivalent. Thus "$P \supset (Q \supset R)$" and "$PQ \supset R$" are equivalent, but their converses "$(Q \supset R) \supset P$" and "$R \supset PQ$" are not equivalent. Thus we see that by making quite insignificant changes in the form of a statement we can induce great changes in its converse.

Still further complications arise when one is considering the converse of a more elaborate statement. When "P" or "Q" are elaborate, the converse of "$P \supset Q$" is often not taken to be either of "$Q \supset P$" or "$\sim P \supset \sim Q$", but some other statement not equivalent to these. One form of statement for which this commonly occurs is "$P \supset (Q \supset R)$", for which the converse is rather often taken to be "$P \supset (R \supset Q)$" or "$P \supset (\sim Q \supset \sim R)$". Rather commonly this is done when P is some fairly trivial condition. Thus consider Fort's Thm. 23 which we cited above. Fort's statement of it is:[2]

"THEOREM 23. *Hypothesis*: $\sum_{n=0}^{\infty} a_n$ diverges. *Conclusion*: $\sum_{n=k}^{\infty} a_n$ diverges, k being any fixed integer."

Clearly this is of the form "$P \supset (Q \supset R)$", where "P", "Q", and "R"

[1] From Bôcher, *op. cit.*

[2] From Fort, *op. cit.*

denote respectively "k is a fixed (positive) integer", "$\sum_{n=0}^{\infty} a_n$ diverges", and "$\sum_{n=k}^{\infty} a_n$ diverges".

After the proof of this Thm. 23, Fort states that the converse is readily proved. Quite clearly, he intends either "$P \supset ({\sim}Q \supset {\sim}R)$" or "$P \supset (R \supset Q)$" as the converse and would not for a moment consider "$(Q \supset R) \supset P$" as the converse.

As another instance of taking "$P \supset (R \supset Q)$" to be the converse of "$P \supset (Q \supset R)$", we quote from pages 100 to 101 of Wentworth and Smith. On page 100 we find stated[1] "*Proposition* VII. In the same circle or in equal circles, if two chords are unequal, they are unequally distant from the center, and the greater chord is at the less distance." On page 101 we find stated[1] "*Proposition* VIII. In the same circle or in equal circles, if two chords are unequally distant from the center, they are unequal, and the chord at the less distance is the greater." Below Proposition VIII is the statement that it is the converse of Proposition VII. Here "In the same circle or in equal circles" plays the role of "P", "chords are unequal" plays the role of "Q", and "distances from the center are unequal" plays the role of "R".

Another situation which sometimes arises is that in which the converse of "$PQ \supset R$" is taken to be "$PR \supset Q$" rather than "$R \supset PQ$". Since "$PQ \supset R$" is equivalent to "$P \supset (Q \supset R)$" and "$PR \supset Q$" is equivalent to "$P \supset (R \supset Q)$", this is really a variant of the previous case where the converse of "$P \supset (Q \supset R)$" was taken to be "$P \supset (R \supset Q)$".

Other interesting situations can be found. Thus in Agnew, 1942, page 113, is to be found:[2]

"THEOREM 6.65. If two differentiable functions are linearly dependent over the interval I, then their Wronskian vanishes over the interval I."

This seems to be simply of the form "$P \supset Q$", and the corresponding statement of the form "$Q \supset P$" would appear to be:[2]

"If their Wronskian vanishes over the interval I, then two differentiable functions are linearly dependent over the interval I."

Hence it would seem appropriate to take the second statement as the converse of the first. Agnew does so and goes on to make the point that, whereas the first statement is true, its converse is false.

The interesting point here is that, although superficially the two statements appear to have the forms "$P \supset Q$" and "$Q \supset P$", this is an illusion due to the peculiarities of English grammar. Actually, if we let "P", "Q", and "R" denote "f and g are differentiable", "f and g are linearly dependent

[1] From Wentworth and Smith, *op. cit.*

[2] From "Differential Equations" by R. P. Agnew, copyright 1942, courtesy of McGraw-Hill Book Company, Inc.

over the interval I", and "the Wronskian of f and g vanishes over the interval I", then the first statement is translated by "$PQ \supset R$", whereas the second statement is translated by "$R \supset (P \supset Q)$". As "$R \supset (P \supset Q)$" is not equivalent to "$R \supset PQ$", we have here another instance of an unorthodox converse. Actually, since "$PQ \supset R$" is equivalent to "$P \supset (Q \supset R)$", and "$R \supset (P \supset Q)$" is equivalent to "$P \supset (R \supset Q)$", we have here essentially another instance in which "$P \supset (Q \supset R)$" and "$P \supset (R \supset Q)$" are taken to be converses. However, this instance has the peculiarity that, as far as the English versions of the statements are concerned, the two statements appear to have the forms "$P \supset Q$" and "$Q \supset P$".

One can find still more unorthodox instances of the notion of a converse. As these occur only occasionally, and with considerable variations, there seems no point in cataloguing them. For the reader who is curious to see one such, we note that a rather startling one occurs in the proof of Thm. 17, on page 25 of Birkhoff and MacLane.

5. Summary of Logical Principles. We summarize the logical principles which were discussed and illustrated in the preceding section.

1. Modus ponens. If "P" and "$P \supset Q$", then "Q".
2. If "P" and "Q", then "PQ".
3. If "$P \supset Q$" and "$Q \supset R$", then "$P \supset R$".
4. If "$\sim Q \supset \sim P$", then "$P \supset Q$".
5. Proof by cases. If "$P \supset R$" and "$Q \supset R$", then "$P \vee Q \supset R$".
6. Proof by cases. If "$P \supset Q$" and "$\sim P \supset Q$", then "Q".
7. Proof of "P" by reductio ad absurdum. Assume "$\sim P$" and deduce "$Q \sim Q$".
8. Proof of "$\sim P$" by reductio ad absurdum. Assume "P" and deduce "$Q \sim Q$".
9. Proof of "$P \supset Q$" by reductio ad absurdum. Assume "$P \sim Q$" and deduce "$R \sim R$".
10. Proof of "$P \supset Q$" by reductio ad absurdum. Assume "$P \sim Q$" and deduce "Q".
11. Proof of "$P \supset Q$" by reductio ad absurdum. Assume "$P \sim Q$" and deduce "$\sim P$".
12. Miscellaneous proofs of "$P \vee Q$". See Ex. II.3.1(l), (m), and (n).
13. Proof of "$P \equiv Q$". Prove "$P \supset Q$" and "$Q \supset P$".
14. Proof of "$P \equiv Q \equiv R \equiv S$". Prove "$P \supset Q$", "$Q \supset R$", "$R \supset S$", and "$S \supset P$".
15. Proof of "$P \equiv Q$". Prove "$P \equiv R$" and "$Q \equiv R$".

EXERCISES

II.5.1. Find illustrations in the mathematical literature of at least six of the fifteen principles listed above.

II.5.2. Find an illustration in the mathematical literature of a true theorem "$P \supset Q$" whose converse "$Q \supset P$" is false.

II.5.3. On page 21 of Fort, 1930, appears the theorem:[1]

"*Hypothesis*: $\sum_{n=0}^{\infty} |a_n|$ converges.

Conclusion: $\sum_{n=0}^{\infty} a_n$ converges and $\left| \sum_{n=0}^{\infty} a_n \right| \leq \sum_{n=0}^{\infty} |a_n|$."

Without looking up the proof, state one of the fifteen principles above which will be used in the proof.

II.5.4. On page 32 of the present text occurs the statement: "AB and CD never meet, for if they met, the point at which they meet would be a point at which planes EF and GH meet." Which of the fifteen principles does this illustrate?

II.5.5. Tell which of the fifteen principles is used in the following proof taken from page 38 of Fort, 1930, in which it is assumed that the a's are all positive.[1]

"THEOREM 49. *Hypothesis*: $\sum_{n=1}^{\infty} a_n$ diverges.

Conclusion: $\sum_{n=1}^{\infty} \frac{a_n}{a_1 + \cdots + a_n}$ diverges.

"Now suppose

$$\sum_{n=1}^{\infty} \frac{a_n}{a_1 + \cdots + a_n} \text{ convergent. Then}$$

$$\sum_{\nu=n+1}^{n+p} \frac{a_\nu}{a_1 + \cdots + a_\nu} \to 0$$

when $n \to \infty$. Consequently it is possible to choose an m such that when $n \geq m$,

$$\left| 1 - \frac{a_1 + \cdots + a_n}{a_1 + \cdots + a_{n+p}} \right| < \frac{1}{2} \text{ for example.}$$

"But for any fixed n when $p \to \infty$

$$\left| 1 - \frac{a_1 + \cdots + a_n}{a_1 + \cdots + a_{n-p}} \right| \to 1, \text{ a contradiction."}$$

II.5.6. Tell which of the fifteen principles is used in the following proof (see Figs. II.5.1 to II.5.3) condensed from pages 118 to 119 of Wentworth and Smith.[2]

An inscribed angle is measured by half the intercepted arc.

[1] From Fort, *op. cit.*

[2] From Wentworth and Smith, *op. cit.*

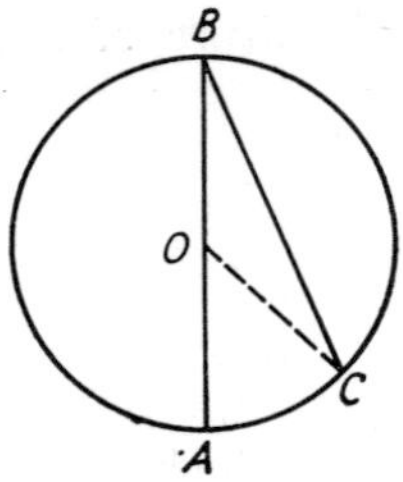

FIG. II.5.1.

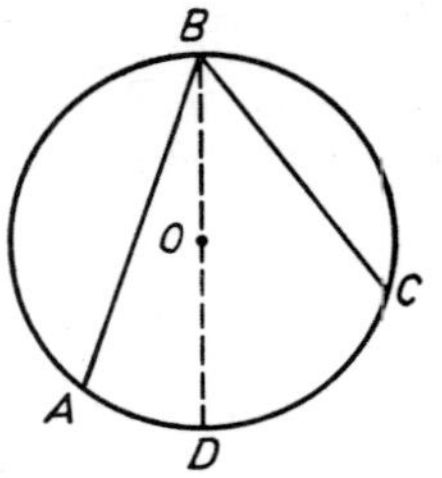

FIG. II.5.2.

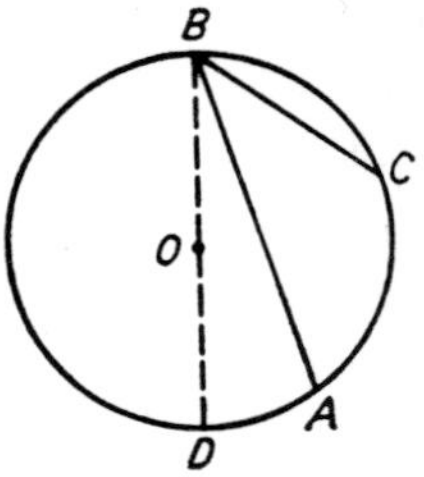

FIG. II.5.3.

Given: A circle with the center O and the inscribed angle B, intercepting the arc AC.

To prove: That $\angle B$ is measured by half the arc AC.

Case 1. When O is on one side, as AB (Fig. II.5.1).

Proof. Draw OC. Then $\angle AOC$ equals $\angle B + \angle C$. But $\angle B = \angle C$. So $\angle B = \frac{1}{2} \angle AOC$. As $\angle AOC$ is measured by arc AC (previous theorem), we conclude that $\angle B$ is measured by half arc AC.

Case 2. When O lies within the angle B (Fig. II.5.2).

Proof. Draw the diameter BD. By Case 1, $\angle ABD$ is measured by half arc AD and $\angle DBC$ is measured by half arc DC. Adding gives $\angle B$ measured by half arc AC.

Case 3. When O lies outside the angle B (Fig. II.5.3).

Proof. Draw the diameter BD. By Case 1, $\angle CBD$ is measured by half arc CD and $\angle ABD$ is measured by half arc AD. Subtracting gives $\angle B$ measured by half arc AC. Q.E.D.

II.5.7. Find a case in the mathematical literature where the word "converse" is used in some peculiar fashion, such as taking "$P \supset (R \supset Q)$" to be the converse of "$P \supset (Q \supset R)$" or taking "$PR \supset Q$" to be the converse of "$PQ \supset R$".

II.5.8. Identify the logical principle in the following quotation from "Through the Looking-glass" by Lewis Carroll:

" 'Everybody that hears me sing it—either it brings the *tears* into their eyes, or else . . . .'

" 'Or else what?' said Alice, for the Knight had made a sudden pause.

" 'Or else it doesn't, you know.' "

CHAPTER III

THE USE OF NAMES

"The name of the song is called *'Haddocks' Eyes.'* "

"Oh, that's the name of the song, is it?" Alice said, trying to feel interested.

"No, you don't understand," the Knight said, looking a little vexed. "That's what the name is *called.* The name really *is, 'The Aged Aged Man.'* "

"Then I ought to have said 'That's what the *song* is called'?" Alice corrected herself.

"No, you oughtn't: that's quite another thing! The *song* is called *'Ways and Means'*: but that's only what it's *called,* you know!"

"Well, what *is* the song, then?" said Alice, who was by this time completely bewildered.

"I was coming to that," the Knight said. "The song really *is 'A-sitting On A Gate'*: and the tune's my own invention."

LEWIS CARROLL

A statement about something generally contains a name of that thing, but it must not contain the thing itself.

Applied to natural objects, this seems quite obvious, since in such case the statement usually could not contain the thing itself. Consider the statement "Georgia is a southern state." This contains the word "Georgia," which is a name of the state in question. Clearly it would be impracticable to replace the word "Georgia" in this statement by the state itself.

Similar considerations apply to "The moon is made of green cheese," "The Atlantic Ocean is wet," "The Equator is long," etc.

For small objects, these considerations are not quite so conclusive. In the statement "This thumbtack is round," one could conceivably erase the words "This thumbtack" and in the empty space stick the thumbtack into the page. One can make rather cogent objections that the resulting conglomeration of two words and a thumbtack is not a statement, but a rebus or charade. In any case, any other statement about that particular thumbtack positively could NOT contain the thumbtack, since the thumbtack has now been preempted to appear in the particular place indicated. Further, and for the same reason, if one wished to repeat the same statement the repetition could not contain the thumbtack but must contain some name of the thumbtack, such as the words "This thumbtack."

For these and other reasons, it is generally agreed that, although one could put together a combination consisting of a thumbtack followed by the words "is round," and although this combination would doubtless convey information, nevertheless the combination does not constitute a statement.

This seems fair enough. Certainly not all means of conveying information are necessarily statements. If a policeman at a busy intersection waves us to stop, he has certainly conveyed information, but hardly in the form of a statement.

To summarize, it is generally agreed about statements that a statement about something must contain a name of that thing, rather than the thing itself. We shall conform with this usage.

Throughout the present text, we are repeatedly making statements about other statements, and by the above dictum the statements which we make must contain names of the statements about which we are speaking. For a word or a statement, one standard procedure for constructing a name is to enclose the word or statement in quotation marks. Thus one writes:

"Georgia is a southern state" contains "Georgia."

This is a statement about the statement "Georgia is a southern state" and the word "Georgia," and so contains names of the statement and the word, to wit, the statement and the word together with surrounding quotation marks.

If one wishes to talk about a name of a statement or of a word, one must use a name of this name. This becomes rather awkward as in the final words of the preceding paragraph, or in the statement:

The name of "Georgia" is " 'Georgia'."

In writing the above statement, we are making a statement about a word and a name of the word, and so must actually use a name of the word and a name of the name of the word. Thus we have to use the awkward double quotation marks to make the simple statement about the particular word "Georgia" that, if one has a word without quotation marks, one forms its name by enclosing it in quotation marks.

Such awkward situations arise only when one is discussing names of words or statements (as we are doing now). Throughout most of the study of logic we make statements only about other statements and not about names of other statements. Thus we have to USE names of statements (requiring use of single quotation marks), but we do not have to discuss names of statements (and so have no need for quotation marks within quotation marks). One place where one does have to discuss names of statements is in the proof of Gödel's theorem that a consistent logic adequate for mathematics is incomplete. In this proof we have to use names of names of statements in order to discuss the names of statements. Failure to comprehend this point is one of the major causes of difficulty in comprehending the proof of Gödel's theorem.

For the greater part of logic, no such difficulties arise. Thus for the greater part of logic one can be rather careless about the use of quotation marks without getting into any difficulty. Such carelessness is usual, and in the future we shall indulge in such carelessness ourselves. Up to now, we have scrupulously tried to be correct. When referring to statements, we have used names of the statements, to wit, the statements enclosed in quotation marks. This has been done consistently, both for statements of English and statements of symbolic logic except in displayed formulas, where the act of displaying was considered tantamount to enclosure in quotation marks. Similarly, use in a truth-value table was considered tantamount to enclosure in quotation marks of the "P", "Q", etc., which required enclosure in quotation marks. We took "T" and "F" as being the names of truth values and hence not requiring enclosure in quotation marks. For them, use in a truth-value table was not considered tantamount to enclosure in quotation marks.

As an illustration of the use of quotation marks when making statements about statements, consider the following sentences of Sec. 1 of Chapter II (which we take the license of quoting without enclosing in quotation marks):

To illustrate, let "P" and "Q" be translations of "It is raining now" and "It is not cloudy now." Then "$(P\&Q)$" is a translation of "It is raining now and it is not cloudy now," and "$\sim P$" and "$\sim Q$" are translations of "It is not raining now" and "It is cloudy now."

In such an explanation, carelessness with quotation marks is inadvisable, and we shall not indulge in it. However, in extensive formal developments, which make up the bulk of many subsequent chapters, one can omit all quotation marks without danger of confusion and with a saving in complexity. In such case, we make such omission without comment.

Be it understood that we are not admitting such omission of quotation marks to be correct; we are merely condoning it as convenient.

This is in line with current mathematical practice in dealing with symbols. A statement such as "If x and y are numbers, then $x + y = y + x$" violates the rule about using names of things when speaking of these things. It should properly be written as "If 'x' and 'y' are numbers, then '$x + y$' = '$y + x$'." However, in the first version (without quotation marks), there can be no more doubt of the meaning intended than in the second. Hence, if it is understood that the first is merely shorthand for the second, there can be no harm in using it.

In a printed text, the "x" and "y" in such statements are customarily written in italics, thereby decreasing the likelihood of any misunderstanding.

It is of interest that there is a place in mathematics where confusion occasionally arises from a failure to preserve a careful distinction between an object and its name. This is in connection with fractions.

The fractions "3/4", "6/8", "9/12", etc., are all names of a certain rational number, which incidentally has many other names such as "0.75", "$\sqrt{0.5625}$", "$\int_0^1 3x^3\,dx$", etc. Thus if one writes "3/4 = 9/12," one is making a statement about the rational number, and names of the rational number appear in the statement. This is as it should be. However, if one writes "3 divides the denominator of 9/12," one is not making a statement about the rational number, but about one of its names. Thus one should write instead "3 divides the denominator of '9/12'."

The chance for confusion here is slight. However, one will occasionally encounter an alert youngster who wishes to know why, if "3/4 = 9/12," one cannot replace "9/12" by "3/4" in the statement "3 divides the denominator of 9/12," whereas it is perfectly correct to replace "9/12 "by "3/4" in the statement "3 is greater than 9/12." The answer, of course, is that "9/12" actually occurs in the second statement, whereas "9/12" does not actually appear in the first statement but only a name of "9/12". Since the first statement is incorrectly written, it appears to contain "9/12" at a point where it really contains a name of "9/12".

The alert youngster may then inquire why one cannot replace "9/12" by "3/4" in the correctly formulated statement "3 divides the denominator of '9/12'," since this also contains "9/12". The answer in this case is that the occurrence of "9/12" in the correct version of the sentence is a purely typographical occurrence, like the "s" in "$\sin x$" or the "d" in "dy/dx". If one is given "$s = d$", one would not think of replacing "s" by "d" in "$\sin x$" or "d" by "s" in "dy/dx". If one had used some other name for "9/12", there would have been no question of substituting "3/4". Thus one might have written "3 divides the denominator of the fraction got by placing a '9' over a bar and a '12' under the bar."

The gist of the matter is that, if we have a statement such as "3 is greater than 9/12" about the rational number 9/12 and containing a name "9/12" of this rational number, one can replace this name by any other name of the same rational number, for instance, "3/4". If we have a statement such as "3 divides the denominator of '9/12' " about a name of a rational number and containing a name of this name, one can replace this name of the name by some other name of the same name, but not in general by the name of some other name, even if it is a name of some other name of the same rational number.

As we said once before, failure to observe such distinctions carefully can seldom lead to confusion in logic and still less seldom in mathematics, and so in much of our text we shall omit the quotation marks that should appear. In so doing, we follow accepted mathematical practice.

Meanwhile, there is one important point concerning names within our symbolic logic. Names are important constituents of statements in symbolic logic even as in more familiar languages. In using the English language, we always assume that our sentences have meaning and that the names which occur in them are the names of something. Not so in our symbolic logic. There is no requirement that a statement of symbolic logic have meaning. Consequently the names which occur in such statements need not be names of anything. This is very convenient, since we are thus entitled to use names without first (or ever) being assured that they are the names of something. We shall amplify this point when we introduce names within our symbolic logic (see Chapter VIII).

CHAPTER IV

AXIOMATIC TREATMENT OF THE STATEMENT CALCULUS

1. The Axiomatic Method of Defining Valid Statements. In effect the axiomatic definition of valid statements is accomplished as follows. Certain statements, chosen rather arbitrarily, are called axioms. We then consider to be valid statements just those statements which are either axioms, or can be derived from several axioms by successive uses of modus ponens.

We shall make the above definition more precise in the next section, but for the moment we wish to discuss certain general aspects of the axiomatic method. In the first place, modus ponens depends only on the forms of the statements involved, and not at all on their meanings. Hence, if the choice of axioms is made to depend upon form only, then the axiomatic definition of valid statement will depend entirely on the forms of the statement. This accords with our stipulation that our symbolic logic shall be independent of the meanings of the statements.

In Chapter II, we learned the method of truth-value tables whereby we could classify certain statements as universally valid. However, this applied only to statement formulas, which are a very specialized type of statement. Unfortunately, the very convenient method of truth-value tables cannot be generalized to general types of statements, for which we must use some more general method. So far, only the axiomatic method is known for handling the most general types of statements. One of the unsolved problems is to find some method other than the axiomatic method for handling the most general types of statements.

It will be some time before we are prepared to give a complete list of axioms. In the present chapter we shall list a subset of the axioms with the following interesting properties. In the first place, any universally valid statement formula can be derived from axioms of this subset by means of modus ponens. In the second place, any statement which can be derived from axioms of this subset by means of modus ponens is a universally valid statement formula. Accordingly, the axioms of this subset are known as the truth-value axioms.

Consider the two properties of the truth-value axioms which we cited in the preceding paragraph. These properties are statements about our symbolic logic, and not statements within our symbolic logic. Accordingly, the proofs which we will give of the statements must be carried out in intuitive logic, and not within the symbolic logic. We have referred earlier to this matter of proving statements about the symbolic logic, and remind the reader that we rigidly restrict ourselves to the use of a very simple intuitive logic for such proofs. We postpone a more extensive discussion of this intuitive logic until the next chapter. However, let us emphasize again the distinction between a proof within the symbolic logic and a proof about the symbolic logic. A proof within the symbolic logic shall be a sequence of uses of modus ponens applied to some set of axioms. Once written out, it can be checked quite mechanically. On the other hand, a proof about the symbolic logic will require more than a rudimentary intelligence for its comprehension, even though we permit only quite simple proofs about the symbolic logic. A typical result that we shall prove about our symbolic logic is that for statements of a particular form proofs within the symbolic logic can be found; in particular, the present chapter will be mainly devoted to an intuitive proof about the symbolic logic that, for each statement formula which always takes the value T, there can be found a proof within the symbolic logic. This intuitive proof will be constructive in that we shall give very explicit directions for writing out the sequence of uses of modus ponens which will constitute the proof within the symbolic logic.

We wish to make one point clear about our use of the word "axiom." Originally the word was used by Euclid to mean a "self-evident truth." This use of the word "axiom" has long been completely obsolete in mathematical circles. For us, the axioms are a set of arbitrarily chosen statements which, together with the rule of modus ponens, suffice to derive all the statements which we wish to derive. This corresponds to the standard mathematical usage of the word "axiom."

2. The Truth-value Axioms. We present in the present chapter just that subset of all the axioms which we have chosen to call the truth-value axioms, namely, a subset such that the axioms of the subset plus all the statements which can be derived from them by successive uses of modus ponens constitute exactly the set of statement formulas which always take the value T. One obvious way to choose such a set of truth-value axioms is to have the truth-value axioms consist of exactly those statement formulas which always take the value T; this procedure is followed by some logicians. However, we consider it more elegant and more instructive to choose a smaller subset of the axioms to be our truth-value axioms, and we do so.

Our truth-value axioms shall consist of an infinite number of statements, but they will be of only three general forms, which we call axiom schemes, to wit:

1. $P \supset PP$.
2. $PQ \supset P$.
3. $P \supset Q . \supset . \sim(QR) \supset \sim(RP)$.

The precise definition of the truth-value axioms is:

If P, Q, and R are statements, not necessarily distinct, then each of the following is an axiom:

1. $P \supset PP$.
2. $PQ \supset P$.
3. $P \supset Q . \supset . \sim(QR) \supset \sim(RP)$.

We shall refer to the three forms above as Axiom schemes 1, 2, and 3, respectively. Any particular axiom having one of these forms will be referred to as an instance of the axiom scheme in question.

Because we can let P and Q be the same, we infer that $PP \supset P$ is an axiom, being an instance of Axiom scheme 2. As another illustration of an axiom, we take P to be $\sim R$ in Axiom scheme 1, and infer that $\sim R \supset \sim R \sim R$ is an axiom. Written in unabbreviated form, this is $\sim(\sim R \sim(\sim R \sim R))$, which is the unabbreviated form of $R \vee \sim R \sim R$. So $R \vee \sim R \sim R$ is also an axiom, being an instance of Axiom scheme 1.

The axioms defined by Axiom schemes 1, 2, and 3 are called the truth-value axioms and are only a subset of all the axioms which we shall eventually present. It is our intention to define our axioms so that they can be identified by reference to their form only and without any reference to their meaning. It will be observed that we have abided by this restriction in defining the truth-value axioms.

We shall show that the truth-value axioms together with the statements which can be derived from them by successive uses of modus ponens constitute exactly the statement formulas which always take the value T. We now define precisely the vague phrase "the statements which can be derived from them by successive uses of modus ponens." We first generalize this to the case where Q is derived not merely from the axioms, but also from certain assumptions $P_1, P_2, \ldots, P_n$. We introduce the notation:

$$P_1, P_2, \ldots, P_n \vdash Q.$$

The intuitive meaning of this is to be that either Q is an axiom or else Q is one of the P's, or else Q is derived from the axioms and the P's by successive uses of modus ponens. The precise definition is as follows:

$P_1, P_2, \ldots, P_n \vdash Q$ indicates that there is a sequence of statements $S_1, S_2, \ldots, S_s$, such that S_s is Q and for each S_i either:

(1) S_i is an axiom.
(2) S_i is a P.
(3) S_i is the same as some earlier S_j.
(4) S_i is derived from two earlier S's by modus ponens.

More precise versions of (3) and (4) are:

(3) There is a j less than i such that S_i and S_j are the same.
(4) There are j and k, each less than i, such that S_k is $S_j \supset S_i$.

In the precise version of (4), S_j is the minor premise, and S_k is the major premise.

The sequence of statements $S_1, S_2, \ldots, S_s$ is called a demonstration of $P_1, P_2, \ldots, P_n \vdash Q$. This sequence $S_1, S_2, \ldots, S_s$ constitutes a proof within the symbolic logic that Q is a logical consequence of the assumptions $P_1, P_2, \ldots, P_n$. That is why the sequence is called a demonstration. The S's which make up the sequence are called the steps of the demonstration. The reader should note the analogy with the more standard mathematical usage of the words "demonstration" and "steps of a demonstration."

By (3), one is permitted to repeat any step of a demonstration as often as desired. In constructing a demonstration, this usually serves no useful purpose, and it would ordinarily be silly to repeat steps. However, it will simplify certain of our proofs of theorems about the symbolic logic if repetition of steps is permitted. As repetition of steps is harmless, we therefore permit it.

Notice that, if a sequence of statements $S_1, S_2, \ldots, S_s$ be written down, then it is a perfectly mechanical procedure to check whether it is or is not a demonstration of $P_1, P_2, \ldots, P_n \vdash Q$.

The symbol "$\vdash$" is called a turnstile. The statement $P_1, P_2, \ldots, P_n \vdash Q$ is read as "$P_1, P_2, \ldots, P_n$ yield Q". In case there are no P's, we write simply $\vdash Q$ and read "yields Q". This case is of especial importance, since it signifies that Q is derived from the axioms alone, without any assumptions $P_1, P_2, \ldots, P_n$. Hence $\vdash Q$ signifies that Q is a consequence of the axioms, or that Q is a provable statement of our symbolic logic.

One point which is made clear by our precise definition of $\vdash Q$ is that, in deriving Q from the axioms by a succession of uses of modus ponens, one can apply modus ponens not merely to the axioms but also to any results derived from them.

Another point about our definition of $P_1, P_2, \ldots, P_n \vdash Q$ is that it states that Q can be derived from the assumptions $P_1, P_2, \ldots, P_n$ with the help of *all* the axioms, and not merely with the help of the truth-value axioms. Temporarily, throughout the remainder of the present section, we shall let $P_1, P_2, \ldots, P_n \vdash^* Q$ denote that Q can be derived from the assumptions $P_1, P_2, \ldots, P_n$ with the help of the truth-value axioms alone. The definition of $P_1, P_2, \ldots, P_n \vdash^* Q$ is just like that of $P_1, P_2, \ldots, P_n \vdash Q$ except that we replace (1) by:

(1*) S_i is a truth-value axiom.

We can now express our earlier clumsy and somewhat vague statement ". . . the truth-value axioms together with the statements which can be derived from them by successive uses of modus ponens constitute exactly the statement formulas which always take the value T" in the neater and more precise form "$\vdash^* Q$ if and only if Q is a statement formula which always takes the value T."

The statement in quotation marks just above is an equivalence. Although it is an intuitive equivalence, nevertheless, many of the remarks in Chapter II about proving equivalences apply, and we can (and shall) prove it by proving the two implications:

If $\vdash^* Q$, then Q is a statement formula which always takes the value T.

If Q is a statement formula which always takes the value T, then $\vdash^* Q$.

We now prove the first of these. Assume $\vdash^* Q$. By the definition of $\vdash^* Q$, there is a sequence of statements $S_1, S_2, \ldots, S_s$ such that S_s is Q and for each S_i either:

(1*) S_i is one of the axioms specified by Axiom schemes 1, 2, or 3.
(3) There is a j less than i such that S_i and S_j are the same.
(4) There are j and k, each less than i such that S_k is $S_j \supset S_i$.

Note the absence of (2), due to the lack of P's before the $\vdash^* Q$.

We now prove by induction on m that S_m is a statement formula which always takes the value T. If $m = 1$, we must have (1*). By making truth-value tables for our three axiom schemes, we verify that each axiom specified by Axiom schemes 1, 2, or 3 is a statement formula which always takes the value T. So S_1 is a statement formula which always takes the value T. Now suppose that each of $S_1, S_2, \ldots, S_m$ is a statement formula which always takes the value T, and put $i = m + 1$. If (1*), we use the same argument as for $m = 1$. If (3), then S_{m+1} is the same as some earlier S, and so is a statement formula which always takes the value T. If (4), then S_k is $S_j \supset S_{m+1}$, where each of S_j and S_k occurs before S_{m+1}. So each of S_j and $S_j \supset S_{m+1}$ is a statement formula which always takes the value T. Inspection of the truth-value table for $\supset$ shows that in this case S_{m+1} must also always take the value T. Also S_{m+1} must be a statement formula.

Since S_m is a statement formula which always takes the value T for each m, we put $m = s$ and infer that Q is a statement formula which always takes the value T.

The converse, "If Q is a statement formula which always takes the value T, then $\vdash^* Q$," is much harder to prove. We devote the next three sections to its proof. However, throughout the next three sections we shall use $\vdash$ instead of $\vdash^*$. We are not doing this with the understanding that $\vdash$ stands for $\vdash^*$, but we actually intend $\vdash$. The point is that the results with $\vdash^*$, while interesting, are not what we shall need for later developments. It is the results with $\vdash$ that we shall need later, and it is these which we shall prove. However, for the benefit of any interested reader, we point out that throughout the next three sections all our proofs are such that all our theorems and proofs would still hold if we should replace $\vdash$ by $\vdash^*$. Thus in Sec. 5 we prove Thm.IV.5.3, which says that, if Q is a statement formula which always takes the value T, then $\vdash Q$. However, our proof would equally well prove "If Q is a statement formula which always takes the value T, then $\vdash^* Q$." As the latter statement is of some interest, we therefore claim that we prove it, even though all that we state at the time and ever make use of afterwards is the weaker statement with $\vdash$.

The weaker result with $\vdash$ is a very useful result, since it gives us quite a handy way of proving $\vdash Q$ for a considerable number of Q's.

We shall refer to this result as the "truth-value theorem."

EXERCISES

IV.2.1. Prove $P \vdash PP$.

IV.2.2. Prove $PP \vdash P$.

IV.2.3. Prove $\sim(\sim PP), \sim P \supset \sim P \vdash P \supset P$. (*Hint.* Put $\sim P$, $\sim P$, and P for P, Q, R in Axiom scheme 3.)

IV.2.4. Prove that, if $P_1, P_2, \ldots, P_n \vdash^* Q$, then $P_1, P_2, \ldots, P_n \vdash Q$.

3. Properties of $\vdash$. Various properties of $\vdash$ are almost obvious, but it is perhaps worth while stating and proving them explicitly.

Theorem IV.3.1. If $P_1, \ldots, P_n \vdash Q$, then $P_1, \ldots, P_n, R_1, \ldots, R_m \vdash Q$.

Proof. Clearly any sequence of S's which will serve for a demonstration of $P_1, \ldots, P_n \vdash Q$ will serve equally well for a demonstration of $P_1, \ldots, P_n, R_1, \ldots, R_m \vdash Q$.

Theorem IV.3.2. If $P_1, \ldots, P_n \vdash Q_1$ and $Q_1, \ldots, Q_m \vdash R$, then $P_1, \ldots, P_n, Q_2, \ldots, Q_m \vdash R$.

Proof. Let $S_1, \ldots, S_s$ be a demonstration of $P_1, \ldots, P_n \vdash Q_1$ and $\Sigma_1, \ldots, \Sigma_\sigma$ be a demonstration of $Q_1, \ldots, Q_m \vdash R$. Then each S is either an axiom or a P or an earlier S or derived from two earlier S's by modus ponens, and S_s is Q_1. Likewise each Σ is either an axiom or a Q or an earlier Σ or derived from two earlier Σ's by modus ponens, and Σ_σ is R. If we now construct a new sequence to consist of all the S's in order followed by all the Σ's in order then we have a demonstration of $P_1, \ldots, P_n, Q_2, \ldots, Q_m \vdash R$. To see this, note that the final step is Σ_σ, which is R. Those Σ's (if any) which are Q_1 are now accounted for as being repetitions of S_s. All S's and all other Σ's are accounted for as before.

Theorem IV.3.3. If $P_1, \ldots, P_n \vdash Q_1, R_1, \ldots, R_m \vdash Q_2$, and $Q_1, \ldots, Q_q \vdash S$, then $P_1, \ldots, P_n, R_1, \ldots, R_m, Q_3, \ldots, Q_q \vdash S$.

Proof. From $P_1, \ldots, P_n \vdash Q_1$ and $Q_1, \ldots, Q_q \vdash S$ we get $P_1, \ldots, P_n, Q_2, \ldots, Q_q \vdash S$ by Thm.IV.3.2. From $R_1, \ldots, R_m \vdash Q_2$ and $P_1, \ldots, P_n, Q_2, \ldots, Q_q \vdash S$ we get $P_1, \ldots, P_n, R_1, \ldots, R_m, Q_3, \ldots, Q_q \vdash S$ by Thm.IV.3.2.

Theorem IV.3.4. $P, P \supset Q \vdash Q$.

Proof. A sequence of S's that will serve as a demonstration of this is clearly:

S_1: P.

S_2: $P \supset Q$.

S_3: Q.

Theorem IV.3.5. If $P_1, \ldots, P_n \vdash Q$ and $R_1, \ldots, R_m \vdash Q \supset S$, then $P_1, \ldots, P_n, R_1, \ldots, R_m \vdash S$.

Proof. In Thm.IV.3.3, take Q_1 to be Q and Q_2 to be $Q \supset S$, and use Thm.IV.3.4.

We note the particularly useful special case of Thm.IV.3.2:

Theorem IV.3.6. If $\vdash Q_1$ and $Q_1, \ldots, Q_m \vdash R$, then $Q_2, \ldots, Q_m \vdash R$.

By applying this successively m times, we deduce:

Theorem IV.3.7. If $\vdash Q_1, \vdash Q_2, \ldots, \vdash Q_m$, and $Q_1, \ldots, Q_m \vdash R$, then $\vdash R$.

This states the obvious, but very useful, principle that, if $Q_1, \ldots, Q_m \vdash R$, and if each of $Q_1, \ldots, Q_m$ can be derived by the axiomatic method, then R can also be derived by the axiomatic method.

Theorem IV.3.8. If $S_1, S_2, \ldots, S_s$ is a demonstration of $P_1, P_2, \ldots, P_n \vdash Q$, then for $1 \leq j \leq s$, $S_1, S_2, \ldots, S_j$ is a demonstration of $P_1, P_2, \ldots, P_n \vdash S_j$.

Theorem IV.3.9. If $R_1, \ldots, R_n$ is any permutation of $P_1, \ldots, P_n$ and if $P_1, \ldots, P_n \vdash Q$, then $R_1, \ldots, R_n \vdash Q$.

Theorem IV.3.10. If $P_1, P_2, \ldots, P_n \vdash Q$, then $P_1, P_1, \ldots, P_1, P_2 \ldots, P_n \vdash Q$, and vice versa.

EXERCISES

IV.3.1. Prove that, if $P \vdash Q$ and $Q \vdash R$, then $P \vdash R$.

IV.3.2. Prove that, if $\vdash P \supset Q$, then $P \vdash Q$.

4. Preliminary Theorems. The reader has become familiar with the use of truth-value tables. As the axiomatic method is quite different, the reader must make a deliberate effort not to carry over to the axiomatic method any habits which he has acquired while using the truth-value tables. Thus by truth-value tables one easily shows the commutativity, associativity, and distributivity of & and **v** (see Ex. II.3.6, II.3.7, II.3.8, and II.3.9). There is accordingly a temptation to make immediate use of these properties in the axiomatic method. Thus, from Axiom scheme 2, $PQ \supset P$, one is tempted to infer $QP \supset P$ immediately by commutativity of &. However, one does not have commutativity of & at first with the axiomatic method, nor is it easy to deduce. Not until Thm.IV.4.13 do we deduce the commutativity of &, and then only in a limited form which does not permit indiscriminate replacement of PQ by QP. Thus $QP \supset P$

is not available until Thm.IV.4.18, which gives a generalized form of both $PQ \supset P$ and $QP \supset P$.

After we have proved the truth-value theorem that $\vdash P$ if P always takes the value T, we can proceed to do anything that we could do with truth-value tables. Until then, we have to proceed very cautiously.

Theorem IV.4.1. $P \supset Q, Q \supset R \vdash \sim(\sim RP)$, where P, Q, and R are statements.

Proof. Let P, Q, and R be statements. Define $S_1, \ldots, S_5$ as follows:

S_1: $P \supset Q$.

S_2: $\sim(Q\sim R)$.

S_3: $P \supset Q. \supset .\sim(Q\sim R) \supset \sim(\sim RP)$.

S_4: $\sim(Q\sim R) \supset \sim(\sim RP)$.

S_5: $\sim(\sim RP)$.

This sequence of S's constitutes a demonstration, as we see by noting the following facts. S_5 is $\sim(\sim RP)$. S_1 and S_2 are $P \supset Q$ and $Q \supset R$. S_3 is an instance of Axiom scheme 3. Also S_3 has the form $S_1 \supset S_4$, so that S_4 is derived by use of modus ponens from S_1 as minor premise and S_3 as major premise. S_4 has the form $S_2 \supset S_5$, so that S_5 is derived by use of modus ponens from S_2 as minor premise and S_4 as major premise.

If we already had the commutativity of &, we could interchange $\sim R$ and P in the conclusion of this theorem, and write $P \supset Q, Q \supset R \vdash P \supset R$. However, we do not yet have commutativity, and so this result must wait awhile.

The fact that Thm.IV.4.1 is true no matter what statements are taken for P, Q, and R is due to the fact that any statements can be taken for P, Q, and R in the axiom schemes and modus ponens. For the same reason, a similar freedom in the choice of P, Q, R, etc., holds for all theorems. This will be taken for granted hereafter, and not mentioned explicitly.

Theorem IV.4.2. $\vdash \sim(\sim PP)$.

Proof. Define $S_1, \ldots, S_5$ as follows:

S_1: $P \supset PP$.

S_2: $\sim(PP\sim P)$.

S_3: $P \supset PP. \supset .\sim(PP\sim P) \supset \sim(\sim PP)$.

S_4: $\sim(PP\sim P) \supset \sim(\sim PP)$.

S_5: $\sim(\sim PP)$.

This sequence of S's constitutes a demonstration. S_5 is $\sim(\sim PP)$. S_1 is an instance of Axiom scheme 1. S_2 is an instance of Axiom scheme 2 with P in place of Q. S_3 is an instance of Axiom scheme 3 with PP in place of Q and P in place of R. S_3 has the form $S_1 \supset S_4$, so that S_4 follows by modus ponens from S_1 and S_3. Similarly, S_5 follows by modus ponens from S_2 and S_4.

We shall not write out in full any more demonstrations, but we shall always give explicit instructions so that anyone who desires can write out any or all of the demonstrations. For instance, instead of writing out the demonstration for Thm.IV.4.2, we could have given the following instructions:

Proof. Put PP for Q and P for R in Thm.IV.4.1. Then $P \supset Q$ becomes an instance of Axiom scheme 1 and $Q \supset R$ becomes an instance of Axiom scheme 2. Then by Thm.IV.3.7, we get $\vdash \sim(\sim PP)$.

Theorem IV.4.3.

I. $\vdash \sim\sim P \supset P$.

II. $\vdash \sim P \mathbf{v} P$.

Proof. Put $\sim P$ for P in Thm.IV.4.2. This gives $\vdash \sim(\sim\sim P \sim P)$, which is the unabbreviated form of both $\vdash \sim\sim P \supset P$ and $\vdash \sim P \mathbf{v} P$.

Let us make one point clear about this matter of substituting $\sim P$ for P in Thm.IV.4.3. This does not mean that one gets a demonstration of $\vdash \sim\sim P \supset P$ by writing down the five steps of the demonstration of $\vdash \sim(\sim PP)$ and adding $\sim(\sim\sim P \sim P)$ as a sixth step with the explanation that it comes from the fifth step by replacing P by $\sim P$. No such procedure for getting a step from a preceding step is permitted by our definition of $\vdash$. What one must do to get a demonstration of $\vdash \sim\sim P \supset P$ is to replace P by $\sim P$ in every step of the demonstration of $\vdash \sim(\sim PP)$. Then all steps that were axioms will again be axioms, all steps that were repetitions of previous steps will again be repetitions of previous steps, and all steps that were derivable from two earlier steps by modus ponens will again be derivable from two earlier steps by modus ponens.

A similar analysis will show that, if one has assumptions to the left of the yields sign, as in Thm.IV.4.1, one can still replace each P, Q, R, etc., by any other statement, provided that one does so for every occurrence on both sides of the yields sign. Thus, from Thm.IV.4.1, we can infer $\sim P \supset Q$, $Q \supset \sim R \vdash \sim\sim R \supset P$, but we cannot infer $P \supset Q, Q \supset R \vdash \sim\sim R \supset P$.

Theorem IV.4.4. $\vdash \sim(QR) \supset (R \supset \sim Q)$.

Proof. Put $\sim\sim Q$ for P in Axiom scheme 3. Take the result as major premise and Thm. IV.4.3 as minor premise, and use modus ponens.

Theorem IV.4.5. $\vdash R \supset \sim\sim R$.

Proof. Put $\sim R$ for Q in Thm.IV.4.4 for major premise, and put R for P in Thm.IV.4.2 for minor premise (and use modus ponens, naturally).

We can rewrite Thm.IV.4.5 as $\vdash P \supset \sim\sim P$. Together with Thm.IV.4.3, this should give $\vdash P \equiv \sim\sim P$. However, we shall not be able to infer $\vdash P \equiv \sim\sim P$ from $\vdash P \supset \sim\sim P$ and $\vdash \sim\sim P \supset P$ until we can prove $P, Q \vdash PQ$, and this will not be proved until late in the section (it follows from Thm.IV.4.22). Even after we get $\vdash P \equiv \sim\sim P$, we shall not be able to substitute P for $\sim\sim P$ and vice versa until in Chapter VI, after we have proved the substitution theorem. Nevertheless, by proving Thm.IV.4.3

and Thm.IV.4.5, we have taken the first steps toward being able to regard P and $\sim\sim P$ as interchangeable.

Theorem IV.4.6. $\vdash Q \supset P. \supset .\sim P \supset \sim Q.$

Proof. Put $\sim P$ for R in Thm.IV.4.4.

Theorem IV.4.7. $\sim P \supset \sim Q \vdash Q \supset P.$

Proof. Put $\sim P$, $\sim Q$, and Q for P, Q, and R in Axiom scheme 3. Use this as a major premise and $\sim P \supset \sim Q$ as a minor premise and infer $\sim(\sim QQ) \supset \sim(Q\sim P)$. Now use this as a major premise and put Q for P in Thm.IV.4.2 for a minor premise.

Notice that at present we cannot infer $\vdash \sim P \supset \sim Q. \supset .Q \supset P$ from Thm.IV.4.7. Later, in Sec. 6, we shall prove the deduction theorem, that if $P \vdash Q$ then $\vdash P \supset Q$, but until this has been proved, we cannot infer $\vdash \sim P \supset \sim Q. \supset .Q \supset P$ from Thm.IV.4.7.

Theorem IV.4.8. $P \supset Q \vdash RP \supset QR.$

Proof. Axiom scheme 3 gives $P \supset Q \vdash \sim(QR) \supset \sim(RP)$. Putting QR and RP for P and Q in Thm.IV.4.7 gives $\sim(QR) \supset \sim(RP) \vdash RP \supset QR$. Then by Thm.IV.3.2 (with $n = 1$, $m = 1$), we infer $P \supset Q \vdash RP \supset QR$.

Theorem IV.4.9. $P \supset Q,\ R \supset S \vdash \sim(\sim(QS)(PR)).$

Proof. From $R \supset S$ by Thm.IV.4.8, we get

(1) $$PR \supset SP.$$

From $P \supset Q$ by Thm.IV.4.8, we get

(2) $$SP \supset QS.$$

From (1) and (2) by Thm.IV.4.1, we get $\sim(\sim(QS)(PR))$.

Theorem IV.4.10. $P \supset Q,\ Q \supset R,\ R \supset S \vdash P \supset S.$

Proof. From $Q \supset R$ we get

(1) $$\sim\sim(Q \supset R)$$

by Thm.IV.4.5. From $R \supset S$, we get $\sim S \supset \sim R$ by Thm.IV.4.6. From $P \supset Q$ and $\sim S \supset \sim R$, we get $\sim(\sim(Q\sim R)(P\sim S))$ by Thm.IV.4.9. This is the same as $\sim(Q \supset R.P\sim S)$. From this, we get $P\sim S \supset \sim(Q \supset R)$ by Thm.IV.4.4. From this, we get $\sim\sim(Q \supset R) \supset \sim(P\sim S)$ by Thm.IV.4.6. Using this as a major premise, and (1) as a minor premise, we get $\sim(P\sim S)$, which is $P \supset S$.

Thm.IV.4.10 is a generalized form of $P \supset Q,\ Q \supset R \vdash P \supset R$. It is interesting that we can prove the generalized form before we prove the simpler form.

Theorem IV.4.11. $\vdash R\sim\sim P \supset PR.$

Proof. Put $\sim\sim P$ and P for P and Q in Thm.IV.4.8 and use Thm.IV.4.3.

Theorem IV.4.12. $\vdash P \supset P$.

Proof. By Axiom scheme 1,

$$(1) \qquad \vdash \sim\sim P \supset \sim\sim P \sim\sim P.$$

By Thm.IV.4.11, with $\sim\sim P$ for R,

$$(2) \qquad \vdash \sim\sim P \sim\sim P \supset P \sim\sim P.$$

By Thm.IV.4.11, with P for R,

$$(3) \qquad \vdash P \sim\sim P \supset PP.$$

By (1), (2), (3), and Thm.IV.4.10,

$$(4) \qquad \vdash \sim\sim P \supset PP.$$

By Axiom scheme 2,

$$(5) \qquad \vdash PP \supset P.$$

By (4), (5), and Thm.IV.4.1, $\vdash \sim(\sim P \sim\sim P)$. This is $\vdash \sim P \supset \sim P$. Then by Thm.IV.4.7, $\vdash P \supset P$.

Theorem IV.4.13. $\vdash RP \supset PR$.

Proof. Put P for Q in Thm.IV.4.8 and use Thm.IV.4.12.

This theorem gives us a limited commutativity of &.

****Theorem IV.4.14.** $P \supset Q, Q \supset R \vdash P \supset R$.

Proof. Put R for S in Thm.IV.4.10 and use Thm.IV.4.12 with R in place of P.

Theorem IV.4.15. $\vdash \sim(PR) \supset \sim(RP)$.

Proof. Put P for Q in Axiom scheme 3 and use Thm.IV.4.12.

Theorem IV.4.16. $P \supset Q, R \supset S \vdash PR \supset QS$.

Proof. From $P \supset Q$ and $R \supset S$ one gets $\sim(\sim(QS)(PR))$ by Thm. IV.4.9. From this by Thm.IV.4.15, one gets $\sim((PR)\sim(QS))$, which is $PR \supset QS$.

Corollary 1. $P \supset Q \vdash PR \supset QR$.

Proof. Take S to be R and use Thm.IV.4.12 with R in place of P.

Corollary 2. $R \supset S \vdash PR \supset PS$.

***Theorem IV.4.17.** $P \supset Q, P \supset R \vdash P \supset QR$.

Proof. Start with $P \supset Q$ and $P \supset R$. By Thm.IV.4.16, $PP \supset QR$. So by Axiom scheme 1 and Thm.IV.4.14, $P \supset QR$.

***Theorem IV.4.18.** $\vdash P_1P_2 \cdots P_n \supset P_m$, where $1 \leq m \leq n$.

Note that we have not yet proved the associativity of &, so that we have to associate to the left in $P_1P_2 \cdots P_n$ and understand it to mean $(\cdots ((P_1P_2)P_3) \cdots P_{n-1})P_n$.

Proof. First let $m < n$. By Axiom scheme 2,

$$\vdash P_1P_2 \cdots P_n \supset P_1P_2 \cdots P_{n-1}$$

$$\vdash P_1P_2 \cdots P_{n-1} \supset P_1P_2 \cdots P_{n-2}$$

$$\cdots\cdots\cdots\cdots\cdots\cdots\cdots\cdots\cdots$$

$$\vdash P_1P_2 \cdots P_mP_{m+1} \supset P_1P_2 \cdots P_m.$$

So by repeated uses of Thm.IV.4.14, we infer $\vdash P_1P_2 \cdots P_n \supset P_1P_2 \cdots P_m$. If $m = 1$, we are done. If $m > 1$, then by Thm.IV.4.13,

$$\vdash P_1P_2 \cdots P_m \supset P_m(P_1P_2 \cdots P_{m-1}).$$

Also by Axiom scheme 2

$$\vdash P_m(P_1P_2 \cdots P_{m-1}) \supset P_m.$$

So by further uses of Thm.IV.4.14, the desired result follows. If $m = n$, we proceed as in the last two displayed formulas.

Theorem IV.4.19. $\vdash (PQ)R \supset P(QR)$.

Note that the rule of association to the left permits us to write this as $\vdash PQR \supset P(QR)$.

Proof. By Thm.IV.4.18,

(1) $$\vdash PQR \supset P,$$

(2) $$\vdash PQR \supset Q,$$

(3) $$\vdash PQR \supset R.$$

By (2) and (3) and Thm.IV.4.17,

(4) $$\vdash PQR \supset QR.$$

Then by (1) and (4) and Thm.IV.4.17, $\vdash PQR \supset P(QR)$.

Theorem IV.4.20. $\vdash P(QR) \supset (PQ)R$.

Proof. By Thm.IV.4.13,

$$\vdash P(QR) \supset (QR)P.$$

By Thm.IV.4.19,

$$\vdash (QR)P \supset Q(RP).$$

By Thm.IV.4.13,

$$\vdash Q(RP) \supset (RP)Q.$$

By Thm.IV.4.19,

$$\vdash (RP)Q \supset R(PQ).$$

By Thm.IV.4.13,

$$\vdash R(PQ) \supset (PQ)R.$$

By repeated uses of Thm.IV.4.14, the desired result follows.

We shall not be able to infer $\vdash (PQ)R \equiv P(QR)$ from these last two lemmas until we have proved $\vdash P \supset (Q \supset PQ)$, which will be Thm.IV.4.22.

Theorem IV.4.21. $\vdash PQ \supset R. \supset .P \supset (Q \supset R)$.

Proof. By Thm.IV.4.20,

(1) $$\vdash P(Q{\sim}R) \supset (PQ){\sim}R.$$

By Thm.IV.4.3, and Thm.IV.4.16, Cor. 2,

$$\vdash P{\sim}{\sim}(Q{\sim}R) \supset P(Q{\sim}R).$$

This is

(2) $$\vdash P{\sim}(Q \supset R) \supset P(Q{\sim}R).$$

By (1) and (2) and Thm.IV.4.14,

$$\vdash P{\sim}(Q \supset R) \supset (PQ){\sim}R.$$

By Thm.IV.4.6,

$$\vdash {\sim}((PQ){\sim}R) \supset {\sim}(P{\sim}(Q \supset R)),$$

which is the desired result.

****Theorem IV.4.22.** $\vdash P \supset (Q \supset PQ)$.

Proof. By Thm.IV.4.12,

$$\vdash PQ \supset PQ.$$

Now use Thm.IV.4.21 (with R replaced by PQ) as a major premise.

By means of this theorem we can deduce $\vdash {\sim}{\sim}P \equiv P$ from Thms.IV.4.3 and IV.4.5, and $\vdash (PQ)R \equiv P(QR)$ from Thms.IV.4.19 and IV.4.20. However, we shall not be able to substitute P for ${\sim}{\sim}P$ or $P(QR)$ for $(PQ)R$ until in Chapter VI, after we have proved the substitution theorem.

Theorem IV.4.23. $P \supset Q, {\sim}P \supset Q \vdash Q$.

Proof. Start with $P \supset Q$ and ${\sim}P \supset Q$. By Thm.IV.4.6, we get ${\sim}Q \supset {\sim}P$ and ${\sim}Q \supset {\sim}{\sim}P$. Then by Thm.IV.4.17, ${\sim}Q \supset {\sim}P{\sim}{\sim}P$. Then by Thm.IV.4.6, ${\sim}({\sim}P{\sim}{\sim}P) \supset {\sim}{\sim}Q$. That is, ${\sim}P \supset {\sim}P. \supset {\sim}{\sim}Q$. Putting ${\sim}P$ for P in Thm.IV.4.12 gives us ${\sim}{\sim}Q$, and then by Thm.IV.4.3, we get Q.

Theorem IV.4.24. $PQ \supset R, P{\sim}Q \supset R \vdash P \supset R$.

Proof. Start with $PQ \supset R$ and $P{\sim}Q \supset R$. By Thm.IV.4.13 and Thm.IV.4.14, we get $QP \supset R$ and ${\sim}QP \supset R$. Then by Thm.IV.4.21, we get $Q \supset (P \supset R)$ and ${\sim}Q \supset (P \supset R)$. So by Thm.IV.4.23, we get $P \supset R$.

Theorem IV.4.25. $P \supset Q \vdash P \supset {\sim}{\sim}Q$.

Proof. Replace R by ${\sim}{\sim}Q$ in Thm.IV.4.14 and use Thm.IV.4.5.

Theorem IV.4.26. $P \supset {\sim}Q \vdash P \supset {\sim}(QR)$.

Proof. By Axiom scheme 2, $\vdash QR \supset Q$. So by Thm.IV.4.6, $\vdash {\sim}Q \supset$

$\sim(QR)$. However, by Thm.IV.4.14, $P \supset \sim Q, \sim Q \supset \sim(QR) \vdash P \supset \sim(QR)$.

Corollary. $P \supset \sim Q \vdash P \supset (Q \supset R)$.

Proof. Put $\sim R$ in place of R.

Theorem IV.4.27. $P \supset \sim R \vdash P \supset \sim(QR)$.

Proof. Start with $P \supset \sim R$. By Thm.IV.4.26, we get $P \supset \sim(RQ)$. By this and Thm.IV.4.15, we get $P \supset \sim(QR)$ by use of Thm.IV.4.14.

Theorem IV.4.28. $P \supset R \vdash P \supset (Q \supset R)$.

Proof. Start with $P \supset R$. By Thm.IV.4.25, $P \supset \sim\sim R$. So by Thm.IV.4.27, $P \supset \sim(Q\sim R)$. That is, $P \supset (Q \supset R)$.

***Corollary.** $\vdash P \supset (Q \supset P)$.

Proof. Replace R by P and use Thm.IV.4.12.

Theorem IV.4.29. $P \supset Q, P \supset \sim R \vdash P \supset \sim(Q \supset R)$.

Proof. Start with $P \supset Q$ and $P \supset \sim R$. Then by Thm.IV.4.17, $P \supset Q\sim R$. So by Thm.IV.4.25, $P \supset \sim\sim(Q\sim R)$. That is, $P \supset \sim(Q \supset R)$.

EXERCISES

IV.4.1. Write out a complete demonstration for Thm.IV.4.5.

IV.4.2. Write out a complete demonstration for Thm.IV.4.7.

IV.4.3. Write out a complete demonstration for Thm.IV.4.8.

IV.4.4. Write out a complete demonstration for Thm.IV.4.9.

IV.4.5. State an upper bound for the minimum number of steps needed for a complete demonstration of $\vdash P \supset P$ and justify your statement.

IV.4.6. Using only results of Sec. 4 or earlier portions of the present exercise, prove:

(a) $\vdash P \vee Q \supset Q \vee P$.
(b) $\vdash P \supset P \vee Q$.
(c) $\vdash P_m \supset P_1 \vee P_2 \vee \cdots \vee P_n$, if $1 \leq m \leq n$.
(d) $P \supset R, Q \supset R \vdash P \vee Q \supset R$.

(*Hint.* Proceed as in the beginning of the proof of Thm.IV.4.23.)

(e) $\vdash P \vee (Q \vee R) \supset (P \vee Q) \vee R$.
(f) $\vdash (P \vee Q) \vee R \supset P \vee (Q \vee R)$.
(g) $\vdash P \supset (Q \supset R) . \supset . PQ \supset R$.
(h) $\vdash (P \vee Q)R \supset PR \vee QR$.

(*Hint.* Prove each of $\vdash P \supset .R \supset PR \vee QR$ and $\vdash Q \supset .R \supset PR \vee QR$ and then use parts (d) and (g).)

(i) $\vdash PR \vee QR \supset (P \vee Q)R$.
(j) $\vdash PQ \vee R \supset (P \vee R)(Q \vee R)$.
(k) $\vdash (P \vee R)(Q \vee R) \supset PQ \vee R$.

(*Hint.* By (h) $\vdash (P\vee R)(Q\vee R) \supset P(Q\vee R)\vee R(Q\vee R)$. Now prove $\vdash P(Q\vee R) \supset PQ\vee R$ and $\vdash R(Q\vee R) \supset PQ\vee R$, and use (d).)

(l) $\vdash PQ\vee P{\sim}Q\vee{\sim}PQ\vee{\sim}P{\sim}Q$.

IV.4.7. Write out a complete demonstration for $\vdash {\sim}P \supset (P \supset Q)$.

IV.4.8. State why one cannot prove Thm.IV.4.20 in the same way that Thm.IV.4.19 was proved.

IV.4.9. Prove $P,Q \vdash PQ$.

5. The Truth-value Theorem. In this section we prove the truth-value theorem to the effect that, if P always takes the value T, then $\vdash P$.

We shall illustrate the method by actually proving

$$\vdash P \supset Q. \supset :.P \supset .Q \supset R: \supset .P \supset R.$$

Let us first show that this always takes the value T, which we do by means of the following abridged truth-value table in which U denotes $P \supset (Q \supset R)$, V denotes $U \supset (P \supset R)$ (that is, V denotes $P \supset .Q \supset R: \supset .P \supset R$), and W denotes $(P \supset Q) \supset V$ (that is, W denotes $P \supset Q. \supset :.P \supset .Q \supset R: \supset .P \supset R$).

P	Q	R	$P \supset Q$	$Q \supset R$	$P \supset (Q \supset R)$ U	$P \supset R$	$U \supset (P \supset R)$ V	$(P \supset Q) \supset V$ W
		T				T	T	T
F		F				T	T	T
T	F	F	F					T
T	T	F		F	F		T	T

The interpretation of the first line of this is that, if R is true, then each of $P \supset R$, $U \supset (P \supset R)$, and $(P \supset Q) \supset V$ is true. The corresponding statements of symbolic logic would be:

(1) $\vdash R \supset (P \supset R)$,

(2) $\vdash R \supset .U \supset (P \supset R)$, i.e. $\vdash R \supset V$,

(3) $\vdash R \supset .(P \supset Q) \supset V$, i.e. $\vdash R \supset W$.

Let us try to prove these. This turns out to be very easy, inasmuch as we have derived theorems which are expressly designed to prove these. (1) follows by the corollary to Thm.IV.4.28, and (2) follows from (1) by Thm.IV.4.28, and (3) follows from (2) by Thm.IV.4.28.

Statements corresponding to the second line of our truth-value table would be:

(4) $$\vdash \sim R \sim P \supset (P \supset R),$$

(5) $$\vdash \sim R \sim P \supset .U \supset (P \supset R),$$

(6) $$\vdash \sim R \sim P \supset .(P \supset Q) \supset V.$$

To derive (4), we first get $\vdash \sim R \sim P \supset \sim P$ by Thm.IV.4.18, and from this we get (4) by the corollary to Thm.IV.4.26. Then we get (5) from (4) and (6) from (5) by Thm.IV.4.28.

Statements corresponding to the third line of our truth-value table would be:

(7) $$\vdash \sim RP \sim Q \supset \sim(P \supset Q),$$

(8) $$\vdash \sim RP \sim Q \supset .(P \supset Q) \supset V.$$

To prove (7), we get $\vdash \sim RP \sim Q \supset P$ and $\vdash \sim RP \sim Q \supset \sim Q$ by Thm. IV.4.18, and then (7) follows by Thm.IV.4.29. From (7), we get (8) by the corollary to Thm.IV.4.26.

Statements corresponding to the fourth line of our truth-value table would be:

(9) $$\vdash \sim RPQ \supset \sim(Q \supset R),$$

(10) $$\vdash \sim RPQ \supset \sim(P \supset (Q \supset R)),$$

(11) $$\vdash \sim RPQ \supset .U \supset (P \supset R),$$

(12) $$\vdash \sim RPQ \supset .(P \supset Q) \supset V.$$

To prove (9), we get $\vdash \sim RPQ \supset Q$ and $\vdash \sim RPQ \supset \sim R$ by Thm.IV.4.18, and then (9) follows by Thm.IV.4.29. Now $\vdash \sim RPQ \supset P$ follows by Thm.IV.4.18, and from this and (9), we get (10) by Thm.IV.4.29. Then (11) follows from (10) by the corollary to Thm.IV.4.26, and finally (12) follows from (11) by Thm.IV.4.28.

By paralleling formally the reasoning embodied in each of the four lines of our truth-value table, we have proved

(3) $$\vdash R \supset W,$$

(6) $$\vdash \sim R \sim P \supset W,$$

(8) $$\vdash \sim RP \sim Q \supset W,$$

(12) $$\vdash \sim RPQ \supset W.$$

Now by (8) and (12), we infer

(13) $$\vdash \sim RP \supset W$$

by Thm.IV.4.24. By (6) and (13), we infer

(14) $$\vdash {\sim}R \supset W$$

by Thm.IV.4.24. Finally, by (3) and (14), we infer $\vdash W$ by Thm.IV.4.23. So we have proved:

Theorem IV.5.1. $\vdash P \supset Q. \supset :.P \supset .Q \supset R: \supset .P \supset R.$

Moreover, we based our proof on a truth-value table, making it plausible that we can base the proofs of other statements on their truth-value tables. We now wish to show rigorously that we can indeed do so.

For actually carrying out a proof, the abridged truth-value table is much shorter, and hence more convenient. However, for proving that we always can carry out a proof, the unabridged truth-value table is more systematic, and hence preferable.

We note that the proof fell into two distinct phases. In the first phase, we were proving statements such as (1) through (12) corresponding to rows of our truth-value table. In the second phase, we combined these statements by means of Thm.IV.4.24 and Thm.IV.4.23. Let us now examine the first phase more carefully.

A logical product such as ${\sim}RPQ$ corresponds to a choice of a set of truth values for P, Q, and R; in this case the choice P is T, Q is T, and R is F. Clearly any such logical product corresponds to a choice of a set of truth values, and vice versa.

Given this choice of truth values, some formulas, such as U, take the value F and other formulas, such as V, take the value T. For a formula U which takes the value F, we wish to prove

(10) $$\vdash {\sim}RPQ \supset {\sim}U,$$

and for a formula V which takes the value T, we wish to prove

(11) $$\vdash {\sim}RPQ \supset V.$$

Incidentally, the departure from alphabetical order in the product ${\sim}RPQ$ was adopted to fit the peculiar arrangement of cases in the abridged truth-value table. For a complete systematic listing of cases, such as occurs in the unabridged truth-value table, the usual alphabetic order would be quite suitable, and we would wish to prove

$$\vdash PQ{\sim}R \supset {\sim}U$$

and

$$\vdash PQ{\sim}R \supset V.$$

These are special cases of the general result proved in the theorem below.

Theorem IV.5.2. Let P_1, P_2, . . . , P_n be statements. Let X be a statement built up from some or all of the P's by use of & and $\sim$, using each P more than once if desired. Let $Q_1, Q_2, \ldots, Q_n$ be some statements satisfying the condition that for some (or no) i's Q_i is P_i, and for the remaining i's (if any) Q_i is $\sim P_i$. Let the value T be assigned to P_i for those i's (if any) for which Q_i is P_i, and let the value F be assigned to P_i for the remaining i's (if any). Let the corresponding value for X be computed by the method of truth-value tables. If the value for X is T, then

$$\vdash Q_1Q_2 \cdots Q_n \supset X,$$

and if the value for X is F, then

$$\vdash Q_1Q_2 \cdots Q_n \supset \sim X.$$

Proof. Proof by induction on the number of symbols in X, counting each occurrence of $\sim$ or a P as a symbol. In other words, we proceed (as in the construction of truth-value tables) from simple statements to more complex statements. First, suppose there is a single symbol in X. Then X must be some P_i. By Thm.IV.4.18,

(a) $$\vdash Q_1Q_2 \cdots Q_n \supset Q_i.$$

Case 1. Q_i is P_i. Then (a) is

$$\vdash Q_1Q_2 \cdots Q_n \supset X.$$

However, in this case the value T is assigned to P_i and hence to X.

Case 2. Q_i is $\sim P_i$. Then (a) is

$$\vdash Q_1Q_2 \cdots Q_n \supset \sim X.$$

However, in this case the value F is assigned to P_i and hence to X.

Now assume the theorem true for k or fewer symbols in X with k a positive integer. We call this assumption the hypothesis of the induction. Let X have $k + 1$ symbols. Hence X has at least two symbols. It was assumed that X was built up by use of & and $\sim$. Hence the last step in building X was either to use an & or to use a $\sim$.

Case 1. The last step was to use an &. So X is AB, where each of A and B has k or fewer symbols.

Subcase I. A has the value T. Then by the hypothesis of the induction

(b) $$\vdash Q_1Q_2 \cdots Q_n \supset A.$$

Subsubcase i. B has the value T giving X the value T. Then by the hypothesis of the induction,

(c) $$\vdash Q_1Q_2 \cdots Q_n \supset B.$$

Then by (b) and (c) and Thm.IV.4.17,

$$\vdash Q_1Q_2 \cdots Q_n \supset AB.$$

This is

$$\vdash Q_1Q_2 \cdots Q_n \supset X.$$

However, this is just what we wish, since in this case X takes the value T.

Subsubcase ii. B has the value F, giving X the value F. Then by the hypothesis of the induction,

$$\vdash Q_1Q_2 \cdots Q_n \supset \sim B.$$

So by Thm.IV.4.27

$$\vdash Q_1Q_2 \cdots Q_n \supset \sim(AB).$$

This is

$$\vdash Q_1Q_2 \cdots Q_n \supset \sim X.$$

However, this is just what we wish, since X takes the value F in this case.

Subcase II. A has the value F, giving X the value F. Then by the hypothesis of the induction,

$$\vdash Q_1Q_2 \cdots Q_n \supset \sim A.$$

So by Thm.IV.4.26

$$\vdash Q_1Q_2 \cdots Q_n \supset \sim(AB).$$

This is

$$\vdash Q_1Q_2 \cdots Q_n \supset \sim X,$$

which is just what we wish since X takes the value F in this case.

Case 2. The last step was to use a $\sim$. So X is $\sim C$, and C has k symbols.

Subcase I. C has the value T, so that X has the value F. By the hypothesis of the induction,

$$\vdash Q_1Q_2 \cdots Q_n \supset C.$$

So by Thm.IV.4.25,

$$\vdash Q_1Q_2 \cdots Q_n \supset \sim\sim C.$$

This is

$$\vdash Q_1Q_2 \cdots Q_n \supset \sim X,$$

which is just what we wish.

Subcase II. C has the value F, so that X has the value T. By the hypothesis of the induction,

$$\vdash Q_1Q_2 \cdots Q_n \supset \sim C.$$

This is

$$\vdash Q_1Q_2 \cdots Q_n \supset X,$$

which is just what we wish.

This theorem takes care of the first phase of any proof based on a truth-value table. If each Q_i is either P_i or $\sim P_i$, then $Q_1Q_2 \cdots Q_n$ represents a choice of a set of truth values for the P's, as indicated in the theorem. The results

$$\vdash Q_1Q_2 \cdots Q_n \supset X$$

or

$$\vdash Q_1Q_2 \cdots Q_n \supset \sim X$$

for various X's correspond to the entries in one row of a truth-value table.

Notice that in the theorem above we assumed X to be built up out of & and $\sim$ alone. That is, each part of X of the form $P \mathbf{v} Q$, $P \supset Q$, or $P \equiv Q$ is written in unabbreviated form before one starts to construct the truth-value table. In constructing an actual truth-value table, this would considerably increase the labor of construction, but for a proof about truth-value tables it allows considerable simplification.

The proof of Thm.IV.5.2 is a particularly interesting example of proof by cases (see Principle 5 in Sec. 5 of Chapter II) in that many of the cases are themselves proofs by cases.

We claimed earlier that all our proofs should be constructive. Let us inquire if the proof above satisfies this requirement. We claim to prove either

$$\vdash Q_1Q_2 \cdots Q_n \supset X$$

or

$$\vdash Q_1Q_2 \cdots Q_n \supset \sim X$$

for each X. That is, we claim the existence of a sequence of steps S_1, S_2, . . . , S_s which is a demonstration of one of the results stated. Have we given instructions for constructing such a sequence of steps? We believe that we have.

To verify this, let us refer back to the proof. We first give instructions for handling each X consisting of only one symbol. In fact Thm.IV.4.18 takes care of this case. The remainder of the theorem assumes that we have available instructions for constructing demonstrations for each X of k or fewer symbols, and furnishes instructions for constructing demonstrations for each X of $k + 1$ symbols. Now given Thm.IV.4.18 which gives instructions for all X's of one symbol, we take $k = 1$ and then have instructions for all X's of two symbols. Now we can take $k = 2$ and get instructions for all X's of three symbols. Proceeding in this way, we can build up a set of instructions for X's of any desired degree of complexity.

In any particular case, the process actually goes through quite easily, as witness the first phase of our proof of Thm.IV.5.1.

We now prove the truth-value theorem:

****Theorem IV.5.3.** Let P_1, P_2, . . . , P_n be statements. Let X be a statement built up from $P_1, P_2, \ldots, P_n$ by use of & and $\sim$, using each P more than once if desired. Let X take the value T whatever sets of values T and F be assigned to $P_1, P_2, \ldots, P_n$. Then $\vdash X$.

The first phase of the proof was taken care of by Thm.IV.5.2, and we now need only carry out the second phase in the manner already indicated in the proof of Thm.IV.5.1. By Thm.IV.5.2, we have

$$\vdash Q_1Q_2 \cdots Q_n \supset X$$

for each set of Q's such that each Q_i is either P_i or $\sim P_i$. In particular, taking Q_n to be first P_n and then $\sim P_n$, we get both

$$\vdash Q_1Q_2 \cdots Q_{n-1}P_n \supset X$$

and

$$\vdash Q_1Q_2 \cdots Q_{n-1}\sim P_n \supset X.$$

So by Thm.IV.4.24,

$$\vdash Q_1Q_2 \cdots Q_{n-1} \supset X.$$

We now repeat this reasoning, letting Q_{n-1} be first P_{n-1} and then $\sim P_{n-1}$, and using Thm.IV.4.24 again to infer

$$\vdash Q_1Q_2 \cdots Q_{n-2} \supset X.$$

We continue in this way down to

$$\vdash Q_1 \supset X.$$

Letting Q_1 be first P_1 and then $\sim P_1$, we get

$$\vdash P_1 \supset X \qquad \text{and} \qquad \vdash \sim P_1 \supset X.$$

Finally, we use Thm.IV.4.23.

Various comments about this theorem are in order. In the first place, we are now free to make use of any statement which always takes the value T. Moreover, if X always takes the value T, one can derive X from the truth-value axioms alone by use of modus ponens. One could verify this by checking through the proofs of all the theorems up to and including Thm.IV.5.3. Or one can observe it more easily by noting that, since only the truth-value axioms have been listed so far, no other axioms could have been used so far.

EXERCISES

IV.5.1. Using only results from Sec. 4, prove:

(a) $\vdash \sim PQR \supset \sim((P \equiv Q) \equiv R)$.
(b) $\vdash \sim PQ\sim R \supset ((P \equiv Q) \equiv R)$.

IV.5.2. We say that our symbolic logic is inconsistent if there is a statement P such that $\vdash P$ and $\vdash \sim P$. Prove that, if our symbolic logic is inconsistent, then $\vdash Q$ for every statement Q.

6. The Deduction Theorem. In this section we prove the important theorem that if $Q \vdash R$ then $\vdash Q \supset R$. Actually, we prove a generalized form of it to the effect that, if $P_1, P_2, \ldots, P_n, Q \vdash R$, then $P_1, P_2, \ldots, P_n \vdash Q \supset R$. This result will be called the deduction theorem.

The reader may wonder how we can prove this theorem before we have stated our complete set of axioms. If we have $Q \vdash R$, this may make use of axioms which we have not yet stated. In such a case, not knowing all the axioms used in $Q \vdash R$, how can we go about proving $\vdash Q \supset R$? Actually, there is no difficulty, since it turns out that the use of axioms in $\vdash Q \supset R$ exactly parallels that in $Q \vdash R$. Hence it suffices to know that we have the same set of axioms available in each case, and the exact forms of the axioms are of no consequence, provided only that our axioms are adequate to prove

$$\vdash P \supset P,$$

$$\vdash P \supset (Q \supset P),$$

and

$$\vdash P \supset Q. \supset :.P \supset .Q \supset R: \supset .P \supset R.$$

As these are Thm.IV.4.12, the corollary to Thm.IV.4.28, and Thm.IV.5.1 our set of axioms does satisfy the proviso.

We now prove the deduction theorem.

****Theorem IV.6.1.** If $P_1, P_2, \ldots, P_n, Q \vdash R$, then $P_1, P_2, \ldots, P_n \vdash Q \supset R$.

Proof. Assume that we have given a demonstration $S_1, S_2, \ldots, S_s$ of $P_1, P_2, \ldots, P_n, Q \vdash R$. Then we wish to show how to construct a demonstration of $P_1, P_2, \ldots, P_n \vdash Q \supset R$. By the definition of $\vdash$, we know that S_s is R and for each S_i either:

(1) S_i is an axiom.

(2) S_i is a P or is Q.

(3) There is a j less than i such that S_i and S_j are the same.

(4) There are j and k, each less than i such that S_k is $S_j \supset S_i$.

We take $Q \supset S_1, Q \supset S_2, \ldots, Q \supset S_s$ to be key steps of our demonstration of $P_1, P_2, \ldots, P_n \vdash Q \supset R$. The last of our key steps, $Q \supset S_s$, is $Q \supset R$, as desired. By filling in additional steps before each of our key steps, we can build up a complete demonstration. We do this as follows.

Case 1. S_i is an axiom. Then before the key step $Q \supset S_i$ we insert the following steps: First a demonstration of $\vdash S_i \supset (Q \supset S_i)$ (see the corollary to Thm.IV.4.28), and then the step S_i. From these, one can proceed to the key step $Q \supset S_i$ by modus ponens.

Case 2. S_i is a P. We proceed as in Case 1.

Case 3. S_i is Q. Then we insert a demonstration of $\vdash Q \supset Q$ (see Thm.IV.4.12). As S_i is Q, the key step $Q \supset S_i$ is a repetition of the last step of the demonstration of $\vdash Q \supset Q$.

Case 4. S_i is the same as an earlier S_j. Then the key step $Q \supset S_i$ is the same as an earlier key step $Q \supset S_j$ and we need not insert any extra steps before $Q \supset S_i$.

Case 5. There are an earlier S_j and an earlier S_k such that S_k is $S_j \supset S_i$. That is, S_j and $S_j \supset S_i$ occur before S_i. Then the key steps $Q \supset S_j$ and $Q \supset (S_j \supset S_i)$ have already occurred. We insert a demonstration of $\vdash Q \supset S_j. \supset :Q \supset (S_j \supset S_i). \supset .Q \supset S_i$ (see Thm.IV.5.1). By modus ponens with the earlier key step $Q \supset S_j$, we can justify the step $Q \supset (S_j \supset S_i). \supset .Q \supset S_i$, which we insert. By modus ponens with the earlier key step $Q \supset (S_j \supset S_i)$ we can justify the key step $Q \supset S_i$.

In Sec. 4 of Chapter II, we made frequent mention of the principle that, if one assumes P and correctly deduces Q, then one can infer $P \supset Q$. The justification of this is carried out in two steps. The first step is to show that, in any case where one assumes P and correctly deduces Q, the deduction can be thrown into a form which is a demonstration of $P \vdash Q$. Then the second step is to infer $\vdash P \supset Q$ by the deduction theorem.

The first step can never be conclusively established, because the notion of "correct deduction" is not precisely defined. In fact, one of our aims in setting up a system of symbolic logic is to give a precise definition, and we intend to take $P \vdash Q$ as a precise definition of "Q can be correctly deduced from P." It is our intention in the succeeding chapters to consider a great many instances in which it is commonly agreed that one has a correct deduction of Q from P, and to show in each of these cases that $P \vdash Q$. We shall exhibit enough instances that we hope that the weight of the evidence will impel a belief on the part of the reader that the precise idea $P \vdash Q$ is indeed an adequate approximation to the less precise idea "Q can be correctly deduced from P."

EXERCISES

IV.6.1. Prove that $P \vdash Q$ if and only if $\vdash P \supset Q$.

CHAPTER V

CLARIFICATION

In Chapter I we stated our aims in very general terms. We are now in a position to be more explicit. We now have shown the beginnings of a system of symbolic logic and have shown how this system may be used as a model for mathematical reasoning. Hence we believe it worth while to pause and restate our intentions more carefully.

There is an intuitive notion of logical correctness which is shared by the majority of mathematicians. There will be disagreement on some of the more abstruse principles, such as the axiom of choice, but if we confine our attention to the more basic principles, there is general agreement. It is our intention to give a precise definition of these basic principles by a mechanical system known as symbolic logic.

Note that we make no claim to justify the basic principles; we claim only that we define them with precision.

We might as well be frank and admit that some of these basic logical principles used by all (or almost all) mathematicians may actually not be valid. There is strong evidence for their validity in that they are in common use by mathematicians, physicists, chemists, engineers, and technical men generally, and the results obtained by them not only are quite satisfactory but are useful almost to the point of being indispensable. However, this evidence is not conclusive. It is a matter of history that infinite series (including even divergent ones) were at one time generally dealt with according to principles which are now believed to be incorrect. Nonetheless, at the time, the results obtained by use of these (incorrect) principles were satisfactory and useful.

Actually, some of the basic principles in common use have been subjected to severe criticism, notably certain uses of reductio ad absurdum. We do not presume to make a judgment in this matter. We include reductio ad absurdum in our symbolic logic (see Sec. 4 of Chapter II), but we do so merely because practically every mathematician uses reductio ad absurdum freely, and not at all because we are able to justify its use.

To reiterate, we shall set up a system of symbolic logic which will define precisely the basic logical principles which are in common use. The system of symbolic logic will in no way justify these principles. In fact, because there is no guarantee that all the principles defined by the symbolic logic are valid, there is equally no guarantee that the symbolic logic is itself valid. In fact, it is perfectly possible that the symbolic logic contains a contradiction; that is, there may be a statement P such that both $\vdash P$ and $\vdash \sim P$. If this were found to be the case, we should certainly have to abandon the present symbolic logic and seek another.

The reader may inquire why we set up a symbolic logic embodying logical principles whose sole justification is that of widespread use. Why not instead set up a symbolic logic embodying only genuinely valid principles? We would if we could, but we don't know how. We know of no way of deciding for sure if a given logical principle is valid. The best criterion we have found as yet for the validity of a logical principle is that of widespread acceptance by careful mathematicians. This is admittedly inconclusive, so that we have to admit the possibility that the logical principles defined by our symbolic logic may be invalid. Our justification for using these principles while retaining doubts of their validity may be summarized in the following considerations:

A. None of these principles is now known to be invalid (although some are under suspicion).

B. From these principles one can derive the existing body of mathematics, which is very useful in the sciences and engineering, and even in daily life.

Let us now look more carefully at the actual structure of our symbolic logic. To make it as precise as possible, we have made it as mechanical as possible. All reference to meaning is avoided, and only the forms of statements are considered. For this reason almost no intelligence is required to check a proof within the symbolic logic, where by a proof we mean an actual demonstration of $\vdash P$. We cannot avoid the use of a minimum of intelligence. Thus, if $S_1, S_2, \ldots, S_s$ is proposed as a demonstration of $\vdash P$, it is required in order to check this that we be able to decide that some of the S's are axioms and that the remaining S's follow from previous S's by modus ponens (or are the same as some previous S's). For this we have to be able to recognize different occurrences of a statement (name of a statement, actually) as occurrences of the same statement (name), to be able to replace occurrences of one statement (name) by occurrences of another statement (name), to be able to associate together properly the left and right ends of pairs of parentheses in a complex statement, etc. The intelligence required to handle these matters is very slight; so that, while we have not completely eliminated intelligence, we have certainly reduced the need for it to the point where it seems justified to claim that the checking procedure is purely mechanical. That is, we have a purely mechanical equivalent of mathematical reasoning.

In the present text, we shall not devote ourselves exclusively to operating within the symbolic logic. Since we wish to make it seem probable that the symbolic logic is a precise definition of the intuitive notion of logical correctness, we shall be presenting a great many instances of ordinary mathematical reasoning for comparison with the symbolic logic. This has already happened in Sec. 4 of Chapter II. Also, in setting up the symbolic logic, we shall proceed by analogy with the intuitive logic, and so shall need to have it before us. This occurred in Sec. 1 of Chapter II and at places in Sec. 3 of Chapter II. Thus we shall expect that in general we shall be considering simultaneously two different logics, the intuitive everyday logic and a mechanical symbolic logic which we are comparing with it.

Still another complicating factor enters the picture as follows. The statement $\vdash P$ means that there is a demonstration whose last step is P. To prove $\vdash P$ we are supposed to exhibit this demonstration, whereupon it is a purely mechanical procedure to check that it is a demonstration. In practice, this ideal arrangement cannot be carried out, simply because the demonstrations become so extremely long as to be completely unmanageable. Thus, in the proofs of Thms.IV.4.1 and IV.4.2, we actually exhibited the demonstrations, but pure lack of space soon forced us to abandon this procedure. If the reader doubts this, let him work Ex. IV.4.4 and IV.4.5. Accordingly, we were compelled to seek other means of proving statements of the form $\vdash P$. There seems no way of doing this without introducing still a third logic. In other words we have to deal simultaneously with the ordinary intuitive logic of mathematics, with a mechanical symbolic logic, and with a constructive intuitive logic which we use to prove things about the symbolic logic. If we should take this third logic to be just the ordinary intuitive logic of mathematics, then we could hardly claim that we are framing a definition of the ordinary intuitive logic of mathematics. Besides, since we do not wish to use this third logic and are forced to only by limitations of time and space, we wish to keep this third logic to a minimum. Further, we desire that the third logic shall have a maximum of trustworthiness, so that if we claim to prove $\vdash P$ there will not be anyone who will question our proof. In order to ensure this, we insist that we shall always either write out a demonstration in full, as in the proofs of Thms. IV.4.1 and IV.4.2, or else give explicit instructions whereby one could write out a demonstration. In some of the proofs, as, for instance, the proof of Thm. IV.5.2, we use proof by mathematical induction on n. This assumes whatever simple properties of positive integers are embodied in the principle of mathematical induction. Even in these more intricate proofs, we still are adhering to our requirement that we must give explicit instructions. In our induction proofs, we give explicit instructions for $n = 1$, and then, assuming instructions available for $n \leq k$ with k a positive integer, we write instructions for $n = k + 1$. Then for any finite value of n, one could write out instructions by working up from $n = 1$, letting k be successively $1, 2, \ldots, n - 1$. Similar remarks hold for the proofs by cases which we sometimes use. We use proof by cases only when we have information which guarantees that our listing of cases is quite exhaustive. Then for each case, appropriate instructions are given.

Thus we restrict our proofs to those which give quite positive evidence of the existence of demonstrations, and thereby justify a high degree of reliance on our conclusions.

To make clear just what is involved, suppose we should relax our requirements and permit proofs by reductio ad absurdum of some of our theorems. Say, for instance, that we should assume that no demonstration exists for some statement, and then deduce a contradiction from our assumption. Most mathematicians would thereby be convinced of the existence of a demonstration for that statement. However, not all would be convinced. Some mathematicians deny the validity of the principle of reductio ad absurdum in such a situation. They would insist that, until we had either shown them a demonstration or given them explicit instructions for writing out a demonstration, we could not really guarantee the existence of a demonstration. We avoid such objections by restricting our proofs to those which give direct positive evidence of the existence of demonstrations.

Let us repeat the relationship of our three logics. There is the purely mechanical symbolic logic. It is operated without reference to meaning. If we wish to prove $\vdash P$ for some P, we must do so purely by reference to the form of P. To prove $\vdash P$ by the purely mechanical procedure prescribed by our symbolic logic is in general much too long a process to be practicable. So we have to permit the use of a slight amount of intuitive, nonmechanical reasoning, to keep our proofs of such results as $\vdash P$ within bounds. We insist that this reasoning be kept simple, direct, and constructive. Be it noted that our proofs of $\vdash P$ still depend purely upon the form of P and not upon its meaning. Thus it is genuinely possible to keep our reasoning about the logic very simple and direct. The connection with the everyday logic of mathematics is as follows. Suppose we have proved $\vdash P$, either quite mechanically, or by use of some simple reasoning based entirely on the form of P. We now give a meaning to P by interpreting the symbols occurring therein (for instance, & is interpreted to be "and"). This meaning will turn out to be a principle of the everyday logic of mathematics. At least, it always has so far in our experience. Conversely, given a basic principle of the everyday logic of mathematics, we have so far been able to find a P which expresses it, and such that $\vdash P$. Needless to say, it is no accident that this happens. We have taken great pains to choose our axioms so as to cause this to happen in general. We have listed a large number of instances to persuade the reader that this happens in general.

Finally, trusting that it does happen in general, we formulate our precise definition of the basic everyday logic of mathematics by saying that it consists of just those logical principles which are meanings of P's for which $\vdash P$.

Needless to say, the meaning of P will not have any connection with the reasoning by which we prove $\vdash P$, since the latter must depend entirely on the form of P.

EXERCISES

V.1.1. If the symbolic logic which we are studying is inconsistent, then:

(a) What can one conclude about the everyday logic of mathematics?
(b) What can one conclude about the simple intuitive logic in which we prove things about our symbolic logic?

CHAPTER VI

THE RESTRICTED PREDICATE CALCULUS

1. Variables and Unknowns. To the layman, the trade-mark of a mathematician is his use of the symbol x to denote an unknown quantity. However, the letters x, y, z, m, n, etc., are used not only to denote unknowns, but also to denote variables. Thus we may write

$$x^2 - 4x + 3 = 0, \tag{VI.1.1}$$

in which x denotes an unknown quantity whose value is to be determined, or we may write

$$\sin^2 x + \cos^2 x = 1, \tag{VI.1.2}$$

in which x denotes a variable for which we may substitute any angle (or any real number, or even any complex number). We may also write

$$\int x^2\, dx = \frac{x^3}{3}, \tag{VI.1.3}$$

$$\int_0^3 x^2\, dx = 9, \tag{VI.1.4}$$

$$\int_0^x y^2\, dy = \frac{x^3}{3}, \tag{VI.1.5}$$

and even

$$\int_0^x x^2\, dx = \frac{x^3}{3}. \tag{VI.1.6}$$

In these, x probably denotes an unknown (or indeterminate) in (VI.1.5), but a variable in the others. However, there is not universal agreement on this point. Usually, in (VI.1.4) one speaks of x as the variable of integration, but some writers insist that x does not really denote a variable (or unknown either) in (VI.1.4), and that (VI.1.4) is merely a conventionalized abbreviation for a very complicated definition. In any case, in (VI.1.3) to (VI.1.6), we certainly have at least two distinct usages of the letter x and perhaps as many as four distinct usages. To make matters still more confusing, in (VI.1.6), two of the occurrences of x are being used in one way and the other two in quite another way. Thus we can replace two of the x's in (VI.1.6) by 3's, and obtain (VI.1.4), but we cannot replace the other two x's by 3's, since this would result in the nonsense

$$\int_0^x 3^2 \, d3 = \frac{x^3}{3};$$

nonetheless, we can replace them by y's to get (VI.1.5).

To cite still other uses of the letter x, we note that, when we speak of x^2 as the result of multiplying x by x, we are using x to denote an indeterminate, but when we speak of the function x^2, we are using x to denote a variable. In the point slope form of the equation of a line

$$y - y_0 = m(x - x_0), \tag{VI.1.7}$$

the x and y denote variables which are the coordinates of a variable point on the line (with the added complication that y may happen not to vary in case $m = 0$), whereas x_0 and y_0 denote constants which are the coordinates of a fixed (but unspecified) point.

There are still other uses of x in mathematics, but they are less common and can be dispensed with.

Additional complications in the usages connected with x arise from carelessness with the use of names. Thus one often says "x is a variable" or "x is an unknown." Actually, of course, x is the twenty-fourth letter of the English alphabet which is temporarily being used as a name of a variable or of an unknown, and a better terminology would be "x denotes a variable" or "x denotes an unknown." In the main we have tried to use the more careful terminology, but on occasion we follow a less accurate wording when the more accurate one sounds awkward.

In our symbolic logic we shall make use of letters such as x, y, z in manners analogous to many of the uses listed above. However, we shall be more systematic and shall introduce various special notations to distinguish different uses of the letters. Such use of different notations for different uses occurs to a limited extent in everyday mathematics. Thus, in analytic geometry and calculus, we have the convention that letters from the early part of the alphabet shall denote constants whereas letters from the latter part of the alphabet shall denote variables. Also, in elementary algebra some writers distinguish between identities, which they write with three bars, and equations, which they write with two bars. Thus they write

$$x^2 - y^2 \equiv (x + y)(x - y) \tag{VI.1.8}$$

but

$$x^2 - 4x + 3 = 0,$$

it being indicated thereby that in the first statement x and y denote variables whose values run over all real (or complex) numbers, whereas in the second statement x denotes an unknown but fixed number whose value is to be determined.

We shall defer many uses of the letter x to later chapters and in the present chapter shall study its use as an unknown (or indeterminate) and as a variable in the particular sense exemplified in the three-bar equivalence of elementary algebra (see equation (VI.1.8) above). The study of these two uses constitutes the restricted predicate calculus.

Before beginning to develop the treatment of these in symbolic logic, let us consider in more detail their use in everyday mathematics.

We cite two instances of the use of variables,

(VI.1.2) $$\sin^2 x + \cos^2 x = 1,$$

(VI.1.8) $$x^2 - y^2 \equiv (x + y)(x - y),$$

and two instances of the use of unknowns (or indeterminates),

(VI.1.1) $$x^2 - 4x + 3 = 0,$$

(VI.1.9) $$x^2 + y = x + y^2.$$

Many philosophers and logicians object to the use of unknowns in statements on the ground that it is difficult (if not impossible) to assign any proper meaning to such statements. Mathematicians have never let such considerations deter them from making common use of unknowns in statements. In our symbolic logic, we insist on paying no attention to meanings and so need not feel the slightest hesitation on this score about using unknowns. Accordingly, we shall use unknowns (or indeterminates) in much the way that they are used in everyday mathematics.

In many cases, statements refer to variables or unknowns without using letters for them, such as:

"If two functions are continuous at a point, their sum is continuous at this point."

This concerns three unknowns, namely, the two unspecified functions and the unspecified point, as will be clearer if one writes the statement in the alternative form:

"If the functions f and g are continuous at a point x, then the function $f + g$ is continuous at the point x."

As used in the three-bar equivalence of elementary algebra, a variable x denotes a quantity which varies over some range. It is permitted that one may substitute for a variable any value in its range. This is clearly exemplified in (VI.1.2) and (VI.1.8). In many uses of variables, this property is not satisfied, as in (VI.1.4), for instance, where one may not substitute

3 for x. This is probably the reason why some writers are reluctant to consider x as a variable in (VI.1.4). Certainly if x is a variable in (VI.1.4), it is a different kind of variable from that which we are presently considering. Accordingly, it will be handled in our symbolic logic in quite a different way from the way we shall handle the x's of (VI.1.2) and (VI.1.8), and will not be considered until a later chapter.

In distinction to a variable, an unknown (or indeterminate) is not supposed to vary. Thus, suppose one starts out to solve for x in (VI.1.1). If x is allowed to vary, so that the value of x in one step of the solution is not the same as the value in the next step, then we shall not be able to justify the next step. Thus we can proceed from

$$x^2 - 4x + 3 = 0$$

to

$$(x - 3)(x - 1) = 0$$

to

$$x = 3 \qquad \text{or} \qquad x = 1$$

only because in each step we have the same value for x as in the preceding step.

To cite a more complicated case, one may look at the proof on pages 14 to 15 of Bôcher, 1907, of:[1]

"THEOREM 1. If two functions are continuous at a point, their sum is continuous at this point."

As we remarked earlier, this is a statement about two unknown functions and an unknown point. Indeed, the proof begins:[1]

"Let f_1 and f_2 be two functions continuous at the point $(c_1, \ldots, c_n) \ldots$."

A hasty survey of Bôcher's proof will indicate that it would break down completely if one should permit a change to some other point or some other pair of functions part way through the proof. That is, the point and functions, though unknown, are not variable.

Nevertheless, there are cases in which we permit an unknown to become a variable, and indeed this occurs in a very important logical principle. To get an instance of this, let us follow the train of thought which Bôcher started when he proved the theorem stated above. He next proves:[1]

"THEOREM 2. If two functions are continuous at a point, their product is continuous at this point."

From these, Bôcher infers that each polynomial is continuous at each point. He then concludes:[1]

"THEOREM 3. Any polynomial is a continuous function for all values of the variables."

[1] From Bôcher, "Introduction to Higher Algebra," copyright 1907 by The Macmillan Company and used with their permission.

In this result, our point has ceased being an unknown and has become a variable. That is, a heretofore fixed point is now allowed to vary. How does this come about? Bôcher does not stop to explain, because this is a standard logical procedure, but had he undertaken to explain, he would likely have given some such explanation as the following:

"We have shown that for a fixed polynomial and a fixed point, the polynomial is continuous at the point. Now let us have a fixed polynomial and a variable point. To show that the polynomial is continuous at the point, choose a value for the point. Holding this value temporarily fixed, we conclude that the polynomial is continuous at that value. But since this was any value, we conclude that the polynomial is continuous at all values."

Putting this principle in general terms, it says that, if one can prove a statement about an unknown, then one can replace the unknown by a variable. The justification is that, whatever value be chosen for the variable, one can, for that value, carry out the proof given for the unknown and hence infer the truth of the theorem for that value. This being so for each value, we infer the theorem for all values.

This principle is widely used. For most theorems involving variables, the proof is usually given with an unknown in place of the variable. Thus to prove

$$\sin^2 x + \cos^2 x = 1,$$

one chooses some unknown (but fixed) x and proves the theorem for that x. One then changes to a variable x.

To cite other instances, consider a typical proof from plane geometry. We quote (a bit freely) from Wentworth and Smith, page 32.[1]

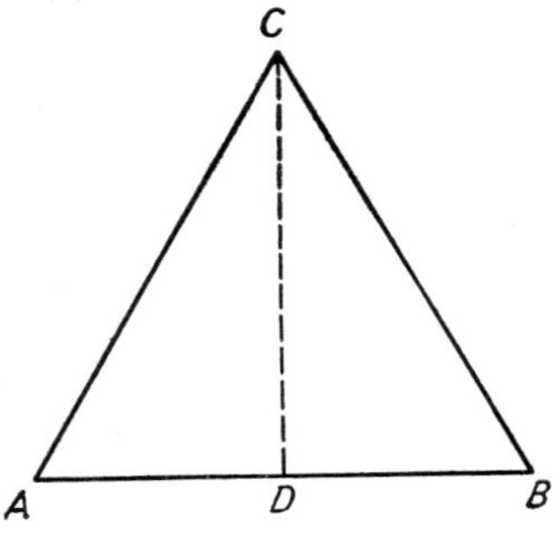

FIG. VI.1.1.

In an isosceles triangle (see Fig. VI.1.1) the angles opposite the equal sides are equal.

Given: The isosceles triangle ABC, with AC equal to BC.

To prove: That $\angle A = \angle B$.

Proof. Suppose CD drawn so as to bisect $\angle ACB$. Then in the triangles ADC and BDC, $AC = BC$ (given), $CD = CD$ (identity), and $\angle ACD = \angle DCB$ (construction). Hence triangle ADC is congruent to triangle BDC, and so $\angle A = \angle B$. Q.E.D.

Clearly, it would ruin this proof completely if halfway through it one should permit the triangle ABC to change into some other isosceles triangle,

[1] From "Plane and Solid Geometry" by George Wentworth and D. E. Smith, copyright 1913, courtesy of Ginn & Company.

say one in which sides AB and BC were equal instead of sides AC and BC. So the proof is carried out for some fixed (but undetermined) isosceles triangle, and only after the proof is complete, and the theorem proved, do we permit the replacement of our fixed, unknown triangle by a variable triangle.

This is the important consideration. It is only in *proved* statements that one can replace an unknown by a variable. In some statement such as

$$x^2 - 4x + 3 = 0$$

which cannot be proved, the x cannot become variable.

Because the same letters are often used for both unknowns and variables, and because in proved theorems unknowns can be changed to variables, the distinction between an unknown and a variable is often not carefully observed in everyday mathematics. Instead, one avoids confusion by paying attention to the meanings of the statements which one is considering. In symbolic logic, where no attention is paid to meanings, we shall have to distinguish between variables and unknowns solely on the basis of the form of the statements in which they occur. This will require a careful attention to details which could be ignored in case one is relying on meaning to prevent confusion. It will also permit a basic simplification of our approach to variables and unknowns. In mathematics, a variable is a shadowy, ill-defined entity which varies over some range and which is denoted by a letter x. In symbolic logic, where we are not concerned with meanings, the variable as such disappears, and we have left only the letter x, now denoting nothing whatever. This has the advantage of freeing us from explaining the difficult concept of a variable. The disadvantage is that our letters x, y, z must now be manipulated by purely mechanical rules, instead of by reference to an intuitive idea of a variable. However, for those who find the intuitive idea of a variable hard to grasp, this disadvantage becomes an advantage.

Although we now operate entirely without variables or unknowns, and only with letters, we still wish to manipulate our letters as though some denoted variables and some unknowns. So, in the next sections, where we set up our rules for manipulating letters, we wish to keep reminding the reader that certain letters are to be treated as though they denoted variables and certain others as though they denoted unknowns (this is not necessary to an understanding of the rules, but we think it will be helpful to our readers). We shall do this by saying that such and such letter is serving as a variable, while such and such other letter is serving as an unknown.

2. Quantifiers. We shall use the same letters to serve both as variables and as unknowns. This is an objectionable procedure, but it leads only to complication and not to fallacy. Also, it conforms to standard mathematical usage, and we follow it. We shall call these letters "variables," even though some occurrences may be serving as unknowns and some as variables. Those occurrences which are serving as unknowns will be called "free" occurrences of the variable and those occurrences which are serving as variables will be called "bound" occurrences. The distinction between free and bound occurrences will be based entirely on the form of the statement, and not at all on its meaning.

We cannot defend this terminology on the ground that it is good, because it is not. It is merely traditional. In the first place, having disposed of the notion of a variable and confined our attention to letters alone, it is very silly to turn around and call these letters "variables," especially since they serve sometimes as variables and sometimes as unknowns. Also, there is certainly nothing about the words "free" or "bound" to suggest serving as unknowns and variables; if anything, the terminology seems just backward. However, it is the accepted terminology.

Besides &, $\sim$, and variables, with which we have acquainted the reader, we now introduce the notation "(x)", namely, a variable enclosed in a pair of parentheses. This combination of symbols is to be prefixed to statements. From the point of view of the symbolic logic, we are quite indifferent to any proposed meaning for this and are concerned only with the formal axioms for it. However, these formal axioms will be much more understandable and easy to remember if we first discuss the interpretation that would be put on "(x)" if one were to consider meanings.

We interpret the prefix "(x)" to denote any one of:

"For all x, . . . ",
"For every x, . . . ",
"For each x, . . . ".

Thus, if we have a statement $F(x)$ containing some occurrences of x, the statement $(x)\ F(x)$ shall have the interpretation that for every possible value of x whatsoever, the statement $F(x)$ is true. Thus we might take $F(x)$ to be

$$x^2 - 1 = (x + 1)(x - 1),$$

and then $(x)\ F(x)$ indicates that, for every possible value of x,

$$x^2 - 1 = (x + 1)(x - 1).$$

It is of course permissible to prefix (x) to $F(x)$ even in those cases where $F(x)$ is not true for every possible value of x. In such case, the result $(x)\ F(x)$ is a false statement. Thus we can and may write

$$(x)\ (x^2 - 4x + 3 = 0),$$

but it is false.

We shall also permit prefixing (x) to a statement P even if it does not contain any occurrences of x. In such case, $(x)\ P$ shall mean the same thing as P. Thus we may write

$$(x)\ (2 + 2 = 4),$$

which merely means "$2 + 2 = 4$," and is true. Also we might write

$$(x)\ (4 \text{ is an odd prime}),$$

which merely means "4 is an odd prime," and is false.

The reader should realize that the meanings indicated above for $(x)\ F(x)$ and $(x)\ P$ are relevant only when we come to interpret our proved statements as logical principles of everyday mathematics. In operating within the symbolic logic, only the forms of our statements are relevant, and on the basis of form alone, it is convenient to be allowed to prefix (x) to any statement whatever, without concern for possible occurrences of x in the statement.

We are now prepared to indicate which occurrences of variables (letters, that is) are free and which are bound. In a statement such as "For all x, $x^2 - 1 = (x + 1)(x - 1)$," clearly x is a variable. So in a corresponding statement $(x)\ F(x)$, we say that all occurrences of x are bound, since they must necessarily be serving as variables. In fact we say that they are bound by (x), and sometimes we speak of prefixing a (x) to $F(x)$ as "binding the occurrences of x in $F(x)$ by (x)."

At the present time we shall not give any further details as to just exactly how the variables occur in a $F(x)$, but we do state the following conditions which they satisfy:

(1) The occurrences of a variable in $\sim P$ are free or bound according as they are free or bound in the part P.

(2) The occurrences of a variable in $P \& Q$ are free or bound according as they are free or bound in the parts P and Q.

(3) All occurrences of x in $(x)\ P$ are bound, but for any other variable the occurrences in $(x)\ P$ are free or bound according as they are free or bound in the part P.

The condition (1) tells us that $\sim$ neither binds nor frees the occurrences of a variable. This agrees with the fact that negating a statement does not alter the status of any unknowns or variables occurring therein. (2) gives similar information about &. (3) tells us that (x) binds all occurrences of x. That is, prefixing a (x) corresponds to the important mathematical operation of changing an unknown to a variable. However, prefixing a (x) does not change the status of any other unknowns or variables except x.

Let us contrast the situations in ordinary mathematics and in symbolic logic. In ordinary mathematics, the x's in

$$x^2 - 1 = (x + 1)(x - 1)$$

would ordinarily denote a variable, but on occasion they might denote an unknown (for instance, throughout a proof of the statement). However, from the statement alone, there is no way to tell which is intended. In symbolic logic we use two different statements to take the place of the single statement of ordinary logic, namely, the two statements

$$x^2 - 1 = (x + 1)(x - 1)$$

and

$$(x)\ (x^2 - 1 = (x + 1)(x - 1)).$$

In the former, all occurrences of x are free and x serves as an unknown. In the latter, all occurrences of x are bound and x serves as a variable. Thus, in symbolic logic one can determine the role of a letter in a statement simply by the form of the statement.

One should take care not to be confused by the fact that the statement

$$x^2 - 1 = (x + 1)(x - 1)$$

occurs in both everyday mathematics and symbolic logic, and has two possible meanings in everyday mathematics but only one meaning in symbolic logic, namely, the less commonly used of its two meanings in everyday mathematics.

The prefix (x) is called the universal quantifier, since $(x)\ F(x)$ signifies that $F(x)$ is universally true. In terms of (x), we can define the existential quantifier $(\mathrm{E}x)$, signifying "For some x . . . ". This is done by noting that $(x)\ {\sim}F(x)$ signifies that $F(x)$ is false for every x, so that its negation ${\sim}(x)\ {\sim}F(x)$ signifies that $F(x)$ must be true for at least one x. So we define $(\mathrm{E}x)\ F(x)$ to be an abbreviation for ${\sim}(x)\ {\sim}F(x)$. Then $(\mathrm{E}x)\ F(x)$ signifies any one of:

"For some x, $F(x)$."
"For at least one x, $F(x)$ is true."
"There is an x such that $F(x)$."
"There exists an x such that $F(x)$."

It is doubtless the last interpretation which suggested the name "existential quantifier" for $(\mathrm{E}x)$.

Notice that since $(\mathrm{E}x)$ contains (x) as a part, all x's in $(\mathrm{E}x)\ F(x)$ are bound.

By combining $(\mathrm{E}x)$ with the notion of equality, we shall later learn how to write such prefixes as "For exactly one x . . . ", "For at least three different x's . . . ", and the like.

If a statement contains occurrences of several variables, $x, y, \ldots,$ it is natural that one may wish to prefix several of $(x), (y), \ldots,$ or $(\mathrm{E}x), (\mathrm{E}y),$

.... Thus since $x^2 - y^2 = (x + y)(x - y)$ is true for every y, we indicate this by prefixing (y), getting $(y)\ (x^2 - y^2 = (x + y)(x - y))$. This statement in turn is true for every x, and we indicate this by prefixing (x), getting $(x)(y)\ (x^2 - y^2 = (x + y)(x - y))$.

This illustration should indicate that the double prefix $(x)(y)$ denotes "For all x and y . . . ". Similarly the triple prefix $(x)(y)(z)$ denotes "For all x, y, and z . . . ". We commonly abbreviate $(x)(y)$ to (x,y), and $(x)(y)(z)$ to (x,y,z), and so on.

In like manner, we see that $(\mathrm{E}x)(\mathrm{E}y)$ denotes "For some x and y . . . ", and $(\mathrm{E}x)(\mathrm{E}y)(\mathrm{E}z)$ denotes "For some x, y, and z . . . ". We abbreviate these to $(\mathrm{E}x,y)$ and $(\mathrm{E}x,y,z)$.

Still other combinations are possible. Thus for each x we can find at least one value of y such that $x^2 + y = x + y^2$ (namely, either $y = x$ or $y = 1 - x$). We express this information by the statement $(x)(\mathrm{E}y)$ $(x^2 + y = x + y^2)$. This is not the same as $(\mathrm{E}y)(x)\ (x^2 + y = x + y^2)$, for the latter states that there is some y such that $x^2 + y = x + y^2$ for every x, which is clearly not so.

We have already called attention to the mathematical statement

$$\int_0^x x^2\,dx = \frac{x^3}{3}$$

in which two occurrences of x are variables of integration and the other two may be unknowns. Similarly, in symbolic logic we can have both bound and free occurrences of x in a single statement. One difference is that there will not be any doubt as to which occurrences are bound and which free. Consider $(\mathrm{E}x)\ (x = 3)$, in which all occurrences of x are bound, and $x = 7$, in which all occurrences of x are free. We can form the logical product of these two and get

$$(x = 7)\&(\mathrm{E}x)\ (x = 3),$$

in which the leftmost occurrence of x is free whereas the other two occurrences of x are bound.

In trying to assign a meaning to this statement, the free and bound occurrences of x have nothing to do with each other. Considered as a statement about x, only the free occurrence of x is involved, and

$$(x = 7)\&(\mathrm{E}y)\ (y = 3)$$

or

$$(x = 7)\&(\mathrm{E}z)\ (z = 3)$$

would be considered to be the same statement about x. In fact all three make the statement that $x = 7$ and there is some object which equals 3.

To make a corresponding statement about y, one would write

$$(y = 7)\&(\mathrm{E}x)\ (x = 3)$$

or

$$(y = 7)\&(\mathrm{E}y)\ (y = 3)$$

or

$$(y = 7)\&(\mathrm{E}z)\ (z = 3),$$

etc., since each of these statements signifies that $y = 7$ and there is some object which equals 3.

This situation is quite analogous to that in which

$$\int_0^x x^2\,dx = \frac{x^3}{3},$$

$$\int_0^x y^2\,dy = \frac{x^3}{3},$$

and

$$\int_0^x z^2\,dz = \frac{x^3}{3}$$

all make the same statement about x, and

$$\int_0^y x^2\,dx = \frac{y^3}{3},$$

$$\int_0^y y^2\,dy = \frac{y^3}{3},$$

and

$$\int_0^y z^2\,dz = \frac{y^3}{3}$$

all make the corresponding statement about y.

We can put this in more general terms. If we have a statement $F(x)$ about x, only free occurrences of x count in the meaning of $F(x)$. So to get a corresponding statement about y, we replace the free occurrences of x by occurrences of y. Notice that this procedure of replacing all free occurrences of x by occurrences of y to get the corresponding statement about y is a purely formal procedure and can be carried out without any reference to meaning.

There are certain obvious cases in which, if we have a statement about x, $F(x)$, and replace all free occurrences of x by occurrences of y, then the resulting statement about y, $F(y)$, is not a corresponding statement about y; to wit, if the original statement contains free occurrences of y as well as x. Thus if

$$F(x) \text{ is } (x - 2)(y + 2) = xy + 2x - 2y - 4,$$

then

$$F(y) \text{ is } (y - 2)(y + 2) = y^2 + 2y - 2y - 4,$$

which is quite a different statement about y. However, in a case like this, one would usually denote the first statement by $F(x,y)$ and the second by $F(y,y)$. In other words, instead of speaking of

$$(x - 2)(y + 2) = xy + 2x - 2y - 4$$

as a statement about x, we usually speak of it as a statement about both x and y; it is clearly then nonsense to ask for a corresponding statement about y alone.

Actually situations of the sort just described cause no trouble if one is careful not to presume that a formula with free occurrences of x does not also contain free occurrences of y. However, there is a more subtle situation that we must guard against in which we can have a statement $F(x)$ with free occurrences of x only, and which therefore is a statement about x only, which is such that, if we replace these free occurrences of x by occurrences of y, then we shall not get a corresponding statement about y. Thus consider

(VI.2.1) $$(x = 7)\&(\mathrm{E}y)\ (y \neq x).$$

This says that $x = 7$ and there is some object which differs from x. If we now replace all free occurrences of x by occurrences of y, we get

(VI.2.2) $$(y = 7)\&(\mathrm{E}y)\ (y \neq y).$$

This says something different about y, to wit, "$y = 7$ and there is some object which differs from itself."

The trouble clearly is that, whereas the occurrence of x is free in

$$(\mathrm{E}y)\ (y \neq x),$$

an occurrence of y in the same position is bound. If we should express our original statement in the quite equivalent form

$$(x = 7)\&(\mathrm{E}z)\ (z \neq x),$$

then we could replace the free occurrences of x by occurrences of y and get

$$(y = 7)\&(\mathrm{E}z)\ (z \neq y)$$

which does say the same thing about y.

A quite analogous situation can occur in everyday mathematics. Thus, consider the statement

$$\int_0^x (2y + x)\, dy = 2x^2.$$

If we replace x by y, we get

$$\int_0^y (2y + y)\, dy = 2y^2,$$

which is not the corresponding statement about y. In fact, the first is a true statement about x, but the second is a false statement about y.

In a situation illustrated by (VI.2.1) and (VI.2.2), in which upon substituting occurrences of y for the free occurrences of x we get a bound occurrence of y where there was a free occurrence of x, we say that the substitution causes confusion. Although we are using the word "confusion," which usually has to do with meaning, we are actually describing a purely formal situation. In fact let us give the following precise and purely formal definition.

If P is a statement and Q is the result of replacing each free occurrence of x (if any) in P by an occurrence of y, then:

(1) If some bound occurrence of y in Q is the result of replacing a free occurrence of x in P by an occurrence of y, then we say that the replacement causes confusion.

(2) If no bound occurrence of y in Q is the result of replacing a free occurrence of x in P by an occurrence of y, then we say that the replacement causes no confusion.

We stated this in a form which allows the possibility that there might be no free occurrences of x in P. In such case, Q would be the same as P, and clearly the replacement would cause no confusion. We also permit P to contain free occurrences of y. Then the case in which the replacement causes no confusion would be characterized by writing $F(x,y)$ for P and $F(y,y)$ for Q, and the meanings of P and Q would be related in a corresponding fashion.

Theorem VI.2.1. If Q is the result of replacing all free occurrences of x in P by occurrences of y, and P is the result of replacing all free occurrences of y in Q by occurrences of x, then neither replacement causes confusion.

Proof. Fix attention on some free occurrences of x in P. It becomes an occurrence of y in Q when we replace all free occurrences of x in P by occurrences of y. Let us now replace all free occurrences of y in Q by occurrences of x. It is assumed that the result of this is P. So our particular occurrence of y must be replaced by an occurrence of x, which can be the case only if this occurrence of y is free in Q. Applying this reasoning in turn to each free occurrence of x in P, we conclude that every free occurrence of x in P becomes a free occurrence of y in Q. Hence this replacement causes no confusion. Similarly, each free occurrence of y in Q becomes a free occurrence of x in P, and this replacement also causes no confusion.

In case P and Q are related as in the hypothesis of this theorem, P will contain no free occurrences of y, and Q will contain no free occurrences of x. Also, by our theorem, it will cause no confusion to replace free occurrences of x in P by occurrences of y, and vice versa. In such case, Q will make exactly the same statement about y that P makes about x. This would generally be characterized by writing $F(x)$ for P and $F(y)$ for Q.

In order to save much repetition of assumptions, we set up the following conventions.

In case we refer to two statements as $F(x,y)$ and $F(y,y)$, it shall be assumed that $F(y,y)$ is the result of replacing each free occurrence of x (if any) in $F(x,y)$ by an occurrence of y and that this replacement causes no confusion. It is not assumed that there actually are free occurrences of either x or y in $F(x,y)$, nor is it assumed that there are not free occurrences of other variables in $F(x,y)$.

In case we refer to two statements as $F(x)$ and $F(y)$, it shall be assumed that $F(y)$ is the result of replacing all free occurrences of x in $F(x)$ by occurrences of y, and $F(x)$ is the result of replacing all free occurrences of y in $F(y)$ by occurrences of x. It is not assumed that there actually are free occurrences of x in $F(x)$, nor is it assumed that there are not free occurrences of variables other than x and y in $F(x)$. Our assumptions do assure that there are no free occurrences of y in $F(x)$ and no free occurrences of x in $F(y)$.

Just as one could write

$$\int_0^1 \int_0^x x^2\,dx\,dx = \int_0^1 \frac{x^3}{3}\,dx = \frac{1}{12},$$

so we could prefix an $(\mathrm{E}x)$ or (x) to

$$(x = 7)\&(\mathrm{E}x)\ (x = 3),$$

getting, for instance,

$$(\mathrm{E}x)\ ((x = 7)\&(\mathrm{E}x)\ (x = 3)).$$

We shall seldom have any occasion to write anything of this sort, but there is no harm in doing so. Since in

$$(x = 7)\&(\mathrm{E}x)\ (x = 3),$$

only the leftmost x is relevant to the meaning of the statement, only this x is bound by the additional $(\mathrm{E}x)$ which we propose to prefix. Or to put it otherwise, since

$$(x = 7)\&(\mathrm{E}x)\ (x = 3)$$

and

$$(x = 7)\&(\mathrm{E}y)\ (y = 3)$$

are supposed to have the same meanings, we attach to $(\mathrm{E}x)\ ((x = 7)\&(\mathrm{E}x)\ (x = 3))$ the same meaning that we would attach to

$$(\mathrm{E}x)\ ((x = 7)\&(\mathrm{E}y)\ (y = 3)).$$

Such questions of meaning arise only when we come to interpret our statements. In the formal manipulations, these matters cause no trouble at all.

A similar matter is the question of the meaning to be given to $(x)(x)\ P$ or $(x)(\mathrm{E}x)\ P$ or $(\mathrm{E}x)(x)\ P$ or $(\mathrm{E}x)(\mathrm{E}x)\ P$. Consider $(x)(x)\ P$. Since all x's in $(x)\ P$ are bound, it follows that, as far as meaning is concerned, $(x)\ P$ contains no x's. In such case $(x)(x)\ P$ has the same meaning as $(x)\ P$. Similarly for the others.

With regard to the omission of parentheses without ambiguity, we shall agree that the abbreviations listed in the left-hand column below have the meanings listed beside them in the right-hand column.

$(x)\ PQ$	$(x)\ (PQ)$
$(x)\ P\&Q$	$(x)\ (P\&Q)$
$(x)\ P\vee Q$	$((x)\ P)\vee Q$
$(x)\ P \supset Q$	$((x)\ P) \supset Q$
$(x)\ P \equiv Q$	$((x)\ P) \equiv Q$

That is, & is weaker than (x), but $\vee$, $\supset$, and $\equiv$ are all stronger than (x). Clearly there is no ambiguity in such forms as $(x)\ {\sim}P$, ${\sim}(x)\ P$, $P(x)\ Q$, $P\vee(x)\ Q$, $P \supset (x)\ Q$, and $P \equiv (x)\ Q$.

We use exactly similar conventions for $(\mathrm{E}x)$. We do not need to choose which of (x) or $(\mathrm{E}x)$ shall be stronger, for there is clearly no ambiguity in such forms as $(x)(\mathrm{E}y)\ P$, $(\mathrm{E}x)(y)(z)\ P$, etc.

The conventions for (x,y) are the same as for (x) and the conventions for $(\mathrm{E}x,y)$ are the same as for $(\mathrm{E}x)$.

Dots can be used to strengthen symbols just as before. Thus the abbreviations in the left-hand column below have the meanings which are listed beside them in the right-hand column.

$(x)\ P.Q$	$((x)\ P)Q$
$(x).P\vee Q$	$(x)\ (P\vee Q)$
$(x).P \supset Q.\vee R$	$((x)\ (P \supset Q))\vee R$
$(x){:}P \supset Q.\vee R$	$(x)\ ((P \supset Q)\vee R)$

Let us now look at some statements of ordinary mathematics which require quantifiers for their translation into symbolic logic. Consider the statement "$f(x)$ is continuous at the point x." First of all, let us write the definition of this in ordinary language:

"For each positive ε there is a positive δ such that whenever $|\ y - x\ | < \delta$ we have $|\ f(y) - f(x)\ | < \varepsilon$."

We adopt $\varepsilon > 0$, $\delta > 0$, $|y - x| < \delta$, and $|f(y) - f(x)| < \varepsilon$ as statements of symbolic logic, and inquire how we shall put them together with quantifiers and logical connections to get a translation of the above statement.

Consider the part "whenever $|y - x| < \delta$ we have $|f(y) - f(x)| < \varepsilon$." If we said merely "if $|y - x| < \delta$, then $|f(y) - f(x)| < \varepsilon$," we would translate it as

$$|y - x| < \delta . \supset .|f(y) - f(x)| < \varepsilon.$$

However, the use of "whenever" strengthens this to

$$(y):|y - x| < \delta . \supset .|f(y) - f(x)| < \varepsilon.$$

That is, the "whenever" converts y into a variable, whereas with "if . . . then . . . ," y might be an unknown.

How shall we say "there is a positive δ such that $F(\delta)$"? If we wished to say merely "there is a δ such that $F(\delta)$," we could write

$$(E\delta)\ F(\delta).$$

To specify that there is a positive δ such that $F(\delta)$, we are claiming that δ simultaneously has the two attributes "δ is positive" and $F(\delta)$. That is, we are claiming

$$\delta > 0.\ F(\delta)$$

for some δ. In other words we claim

$$(E\delta).\delta > 0.\ F(\delta).$$

So "there is a positive δ such that whenever $|y - x| < \delta$ we have $|f(y) - f(x)| < \varepsilon$" becomes

$$(E\delta):\delta > 0:(y):|y - x| < \delta . \supset .|f(y) - f(x)| < \varepsilon.$$

How can we write "For each positive ε, $G(\varepsilon)$"? By analogy with our treatment of δ, one might be tempted to write

$$(\varepsilon).\varepsilon > 0.\ G(\varepsilon).$$

This is completely wrong. The logical product

$$\varepsilon > 0.\ G(\varepsilon)$$

asserts that ε both is positive and possesses the property $G(\varepsilon)$. Then

$$(\varepsilon).\varepsilon > 0.\ G(\varepsilon)$$

asserts this for each ε. In other words, it states that every ε is positive in addition to asserting $G(\varepsilon)$ for each ε. This is quite absurd and is quite a different thing from asserting $G(\varepsilon)$ for every positive ε.

Actually, the form we are seeking is

$$(\varepsilon).\ \varepsilon > 0 \supset G(\varepsilon),$$

as should become apparent from a study of this form. If we have this statement given then certainly we can conclude $G(\varepsilon)$ whenever we have $\varepsilon > 0$. Also, from this statement alone, we cannot conclude $G(\varepsilon)$ for any ε for which it is false that $\varepsilon > 0$, although (and this is proper) it is not forbidden that $G(\varepsilon)$ be true for some ε for which $\varepsilon > 0$ is false.

So we get finally as the translation of "$f(x)$ is continuous at the point x" the statement

$$(\varepsilon):.\varepsilon > 0. \supset :(\mathrm{E}\delta):\delta > 0:(y):|\ y - x\ | < \delta. \supset .|\ f(y) - f(x)\ | < \varepsilon.$$

We say that $f(x)$ is continuous in an interval if it is continuous at each point of the interval. If we translate "x is in the interval (a,b)" by the familiar formula $a \leq x \leq b$, then we can translate "$f(x)$ is continuous in the interval (a,b)" by

$$(x)::a \leq x \leq b. \supset :.(\varepsilon):.\varepsilon > 0. \supset :(\mathrm{E}\delta):\delta > 0:(y):$$
$$|\ y - x\ | < \delta. \supset .|\ f(y) - f(x)\ | < \varepsilon.$$

Often when we are speaking of continuity in an interval, we modify the definition of continuity at the end points so as to require that y as well as x be in the interval (see Hardy, 1947, page 186). This revised definition would be translated as:

$$(x)::a \leq x \leq b. \supset :.(\varepsilon):.\varepsilon > 0. \supset :(\mathrm{E}\delta):\delta > 0:(y):a \leq y \leq b.$$
$$|\ y - x\ | < \delta. \supset .|\ f(y) - f(x)\ | < \varepsilon.$$

We say that $f(x)$ is uniformly continuous in the interval (a,b) if for each positive ε there is a positive δ such that whenever x and y are in the interval (a,b) and $|\ y - x\ | < \delta$ we have $|\ f(y) - f(x)\ | < \varepsilon$. This would be translated as

$$(\varepsilon)::\varepsilon > 0. \supset :.(\mathrm{E}\delta):.\delta > 0:.(x):.a \leq x \leq b. \supset :(y):a \leq y \leq b.$$
$$|\ y - x\ | < \delta. \supset .|\ f(y) - f(x)\ | < \varepsilon.$$

From a formal point of view, the only difference in the two statements is in the location of the part

$$(x).a \leq x \leq b \supset .$$

However, both formally and intuitively this change is quite important.

The mathematical literature is composed mainly of statements which require the use of quantifiers to translate them into symbolic logic so that we shall see many more examples of the use of quantifiers.

We should like to caution the reader against the word "any." Sometimes "any" means "each" and sometimes it means "some." Thus, sometimes "for any x . . ." means (x), and sometimes "for any x . . ." means $(\mathrm{E}x)$. We shall quote literally two examples from the mathematical literature. In the first, the author intended "each" when he wrote "any," and in the second the author intended "some" when he wrote "any." The statements are "If $x_1, \ldots, x_n$ are real numbers, and if for any x_i we have $x_i = 0$, then $x_1^2 + \cdots + x_n^2 = 0$," and "If $x_1, \ldots, x_n$ are vectors, and if for any x_i we have $x_i = 0$, then the set of vectors are linearly dependent."

If one wishes to be sure that one will be understood, one should never use "any" in a place where either of "each" or "some" can be used. However, there are cases in which use of "any" is correct and neither of "each" or "some" can be used. For instance, "I will not violate any law." The statement "I will not violate each law" has quite a different meaning, and the statement "I will not violate some law" might be interpreted to mean that there is a particular law which I am determined not to violate.

Nonetheless, many writers use "any" in places where "each" or "some" would be preferable.

EXERCISES

VI.2.1. Using $x > 0$ and $x^2 > 0$ as statements of symbolic logic, write a translation for "$x^2 > 0$ whenever $x > 0$."

VI.2.2. Using $a \leq b + c$, $c > 0$, and $a \leq b$ as statements of symbolic logic, write a translation for "If $a \leq b + c$ whenever $c > 0$, then $a \leq b$."

VI.2.3. If $F(f(n))$, $G(f(n))$, and $H(f(n))$ are translations of "$f(n)$ is a polynomial with integral coefficients," "$f(n)$ is a constant," and "$f(n)$ is a prime," write a translation of "No polynomial $f(n)$ with integral coefficients, other than a constant, can be prime for all n."

VI.2.4. If $F(x)$ and $G(x,y)$ are translations of "x is the product of a finite number of factors" and "y is a factor of x" and we accept statements of the form "$z = 0$" as statements of symbolic logic, write a translation of "If the product of a finite number of factors is zero, at least one of the factors must be zero."

VI.2.5. If $F(x)$ is a translation of "x is an integer" and we permit use of the symbol e and statements of the form $x = y/z$ and $x = 0$ in symbolic logic, write a translation of "e is irrational."

VI.2.6. Using $(f,\phi_n) = 0$ and $f = 0$ as statements of symbolic logic, write a translation for "$(f,\phi_n) = 0$ for every n implies $f = 0$."

VI.2.7. If $F(f(x))$ and $G(f(x),a)$ are translations of "$f(x)$ is a polynomial in x," and "a is a coefficient of $f(x)$" and we accept statements of the form $f(x) = 0$ and $a = 0$ as statements of symbolic logic, write a translation of "a necessary and sufficient condition that a polynomial in x vanish identically is that all its coefficients be zero."

VI.2.8. If $F(x,y)$ and $G(x,y,z)$ are translations of "x divides y" and "x is the greatest common divisor of y and z" write a translation of "Every common divisor of a and b divides their greatest common divisor."

VI.2.9. If $F(x)$ and $G(x)$ are translations of "x is an odd prime" and "x is an integer" and we accept statements of the form $1 + x^2 + y^2 = mp$ and $0 < m < p$ as statements of symbolic logic, write a translation of "If p is an odd prime, then there are integers x and y such that $1 + x^2 + y^2 = mp$ for some integer m with $0 < m < p$."

VI.2.10. If $F(x)$ and $G(x)$ are translations of "x is an integer of $k(\rho)$" and "x is an integer" and we accept statements of the form $\alpha = a + b\rho$ as statements of symbolic logic, write a translation of "The integers of $k(\rho)$ are the numbers $\alpha = a + b\rho$ with integral a, b."

VI.2.11. If $F(x)$ is a translation of "x is an integer" and we accept statements of the form $0 < x < 1$ as statements of symbolic logic, write a translation of "There is no integer between 0 and 1."

VI.2.12. If $F(x)$ is a translation of "x is a rational number" and we accept statements of the form $x = y$ and $x < y$ as statements of symbolic logic, write a translation of "There is a rational between any two rationals."

VI.2.13. If $F(x)$ and $G(x)$ are translations of "x is a rational number" and "x is a member of S" and we accept statements of the form $x < y$ as statements of symbolic logic, write a translation of "Every rational member of S is less than every rational nonmember of S."

VI.2.14. If $G(x)$ is a translation of "x is a member of S" and we accept statements of the form $x = y$ and $x < y$ as statements of symbolic logic, write a translation of "S has a greatest member."

VI.2.15. If $G(x)$ is a translation of "x is a member of S" and we accept statements of the form $x = y$, $x > 0$, and $|x - y| < z$ as statements of symbolic logic, write a translation for "For every positive ε there is a member of S different from x whose distance from x is less than ε."

VI.2.16. If $G(x)$ is a translation of "x is a member of S" and we accept statements of the form $x = y$ as statements of symbolic logic, write translations of:

(a) S has at least two members.
(b) S does not have at least two members.
(c) S has exactly one member.

VI.2.17. Find a statement $F(x,y)$ of mathematics such that $(x)(\mathrm{E}y)$ $F(x,y)$ is true but $(\mathrm{E}y)(x)$ $F(x,y)$ is false.

VI.2.18. If the occurrences of the variables x and y in $x = y$ are free, identify which occurrences of variables are bound and which free in the following statements:

(a) $(\mathrm{E}y).y = x.$
(b) $(\mathrm{E}z)(y){:}z = y. \equiv .y = x.$

(c) $x = y: \equiv :(z):x = z. \equiv .y = z.$
(d) $y = x. \supset .(Ey).y = x.$

VI.2.19. If $G(x)$ is a translation of "x is a positive integer" and we accept statements of the form $x > 0$, $x > y$, and $| a_x - a_y | < z$ as statements of symbolic logic, write a translation for "For every positive ε there is a positive integer m such that for every greater positive integer n, $| a_m - a_n | < \varepsilon$."

3. Axioms for the Restricted Predicate Calculus. We now get down to formal matters, and state some axioms. Before doing so, we wish to discuss one important characteristic which our axioms should have. We stated earlier the important principle that, if one can prove a statement about an unknown, then one can replace the unknown by a variable. Within our symbolic logic, this will take the form:

If $\vdash F(x)$, then $\vdash (x)\ F(x)$.

In order to be able to prove this, we have to define our axioms in such a way that, if $F(x)$ is an axiom, then so is $(x)\ F(x)$, and, in general, if P is an axiom, then $(x_1)(x_2) \cdots (x_n)\ P$ is an axiom. This we do as follows:

If P, Q, and R are statements, not necessarily distinct, and $x, x_1, x_2, \ldots, x_n$ are variables, not necessarily distinct, then each of the following is an axiom:

1. $(x_1)(x_2) \cdots (x_n)\ (P \supset PP)$.
2. $(x_1)(x_2) \cdots (x_n)\ (PQ \supset P)$.
3. $(x_1)(x_2) \cdots (x_n)\ (P \supset Q. \supset .\sim(QR) \supset \sim(RP))$.
4. $(x_1)(x_2) \cdots (x_n)\ ((x).P \supset Q: \supset :(x)\ P. \supset .(x)\ Q)$.

If $x, x_1, x_2, \ldots, x_n$ are variables, not necessarily distinct, and P is a statement with no free occurrences of x, then the following is an axiom:

5. $(x_1)(x_2) \cdots (x_n)\ (P \supset (x)\ P)$.

If $x, y, x_1, x_2, \ldots, x_n$ are variables, not necessarily distinct, and P is a statement, and Q is the result of replacing each free occurrence (if any) of x in P by an occurrence of y, and no bound occurrence (if any) of y in Q is the result of replacing a free occurrence of x in P by an occurrence of y, then the following is an axiom:

6. $(x_1)(x_2) \cdots (x_n)\ ((x)\ P \supset Q)$.

By the conventions which we set up in the previous section, we could simplify this last to:

If $x, y, x_1, x_2, \ldots, x_n$ are variables, not necessarily distinct, then the following is an axiom:

6. $(x_1)(x_2) \cdots (x_n)\ ((x)\ F(x,y) \supset F(y,y))$.

We note that, in each of the above, it is permitted that $n = 0$, so that

1. $P \supset PP$.
2. $PQ \supset P$.
3. $P \supset Q. \supset .\sim(QR) \supset \sim(RP)$.
4. $(x).P \supset Q: \supset :(x)\ P. \supset .(x)\ Q$.
5. $P \supset (x)\ P$ if no free occurrences of x in P.
6. $(x)\ F(x,y) \supset F(y,y)$.

are axioms.

We shall refer to the forms indicated above as Axiom schemes 1 to 6. Subsequent axiom schemes which we shall add in later chapters will be referred to as Axiom schemes 7, 8, ...

The type of axiom scheme, of the form

$$(x_1)(x_2) \cdots (x_n)\ P,$$

will be used in stating all future axioms. For this reason, the following theorem will be obvious.

Theorem VI.3.1. If P is an axiom and x is a variable, then $(x)\ P$ is an axiom.

We might point out certain properties of Axiom schemes 1 to 6. Axiom schemes 1 to 3 are just the truth-value axioms added to in such a way as to make Thm.VI.3.1 true. Axiom scheme 4 is important for the proof that if $\vdash P$ then $\vdash (x)\ P$. Axiom schemes 5 and 6 tell us that, if P has no free occurrences of x, then $\vdash P \equiv (x)\ P$; for we get $\vdash P \supset (x)\ P$ by Axiom scheme 5, and by putting P for $F(x,y)$ in Axiom scheme 6, we get $\vdash (x)\ P \supset P$. The result "$\vdash P \equiv (x)\ P$ if there are no free occurrences of x in P" accords with our convention that, if there are no x's in P, then we shall attach the same meaning to $(x)\ P$ as to P. Finally Axiom scheme 6 gives a formal expression of the principle that one can replace a variable by any one of its values.

In Chapter VIII we shall discuss another type of variable, such as in

$$\int_0^3 x^2\, dx = 9,$$

for which one cannot replace the variable by any of its values.

EXERCISES

VI.3.1. Find a statement P that would arise naturally in a mathematical discussion such that, if Q is the result of replacing each free occurrence of x in P by an occurrence of y, then $(x)\ P \supset Q$ is false. Explain why your particular example does not violate Axiom scheme 6.

VI.3.2. Prove that the following statement is true about each statement

P which is derivable from the Axiom schemes 1 to 6 by means of modus ponens:

"If in P we replace all occurrences of variables whatever by occurrences of the particular variable x, and if we further remove from P all quantifiers whatever, then the resulting expression Q is built up from various statements $R_1, \ldots, R_r$ (clearly the only variable occurring in any of the R's is x) by means of $\sim$ and & alone, and is of such a form that no matter what set of truth values we assign to the R's, the corresponding value of Q is truth."

(*Hint.* Use induction on the number of steps in the demonstration of $\vdash P$.)

VI.3.3. Using the previous exercise, prove that one cannot derive a contradiction from Axiom schemes 1 to 6 by use of modus ponens.

4. The Generalization Principle. The generalization principle is that, if P is proved, one may infer $(x)\ P$.

***Theorem VI.4.1.** If P is a statement and x is a variable and $\vdash P$, then $\vdash (x)\ P$.

Proof. Let $S_1, S_2, \ldots, S_s$ be a demonstration of $\vdash P$. Then S_s is P, and for each S_i either:

(1) S_i is an axiom.

(2) There is a j less than i such that S_i and S_j are the same.

(3) There are j and k, each less than i such that S_k is $S_j \supset S_i$.

We take $(x)\ S_1, (x)\ S_2, \ldots, (x)\ S_s$ to be key steps of our demonstration of $\vdash (x)\ P$. The last of our key steps, $(x)\ S_s$, is $(x)\ P$, as desired. By filling in additional steps before each of our key steps, we can build up a complete demonstration. We do this as follows.

Case 1. S_i is an axiom. Then by Thm.VI.3.1, $(x)\ S_i$ is also an axiom.

Case 2. S_i is the same as an earlier S_j. Then $(x)\ S_i$ is the same as an earlier $(x)\ S_j$.

Case 3. There are an earlier S_j and an earlier S_k such that S_k is $S_j \supset S_i$. That is, S_j and $S_j \supset S_i$ occur before S_i. Then the key steps $(x)\ S_j$ and $(x).S_j \supset S_i$ have already occurred. Insert the steps

$$(x).S_j \supset S_i : \supset :(x)\ S_j \supset (x)\ S_i$$

$$(x)\ S_j \supset (x)\ S_i.$$

The first is an instance of Axiom scheme 4. Using the first as major premise and $(x).S_j \supset S_i$ as minor premise, we infer the second by modus ponens. Then we can use the second as major premise and $(x)\ S_j$ as minor premise to infer $(x)\ S_i$ by modus ponens.

This theorem states the generalization principle that, if one has proved a statement $F(x)$ containing the unknown x, one may generalize the unknown

x and infer $F(x)$ with a variable x, that is, $(x)\ F(x)$. Incidentally, it is interesting to contrast the justification which we gave early in this chapter of the generalization principle with the proof just given of Thm.VI.4.1. Our earlier justification depended on meaning and was carried out in the everyday intuitive logic of mathematics. The proof of Thm.VI.4.1, on the other hand, is carried out in the constructive intuitive logic and depends entirely on the forms of the statements involved.

The generalization principle is so important that we wish to cite further instances of it. First, though, we wish to cite two results which look rather like instances of the generalization principle, but which are not, namely:

If a continuous function is not zero at some point, x, then for all points in some neighborhood of x, the function is not zero.

If three parallel lines cut equal segments from one transversal, they cut equal segments from all transversals.

The reader should study these until he is sure he understands why they are not instances of the generalization principle.

We turn now to some genuine instances of the generalization principle. An important class of theorems whose proofs make use of the generalization principle are the locus theorems of geometry. Thus let us look at the locus theorem which we quoted on pages 41 and 42 of this text. Here it was assumed that YO is the perpendicular bisector of AB, and we wished to prove that every P on YO is equidistant from A and B and every P off YO is not equidistant from A and B. That is, we wished to prove:

$$(P){:}P \text{ on } YO. \supset .PA = PB,$$

$$(P){:}{\sim}(P \text{ on } YO). \supset .PA \neq PB.$$

Suppose we look carefully at the proof of the first of these (the proof of the second involves the same logical principles). Having assumed YO the perpendicular bisector of AB, Wentworth and Smith say:[1]

"Let P be any point in YO, . . ."

That is, they choose P an arbitrary, undetermined point of YO, which must nevertheless temporarily stay fixed so that they can construct some triangles and prove them congruent and infer $PA = PB$. That is, Wentworth and Smith first prove

(VI.4.1) $$W, P \text{ on } YO \vdash PA = PB$$

where P is an unknown and W stands for the statement that YO is the perpendicular bisector of AB. From this they proceed tacitly to

(VI.4.2) $$W \vdash P \text{ on } YO. \supset .PA = PB,$$

[1] From Wentworth and Smith, *op. cit.*

(VI.4.3) $W \vdash (P){:}P$ on $YO. \supset .PA = PB,$

(VI.4.4) $\vdash W \supset :(P){:}P$ on $YO. \supset .PA = PB.$

We can proceed from (VI.4.1) to (VI.4.2) and from (VI.4.3) to (VI.4.4) by use of the deduction theorem. The step from (VI.4.2) to (VI.4.3) uses the generalization principle. However, we cannot carry out this step by use of Thm.VI.4.1, because Thm.VI.4.1 says merely that, if $\vdash V$, then $\vdash (P)\ V$, whereas to go from (VI.4.2) to (VI.4.3) we need to know that, if $W \vdash V$, then $W \vdash (P)\ V$.

Actually, the step from (VI.4.2) to (VI.4.3) violates our proviso that one can apply the generalization principle only to *proved* statements. In (VI.4.2), the statement

$$P \text{ on } YO. \supset .PA = PB$$

is not proved, but only deduced from the assumption W.

One is tempted to jump to the conclusion that one can apply the generalization principle not merely to proved statements but also to statements which have been correctly deduced from some assumption. However, this is not so. If it were so, we could proceed as follows. Applying the generalization principle to (VI.4.1) we get

(VI.4.5) W, P on $YO \vdash (P).PA = PB.$

However, $(Q).QA = QB$ is the same as $(P).PA = PB$. So we conclude

$$W, P \text{ on } YO \vdash (Q).QA = QB.$$

This says that, if YO is the perpendicular bisector of AB and P is on YO, then every point Q is equidistant from A and B.

This is clearly absurd.

Thus we see that it is not permissible to apply the generalization principle in (VI.4.1), but it is apparently permissible to apply the generalization principle to (VI.4.2) to get (VI.4.3). To get an explanation of this discrepancy, let us review the intuitive reasoning that one might use to justify deriving (VI.4.3) from (VI.4.2). In (VI.4.2) we showed that for some particular P we can deduce P on $YO. \supset .PA = PB$ from W. Can we conclude that this can be done for each P? Can we, for instance, conclude that we can deduce Q on $YO. \supset .QA = QB$ from W? The answer is "Yes," for it suffices to repeat the proof of (VI.4.2) with Q in place of P. Thus we can infer $(P){:}P$ on $YO. \supset .PA = PB$ from W.

If now we try to reason analogously to deduce (VI.4.5) from (VI.4.1) it becomes immediately apparent why this deduction fails. If we replace P by Q in the proof of (VI.4.1), we do not get W, P on $YO \vdash QA = QB$; we get instead W, Q on $YO \vdash QA = QB$. In other words, the critical point in going from (VI.4.2) to (VI.4.3) is that W does not depend on P, so that if we replace P by Q in the proof of (VI.4.2) we get a proof of $W \vdash Q$ on $YO. \supset .QA = QB$ and so (VI.4.3) holds. Had W depended on P, then we could not have applied the generalization principle to (VI.4.2) any more than to (VI.4.1).

A rather obvious way of putting this is that, if any of our assumptions depend on P, as "P on YO" in (VI.4.1), then they put a restriction on P which prevents use of the generalization principle. However, if none of our assumptions depend on P, as W does not depend on P in (VI.4.2), then our deduction is completely unrestricted as far as P is concerned, and use of the generalization principle is legitimate.

Quite clearly, the conditions expressed above can be stated in a manner which depends only on the forms of the statements involved, and not at all on their meanings. We shall do so in the following theorem.

****Theorem VI.4.2.** If $P_1, P_2, \ldots, P_n, Q$ are statements, not necessarily distinct, and x is a variable which has no free occurrences in any of $P_1, P_2, \ldots, P_n$, and if $P_1, P_2, \ldots, P_n \vdash Q$, then $P_1, P_2, \ldots, P_n \vdash (x)\ Q$.

Proof. Let $S_1, S_2, \ldots, S_s$ be a demonstration of $P_1, P_2, \ldots, P_n \vdash Q$. Then S_s is Q, and for each S_i either:

(1) S_i is an axiom.

(2) S_i is a P.

(3) There is a j less than i such that S_i and S_j are the same.

(4) There are j and k, each less than i such that S_k is $S_j \supset S_i$.

We take $(x)\ S_1, (x)\ S_2, \ldots, (x)\ S_s$ to be key steps of our demonstration and proceed to fill in additional steps as in the proof of Thm.VI.4.1 in the cases (1), (3), and (4). In the case (2), where S_i is a P, we insert S_i and $S_i \supset (x)\ S_i$ as extra steps before the key step $(x)\ S_i$. Because S_i is a P, it is acceptable as a step of our demonstration. Also, since there are no free occurrences of x in any of the P's, there are no free occurrences of x in S_i, and so $S_i \supset (x)\ S_i$ is an instance of Axiom scheme 5. With S_i and $S_i \supset (x)\ S_i$ inserted, we get the key step $(x)\ S_i$ by modus ponens.

This theorem enables us to use the generalization principle in symbolic logic whenever it would be considered right to use it in everyday mathematics, and only then. For this reason, we shall often refer to Thm.VI.4.2 as the generalization theorem.

The generalization principle is so widely used in everyday mathematics that it is usually taken for granted and used without specific mention. We shall cite one instance of its use which is out of the ordinary in that there is explicit mention of the generalization principle.

On page 275, Wentworth and Smith state the definition:[1]

"If a straight line drawn to a plane is perpendicular to every straight

[1] *Ibid.*

line that passes through its foot and lies in the plane, it is said to be *perpendicular* to the plane."

On the next page, they state and prove:[1]

"If a line is perpendicular to each of two other lines at their point of intersection, it is perpendicular to the plane of the two lines."

We shall quote only the beginning of the proof and the step at which the generalization principle is used. The proof begins:[1]

"Given the line AO perpendicular to the lines OP and OR at O.

"To prove that AO is perpendicular to the plane MN of these lines.

"*Proof.* Through O draw in MN any other line OQ, ..."

Now various other lines are drawn, and triangles are proved congruent, and finally it is shown that OQ is perpendicular to AO. Then comes the use of the generalization principle:[1]

"Therefore AO is perpendicular to any and hence to every line in MN through O."

EXERCISES

VI.4.1. Find an illustration in the mathematical literature of the use of the generalization principle.

VI.4.2. Write out a complete demonstration of $\vdash (x)\sim(\sim PP)$.

VI.4.3. If there are no free occurrences of x in P, prove

$$\vdash (x).P \supset Q : \supset :P \supset (x)\, Q.$$

5. The Equivalence and Substitution Theorems. Although we can now prove $\vdash P \equiv \sim\sim P$, we still have not proved that we can replace P by $\sim\sim P$ or $\sim\sim P$ by P whenever desired. In ordinary mathematics, where one goes by meaning, such a replacement would be immediately sanctioned, since P and $\sim\sim P$ have the same meaning. More generally, any time we have proved $\vdash A \equiv B$, we should expect to be able to replace A by B or vice versa. In this section, we shall prove the substitution theorem, which says that we can indeed replace A by B if we have $\vdash A \equiv B$.

We cannot prove the substitution theorem in full generality at the present time. Thus we shall have to give a second proof at a later time when full generality is attainable. Nonetheless, the present form of the substitution theorem will be of sufficient value to warrant proving it now, even though this will involve some duplication later when we prove the more general form.

***Theorem VI.5.1.** $\vdash (x)\, P \supset P$.

Proof. $(x)\, P \supset P$ is an axiom, namely, an instance of Axiom scheme 6. To see this, let us refer back to the first, unsimplified version of Axiom scheme 6. There let us take y to be the same as x. Then Q is the result of

[1] *Ibid.*

replacing all free occurrences of x in P by occurrences of x, so that Q is P and the replacement causes no confusion, and we can indeed apply Axiom scheme 6.

Theorem VI.5.2. $\vdash (x).PQ: \supset :(x)\ P.(x)\ Q.$

Proof. By Thm.IV.4.17, it suffices to prove each of

$$\vdash (x).PQ: \supset :(x)\ P,$$

$$\vdash (x).PQ: \supset :(x)\ Q.$$

The proofs of these are very similar, and so we give a proof for the second only. By the deduction theorem (Thm.IV.6.1), it suffices to prove

$$(x).PQ \vdash (x)\ Q,$$

and by the generalization theorem (Thm.VI.4.2), it suffices to prove

$$(x).PQ \vdash Q$$

(since clearly there are no free occurrences of x in $(x).PQ$). To prove this latter, we have

$$\vdash (x).PQ: \supset :PQ$$

by Thm.VI.5.1 and

$$\vdash PQ \supset Q$$

by Thm.IV.4.18.

An alternative proof would be as follows. By Thm.IV.4.18,

$$\vdash PQ \supset Q.$$

So by Thm.VI.4.1,

$$\vdash (x):PQ \supset Q.$$

But by Axiom scheme 4

$$\vdash (x):PQ \supset Q.: \supset :.(x).PQ: \supset :(x)\ Q.$$

So by modus ponens

$$\vdash (x).PQ: \supset :(x)\ Q.$$

Theorem VI.5.3. $\vdash (x).P \equiv Q: \supset :(x)\ P \equiv (x)\ Q.$

Proof. By Thm.VI.5.2,

$$\vdash (x).P \equiv Q: \supset :(x).P \supset Q:(x).Q \supset P.$$

However, by Axiom scheme 4,

$$\vdash (x).P \supset Q: \supset :(x)\ P \supset (x)\ Q,$$

$$\vdash (x).Q \supset P: \supset :(x)\ Q \supset (x)\ P.$$

So by Thm.IV.4.16,

$$\vdash (x).P \supset Q:(x).Q \supset P: \supset :(x)\ P \equiv (x)\ Q.$$

We now prove the equivalence theorem.

In both the equivalence theorem and the substitution theorem there occurs a complicated hypothesis. Rather than write it out twice in the statements of the two theorems, we temporarily denote it by Hypothesis H_1.

Hypothesis H_1. $P_1, P_2, \ldots, P_n, A, B$ are statements and $x_1, x_2, \ldots, x_a$ are variables. W is built up out of some or all of the P's and A and B by means of &, $\sim$, and (x), where each time (x) is used, x is one of $x_1, x_2, \ldots, x_a$, and where one may use each P or each x or A or B more than once if desired. V is the result of replacing some or none of the A's in W by B's.

The equivalence theorem then takes the form:

Theorem VI.5.4. Assume Hypothesis H_1. Let $y_1, y_2, \ldots, y_b$ be variables such that there are no free occurrences of any of the x's in $(y_1)(y_2) \cdots (y_b)\ (A \equiv B)$. Then

$$\vdash (y_1)(y_2) \cdots (y_b)\ (A \equiv B). \supset .W \equiv V.$$

Proof. Proof by induction on the number of symbols in W, counting as a symbol each occurrence of a P, or of A or of B or of $\sim$ or of a (x). Temporarily let X denote $(y_1)(y_2) \cdots (y_b)\ (A \equiv B)$.

Let W have one symbol. Then W is A, B, or a P.

Case 1. W is A.

Subcase I. A is replaced by B. Then V is B. So $W \equiv V$ is $A \equiv B$. By b uses of Thm.VI.5.1, we get

$$\vdash X \supset .A \equiv B.$$

That is,

$$\vdash X \supset .W \equiv V.$$

Subcase II. A is not replaced by B. Then V is A and $W \equiv V$ is $A \equiv A$. By the truth-value theorem,

$$\vdash X \supset .A \equiv A.$$

That is,

$$\vdash X \supset .W \equiv V.$$

Case 2. W is B or a P. Then V is the same and $W \equiv V$ is $W \equiv W$. By the truth-value theorem,

$$\vdash X \supset .W \equiv W.$$

That is,

$$\vdash X \supset .W \equiv V.$$

Assume the theorem if W has k or fewer symbols, where k is a positive integer, and let W have $k + 1$ symbols. Then W has at least two symbols, and so must be either $\sim Q$ or QR or $(x)\ Q$, where Q (and R) has k or fewer symbols.

Case 1. W is $\sim Q$. Then V is $\sim S$, where S is the result of replacing some or none of the A's in Q by B's. So by the hypothesis of the induction

$$\vdash X \supset .Q \equiv S.$$

By the truth-value theorem,

$$\vdash Q \equiv S. \supset .\sim Q \equiv \sim S.$$

So

$$\vdash X \supset .\sim Q \equiv \sim S.$$

That is,

$$\vdash X \supset .W \equiv V.$$

Case 2. W is QR. Then V is ST, where S and T are the results of replacing some or none of the A's in Q and R by B's. So by the hypothesis of the induction

$$\vdash X \supset .Q \equiv S,$$

$$\vdash X \supset .R \equiv T.$$

By Thm.IV.4.17,

$$\vdash X \supset .Q \equiv S.R \equiv T.$$

By the truth-value theorem

$$\vdash Q \equiv S.R \equiv T. \supset .QR \equiv ST.$$

So

$$\vdash X \supset .QR \equiv ST.$$

That is,

$$\vdash X \supset .W \equiv V.$$

Case 3. W is $(x)\ Q$. Then V is $(x)\ S$, where S is the result of replacing some or none of the A's in Q by B's. So by the hypothesis of the induction

$$\vdash X \supset .Q \equiv S.$$

So

$$X \vdash Q \equiv S.$$

By the generalization theorem

$$X \vdash (x)\ (Q \equiv S),$$

since part of the hypothesis of our theorem is that there are no free occurrences of x in X. Then by the deduction theorem

$$\vdash X \supset (x)\ (Q \equiv S).$$

Then by Thm.VI.5.3,

$$\vdash X \supset .(x)\ Q \equiv (x)\ S.$$

That is,

$$\vdash X \supset .W \equiv V.$$

There is a somewhat weaker version of the equivalence theorem which is often useful, namely:

****Theorem VI.5.5.** Assume Hypothesis H_1. If $\vdash A \equiv B$, then $\vdash W \equiv V$.

Proof. Clearly there are no free occurrences of the x's in $(x_1)(x_2) \cdots (x_a)\ (A \equiv B)$. So by the previous theorem

$$\vdash (x_1)(x_2) \cdots (x_a)\ (A \equiv B). \supset .W \equiv V.$$

If now we have $\vdash A \equiv B$, then by a uses of Thm.VI.4.1, we get

$$\vdash (x_1)(x_2) \cdots (x_a)\ (A \equiv B).$$

Then by modus ponens

$$\vdash W \equiv V.$$

We now prove the substitution theorem.

****Theorem VI.5.6.** Assume Hypothesis H_1. If $\vdash A \equiv B$ and $\vdash W$, then $\vdash V$.

Proof. If $\vdash A \equiv B$, then $\vdash W \equiv V$ by the previous theorem. However,

$$\vdash W \equiv V. \supset .W \supset V$$

by Axiom scheme 2, and so $\vdash W \supset V$ by modus ponens. If in addition, $\vdash W$, then $\vdash V$ by modus ponens.

Although the substitution theorem is an easy deduction from the equivalence theorem, the two theorems differ widely in their applications. If we have $\vdash A \equiv B$, the equivalence theorem allows us to infer various equivalences of the form $\vdash W \equiv V$, whereas the substitution theorem allows us to substitute occurrences of B for occurrences of A in proved theorems. That is, given the proved theorem $\vdash W$, we can substitute occurrences of B for occurrences of A in it and get $\vdash V$.

There is little use of the equivalence theorems or the substitution theorem in everyday mathematics. This is because very commonly, if one has $\vdash A \equiv B$, it is considered that A and B have the same meaning, and so if we replace A by B, we make no change in the meaning, and so there is no need to justify the replacement. In symbolic logic, where the form alone is considered, the substitution theorem is quite important. However, occasionally in fairly complex situations, where the meaning is not easy to follow, the substitution theorem may be used in ordinary mathematics. Thus, in Landau, 1930, page 44, it is shown that the condition stated in Satz 120 is equivalent to the second condition in the definition of a "Schnitt", and it is then concluded that the former may replace the latter in the definition of a "Schnitt". This is a clear-cut instance of the use of the substitution theorem.

EXERCISES

VI.5.1. Using $\vdash P \equiv \sim\sim P$, prove $\vdash Q \supset (x)\ P. \equiv .\sim(Q(\mathrm{E}x)\sim P)$.

VI.5.2. Without using the substitution theorem or either version of the equivalence theorem, prove $\vdash Q \supset (x)\ P. \equiv .\sim(Q(\mathrm{E}x)\sim P)$.

VI.5.3. Prove $\vdash (x).P \equiv Q{:} \supset {:}(x).\ P \supset R. \equiv .(x).Q \supset R.$

VI.5.4. If there are no free occurrences of x in P, prove $\vdash (x).P \equiv Q{:} \supset {:}P \equiv (x)\ Q.$

VI.5.5. If there are no free occurrences of x in Q, prove $\not\vdash (x).P \equiv Q{:} \supset {:}P \equiv (x)\ Q.$

6. Useful Equivalences. The substitution theorem gives us a useful application for equivalences. Accordingly, we collect a large number of equivalences in the present section. We remark that, from a given set of equivalences, one can derive new ones by use of the equivalence theorems of the preceding section. Also, because of

$$\vdash P \equiv Q. \supset .Q \equiv P,$$

which follows from the truth-value theorem, the order of an equivalence is reversible. One should not forget that equivalences can be combined by use of

$$\vdash P \equiv Q.Q \equiv R. \supset .P \equiv R.$$

One can prove a large number of equivalences by means of the truth-value theorem. We have collected a group of such equivalences in the next theorem.

Theorem VI.6.1.

I. $\vdash P \equiv PP.$
**II. $\vdash P \equiv \sim\sim P.$
III. $\vdash P \equiv P\mathsf{v}P.$
IV. $\vdash P \equiv .P.Q\mathsf{v}\sim Q.$
V. $\vdash P \equiv P\mathsf{v}Q\sim Q.$
VI. $\vdash P \equiv PQ\mathsf{v}P\sim Q.$
VII. $\vdash P \equiv .P\mathsf{v}Q.P\mathsf{v}\sim Q.$
VIII. $\vdash P \equiv .P.P\mathsf{v}Q.$
IX. $\vdash P \equiv P\mathsf{v}PQ.$
X. $\vdash P \equiv .P\mathsf{v}Q.Q \supset P.$
XI. $\vdash P \equiv {:}Q \equiv .P \equiv Q.$
XII. $\vdash P \equiv .P \equiv Q\mathsf{v}\sim Q.$
XIII. $\vdash \sim P \equiv .P \equiv Q\sim Q.$
**XIV. $\vdash PQ \equiv QP.$
**XV. $\vdash P\mathsf{v}Q \equiv Q\mathsf{v}P.$
**XVI. $\vdash (PQ)R \equiv P(QR).$

**XVII. $\vdash (P\vee Q)\vee R \equiv P\vee(Q\vee R)$.
**XVIII. $\vdash P.Q\vee R. \equiv .PQ\vee PR$.
**XIX. $\vdash P\vee QR. \equiv .P\vee Q.P\vee R$.
XX. $\vdash P \supset R.Q \supset R. \equiv .P\vee Q \supset R$.
XXI. $\vdash P \supset Q.P \supset R. \equiv .P \supset QR$.
XXII. $\vdash P\vee.Q \supset R{:} \equiv {:}P\vee Q. \supset .P\vee R$.
XXIII. $\vdash P\vee.Q \equiv R{:} \equiv {:}P\vee Q. \equiv .P\vee R$.
XXIV. $\vdash P \supset Q\vee R. \equiv .P \supset Q.\vee.P \supset R$.
XXV. $\vdash PQ \supset R. \equiv .P \supset R.\vee.Q \supset R$.
XXVI. $\vdash P \supset .Q \supset R{:} \equiv {:}P \supset Q. \supset .P \supset R$.
XXVII. $\vdash P \supset .Q \equiv R{:} \equiv {:}P \supset Q. \equiv .P \supset R$.
XXVIII. $\vdash P\vee Q \equiv \sim(\sim P\sim Q)$.
XXIX. $\vdash PQ \equiv \sim(\sim P\vee\sim Q)$.
XXX. $\vdash \sim(P\vee Q) \equiv \sim P\sim Q$.
XXXI. $\vdash \sim(PQ) \equiv \sim P\vee\sim Q$.
XXXII. $\vdash PQ. \equiv .P\vee\sim Q.Q$.
XXXIII. $\vdash P\vee Q \equiv P\sim Q\vee Q$.
XXXIV. $\vdash PQ. \equiv .P.P \supset Q$.
XXXV. $\vdash P\vee Q. \equiv {:}P \supset Q. \supset Q$.
XXXVI. $\vdash PQ. \equiv .P\vee Q.P\vee\sim Q.\sim P\vee Q$.
XXXVII. $\vdash P\vee Q \equiv PQ\vee P\sim Q\vee\sim PQ$.
XXXVIII. $\vdash PQ. \equiv .P\vee Q.P \equiv Q$.
XXXIX. $\vdash P\vee Q. \equiv .PQ\vee.P \equiv \sim Q$.
XL. $\vdash \sim(PQ) \equiv P\sim Q\vee\sim PQ\vee\sim P\sim Q$.
XLI. $\vdash \sim(P\vee Q). \equiv .P\vee\sim Q.\sim P\vee Q.\sim P\vee\sim Q$.
XLII. $\vdash P \supset Q. \equiv .\sim(P\sim Q)$.
**XLIII. $\vdash P \supset Q. \equiv .\sim P\vee Q$.
**XLIV. $\vdash P \supset Q. \equiv .\sim Q \supset \sim P$.
XLV. $\vdash P \supset \sim Q. \equiv .Q \supset \sim P$.
XLVI. $\vdash \sim P \supset Q. \equiv .\sim Q \supset P$.
XLVII. $\vdash P \supset Q. \equiv .P \supset PQ$.
XLVIII. $\vdash P \supset Q. \equiv .P\vee Q \supset Q$.
XLIX. $\vdash P \supset Q. \equiv .P \equiv PQ$.
L. $\vdash P \supset Q. \equiv .P\vee Q \equiv Q$.
LI. $\vdash P \supset Q. \equiv .PQ\vee\sim PQ\vee\sim P\sim Q$.
LII. $\vdash PQ{:} \equiv {:}P \equiv .P \supset Q$.
LIII. $\vdash P\vee Q{:} \equiv {:}Q \equiv .P \supset Q$.
LIV. $\vdash P \equiv Q. \equiv .P \supset Q.Q \supset P$.
LV. $\vdash P \equiv Q. \equiv .P \supset Q.\sim P \supset \sim Q$.
LVI. $\vdash P \equiv Q. \equiv .P\vee\sim Q.\sim P\vee Q$.
LVII. $\vdash P \equiv Q. \equiv .\sim P \equiv \sim Q$.
LVIII. $\vdash P \equiv \sim Q. \equiv .\sim P \equiv Q$.

LIX. $\vdash P \equiv Q. \equiv .PQ\mathbf{v}{\sim}P{\sim}Q.$

LX. $\vdash P \equiv Q. \equiv .{\sim}(P \equiv {\sim}Q).$

LXI. $\vdash {\sim}(P \equiv Q) \equiv P{\sim}Q\mathbf{v}{\sim}PQ.$

LXII. $\vdash {\sim}(P \equiv Q). \equiv .P\mathbf{v}Q.{\sim}P\mathbf{v}{\sim}Q.$

**LXIII. $\vdash PQ \supset R: \equiv :P \supset .Q \supset R.$

**LXIV. $\vdash P \supset .Q \supset R: \equiv :Q \supset .P \supset R.$

LXV. $\vdash P{\sim}P \equiv Q{\sim}Q.$

LXVI. $\vdash P\mathbf{v}{\sim}P \equiv Q\mathbf{v}{\sim}Q.$

LXVII. $\vdash P \supset .Q \equiv PQ.$

LXVIII. $\vdash P \supset .P \equiv P\mathbf{v}Q.$

LXIX. $\vdash P \supset :Q \equiv .P \supset Q.$

LXX. $\vdash P \supset :P \equiv .Q \supset P.$

LXXI. $\vdash P \supset :Q \supset .P \equiv Q.$

LXXII. $\vdash {\sim}P \supset .P \equiv PQ.$

LXXIII. $\vdash {\sim}P \supset .Q \equiv P\mathbf{v}Q.$

LXXIV. $\vdash {\sim}P \supset :{\sim}Q \supset .P \equiv Q.$

LXXV. $\vdash {\sim}P \equiv :{\sim}Q \equiv .P \equiv Q.$

We note one useful consequence of the substitution theorem in connection with the above list of equivalences. Since we have the commutative and associative laws for the logical product (Parts XIV and XVI), we can prove any two products of several factors equivalent regardless of their order and the method of inserting parentheses. Hence any such product may be substituted for any other such in any statement. Hence we no longer need distinguish such products, but may write $P_1P_2 \cdots P_n$ as standing indifferently for any product of the factors $P_1, P_2, \ldots, P_n$ regardless of order and grouping.

Similar remarks apply to the logical sum.

Although we have not listed above all equivalences provable by truth values that have ever been used, we have listed all that are in common use, and many less common ones. We have even listed several variations of some of the more useful ones. Thus XLV and XLVI are variations of the very important XLIV. On the other hand, we have not listed

$$\vdash PQ. \equiv .P.{\sim}P\mathbf{v}Q$$

and

$$\vdash P\mathbf{v}Q \equiv P\mathbf{v}{\sim}PQ$$

which are variations of XXXII and XXXIII got by interchanging the roles of P and Q.

We call attention to LXXI. From this, we see that, if $\vdash P$ and $\vdash Q$, then $\vdash P \equiv Q$, and we may substitute Q for P or vice versa. In effect, any two true statements are equivalent and one may be substituted for the other in any statement. Correspondingly, by LXXIV, if $\vdash \sim P$ and $\vdash \sim Q$, then $\vdash P \equiv Q$, and we may substitute Q for P or vice versa. In effect, any two false statements are equivalent, and one may be substituted for the other in any statement.

There are many useful equivalences involving quantifiers. We now state and prove some of these.

Theorem VI.6.2.

I. $\vdash (\mathrm{E}x)\ P \equiv \sim(x) \sim P$.

II. $\vdash (x)\ P \equiv \sim(\mathrm{E}x) \sim P$.

III. $\vdash \sim(\mathrm{E}x)\ P \equiv (x) \sim P$.

IV. $\vdash \sim(x)\ P \equiv (\mathrm{E}x) \sim P$.

Proof. If we write the left side of Part I in unabbreviated form, we see that it is identical with the right side, so that Part I is an instance of $\vdash Q \equiv Q$, and follows from the truth-value theorem. As Part I is proved for every P and x, it will remain true if we replace P by $\sim P$, so that we get

$$\vdash (\mathrm{E}x) \sim P \equiv \sim(x) \sim\sim P.$$

By Thm.VI.6.1, Part II, we are entitled to replace the $\sim\sim P$ by P, which gives us

$$\vdash (\mathrm{E}x) \sim P \equiv \sim(x)\ P,$$

and we readily infer Part IV. Now by Thm.VI.6.1, Part LVIII, we get Part III from Part I, and Part II from Part IV.

We now wish to introduce a powerful means of proving equivalences, known as the duality theorem. The statement of the theorem involves the notion of the dual of a statement. To define this notion, we must temporarily not think of $P \mathbf{v} Q$ and $(\mathrm{E}x)\ P$ being defined as $\sim(\sim P \sim Q)$ and $\sim(x) \sim P$, but must temporarily think of $\mathbf{v}$ and $(\mathrm{E}x)$ as basic operators on the same footing with $\sim$, & and (x). Now let $P_1, P_2, \ldots, P_n$ be statements, and let W be built up out of some or all of the P's by use of $\sim$, &, $\mathbf{v}$, (x), and $(\mathrm{E}x)$, where we may use each P as often as desired, and may use whatever variables we like in the (x) and $(\mathrm{E}x)$, and as often as desired. Then the dual of W is got from W by replacing products by sums, sums by products, (x) by $(\mathrm{E}x)$, $(\mathrm{E}x)$ by (x), and each P_i by $\sim P_i$. In case any occurrence of a P_i already has a $\sim$ attached in front of it in W, we shall get a $\sim\sim P_i$ at that place upon forming the dual, and since we can replace this by P_i, we might as well do so and count this replacement as part of the operation of forming the dual. Accordingly, we combine these two operations into a single operation which we call the operation of forming the dual. We define the combined operation as follows.

The dual of W is that statement which one gets from W by simultaneously performing the following changes:

1. If an occurrence of P_i does not have a $\sim$ attached, attach one.
2. If an occurrence of P_i does have a $\sim$ attached, take it off.
3. Replace each & by $\vee$ and vice versa.
4. Replace each (x) by $(\mathrm{E}x)$ and vice versa.

Clearly changes 1 and 2 are intended to produce the same result as replacing each P_i by $\sim P_i$, and then removing each $\sim\sim$ produced by this. In other words, changes 1 and 2 refer only to $\sim$'s attached directly to P's, and if a $\sim$ is attached to a more complex part, this is not to be tampered with.

To illustrate the idea of a dual, we shall list several statements in a column below, with their duals in a column to the right.

P	$\sim P$
$\sim P$	P
$(\mathrm{E}x)\ P{\sim}Q$	$(x).\ {\sim}P{\vee}Q$
$\sim(x)\ (\mathrm{E}y).P{\vee}{\sim}Q{\vee}RS$ . . .	$\sim(\mathrm{E}x)\ (y).\ {\sim}PQ({\sim}R{\vee}{\sim}S)$
$\sim({\sim}P(x)\ Q)$	$\sim(P{\vee}(\mathrm{E}x)\ {\sim}Q)$

Although we took the statements on the right to be the duals of the statements on the left, we see that the statements on the left are duals of the statements on the right. Indeed, inspection of our definition of a dual makes it clear that, if we take the dual of a dual, we return to the original statement.

Note that the definition of a dual is relative to the P's. That is, in forming a dual, we operate entirely outside the P's, and if the P's themselves have structure, we make no changes within the P's.

One must watch the omission of parentheses in forming duals. Thus the dual of $PQ{\vee}R$ is $({\sim}P{\vee}{\sim}Q){\sim}R$ rather than ${\sim}P{\vee}{\sim}Q{\sim}R$. This is because $PQ{\vee}R$ really means $(PQ){\vee}R$ whereas ${\sim}P{\vee}{\sim}Q{\sim}R$ means ${\sim}P{\vee}({\sim}Q{\sim}R)$.

We remark again that, for the purposes of taking duals, $\vee$ is counted as a basic symbol. Thus, although $P{\vee}Q$ and ${\sim}({\sim}P{\sim}Q)$ are really the same, for the purpose of taking duals we count them as different; indeed they have different duals, to wit, ${\sim}P{\sim}Q$ and ${\sim}(P{\vee}Q)$, respectively. However, though these duals are different, they are equivalent. Indeed, it will turn out to be the case that equivalent statements have equivalent duals.

If W contains parts of the form $P \supset Q$ or $P \equiv Q$, these must be expressed in terms of $\sim$, &, and $\vee$ before forming the dual. One could express $P \supset Q$ as ${\sim}(P{\sim}Q)$, but a neater dual will result if we express $P \supset Q$ as ${\sim}P{\vee}Q$. Similarly, it is best to express $P \equiv Q$ as ${\sim}P{\vee}Q.P{\vee}{\sim}Q$.

We shall write W^* for the dual of W. Clearly, if W^* and V^* are the duals of W and V, then $W^* \vee V^*$ is the dual of WV, W^*V^* is the dual of $W \vee V$, (Ex) W^* is the dual of (x) W, (x) W^* is the dual of (Ex) W, and $\sim W^*$ is the dual of $\sim W$ except when W consists of a single P_i. In the latter case, the dual of $\sim W$ is the dual of $\sim P_i$ and is P_i, whereas $\sim W^*$ is $\sim\sim P_i$.

We now state the duality theorem.

****Theorem VI.6.3.** If W^* is the dual of W, then $\vdash \sim W \equiv W^*$.

Proof. Proof by induction on the number of symbols in W, counting as a symbol each occurrence of a P, $\sim$, (x), or (Ex). First let W consist of a single symbol. Then W is P_i, W^* is $\sim P_i$, and so

$$\vdash \sim W \equiv W^*.$$

Now assume the theorem true if W has k or fewer symbols where k is a positive integer and let W have $k + 1$ symbols. Then W has at least two symbols. By our assumption on the structure of W, W must have one of the forms $\sim Q$, QR, $Q \vee R$, (x) Q, or (Ex) Q, where Q and R have k or fewer symbols.

Case 1. W is $\sim Q$.

Subcase I. Q is a single symbol, P_i. Then W^* is P_i and $\sim W$ is $\sim\sim P_i$. But we have $\vdash \sim\sim P_i \equiv P_i$. That is

$$\vdash \sim W \equiv W^*.$$

Subcase II. Q has more than one symbol. Then W^* is $\sim Q^*$. By the hypothesis of the induction, $\vdash \sim Q \equiv Q^*$. So by Thm.VI.6.1, Part LVII, $\vdash \sim\sim Q \equiv \sim Q^*$. That is,

$$\vdash \sim W \equiv W^*.$$

Case 2. W is QR. Then W^* is $Q^* \vee R^*$. Moreover, we have $\vdash \sim Q \equiv Q^*$ and $\vdash \sim R \equiv R^*$. Since $\vdash \sim(QR) \equiv \sim Q \vee \sim R$ by Thm.VI.6.1, Part XXXI, we get $\vdash \sim(QR) \equiv Q^* \vee R^*$ by two uses of the substitution theorem. That is,

$$\vdash \sim W \equiv W^*.$$

Case 3. W is $Q \vee R$. Similar to Case 2, except for using Part XXX of Thm.VI.6.1.

Case 4. W is (x) Q. Then W^* is (Ex) Q^*. Moreover, we have $\vdash \sim Q \equiv Q^*$. By Thm.VI.6.2, Part IV, $\vdash \sim(x)\, Q \equiv (\mathrm{E}x) \sim Q$. By the substitution theorem, $\vdash \sim(x)\, Q \equiv (\mathrm{E}x)\, Q^*$. That is,

$$\vdash \sim W \equiv W^*.$$

Case 5. W is (Ex) Q. Similar to Case 4, except for using Part III of Thm.VI.6.2.

We cite below numerous instances of the duality theorem which have already occurred, together with the W and W^* involved in each case.

Instance	W	W^*
Thm.VI.6.1, Part II	$\sim P$	P
Thm.VI.6.1, Part XXVIII	$\sim P \sim Q$	$P \vee Q$
Thm.VI.6.1, Part XXIX	$\sim P \vee \sim Q$	PQ
Thm.VI.6.1, Part XXX	$P \vee Q$	$\sim P \sim Q$
Thm.VI.6.1, Part XXXI	PQ	$\sim P \vee \sim Q$
Thm.VI.6.1, Part XLII	$P \sim Q$	$P \supset Q$
Thm.VI.6.1, Part LXI	$P \equiv Q$	$P \sim Q \vee \sim PQ$
Thm.VI.6.2, Part I	$(x) \sim P$	$(\mathrm{E}x)\ P$
Thm.VI.6.2, Part II	$(\mathrm{E}x) \sim P$	$(x)\ P$
Thm.VI.6.2, Part III	$(\mathrm{E}x)\ P$	$(x) \sim P$
Thm.VI.6.2, Part IV	$(x)\ P$	$(\mathrm{E}x) \sim P$

We note that from the duality theorem it follows that, if two statements are equivalent, then their duals are likewise equivalent. For if $\vdash W \equiv V$, then $\vdash \sim W \equiv \sim V$, and this with $\vdash \sim W \equiv W^*$ and $\vdash \sim V \equiv V^*$ gives $\vdash W^* \equiv V^*$.

A rather more startling and important consequence of the duality theorem is embodied in the following theorem, which we shall call the corollary to the duality theorem.

Theorem VI.6.4. Let $P_1, P_2, \ldots, P_n$ be statements, and let W and V be built up out of some or all of the P's by use of $\sim$, &, $\vee$, (x), and $(\mathrm{E}x)$, where we may use each P as often as desired, and may use whatever variables we like in the (x) and $(\mathrm{E}x)$, and as often as desired. Let X and Y be the results of replacing & by $\vee$, $\vee$ by &, (x) by $(\mathrm{E}x)$, and $(\mathrm{E}x)$ by (x) in W and V, respectively. If $\vdash W \equiv V$, and if this would continue to hold if we replace each P_i by $\sim P_i$, then $\vdash X \equiv Y$.

Proof. Since $\vdash W \equiv V$ continues to hold if we replace each P_i by $\sim P_i$, let us make this replacement. Call the result $\vdash W_1 \equiv V_1$. Then $\vdash \sim W_1 \equiv \sim V_1$. However, $\vdash \sim W_1 \equiv W_1{}^*$ and $\vdash \sim V_1 \equiv V_1{}^*$. So $\vdash W_1{}^* \equiv V_1{}^*$. However, clearly $W_1{}^*$ is X, and $V_1{}^*$ is Y, and our theorem is proved.

In most of the cases encountered so far in which $\vdash W \equiv V$ has been proved, it holds no matter what we substitute for the P_i, and therefore certainly in case we merely put $\sim P_i$ for each P_i. In such a general case, $\vdash X \equiv Y$ likewise holds no matter what we substitute for the P_i, as one can easily see by going through the proof of Thm.VI.6.4. Notice that the same changes which we applied to W and V to get X and Y will, if applied in turn to X and Y, give us W and V back again. So the relation between $\vdash W \equiv V$ and $\vdash X \equiv Y$ is a reciprocal one. If either holds regardless of what we substitute for the P_i, then we can deduce the other by the theorem just proved.

We have already given many pairs of equivalences related as $W \equiv V$ and $X \equiv Y$ are related. For instance, among the parts of Thm.VI.6.1 occur the pairs I and III, IV and V, VI and VII, VIII and IX, XIV and XV, XVI and XVII, XVIII and XIX, XXVIII and XXIX, XXX and XXXI, XXXII and XXXIII, XXXVI and XXXVII, and XL and XLI. Also in Thm.VI.6.2, Parts I and II are a pair and Parts III and IV are a pair.

Theorem VI.6.5.

★I. $\vdash (x).PQ: \equiv :(x)\ P.(x)\ Q.$

★II. $\vdash (\mathrm{E}x).P\mathbf{v}Q: \equiv :(\mathrm{E}x)\ P\mathbf{v}(\mathrm{E}x)\ Q.$

Proof of Part I. Thm.VI.5.2 gives half of Part I. To get the other half, it suffices to prove

$$(x)\ P.(x)\ Q \vdash PQ,$$

since we can then apply successively the generalization theorem, and the deduction theorem. If we start with $(x)\ P.(x)\ Q$, we get $(x)\ P$ and $(x)\ Q$ by Thm.IV.4.18, then P and Q by Thm.VI.5.1, and finally PQ by Thm. IV.4.22.

Part II follows from Part I by the corollary to the duality theorem.

Theorem VI.6.6. If there are no free occurrences of x in Q, then:

I. $\vdash (x)\ Q \equiv Q.$

II. $\vdash (\mathrm{E}x)\ Q \equiv Q.$

★III. $\vdash (x).PQ: \equiv :(x)\ P.Q.$

★IV. $\vdash (\mathrm{E}x).P\mathbf{v}Q: \equiv :(\mathrm{E}x)\ P.\mathbf{v}Q.$

★V. $\vdash (x).P\mathbf{v}Q: \equiv :(x)\ P.\mathbf{v}Q.$

★VI. $\vdash (\mathrm{E}x).PQ: \equiv :(\mathrm{E}x)\ P.Q.$

★VII. $\vdash (x).P \supset Q: \equiv :(\mathrm{E}x)\ P. \supset Q.$

VIII. $\vdash (\mathrm{E}x).P \supset Q: \equiv :(x)\ P. \supset Q.$

★IX. $\vdash (x).Q \supset P: \equiv :Q \supset (x)\ P.$

X. $\vdash (\mathrm{E}x).Q \supset P: \equiv :Q \supset (\mathrm{E}x)\ P.$

Proof of Part I. By Thm.VI.5.1, $\vdash (x)\ Q \supset Q$, and by Axiom scheme 5, $\vdash Q \supset (x)\ Q$.

Part II follows from Part I by the corollary to the duality theorem. Note that Part I does not hold regardless of what we substitute for Q, since it would not hold if we substitute for Q a statement with free occurrences of x. However, Part I will still hold if we replace Q by $\sim Q$, since if Q has no free occurrences of x, $\sim Q$ likewise has no free occurrences of x. Hence we can apply Thm.VI.6.4.

Proof of Part III. By Part I and the substitution theorem, we can replace $(x)\ Q$ by Q in Part I of Thm.VI.6.5.

Part IV follows from Part III by the corollary to the duality theorem.

Proof of Part X. Put $\sim Q$ for Q in Part IV and use Thm.VI.6.1, Part XLIII.

Proof of Part IX. By Axiom scheme 4, $\vdash (x).Q \supset P: \supset :(x)\ Q. \supset .(x)\ P.$ So by Part I and the substitution theorem, we get

$$\vdash (x).Q \supset P: \supset :Q \supset (x)\ P.$$

To get the converse, note that, by Thm.VI.5.1,

$$Q \supset (x)\ P \vdash Q \supset P.$$

So, by the generalization theorem and the deduction theorem,

$$\vdash Q \supset (x)\ P: \supset :(x).Q \supset P$$

Proof of Part VIII. Put $\sim P$ for P in Part IV and use Thm.VI.6.1, Part XLIII and Thm.VI.6.2, Part IV.

Proof of Part VII. Put $\sim P$ and $\sim Q$ for P and Q in Part IX and use Thm.VI.6.1, Parts XLIV and XLVI.

Proof of Part V. Replace Q by $\sim Q$ in Part IX and use Thm.VI.6.1, Parts XLIII and II.

Part VI follows from Part V by the corollary to the duality theorem.

This theorem which we have just proved tells us what we can do with a quantified statement when part of the statement does not involve the variable of quantification.

Theorem VI.6.7.

★★I. $\vdash (x)(y)\ P \equiv (y)(x)\ P.$

★★II. $\vdash (\mathrm{E}x)(\mathrm{E}y)\ P \equiv (\mathrm{E}y)(\mathrm{E}x)\ P.$

Proof of Part I. By two uses of Thm.VI.5.1,

$$(x)(y)\ P \vdash P.$$

So, by two uses of the generalization theorem,

$$(x)(y)\ P \vdash (y)(x)\ P.$$

Then, by the deduction theorem,

$$\vdash (x)(y)\ P \supset (y)(x)\ P.$$

In a similar manner, we prove

$$\vdash (y)(x)\ P \supset (x)(y)\ P.$$

Part II follows from Part I by the corollary to the duality theorem.

The parts of this theorem would ordinarily be abbreviated to $\vdash (x,y)\ P \equiv (y,x)\ P$ and $\vdash (\mathrm{E}x,y)\ P \equiv (\mathrm{E}y,x)\ P$.

It is clear that the proof we gave for Part I would prove

$$\vdash (x,y,z)\ P \equiv (y,z,x)\ P$$

or any similar generalization of Part I. From such a generalization of Part I, we can deduce the corresponding generalization of Part II. We shall feel free to use such generalizations in the future, and for justification will merely refer to the theorem just proved.

Theorem VI.6.8.

**I. $\vdash (x)\ F(x) \equiv (y)\ F(y)$.

**II. $\vdash (\mathrm{E}x)\ F(x) \equiv (\mathrm{E}y)\ F(y)$.

By our convention with regard to the use of $F(x)$ and $F(y)$, this theorem is to be considered as a shorthand way of stating the following result.

Theorem VI.6.8. Let x and y be variables and P and Q be statements. Let Q be the result of replacing all free occurrences of x in P by occurrences of y, and P be the result of replacing all free occurrences of y in Q by occurrences of x. Then:

I. $\vdash (x)\ P \equiv (y)\ Q$.

II. $\vdash (\mathrm{E}x)\ P \equiv (\mathrm{E}y)\ Q$.

Proof of Part I. By Thm.VI.2.1, the replacement of x by y to go from $F(x)$ to $F(y)$ causes no confusion, and so

$$\vdash (x)\ F(x) \supset F(y)$$

is an instance of Axiom scheme 6. So

$$(x)\ F(x) \vdash F(y).$$

Clearly there are no free occurrences of y in $(x)\ F(x)$, for if y is the same variable as x, then the (x) in front binds all occurrences, whereas if y is a variable different from x, then by our construction of $F(x)$ from $F(y)$ there are no free occurrences of y in $F(x)$ and hence none in $(x)\ F(x)$. So we can apply the generalization theorem to get

$$(x)\ F(x) \vdash (y)\ F(y .$$

Then the deduction theorem gives

$$\vdash (x)\ F(x) \supset (y)\ F(y).$$

In a similar manner, we get

$$\vdash (y)\ F(y) \supset (x)\ F(x).$$

Part II follows from Part I by the corollary to the duality theorem, but in order to be sure that we do not have any troubles about confusion of variables, it is perhaps worth while to give a detailed proof. If $F(x)$ and $F(y)$ satisfy the specified requirements on variables, so do $\sim F(x)$ and $\sim F(y)$. So by Part I

$$\vdash (x) \sim F(x) \equiv (y) \sim F(y).$$

Then

$$\vdash \sim(x)\sim F(y) \equiv \sim(y)\sim F(y)$$

by Thm.VI.6.1, Part LVII. This is Part II.

Because of this theorem, we can usually avoid having a statement in which a given variable has both free and bound occurrences. Thus, instead of $F(x) \mathbf{v} (x)\, G(x)$ we can use the equivalent statement $F(x) \mathbf{v} (y)\, G(y)$, where we are careful to choose a y which does not occur in $F(x)$.

The duality theorem is often very useful in connection with proofs by reductio ad absurdum. We recall that the standard procedure for proving P by reductio ad absurdum is to assume $\sim P$ and deduce $Q \sim Q$. Because of the duality theorem we now have available three variants of this, namely:

"Assume P^* and deduce $Q \sim Q$."

"Assume $\sim P$ and deduce QQ^*."

"Assume P^* and deduce QQ^*."

If P is a direct statement (that is, P does not begin with a $\sim$), then $\sim P$ is a negative statement and so is awkward to deal with, whereas P^* is a direct statement and generally more agreeable to work with. Thus, suppose P is the statement that a function is unifcrmly continuous in an interval (a,b), which we earlier wrote out (see page 98). Then if we wish to prove by reductio ad absurdum that P is true, it will be much more effective to assume P^* than $\sim P$. We write P^* below:

$$(\mathrm{E}\varepsilon)::\varepsilon > 0:.(\delta):.\delta > 0. \supset :(\mathrm{E}x):a \leq x \leq b:(\mathrm{E}y).a \leq y \leq b.|\,y - x\,| < \delta. \\ \sim(|\,f(y) - f(x)\,| < \varepsilon).$$

If we take $|\,f(y) - f(x)\,| \geq \varepsilon$ as equivalent to $\sim(|\,f(y) - f(x)\,| < \varepsilon)$, and note that we can put $a \leq x \leq b$ inside $(\mathrm{E}y)$ since there are no free y's in $a \leq x \leq b$ (see Thm.VI.6.6, Part VI), we can write P^* in the following equivalent form

$$(\mathrm{E}\varepsilon):\varepsilon > 0:(\delta):\delta > 0. \supset .(\mathrm{E}x,y).a \leq x \leq b.a \leq y \leq b.|\,y - x\,| < \delta. \\ |\,f(y) - f(x)\,| \geq \varepsilon.$$

This is clearly a direct statement from which one could expect to prove numerous consequences, and is quite a contrast to the purely negative statement $\sim P$.

Although the duality theorem is not widely known among mathematicians, an experienced analyst will have woıked out enough special cases of it so that derivation of the above statement as a way of saying that the function f is not uniformly continuous in the interval (a,b) will not seem startling. However, the novice finds such transformations fairly difficult and would be helped by a knowledge of the duality theorem.

EXERCISES

VI.6.1. Write the duals of:

(a) $(x){:}.P \supset {:}(\mathrm{E}y){:}Q{:}(z).R \supset S.$
(b) $(\mathrm{E}x).P\mathbf{v}(y)\ Q{:}(u)(\mathrm{E}v) \sim R.$
(c) $P \supset (x)\ Q\mathbf{v}(\mathrm{E}y)\ RS.$

VI.6.2. Write out a complete demonstration of $(x)\ F(x) \vdash (y)\ F(y)$.
VI.6.3. Prove:

(a) $\vdash (x)\ P\mathbf{v}(x)\ Q{:} \supset {:}(x).P\mathbf{v}Q.$
(b) $\vdash (\mathrm{E}x).PQ{:} \supset {:}(\mathrm{E}x)\ P.(\mathrm{E}x)\ Q.$

VI.6.4. Find examples to show why one would not expect to be able to prove either of:

(a) $(x).P\mathbf{v}Q{:} \supset {:}(x)\ P\mathbf{v}(x)\ Q.$
(b) $(\mathrm{E}x)\ P.(\mathrm{E}x)\ Q{:} \supset {:}(\mathrm{E}x).PQ.$

VI.6.5. Prove:

(a) $\vdash (x).P \supset Q{:} \supset {:}(\mathrm{E}x)\ P \supset (\mathrm{E}x)\ Q.$
(b) $\vdash (x).P \equiv Q{:} \supset {:}(\mathrm{E}x)\ P \equiv (\mathrm{E}x)\ Q.$

VI.6.6. Write out a complete demonstration of $\vdash (x)(y)\ P \supset (x)\ P$.
VI.6.7. Write out a complete demonstration of $(x)(y)\ P \vdash (y)(x)\ P$.
VI.6.8. Supply the conditions on free and bound variables needed to make the following statement valid, and prove the resulting valid statement

$$\vdash (\mathrm{E}x)\ F(x). \equiv .(\mathrm{E}x,y).F(x)\mathbf{v}F(y).$$

VI.6.9. Let $P_1, \ldots, P_n$ be statements (which may contain free occurrences of various variables) and let W be built up out of the P's by means of $\sim$, &, and (x) for various x's. Prove that there are statements $Q_1, \ldots, Q_m$, which are the same as the P's or are got from them by replacing various free occurrences of variables by occurrences of other variables, and there is a V built from the Q's by means of $\sim$ and & alone (not using any quantifiers) and there is a string of quantifiers (Q) (some existential and some universal) such that $\vdash W \equiv (Q)\ V$. (*Hint.* Use induction on the number of symbols in W.)

7. The Formal Analogue of an Act of Choice. The statement $P_1, P_2, \ldots, P_n \vdash Q$ means in effect that we can get from the P's and the axioms to Q by successive uses of modus ponens. Now modus ponens is a rule, "If P and $P \supset Q$, then Q," by which one can go from valid statements to a new valid statement.

One might ask why we restrict ourselves to use of the single rule of modus ponens. Actually, in effect we do not so restrict ourselves. Any time one proves a theorem such as $\vdash \sim\sim P \supset P$ or $\vdash P \supset Q. \supset .\sim Q \supset \sim P$, one has in effect an additional rule such as "If $\sim\sim P$, then P" or "If $P \supset Q$, then $\sim Q \supset \sim P$." However, these additional rules merely involve the use of modus ponens with a proved theorem of the form $\vdash W \supset V$, and there seems no point in stating such formal rules as long as we have modus ponens and have stated the corresponding theorem. Even more complicated rules can easily be got from proved theorems by modus ponens. Thus, from Thm.IV.4.22, $\vdash P \supset (Q \supset PQ)$, by two uses of modus ponens, we infer the rule "If P and Q, then PQ."

However, there are some useful rules which cannot be got by combining modus ponens with a proved theorem of the form $\vdash W \supset V$. Such a one is justified by Thm.VI.4.1. The corresponding rule would be "If P, then $(x)\ P$." We shall refer to it as the generalization rule, or more shortly as "rule G." This cannot be derived by modus ponens from $\vdash P \supset (x)\ P$, because this statement is false so far as we know. Certainly it should be false, for if it were true we could infer $\vdash (x).P \supset (x)\ P$ by Thm.VI.4.1, and then get $\vdash (\mathrm{E}x)\ P \supset (x)\ P$ by Thm.VI.6.6, Part VII. As $(\mathrm{E}x)\ P \supset (x)\ P$ represents a false statement, $\vdash (\mathrm{E}x)\ P \supset (x)\ P$ certainly should be false.

The fact that we are using only the rule of modus ponens appears in our definition of $\vdash$. If we admit the use of rule G as well as modus ponens, we must change our definition of $\vdash$. Notice further that we cannot permit unrestricted use of rule G. This is indicated in Thm.VI.4.2, where one is permitted to use rule G in case x has no free occurrences in any of $P_1, P_2, \ldots, P_n$. With this restriction in mind, we state a definition for $P_1, P_2, \ldots, P_n \vdash_G Q$, which will make it say in effect that we can get from the P's and the axioms to Q by successive uses of the two rules, modus ponens and rule G. Note that we reserve $\vdash$ for demonstrations which use only modus ponens, and write $\vdash_G$ whenever we permit uses of rule G.

The precise definition is as follows:

$P_1, P_2, \ldots, P_n \vdash_G Q$ indicates that there is a sequence of statements $S_1, S_2, \ldots, S_s$, such that S_s is Q and for each S_i either:

(1) S_i is an axiom.
(2) S_i is a P.
(3) There is a j less than i such that S_i and S_j are the same.
(4) There are j and k, each less than i, such that S_k is $S_j \supset S_i$.
(5) There is a variable x, which does not occur free in any of $P_1, P_2, \ldots, P_n$, and a j less than i such that S_i is $(x)\ S_j$.

We call attention to the fact that (1) to (4) are exactly as in the definition of $\vdash$. It is condition (4) that permits the use of modus ponens, and condition (5) that permits the use of rule G. The sequence of S's is called a demonstration of $P_1, P_2, \ldots, P_n \vdash_G Q$, and the S's are called steps.

We characterize the various steps S_i according to which of the five cases they come under. S's covered by (1) are axioms, S's covered by (2) are P's, S's covered by (3) are repetitions, S's covered by (4) are results of modus ponens, and S's covered by (5) are results of rule G. In general any given step will come under only one case. However, one can conceive of artificial situations in which a step could be justified by either of two cases. In such a case, we shall take as the justification that case having the smaller number. Having thus assured that there is a unique case assigned to each step, we can now speak of the number of uses of modus ponens and the number of uses of rule G. To be explicit, each S_i which comes under case (4) constitutes a use of modus ponens, and each S_i which comes under case (5) constitutes a use of rule G. We can further speak of the first, second, third, etc., uses of modus ponens or rule G. Moreover, whenever we use rule G to get a step S_i, the S_i has the form $(x)\ S_j$, and the use of rule G consisted in attaching the (x) in front of the S_j. The x is said to be the x involved in this use of rule G.

Theorem VI.7.1. If $P_1, P_2, \ldots, P_n \vdash_G Q$, then $P_1, P_2, \ldots, P_n \vdash Q$.

Proof. Proof by induction on the number of uses of rule G in the demonstration of $P_1, P_2, \ldots, P_n \vdash_G Q$. If there are zero uses, then the theorem is obvious. Let us now assume the theorem true whenever there are n or fewer uses of rule G in the demonstration ($n \geq 0$), and let us have a demonstration with $n + 1$ uses of rule G. Let S_α be the first step in the demonstration for which rule G was used. Then there is a β less than α and a variable x, which has no free occurrences in any of $P_1, P_2, \ldots, P_n$, such that S_α is $(x)\ S_\beta$. Since S_α is the first use of rule G, the steps $S_1, S_2, \ldots, S_\beta$ constitute a demonstration of $P_1, P_2, \ldots, P_n \vdash S_\beta$. Because there are no free occurrences of x in any of $P_1, P_2, \ldots P_n$, it follows by Thm.VI.4.2 that there is a demonstration of $P_1, P_2, \ldots, P_n \vdash (x)\ S_\beta$. Let $T_1, T_2, \ldots, T_t$ be this demonstration. Then T_t is $(x)\ S_\beta$ which is S_α. Now in the demonstration $S_1, S_2, \ldots, S_s$, replace the single step S_α by the sequence of steps $T_1, T_2, \ldots, T_t$. As T_t is S_α, we still have all the S's present, and in their original order, so that we have another demonstration of $P_1, P_2, \ldots, P_n \vdash_G Q$. However, whereas formerly S_α was derived from S_β by a use of rule G, now S_α is derived without a use of rule G by means of the steps $T_1, T_2, \ldots, T_t$. So our new demonstration has only n uses of rule G, and by our hypothesis of induction there is a demonstration of $P_1, P_2, \ldots, P_n \vdash Q$.

This theorem is a generalized form of Thm.VI.4.2. Thm.VI.4.2 covered the case where there is a single use of rule G, and this occurs in the last step of the demonstration.

Thm.VI.7.1 says that whatever can be proved by use of rule G can be proved without it. Hence we do not really need rule G and are justified in using merely modus ponens. On the other hand, Thm.VI.7.1 also justifies the point of view that we might as well use rule G, since it will not lead to any results that we could not get without it. This is our point of view. In general, a demonstration of $P_1, P_2, \ldots, P_n \vdash_G Q$ will have many fewer steps than the corresponding demonstration of $P_1, P_2, \ldots, P_n \vdash Q$. Thus it is easier to find a demonstration of $P_1, P_2, \ldots, P_n \vdash_G Q$, in spite of the fact that we are assured by Thm.VI.7.1 that there must be a demonstration of $P_1, P_2, \ldots, P_n \vdash Q$ whenever there is a demonstration of $P_1, P_2, \ldots, P_n \vdash_G Q$.

There is another rule which is also very useful. Like rule G, we do not really need it, in the sense that we can always manage to do without it; however, we manage to do without it only at the cost of making our demonstrations much more lengthy and laborious. So, as with rule G, we shall use this other rule but shall prove a theorem to the effect that whatever results we get by using it can be got by the single rule of modus ponens.

In order to motivate this rule, let us look at an instance of its use in everyday mathematics. On pages 14 to 15 of Bôcher, 1907, is proved the theorem that, if two functions are continuous at a point, their sum is continuous at this point. We now quote this proof (except for the minor change of using functions of a single variable, instead of functions of several variables).[1]

"Let f_1 and f_2 be two functions continuous at the point c and let k_1 and k_2 be their respective values at this point. Then, no matter how small the positive quantity ε may be chosen, we may take δ_1 and δ_2 so small that

$$|f_1 - k_1| < \tfrac{1}{2}\varepsilon \qquad \text{when } |x - c| < \delta_1,$$
$$|f_2 - k_2| < \tfrac{1}{2}\varepsilon \qquad \text{when } |x - c| < \delta_2.$$

Accordingly

$$|f_1 - k_1| + |f_2 - k_2| < \varepsilon \qquad \text{when } |x - c| < \delta,$$

where δ is the smaller of the two quantities δ_1 and δ_2; and since

$$|A| + |B| \geq |A + B|,$$

we have

$$|f_1 - k_1 + f_2 - k_2| = |(f_1 + f_2) - (k_1 + k_2)| < \varepsilon \quad \text{when } |x - c| < \delta.$$

Hence $f_1 + f_2$ is continuous at the point c."

[1] From Bôcher, *op. cit.*

Let us focus our attention on the phrase "we may take δ_1 and δ_2 . . . ". We had the hypothesis that f_1 and f_2 are continuous at c, namely, (for $i = 1, 2$)

$$(\varepsilon)::\varepsilon > 0. \supset :.(\exists\delta):.\delta > 0:(x):| x - c | < \delta. \supset .| f_i(x) - k_i | < \varepsilon.$$

We have "chosen" an arbitrary positive ε and taken the ε of our hypotheses to be $\varepsilon/2$, and so now have

$$\text{(VI.7.1)} \quad (\mathrm{E}\delta):.\delta > 0:(x):| x - c | < \delta. \supset .| f_i(x) - k_i | < \tfrac{1}{2}\varepsilon.$$

Now what is the procedure by which we "take δ_1 and δ_2"? Clearly it cannot be the same that we used when we "chose" a positive ε. There are no restrictions on ε. We are free to choose any one that pleases us. Our own convenience is the only criterion. This is not the case when we come to "take" a δ. The statement (VI.7.1) assures us that there are δ's having the property that we wish. However, it gives us no criteria for choosing them.

The usual mathematical treatment offers no solution to this impasse. The standard procedure, as illustrated by Bôcher's proof, is to assume that somehow, by unexplained magic, we have got hold of the δ's we wish, and then to proceed from there. From the point of view of symbolic logic, the step amounts to proceeding (without explanation or justification) from (VI.7.1) to

$$\delta_i > 0:(x):| x - c | < \delta_i. \supset .| f_i(x) - k_i | < \tfrac{1}{2}\varepsilon.$$

That is, at this step, use is made of a rule "If $(\mathrm{E}x)\ F(x)$, then $F(y)$." In the case at hand, the rule is used twice, once to go from $(\mathrm{E}\delta) F_1(\delta)$ to $F_1(\delta_1)$, and once to go from $(\mathrm{E}\delta)\ F_2(\delta)$ to $F_2(\delta_2)$.

It is not our intent to furnish any philosophical justification for such a rule. We merely observe that it is commonly used in mathematics, and so we seek to justify its use in symbolic logic. Actually, if we succeed in justifying its use in symbolic logic, where nothing more extravagant than modus ponens has been assumed, this will furnish justification of a sort for its use in everyday mathematics.

What is involved psychologically in going from $(\mathrm{E}x)\ F(x)$ to $F(y)$ seems to be the following. $(\mathrm{E}x)\ F(x)$ says that there is at least one x which makes $F(x)$ true. From among such x's, let us "choose" one, and call it y. Then y is an unknown, fixed quantity having the property $F(y)$.

Explaining the step from $(\mathrm{E}x)\ F(x)$ to $F(y)$ as depending on an act of choice does not justify it, but it does generate certain inhibitions about the use of the step which prevent us from using it improperly. For it is not always permissible to go from $(\mathrm{E}x)\ F(x)$ to $F(y)$, and without some criterion for when the step is suitable, we should get into trouble by using it.

Since the rule "If (Ex) $F(x)$, then $F(y)$" corresponds to a hypothetical act of choice, we shall call it the rule of choice, or more briefly, rule C. In the symbolic logic, where reference to meaning is not permitted, we must manage somehow to state the conditions for the use of rule C in a manner which depends only on the forms of the statements involved. This we shall do.

We must realize first of all that rule C, like rule G and modus ponens, is something which is used in a demonstration. We shall make this more explicit later by generalizing the notion $\vdash$ again. Accordingly, the restrictions on rule C are on its use in a demonstration and depend on the particular demonstration being considered. Thus a certain use of rule C may be legitimate in one demonstration and not legitimate in a second demonstration. We have encountered this situation already in connection with rule G. If x has no free occurrences in P but does have free occurrences in R, one could use rule G to go from S to $(x)\ S$ in a demonstration of $P \vdash_G Q$, but not in a demonstration of $R \vdash_G Q$.

In order to formulate the restrictions on rule C, let us analyze the inhibitions inherent in thinking of it as an act of choice. In the first place, if we have (Ex) $F(x)$ and "choose" a y so that $F(y)$, then our y is not only fixed and unknown, but restricted. It cannot be just any quantity, as some unknowns can. Hence we cannot expect to use the generalization principle with this y. Or to put it in formal terms, if we use rule C to get from (Ex) $F(x)$ to $F(y)$ with some y, then we cannot later in our demonstration use rule G to go from $G(y)$ to $(y)\ G(y)$ with this same y. This restriction on later uses of rule G does not apply merely to the variable y, but to every variable which occurs free in $F(y)$. This may seem unnecessarily severe, but if we have a look at the meanings involved, we see that it is inescapable. Let $F(x,z)$ denote: "x is a prime greater than the prime z." Then (Ex) $F(x,z)$ is true for each prime z and is merely a statement of Euclid's theorem that there are an infinity of primes. Now "choose" a y such that $F(y,z)$. We certainly have restricted y by so doing, but we have also restricted z. For whereas (Ex) $F(x,z)$ is true for *every* prime z, $F(y,z)$ is true only for those prime z's which are less than y, and it would now be wholly inappropriate to use rule G with z.

In applying rule C to get $F(y)$ from (Ex) $F(x)$, certain precautions on the choice of the letter y must be observed. Note that the choice of a letter y to appear in $F(y)$ is quite a different matter from actually choosing one of the quantities which make $F(x)$ true. The letter y does not make $F(y)$ true. It merely stands in $F(y)$ and denotes some quantity which makes $F(x)$ true. The letter y is a name, and if we are ignoring meanings (as we are) we can choose a name without choosing the quantity of which it is a name. Our restrictions on y are essentially that it should not be a name that has already been assigned to some other fixed or restricted quantity, for if it were, this would amount to assuming that the quantity which we are choosing as one of those which make $F(x)$ true happens to be a previously assigned quantity; certainly a dubious assumption.

Formally, the restriction on the letter y when we go from $(\mathrm{E}x)\ F(x)$ to $F(y)$ by rule C is merely the following. In the first place, y should not occur free in any of the P's which precede the $\vdash$ sign. These P's are all assumptions, and any y which occurs free in a P is therefore subject to a restriction. Furthermore, if at some previous point in our demonstration we have used rule C to go from $(\mathrm{E}v)\ G(v)$ to $G(w)$, then y must not have occurred free in $G(w)$. We call attention to the fact that Bôcher observed this restriction in his proof. His first use of rule C was to go from $(\mathrm{E}\delta)\ F_1(\delta)$ to $F_1(\delta_1)$, and his second use was to go from $(\mathrm{E}\delta)\ F_2(\delta)$ to $F_2(\delta_2)$, and he used different letters, δ_1 and δ_2, in the two cases.

One final point, and we have all the necessary restrictions. If $(\mathrm{E}x)\ F(x)$ is true, and we use rule C to infer $F(y)$, no one claims that $F(y)$ is true. Although we pretend to choose y so that $F(y)$ is true, we know that usually we have not sufficient information to allow us actually to make such a choice. So $F(y)$ has a sort of quasi truth, in that, if an omniscient being were performing the proof, he could actually choose a y. All subsequent statements which contain y also have only the same sort of quasi truth. However, if we later derive statements which do not contain y, they do not depend on the actual choice of y, but only on the theoretical possibility of choosing y, which possibility is supposedly guaranteed by the statement $(\mathrm{E}x)\ F(x)$. So statements which do not contain y will be genuinely true. To put this in terms of a demonstration, if we get Q from $P_1, P_2, \ldots, P_n$ and the axioms by modus ponens, rule G, and rule C, then we only have $P_1, P_2, \ldots, P_n \vdash Q$ in case Q does not contain any y used with rule C.

We have now compiled a list of restrictions based on the idea that rule C is the formal equivalent of an act of choice. We next have to show that this list of restrictions is adequate. To show this, we define $P_1, P_2, \ldots, \vdash_C Q$ to mean that one can get Q from the P's and the axioms by modus ponens, rule G, and rule C, subject to all the stated restrictions, and then prove that, whenever we have $P_1, P_2, \ldots, P_n \vdash_C Q$, then we have $P_1, P_2, \ldots, P_n \vdash Q$. This will then tell us that we do not need to use rule C (or rule G), and equally it will tell us that we may perfectly well use it if we wish.

Actually, it turns out to be inconvenient to embody all our restrictions in the definition of $\vdash_C$. So we embody most of our restrictions in the definition of $\vdash_C$, and insert the remaining restrictions as an additional hypothesis in the theorem which says that, if $P_1, P_2, \ldots, P_n \vdash_C Q$, then $P_1, P_2, \ldots, P_n \vdash Q$.

The precise definition of $\vdash_C$ is as follows.

$P_1, P_2, \ldots, P_n \vdash_C Q$ indicates that there is a sequence of statements $S_1, S_2, \ldots, S_s$, such that S_s is Q, and for each S_i either:

(1) S_i is an axiom.

(2) S_i is a P.

(3) There is a j less than i such that S_i and S_j are the same.

(4) There are j and k, each less than i, such that S_k is $S_j \supset S_i$.

(5) There is a variable x, which does not occur free in any of $P_1, P_2, \ldots, P_n$, or in any earlier step which is a result of rule C, and there is a j less than i such that S_i is $(x)\ S_j$.

(6) There are variables x and y, not necessarily distinct, such that y does not occur free in any of $P_1, P_2, \ldots, P_n$, or in any earlier step which is a result of rule C, and there is a j less than i such that S_j is $(\mathrm{E}x)\ W$ where W is the result of replacing all free occurrences of y in S_i by occurrences of x and S_i is the result of replacing all free occurrences of x in W by occurrences of y.

We still have to define which steps are results of rule C. These will be the steps covered by case (6) above, except that as before we arrange that each step shall be covered by a unique case by agreeing that, whenever a step can be justified by two different cases, we shall take as the justification that case having the smaller number. Among other things, this ensures that we use rule G and rule C as few times as possible.

As usual, the sequence of S's is called a demonstration, and the S's are called the steps of the demonstration.

By our conventions, we could shorten the latter portion of case (6) to: "... and there is a j less than i such that S_j is $(\mathrm{E}x)\ F(x)$ and S_i is $F(y)$."

In this case, we say that $F(y)$ is derived from $(\mathrm{E}x)\ F(x)$ by a use of rule C with y.

****Theorem VI.7.2.** Suppose that $P_1, P_2, \ldots, P_n \vdash_C Q$. Furthermore, let $y_1, y_2, \ldots, y_m$ be the y's with which rule C is used in the given demonstration of $P_1, P_2, \ldots, P_n \vdash_C Q$. If none of these y's occur free in Q, then $P_1, P_2, \ldots, P_n \vdash Q$.

Proof. Let $S_1, S_2, \ldots, S_s$ be the steps of the given demonstration of $P_1, P_2, \ldots, P_n \vdash_C Q$. Let $F_1(y_1), F_2(y_2), \ldots, F_m(y_m)$ be the steps which are results of rule C, in the order in which they occur in the demonstration $S_1, S_2, \ldots, S_s$, and let $y_1, y_2, \ldots, y_m$ be the y's with which these uses of rule C are made. Define α_i to be the greatest α such that the step $F_\alpha(y_\alpha)$ does not occur later than the step S_i (for those i's such that S_i occurs before $F_1(y_1)$, we take $\alpha_i = 0$).

Lemma A. For $1 \leq i \leq s$,

$$P_1, P_2, \ldots, P_n, F_1(y_1), F_2(y_2), \ldots, F_{\alpha_i}(y_{\alpha_i}) \overset{i}{\vdash} S_i.$$

(If S_i precedes $F_1(y_1)$, then $\alpha_i = 0$ and this takes the form $P_1, P_2, \ldots, P_n \vdash S_i$.)

Proof. We prove this by induction on i. If $i = 1$, then S_i must be an axiom or a P, and the lemma is obvious. Now assume the lemma true for $i \leq k$, and let $i = k + 1$. If S_i is an axiom or a P, our lemma is obvious. Let S_i be a repetition of an earlier S_j. Then by hypothesis,

$$P_1, P_2, \ldots, P_n, F_1(y_1), F_2(y_2), \ldots, F_{\alpha_j}(y_{\alpha_j}) \vdash S_j.$$

If $\alpha_j = \alpha_i$, then we have our result, since S_j is the same as S_i. If $\alpha_j \neq \alpha_i$, then clearly $\alpha_j < \alpha_i$, since $j < i$. So we can get the desired result by inserting the additional hypotheses

$$F_{\alpha_j+1}(y_{\alpha_j+1}), F_{\alpha_j+2}(y_{\alpha_j+2}), \ldots, F_{\alpha_i}(y_{\alpha_i})$$

before the $\vdash$ sign.

If S_i is the result of modus ponens, then we have S_j and S_k, each previous to S_i, and such that S_k is $S_j \supset S_i$. So by hypothesis we have

$$P_1, P_2, \ldots, P_n, F_1(y_1), F_2(y_2), \ldots, F_{\alpha_j}(y_{\alpha_j}) \vdash S_j,$$

$$P_1, P_2, \ldots, P_n, F_1(y_1), F_2(y_2), \ldots, F_{\alpha_k}(y_{\alpha_k}) \vdash S_j \supset S_i.$$

If necessary, we adjoin additional assumptions before the $\vdash$ sign, and so infer

$$P_1, P_2, \ldots, P_n, F_1(y_1), F_2(y_2), \ldots, F_{\alpha_i}(y_{\alpha_i}) \vdash S_j,$$

$$P_1, P_2, \ldots, P_n, F_1(y_1), F_2(y_2), \ldots, F_{\alpha_i}(y_{\alpha_i}) \vdash S_j \supset S_i.$$

If now we write out in succession the steps of these two demonstrations and add a final step S_i, we shall have a demonstration of

$$P_1, P_2, \ldots, P_n, F_1(y_1), F_2(y_2), \ldots, F_{\alpha_i}(y_{\alpha_i}) \vdash S_i.$$

If S_i is the result of rule G, then S_i has the form $(x)\ S_j$ where j is less than i and x does not occur free in any of

$$P_1, P_2, \ldots, P_n, F_1(y_1), F_2(y_2), \ldots, F_{\alpha_i}(y_{\alpha_i});$$

this restriction on the free occurrences of x being exactly the condition that was imposed in the definition of $\vdash_C$. By hypothesis

$$P_1, P_2, \ldots, P_n, F_1(y_1), F_2(y_2), \ldots, F_{\alpha_j}(y_{\alpha_j}) \vdash S_j.$$

So

$$P_1, P_2, \ldots, P_n, F_1(y_1), F_2(y_2), \ldots, F_{\alpha_i}(y_{\alpha_i}) \vdash S_j.$$

Hence by the generalization theorem (Thm.VI.4.2), recalling that $(x)\ S_j$ is S_i,

$$P_1, P_2, \ldots, P_n, F_1(y_1), F_2(y_2), \ldots, F_{\alpha_i}(y_{\alpha_i}) \vdash S_i.$$

If S_i is the result of rule C, then S_i is $F_{\alpha_i}(y_{\alpha_i})$ by the definition of α_i, and the demonstration of

$$P_1, P_2, \ldots, P_n, F_1(y_1), F_2(y_2), \ldots, F_{\alpha_i}(y_{\alpha_i}) \vdash S_i$$

consists of the single step S_i, which we justify by noting that it is just $F_{\alpha_i}(y_{\alpha_i})$.

Lemma B.

$$P_1, P_2, \ldots, P_n, F_1(y_1), F_2(y_2), \ldots, F_m(y_m) \vdash Q.$$

This follows from Lemma A by putting $i = s$.

Lemma C. For each α with $1 \leq \alpha \leq m$, there is an x_α such that

$$P_1, P_2, \ldots, P_n, F_1(y_1), F_2(y_2), \ldots, F_{\alpha-1}(y_{\alpha-1}) \vdash (\mathrm{E}x_\alpha)F_\alpha(x_\alpha).$$

Proof. To prove this, consider the step $F_\alpha(y_\alpha)$. This is derived by rule C from some earlier S_j of the form $(\mathrm{E}x_\alpha)\ F_\alpha(x_\alpha)$. By Lemma A, we have

$$P_1, P_2, \ldots, P_n, F_1(y_1), F_2(y_2), \ldots, F_{\alpha_j}(y_{\alpha_j}) \vdash (\mathrm{E}x_\alpha)F_\alpha(x_\alpha).$$

Since S_j occurs before $F_\alpha(y_\alpha)$, we have $\alpha_j < \alpha$ and so $\alpha_j \leq \alpha - 1$, and our lemma follows.

Lemma D. For $0 \leq \beta \leq m$,

$$P_1, P_2, \ldots, P_n, F_1(y_1), F_2(y_2), \ldots, F_{m-\beta}(y_{m-\beta}) \vdash Q.$$

Proof. We prove this by induction on β. If $\beta = 0$, our lemma follows by Lemma B. Assume the lemma for β $(0 \leq \beta \leq m)$, and prove it for $\beta + 1$. Since the lemma is true for β, we have

$$P_1, P_2, \ldots, P_n, F_1(y_1), F_2(y_2), \ldots, F_{m-\beta}(y_{m-\beta}) \vdash Q.$$

So by the deduction theorem

$$P_1, P_2, \ldots, P_n, F_1(y_1), F_2(y_2), \ldots, F_{m-(\beta+1)}(y_{m-(\beta+1)}) \vdash F_{m-\beta}(y_{m-\beta}) \supset Q.$$

Now $y_{m-\beta}$ does not occur free in any of

$$P_1, P_2, \ldots, P_n, F_1(y_1), F_2(y_2), \ldots, F_{m-(\beta+1)}(y_{m-(\beta+1)}),$$

this restriction on the free occurrences of $y_{m-\beta}$ being exactly the condition that was imposed in the definition of $\vdash_C$. So by the generalization theorem

$$P_1, P_2, \ldots, P_n, F_1(y_1), F_2(y_2), \ldots, F_{m-(\beta+1)}(y_{m-(\beta+1)})$$
$$\vdash (y_{m-\beta}).F_{m-\beta}(y_{m-\beta}) \supset Q.$$

By the hypothesis of our theorem, $y_{m-\beta}$ does not occur free in Q. So by Thm.VI.6.6, Part VII,

$$\vdash (y_{m-\beta}).F_{m-\beta}(y_{m-\beta}) \supset Q: \equiv :(\mathrm{E}y_{m-\beta})F_{m-\beta}(y_{m-\beta}). \supset Q.$$

Also, by Thm.VI.6.8, Part II,

$$\vdash (\mathrm{E}y_{m-\beta})F_{m-\beta}(y_{m-\beta}) \equiv (\mathrm{E}x_{m-\beta})F_{m-\beta}(x_{m-\beta}).$$

Hence we have

$$P_1, P_2, \ldots, P_n, F_1(y_1), F_2(y_2), \ldots, F_{m-(\beta+1)}(y_{m-(\beta+1)})$$
$$\vdash (\mathrm{E}x_{m-\beta})F_{m-\beta}(x_{m-\beta}) . \supset Q.$$

However, by Lemma C

$$P_1, P_2, \ldots, P_n, F_1(y_1), F_2(y_2), \ldots, F_{m-(\beta+1)}(y_{m-(\beta+1)})$$
$$\vdash (\mathrm{E}x_{m-\beta})F_{m-\beta}(x_{m-\beta}).$$

So we conclude

$$P_1, P_2, \ldots, P_n, F_1(y_1), F_2(y_2), \ldots, F_{m-(\beta+1)}(y_{m-(\beta+1)}) \vdash Q,$$

and our induction step is complete. Accordingly, our lemma is proved by induction.

Our theorem now follows by putting $\beta = m$ in Lemma D.

Because of the above theorem, we are relatively free to use rule C whenever convenient. It is true that, in our definition of $\vdash_C$ and in our statement of the above theorem, many restrictions on the use of rule G and rule C are listed. Actually these correspond precisely to the inhibitions that would quite properly arise if one were thinking of rule C as being the act of "choosing" a y to be one of the x's which make $F(x)$ true. Consequently, in any situation in everyday mathematics in which it would be considered legitimate to make such an act of choice, we shall find our restrictions satisfied and shall be able to use rule C.

Let it be recalled that rule C, together with its attendant restrictions, is purely formal and depends entirely on the forms of the statements involved. Thus our Thm.VI.7.2, which we just proved, enables us to replace the psychological process of "choosing" a y to be one of the x's which make $F(x)$ true by a purely formal process. This replacement constitutes a considerable logical advance. There are numerous connotations of the act of choosing which are disturbing to many mathematicians who are careful in their reasoning. This is particularly the case when $(\mathrm{E}x)\ F(x)$ has been proved by reductio ad absurdum or some indirect process which gives no clues whatever as to how one might proceed to find one of the x's which make $F(x)$ true. It is quite worth while to dispense with these disturbing connotations, even if it means replacing them by a collection of somewhat arbitrary rules.

As permitted by Thm.VI.7.2, we shall make constant use of rule G and rule C hereafter. This will result in a great simplification in our proofs, in spite of the complexities in the restrictions given in the definition of $\vdash_C$ and in the hypothesis of Thm.VI.7.2. One reason for the simplification is that in general a demonstration of

$$P_1, P_2, \ldots, P_n \vdash_C Q$$

is tremendously shorter than the corresponding demonstration of

$$P_1, P_2, \ldots, P_n \vdash Q.$$

Although we no longer write out any demonstrations in full, but merely give instructions for writing them out, there is still an advantage in dealing with shorter demonstrations, since fewer instructions will be required.

Besides the fact that we get shorter demonstrations by use of rule G and rule C, there is the important consideration that demonstrations are easier to discover if we permit the use of rule G and rule C. This is because rule G and rule C correspond rather closely to operations commonly used in everyday mathematics. This consideration is less important once the demonstration has been discovered, but even the person who is merely following demonstrations written out by someone else will find them easier to follow if they embody familiar operations, such as rule G and rule C, rather than the very involved and unfamiliar operations needed if we do not allow the use of rule G and rule C (see the proof of Thm.VI.7.2, for instance).

To a considerable extent, rule G and rule C enable us to deal with unquantified statements rather than with quantified ones. Thus suppose we have some quantified statements. By Thm.VI.5.1, we can remove the universal quantifiers, and by rule C, we can remove the existential quantifiers. We then proceed, unhampered by quantifiers. At the end, we may have to put back the quantifiers. Rule G is available for the purpose of attaching universal quantifiers. For the purpose of attaching existential quantifiers, we have the following theorem:

***Theorem VI.7.3.** $\vdash F(y,y) \supset (\mathrm{E}x)\, F(x,y)$.

Proof. By Axiom scheme 6, $\vdash (x){\sim}F(x,y) \supset {\sim}F(y,y)$. So by Thm.VI.6.1, Part XLV, $\vdash F(y,y) \supset {\sim}(x){\sim}F(x,y)$. This is our theorem.

****Corollary.** $\vdash P \supset (\mathrm{E}x)\, P$.

Proof. Take y to be the same as x.

We now give four theorems whose proofs follow the routine just indicated, namely, one first removes quantifiers, then performs some simple operations, and then replaces the quantifiers.

Theorem VI.7.4.

I. $\vdash (\mathrm{E}x).PQ: \supset :(\mathrm{E}x)\, P.(\mathrm{E}x)\, Q$.

II. $\vdash (x)\, P.\mathbf{v}.(x)\, Q: \supset :(x).P\mathbf{v}Q$.

Proof of Part I. We first undertake to prove

$$(\mathrm{E}x)\, PQ \vdash_C (\mathrm{E}x)\, P.(\mathrm{E}x)\, Q.$$

We start with $(\mathrm{E}x).PQ$. Then by rule C with x, PQ. So by Thm. IV.4.18, P and Q. So by Thm.VI.7.3, corollary, $(\mathrm{E}x)\, P$ and $(\mathrm{E}x)\, Q$. Finally by Thm.IV.4.22, $(\mathrm{E}x)\, P.(\mathrm{E}x)\, Q$. Accordingly, we can infer that there is a demonstration of

$$(\mathrm{E}x)\, PQ \vdash_C (\mathrm{E}x)\, P.(\mathrm{E}x)\, Q$$

as soon as we have shown that the given restrictions are satisfied. When we referred to Thm.IV.4.18, Thm.VI.7.3, corollary, and Thm.IV.4.22, we skipped over large numbers of steps. Could any of these steps involve rule G or rule C? No, because the theorems quoted all involved a $\vdash$ and not a $\vdash_G$ or $\vdash_C$. So the only use of rule C is that indicated, by which we went from $(\mathrm{E}x).PQ$ to PQ. This use of rule C is permissible since it involves x, which does not occur free in $(\mathrm{E}x)\ PQ$. Also there are no uses of rule G. Accordingly, our restrictions are satisfied, and we know that there is a demonstration of

$$(\mathrm{E}x)\ PQ \vdash_C (\mathrm{E}x)\ P.(\mathrm{E}x)\ Q.$$

Moreover, the only use of rule C in this demonstration is with x, which does not occur free in $(\mathrm{E}x)\ P.(\mathrm{E}x)\ Q$. So by Thm.VI.7.2,

$$(\mathrm{E}x)\ PQ \vdash (\mathrm{E}x)\ P.(\mathrm{E}x)\ Q.$$

Then Part I follows by the deduction theorem.

Proof of Part II. In Part I, replace P and Q by $\sim P$ and $\sim Q$. This gives

$$\vdash (\mathrm{E}x).{\sim}P{\sim}Q:\ \supset\ :(\mathrm{E}x)\ {\sim}P.(\mathrm{E}x)\ {\sim}Q.$$

So

$$\vdash {\sim}((\mathrm{E}x)\ {\sim}P.(\mathrm{E}x)\ {\sim}Q)\ \supset\ .{\sim}(\mathrm{E}x).{\sim}P{\sim}Q.$$

However, by the duality theorem,

$$\vdash {\sim}((\mathrm{E}x)\ {\sim}P.(\mathrm{E}x)\ {\sim}Q):\ \equiv\ :(x)\ P.\mathbf{v}.(x)\ Q$$

$$\vdash {\sim}(\mathrm{E}x).{\sim}P{\sim}Q:\ \equiv\ :(x).P\mathbf{v}Q.$$

So Part II follows.

In the preceding proof we made quite a bother over showing that we had satisfied the various restrictions involved in the definition of $\vdash_C$ and in the hypothesis of Thm.VI.7.2. By proceeding in a systematic manner, we can check on these restrictions rather easily. First of all, each time we use rule C, we should note the $F_\alpha(y_\alpha)$ which results, and the y_α which we use. Then at the end of the demonstration, it is very easy to check if any of these y_α's occur free in Q. This takes care of the hypothesis of Thm.VI.7.2. There still remain the restrictions embodied in the definition of $\vdash_C$. Note that there are restrictions only on the use of rule G and rule C, and that for any given use of rule G or rule C the restriction depends only on the P's and the previously occurring $F_\alpha(y_\alpha)$'s. So one can check the restrictions on a given use of rule G or rule C at the time the rule is used. Also, the restrictions merely involve the question whether a given variable occurs free in the P's or the previous $F_\alpha(y_\alpha)$'s, which can be easily checked if one is keeping a list of the $F_\alpha(y_\alpha)$'s.

Furthermore, whenever we skip over a sequence of steps by referring to a previously proved theorem $\vdash A$, there is nothing to check, since the steps of the demonstration of $\vdash A$ involve no uses of rule G or rule C. Also, since there are no uses of rule C, the demonstration of $\vdash A$ will not produce any $F_\alpha(y_\alpha)$ that we should add to our list.

In summary, if we compile a list of the $F_\alpha(y_\alpha)$ and y_α as we go along, it is very simple to check the restrictions involved in the definition of $\vdash_C$, since one merely checks each use of rule G or rule C at the time of its use by reference to the P's and the previously occurring $F_\alpha(y_\alpha)$'s. Also at the end, we have a complete list of the y_α's, and can readily check if any of them occur free in Q.

Bearing this in mind, let us now look at the proofs of the remaining three illustrative theorems.

Theorem VI.7.5. $\vdash (\mathrm{E}x)(y)\ P \supset (y)(\mathrm{E}x)\ P$.

Proof. Start with $(\mathrm{E}x)(y)\ P$. As x does not occur free in this, we can use rule C with x and get $(y)\ P$. Then by Thm.VI.5.1, P. Then by Thm.VI.7.3, corollary, $(\mathrm{E}x)\ P$. As y does not occur free in $(\mathrm{E}x)(y)\ P$ or $(y)\ P$, we can use rule G with y and get $(y)(\mathrm{E}x)\ P$. So we have shown

$$(\mathrm{E}x)(y)\ P \vdash_C (y)(\mathrm{E}x)\ P.$$

As x does not occur free in $(y)(\mathrm{E}x)\ P$, we infer

$$(\mathrm{E}x)(y)\ P \vdash (y)(\mathrm{E}x)\ P$$

by Thm.VI.7.2.

Theorem VI.7.6. $\vdash (x).P \supset Q : \supset :(\mathrm{E}x)\ P. \supset .(\mathrm{E}x)\ Q$.

Proof. Start with $(x).P \supset Q$ and $(\mathrm{E}x)\ P$. By Thm.VI.5.1, $P \supset Q$. As x does not occur free in $(x).P \supset Q$ or $(\mathrm{E}x)\ P$, we can use rule C with x to get P from $(\mathrm{E}x)\ P$. Then from P and $P \supset Q$ by modus ponens, we get Q. Finally, by Thm.VI.7.3, corollary, $(\mathrm{E}x)\ Q$. So

$$(x).P \supset Q,\ (\mathrm{E}x)\ P \vdash_C (\mathrm{E}x)\ Q.$$

As x does not occur free in $(\mathrm{E}x)\ Q$, we get

$$(x).P \supset Q,\ (\mathrm{E}x)\ P \vdash (\mathrm{E}x)\ Q.$$

Then our theorem follows by two uses of the deduction theorem.

Theorem VI.7.7. $\vdash (\mathrm{E}x).P \supset Q : \supset :(x)\ P. \supset .(\mathrm{E}x)\ Q$.

Proof. Start with $(\mathrm{E}x).P \supset Q$ and $(x)\ P$. By rule C with x, $P \supset Q$, and by Thm.VI.5.1, P. So by modus ponens, Q. Finally by Thm.VI.7.3, corollary, $(\mathrm{E}x)\ Q$. So

$$(\mathrm{E}x).P \supset Q,\ (x)\ P \vdash_C (\mathrm{E}x)\ Q.$$

So

$$(\mathrm{E}x).P \supset Q,\ (x)\ P \vdash (\mathrm{E}x)\ Q.$$

It will be instructive to go back and review Bôcher's proof that the sum of two continuous functions is continuous; in particular let us rewrite it as a formal proof involving rule G and rule C, with appropriate use of Thm.VI.7.2. As we shall now add, in full detail, all the logical steps which Bôcher takes for granted, our formalized version will be much longer than Bôcher's original. We mention this in order to point out that the extra length is due to the insertion of omitted steps, rather than to the use of formal logic instead of intuitive logic.

Let $A_i (i = 1, 2)$ denote

$$(\varepsilon):.\varepsilon > 0. \supset :(E\delta):\delta > 0:(x):| x - c | < \delta. \supset .| f_i(x) - f_i(c) | < \varepsilon;$$

that is, A_i denotes the statement "f_i is continuous at the point c." Then the theorem we are to prove is:

$$\vdash A_1\&A_2. \supset ::(\varepsilon):.\varepsilon > 0. \supset :(E\delta):\delta > 0:(x):| x - c | < \delta. \supset . \\ | f_1(x) + f_2(x) - f_1(c) - f_2(c) | < \varepsilon.$$

Because of the generalization theorem (Thm.VI.4.2) and the deduction theorem, it will suffice to prove

$$A_1\&A_2 \vdash \varepsilon > 0. \supset :(E\delta):\delta > 0:(x):| x - c | < \delta. \supset . \\ | f_1(x) + f_2(x) - f_1(c) - f_2(c) | < \varepsilon.$$

Because of the deduction theorem, it will suffice to prove

$$A_1\&A_2, \varepsilon > 0 \vdash (E\delta):\delta > 0:(x):| x - c | < \delta. \supset . \\ | f_1(x) + f_2(x) - f_1(c) - f_2(c) | < \varepsilon.$$

So let us start with

(1) $$A_1\&A_2$$

(2) $$\varepsilon > 0.$$

We are now at the point corresponding to Bôcher's clause[1] "Then, no matter how small the positive quantity ε may be chosen," but must insert several steps before we can proceed with the rest of his sentence[1] "we may take δ_1 and δ_2 . . . ". By Axiom scheme 6, we have for $i = 1, 2$,

$$\vdash A_i. \supset :.\varepsilon/2 > 0. \supset :(E\delta):\delta > 0:(x):| x - c | < \delta. \supset . \\ | f_i(x) - f_i(c) | < \varepsilon/2.$$

However, from our assumption (1), we get A_1 and A_2, and so by modus ponens, we get for $i = 1, 2$,

$$\varepsilon/2 > 0. \supset :(E\delta):\delta > 0:(x):| x - c | < \delta. \supset .| f_i(x) - f_i(c) | < \varepsilon/2.$$

[1] From Bôcher, *op. cit.*

From our assumption (2), we get $\varepsilon/2 > 0$ (this is one of the few steps in this proof which is not purely logical), and so by modus ponens, we get for $i = 1, 2$,

$$(E\delta):\delta > 0:(x):|\, x - c \,| < \delta. \supset .|\, f_i(x) - f_i(c) \,| < \varepsilon/2.$$

Now by rule C, we get

$$(3) \qquad \delta_1 > 0:(x):|\, x - c \,| < \delta_1. \supset .|\, f_1(x) - f_1(c) \,| < \varepsilon/2.$$

By rule C again, we get

$$(4) \qquad \delta_2 > 0:(x):|\, x - c \,| < \delta_2. \supset .|\, f_2(x) - f_2(c) \,| < \varepsilon/2.$$

This brings us to the end of that sentence in Bôcher's proof.

Now take δ the smaller of δ_1 and δ_2 (the logic involved in this step will be discussed in Chapter VIII). Then we have

$$(5) \qquad \delta > 0,$$

$$(6) \qquad \delta \leq \delta_1,$$

$$(7) \qquad \delta \leq \delta_2.$$

By (6) and (7), we get

$$(8) \qquad |\, x - c \,| < \delta. \supset .|\, x - c \,| < \delta_1,$$

$$(9) \qquad |\, x - c \,| < \delta. \supset .|\, x - c \,| < \delta_2.$$

(This is another step which is not purely logical.) By (3), (4), and Axiom scheme 6, we get

$$|\, x - c \,| < \delta_1. \supset .|\, f_1(x) - f_1(c) \,| < \varepsilon/2,$$

$$|\, x - c \,| < \delta_2. \supset .|\, f_2(x) - f_2(c) \,| < \varepsilon/2.$$

By (8) and (9), we get

$$|\, x - c \,| < \delta. \supset .|\, f_1(x) - f_1(c) \,| < \varepsilon/2,$$

$$|\, x - c \,| < \delta. \supset .|\, f_2(x) - f_2(c) \,| < \varepsilon/2.$$

By Thm.IV.4.17,

$$(10) \qquad |\, x - c \,| < \delta. \supset :|\, f_1(x) - f_1(c) \,| < \varepsilon/2.|\, f_2(x) - f_2(c) \,| < \varepsilon/2.$$

However,

$$(11) \qquad |\, f_1(x) - f_1(c) \,| < \varepsilon/2.|\, f_2(x) - f_2(c) \,| < \varepsilon/2: \supset :$$
$$|\, f_1(x) + f_2(x) - f_1(c) - f_2(c) \,| < \varepsilon$$

(This is our third step which is not purely logical. Bôcher makes two steps out of it, since he is more interested in the mathematics of the proof than in the logic.) By (10) and (11),

$$| x - c | < \delta . \supset .| f_1(x) + f_2(x) - f_1(c) - f_2(c) | < \varepsilon.$$

As x does not occur free in either (1), (2), (3), or (4), we can use rule G and get

$$(x):| x - c | < \delta . \supset .| f_1(x) + f_2(x) - f_1(c) - f_2(c) | < \varepsilon.$$

By (5), we get

$$\delta > 0:(x):| x - c | < \delta . \supset .| f_1(x) + f_2(x) - f_1(c) - f_2(c) | < \varepsilon.$$

Finally, by Thm.VI.7.3,

$$(\mathrm{E}\delta):\delta > 0:(x):| x - c | < \delta . \supset .| f_1(x) + f_2(x) - f_1(c) - f_2(c) | < \varepsilon.$$

So we have proved

$$A_1 \& A_2,\ \varepsilon > 0 \vdash_C (\mathrm{E}\delta):\delta > 0:(x):| x - c | < \delta . \supset . \\ | f_1(x) + f_2(x) - f_1(c) - f_2(c) | < \varepsilon.$$

As neither δ_1 nor δ_2 occurs at all in the conclusion, we can use Thm. VI.7.2 and replace $\vdash_C$ by $\vdash$. Then, as indicated earlier, we can conclude the proof by using the deduction theorem and the generalization theorem.

EXERCISES

VI.7.1. Prove:

(a) $\vdash (x)\ P \supset (\mathrm{E}x)\ P$.
(b) $\vdash (\mathrm{E}x)\ F(x). \equiv .(\mathrm{E}x,y).F(x) \mathbf{v} F(y)$.
(c) $\vdash (\mathrm{E}x)\ P.(x)\ Q. \supset .(\mathrm{E}x).PQ$.
(d) $\vdash (x,y).P \supset Q: \supset :(x,y)\ P. \supset .(x,y)\ Q$.
(e) $\vdash (x)(\mathrm{E}y).P \supset Q: \supset :(\mathrm{E}x)(y)\ P. \supset .(\mathrm{E}x,y)\ Q$.
(f) $\vdash (x).P \mathbf{v} Q: \supset :(x)\ P. \mathbf{v}. (\mathrm{E}x)\ Q$.
(g) $\vdash (x)\ P. \mathbf{v}. (\mathrm{E}x)\ Q: \supset :(\mathrm{E}x).P \mathbf{v} Q$.
(h) $\vdash (\mathrm{E}x)\ P. \supset .(x)\ Q: \supset :(x).P \supset Q$.
(i) $\vdash (\mathrm{E}x)\ P. \supset .(\mathrm{E}x)\ Q: \supset :(\mathrm{E}x).P \supset Q$.
(j) $\vdash (x)\ P. \supset .(x)\ Q: \supset :(\mathrm{E}x).P \supset Q$.

VI.7.2. If there are no free occurrences of y in P and no free occurrences of x in Q, prove:

(a) $\vdash (x)\ P.(y)\ Q: \equiv :(x,y).PQ$.
(b) $\vdash (x)(\mathrm{E}y).PQ: \equiv :(\mathrm{E}y)(x).PQ$.
(c) $\vdash (y)\ Q. \supset .(\mathrm{E}x)\ P: \equiv :(\mathrm{E}x,y).Q \supset P$.

VI.7.3. Find the flaws in the following invalid proofs of incorrect statements:

(a) To prove $(\mathrm{E}x)\ P \vdash (x)\ P$. Start with $(\mathrm{E}x)\ P$. Then P by rule C. Then $(x)\ P$ by rule G. So $(\mathrm{E}x)\ P \vdash_C (x)\ P$. So $(\mathrm{E}x)\ P \vdash (x)\ P$.

(b) To prove $(\mathrm{E}x)\ P \vdash P$. Start with $(\mathrm{E}x)\ P$. Then P by rule C. So $(\mathrm{E}x)\ P \vdash_C P$. So $(\mathrm{E}x)\ P \vdash P$.

(c) To prove $\vdash (\mathrm{E}x)\ P \supset P$. We use reductio ad absurdum. So start with $(\mathrm{E}x)\ P.{\sim}P$. Then $(\mathrm{E}x)\ P$ and ${\sim}P$. So by rule C, P and ${\sim}P$. So $P{\sim}P$. So $(x)\ Q.{\sim}(x)\ Q$ by Thm.VI.6.1, Part LXV. So $(\mathrm{E}x)\ P.{\sim}P \vdash_C (x)\ Q.{\sim}(x)\ Q$. So $(\mathrm{E}x)\ P.{\sim}P \vdash (x)\ Q.{\sim}(x)\ Q$. So $\vdash (\mathrm{E}x)\ P.{\sim}P :\supset: (x)\ Q.{\sim}(x)\ Q$. So $\vdash {\sim}((\mathrm{E}x)\ P.{\sim}P)$ by Ex. II.3.1, Part (f). This is $\vdash (\mathrm{E}x)\ P \supset P$.

(d) To prove $(\mathrm{E}x)\ P.(\mathrm{E}x)\ Q \vdash (\mathrm{E}x)\ PQ$. Start with $(\mathrm{E}x)\ P.(\mathrm{E}x)\ Q$. Then $(\mathrm{E}x)\ P$ and $(\mathrm{E}x)\ Q$. So by rule C, P and Q. So PQ. So $(\mathrm{E}x)\ PQ$ by Thm.VI.7.3. So $(\mathrm{E}x)\ P.(\mathrm{E}x)\ Q \vdash_C (\mathrm{E}x)\ PQ$. So $(\mathrm{E}x)\ P.(\mathrm{E}x)\ Q \vdash (\mathrm{E}x)\ PQ$.

(e) To prove $(y)(\mathrm{E}x)\ P \vdash (\mathrm{E}x)(y)\ P$. Start with $(y)(\mathrm{E}x)\ P$. Then $(\mathrm{E}x)\ P$ by Thm.VI.5.1. Then P by rule C. Then $(y)\ P$ by rule G. Then $(\mathrm{E}x)(y)\ P$ by Thm.VI.7.3. So $(y)(\mathrm{E}x)\ P \vdash_C (\mathrm{E}x)(y)\ P$. So $(y)(\mathrm{E}x)\ P \vdash (\mathrm{E}x)(y)\ P$.

(f) To prove $(x).P \supset Q, (\mathrm{E}x)\ P \vdash (x)\ Q$. Start with $(x).P \supset Q$ and $(\mathrm{E}x)\ P$. Then $P \supset Q$ by Thm.VI.5.1 and P by rule C. So Q by modus ponens. So $(x)\ Q$ by rule G. So $(x).P \supset Q, (\mathrm{E}x)\ P \vdash_C (x)\ Q$. So $(x).P \supset Q, (\mathrm{E}x)\ P \vdash (x)\ Q$.

(g) To prove $(\mathrm{E}x).P \supset Q, (\mathrm{E}x)\ P \vdash (\mathrm{E}x)\ Q$. Start with $(\mathrm{E}x).P \supset Q$ and $(\mathrm{E}x)\ P$. Then $P \supset Q$ and P by rule C. So Q by modus ponens. So $(\mathrm{E}x)\ Q$ by Thm.VI.7.3. So $(\mathrm{E}x).P \supset Q, (\mathrm{E}x)\ P \vdash_C (\mathrm{E}x)\ Q$. So $(\mathrm{E}x).P \supset Q, (\mathrm{E}x)\ P \vdash (\mathrm{E}x)\ Q$.

(h) To prove $(x).P \supset Q, (\mathrm{E}x)\ P \vdash Q$. Start with $(x).P \supset Q$ and $(\mathrm{E}x)\ P$. Then $P \supset Q$ by Thm.VI.5.1 and P by rule C. So Q by modus ponens. So $(x).P \supset Q, (\mathrm{E}x)\ P \vdash_C Q$. So $(x).P \supset Q, (\mathrm{E}x)\ P \vdash Q$.

8. Restricted Quantification. The expression $(x)\ F(x)$ indicates that $F(x)$ is true where x is any logical entity whatsoever. In practical mathematical discussions this amount of generality is far more than is desirable or useful. For instance, instead of "For all x, $A(x)$" or "There is an x such that $A(x)$," one will usually find in mathematical discussions such expressions as "For all positive integers, x, $A(x)$," or "There is a prime, $p \equiv 1$ (mod 4), such that $A(p)$," or "For each $\varepsilon > 0$, $A(\varepsilon)$," etc. Even when such expressions as "For all x, $A(x)$," or "There is an x such that $A(x)$," do occur in mathematical discussions, it is almost always understood tacitly that there are certain restrictions on the x, and that what is meant is something like "For all real numbers, x, $A(x)$," or "There is an angle, x, such that $A(x)$."

In short, the types of quantifiers which are useful in mathematics take the general forms "For all x of kind K, $A(x)$" or "There is an x of kind K such that $A(x)$." We refer to these as restricted quantifiers.

It is very easy to express restricted quantifiers in symbolic logic. Let $K(x)$ and $F(x)$ be translations of "x is of kind K" and "$A(x)$." Then $(x).K(x) \supset F(x)$ and $(\mathrm{E}x)\ K(x)F(x)$ are the translations of "For all x of kind K, $A(x)$" and "There is an x of kind K such that $A(x)$." Thus the translation of restricted quantifiers presents no problem. However, there is another question besides mere translation, namely, a question of convenience. In ordinary mathematics the device of restricting certain letters to denote values from specified ranges saves a large amount of repetition of hypotheses and reiteration of restrictive conditions. Thus one may find it stated in the beginning of some text that, throughout the text, x and y shall denote real numbers, δ and ε shall denote positive real numbers, m and n shall denote positive integers, etc. Then such conditions need not be inserted in the statements of theorems, or in the proofs, or in definitions, or in discussions. The resulting abridgment not only saves space but facilitates comprehension.

One can partially adopt such conventions in symbolic logic, and it is quite worth while to do so. The procedure is not difficult. If there is some condition, $K(x)$, which we wish to impose on certain quantities throughout a given discussion, we choose certain letters which are to denote quantities satisfying the condition $K(x)$ throughout our discussion. Suppose we choose α and β for this purpose. Then throughout our discussion we understand $(\alpha)\ F\ (\alpha)$ to be an abbreviation for $(x).K(x) \supset F(x)$, and we understand $(\mathrm{E}\alpha)\ F(\alpha)$ to be an abbreviation for $(\mathrm{E}x)\ K(x)F(x)$. Similarly for β. In such case we speak of (α) and $(\mathrm{E}\alpha)$ as restricted quantifiers.

One can at the same time have other letters denoting quite different quantities. Thus, at the same time that we interpret (α), (β), $(\mathrm{E}\alpha)$, and $(\mathrm{E}\beta)$ as indicated above, we can agree that $(\gamma)\ F(\gamma)$ shall denote $(x).L(x) \supset F(x)$ and $(\mathrm{E}\gamma)\ F(\gamma)$ shall denote $(\mathrm{E}x)\ L(x)F(x)$. And we can at the same time let $(\delta)\ F(\delta)$ or $(\varepsilon)\ F(\varepsilon)$ denote $(x).x > 0 \supset F(x)$, and let $(\mathrm{E}\delta)\ F(\delta)$ or $(\mathrm{E}\varepsilon)\ F(\varepsilon)$ denote $(\mathrm{E}x){:}x > 0.F(x)$. One can mix the various kinds of quantifiers. Thus

$$(\alpha,\gamma)\ F(\alpha,\gamma)$$

would denote

$$(x){:}K(x).\supset.(y).L(y) \supset F(x,y),$$

or any of the equivalent forms

$$(x,y):K(x). \supset .L(y) \supset F(x,y),$$

$$(x,y):K(x)L(y). \supset .F(x,y),$$

$$(y,x):L(y)K(x). \supset .F(x,y),$$

$$(y,x):L(y). \supset .K(x) \supset F(x,y),$$

$$(y):L(y). \supset .(x).K(x) \supset F(x,y).$$

The last of these is just what we would denote by $(\gamma,\alpha)\ F(\alpha,\gamma)$. So we have

$$\vdash (\alpha,\gamma)\ P \equiv (\gamma,\alpha)\ P$$

even when α and γ are restricted quantifiers, and even when we do not have the same restriction on each of α and γ.

However, even with different restrictions on α and γ, we cannot infer the equivalence of $(\mathrm{E}\alpha)(\gamma)\ P$ and $(\gamma)(\mathrm{E}\alpha)\ P$.

We notice that by Thm.VI.6.8 it is quite immaterial whether we interpret $(\alpha)\ F(\alpha)$ as $(x).K(x) \supset F(x)$ or $(y).K(y) \supset F(y)$, provided that we observe the restrictions implied by our conventions in writing $F(\alpha)$, $F(x)$, $F(y)$, $K(\alpha)$, $K(x)$, $K(y)$, namely, that $F(x)$ is the result of replacing all free occurrences of α in $F(\alpha)$ by occurrences of x and $F(\alpha)$ is the result of replacing all free occurrences of x in $F(x)$ by occurrences of α, with similar understandings for $K(\alpha)$ and $K(x)$, $F(x)$ and $F(y)$, and $K(x)$ and $K(y)$. Such an understanding is necessary to assure that $(x).K(x) \supset F(x)$ has the meaning intended for $(\alpha)\ F(\alpha)$.

The above conventions ensure that, if we have $(\alpha)\ F(\alpha)$ where $F(\alpha)$ contains no free occurrences of α, then we must choose an x which does not occur free in $F(\alpha)$ when we write $(x).K(x) \supset F(x)$ as the interpretation of $(\alpha)\ F(\alpha)$. Then x will not occur free in $F(x)$, and $F(\alpha)$ and $F(x)$ are the same.

We now state the remarkable fact that, if we confine our attention to formulas with no free occurrences of the quantified variable, then all the theorems which we have proved for unrestricted quantifiers hold also for restricted quantifiers, except that a few of them require the hypotheses $(\mathrm{E}x)\ K(x)$, $(\mathrm{E}x)\ L(x)$, $(\mathrm{E}x).x > 0$, etc. This requirement means that, if we are going to deal with restricted quantifiers, our restriction should not be so severe that it is not satisfied by any quantities at all. In practical cases, the restrictions $K(x)$, $L(x)$, etc., will usually be conditions such as "x is a real number," or "x is a vector," or the like, and we shall certainly have $(\mathrm{E}x)\ K(x)$, $(\mathrm{E}x)\ L(x)$, etc.

The easiest way to verify that the theorems with no free occurrences of the quantified variables, which we have proved, hold also for restricted quantifiers is to check them one by one. Actually, in most cases all that is required is to write the interpretation of the given theorem, and it is then a simple exercise to prove it.

We should consider first our axioms. Suppose $(x)\ F(x)$ is an axiom; can we prove $(\alpha)\ F(\alpha)$? This latter signifies $(x).K(x) \supset F(x)$. Since $(x)\ F(x)$ is an axiom, we have $\vdash (x)\ F(x)$. Then $\vdash F(x)$ by Thm.VI.5.1. However, by Thm.IV.4.28, corollary, $\vdash F(x). \supset .K(x) \supset F(x)$. So $\vdash K(x) \supset F(x)$. Then by Thm.VI.4.1, $\vdash (x).K(x) \supset F(x)$. That is, $\vdash (\alpha)\ F(\alpha)$.

This takes care of all axioms of the form $(x)\ F(x)$.

Now consider $(x).F(x) \supset G(x): \supset :(x)\ F(x). \supset .(x)\ G(x)$, one of the instances of Axiom scheme 4.

Since this does not have the form $(x)\ F(x)$, it is not covered by our earlier analysis. We must prove

$$\vdash (\alpha).F(\alpha) \supset G(\alpha): \supset :(\alpha)\ F(\alpha). \supset .(\alpha)\ G(\alpha).$$

This signifies

$$\vdash (x):K(x) \supset .F(x) \supset G(x).: \supset :.(x).K(x) \supset F(x): \supset :(x).K(x) \supset G(x).$$

We prove without difficulty

$$(x):K(x) \supset .F(x) \supset G(x),\ (x).K(x) \supset F(x),\ K(x) \vdash G(x).$$

Then by the deduction theorem and the generalization theorem, we get

$$(x):K(x) \supset .F(x) \supset G(x),\ (x).K(x) \supset F(x) \vdash (x).K(x) \supset G(x).$$

Then the desired result follows by two more uses of the deduction theorem.

Now consider $P \supset (x)\ P$, where there are no free occurrences of x in P. This is an instance of Axiom scheme 5. We wish to prove $\vdash P \supset (\alpha)\ P$, where α does not occur free in P. This signifies $\vdash P \supset .(x).K(x) \supset P$, where x does not occur free in P. By Thm.IV.4.28, corollary, we have $\vdash P \supset .K(x) \supset P$. So by Thm.VI.4.1, $\vdash (x):P \supset .K(x) \supset P$. So by Thm. VI.6.6, Part IX, $\vdash P \supset .(x).K(x) \supset P$.

Axiom scheme 6 can involve free occurrences of the quantified variable, and so we are not concerned with it at the moment. Likewise Thm.VI.4.1, Thm.VI.4.2, and Thm.VI.5.1. We postpone Thm.VI.5.2 because it is a special case of Thm.VI.6.5, which we shall take up in its place.

Now consider Thm.VI.5.3. We wish to prove

$$\vdash (\alpha).F(\alpha) \equiv G(\alpha): \supset :(\alpha)\ F(\alpha). \equiv .(\alpha)\ G(\alpha).$$

This signifies

$$\vdash (x):K(x) \supset .F(x) \equiv G(x).: \supset :.(x).K(x) \supset F(x): \equiv :(x).K(x) \supset G(x).$$

This is easily proved, since we can prove each of

$$\vdash (x){:}K(x) \supset .F(x) \equiv G(x).{:} \supset {:}.(x).K(x) \supset F(x){:} \supset {:}(x).K(x) \supset G(x)$$

and

$$\vdash (x){:}K(x) \supset .F(x) \equiv G(x).{:} \supset {:}.(x).K(x) \supset G(x){:} \supset {:}(x).K(x) \supset F(x)$$

by the procedure used for Axiom scheme 4.

In case some of the y's are restricted quantifiers which occur free in $W \equiv V$, Thm.VI.5.4 will not hold. However, Thm.VI.5.5 and Thm.VI.5.6 hold in any case. The method of proof is very easy, and we illustrate with an example. Suppose we have $\vdash F(\alpha) \equiv G(\alpha)$, and wish to prove

$$\vdash P \supset (\alpha)\ F(\alpha). \equiv .P \supset (\alpha)\ G(\alpha).$$

The latter signifies

$$\vdash P \supset .(x).K(x) \supset F(x){:} \equiv {:}P \supset .(x).K(x) \supset G(x).$$

By Thm.VI.6.8, this is equivalent to

$$\vdash P \supset .(\alpha).K(\alpha) \supset F(\alpha){:} \equiv {:}P \supset .(\alpha).K(\alpha) \supset G(\alpha),$$

in which, momentarily for the purposes of a proof, we are not considering the α as a restricted quantifier. Now this latter follows from $\vdash F(\alpha) \equiv G(\alpha)$ by Thm.VI.5.5.

Thm.VI.6.2 is a special case of the duality theorem, and so we proceed directly to the duality theorem, Thm.VI.6.3. We first have to generalize the definition of a dual. In addition to replacing (x) by $(\mathrm{E}x)$ and vice versa, we replace (α) by $(\mathrm{E}\alpha)$ and vice versa, and similarly for any other letter denoting a restricted quantity. In a word, we treat restricted quantifiers just like unrestricted quantifiers when forming the dual. To prove the duality theorem, we show that, if we write out $(\alpha)\ F(\alpha)$ without restricted quantifiers and take the dual in the usual manner, we merely get what $(\mathrm{E}\alpha)\ F^*(\alpha)$ signifies, and vice versa (where $F^*(\alpha)$ is the dual of $F(\alpha)$). If we write $(\alpha)\ F(\alpha)$ with an unrestricted quantifier, we get $(x).K(x) \supset F(x)$, which is equivalent to $(x).\sim K(x) \vee F(x)$, whose dual is $(\mathrm{E}x).K(x).F^*(x)$, which is just $(\mathrm{E}\alpha)\ F^*(\alpha)$ written with an unrestricted quantifier. Similarly, we proceed from $(\mathrm{E}\alpha)\ F^*(\alpha)$ back to $(\alpha)\ F(\alpha)$ if we take the dual of the corresponding statement written with an unrestricted quantifier. So the duality theorem is easily verified.

Likewise the important corollary to the duality theorem, namely, Thm.VI.6.4, also holds, it being proved exactly as when we were dealing only with unrestricted quantification. By means of it, we can get Part II of Thm.VI.6.5 from Part I; Parts II, IV, and V of Thm.VI.6.6 from Parts I, III, and VI; Part II of Thm.VI.6.7 from Part I; and Part II of Thm.VI.6.8 from Part I.

Now let us look at Part I of Thm.VI.6.5. We desire to prove

$$\vdash (\alpha).F(\alpha).G(\alpha): \equiv :(\alpha)\ F(\alpha).(\alpha)\ G(\alpha).$$

This signifies

$$\vdash (x):K(x) \supset .F(x).G(x).: \equiv :.(x).K(x) \supset F(x):(x).K(x) \supset G(x).$$

One easily proves

$$(x):K(x) \supset .F(x).G(x),\ K(x) \vdash F(x)$$

and so gets

$$\vdash (x):K(x) \supset .F(x).G(x).: \supset :.(x).K(x) \supset F(x).$$

Similarly

$$\vdash (x):K(x) \supset .F(x).G(x).: \supset :.(x).K(x) \supset G(x),$$

and we have half of our theorem. Conversely, we easily get

$$(x).K(x) \supset F(x):(x).K(x) \supset G(x),\ K(x) \vdash F(x).G(x),$$

which gives the other half of our theorem.

Now let us look at Part I of Thm.VI.6.6. We desire to prove $\vdash (\alpha)\ Q \equiv Q$, where there are no free occurrences of α in Q. This signifies $\vdash (x).K(x) \supset Q: \equiv Q$, where x does not occur free in Q. Since we are assuming $\vdash (\mathrm{E}x)\ K(x)$, we have by Thm.VI.6.1, Part LXIX, $\vdash Q \equiv :(\mathrm{E}x)\ K(x). \supset .Q$. So by Thm.VI.6.6, Part VII, $\vdash Q \equiv :(x).K(x) \supset Q$.

We now get Part III of Thm.VI.6.6 by the same proof that was used when dealing with unrestricted quantifiers.

We now consider Part VI of Thm.VI.6.6. We desire to prove $\vdash (\mathrm{E}\alpha): F(\alpha).Q.: \equiv :.(\mathrm{E}\alpha).F(\alpha):Q$. This signifies $\vdash (\mathrm{E}x):K(x).F(x).Q.: \equiv :.(\mathrm{E}x). K(x).F(x):Q$. This is an easy consequence of Thm.VI.6.6, Part VI, if we take P to be $K(x)F(x)$.

We now quickly conclude the rest of Thm.VI.6.6, because we get Part VII by putting $\sim P$ for P in Part V, Part VIII by putting $\sim P$ for P in Part IV, Part IX by putting $\sim Q$ for Q in Part V, and Part X by putting $\sim Q$ for Q in Part IV.

We have already indicated how to prove Part I of Thm.VI.6.7.

Now consider Part I of Thm.VI.6.8. We wish to prove $\vdash (\alpha)\ F(\alpha) \equiv (\beta)\ F(\beta)$.

CAUTION. Unless α and β have the same restrictions, this is not true.

As we are assuming α and β both subject to the restriction $K(x)$, this signifies $\vdash (x).K(x) \supset F(x): \equiv :(y).K(y) \supset F(y)$, which is immediate.

Had we tried to prove $\vdash (\alpha)\ F(\alpha) \equiv (\gamma)\ F(\gamma)$, we should have been trying to prove $\vdash (x).K(x) \supset F(x): \equiv :(y).L(y) \supset F(y)$, which in general is not true unless one assumes some special relationships between $F(x)$, $K(x)$, and $L(x)$.

Part I of Thm.VI.7.4 would read

$$\vdash (\mathrm{E}\alpha).F(\alpha).G(\alpha): \supset :(\mathrm{E}\alpha)\ F(\alpha):(\mathrm{E}\alpha)\ G(\alpha),$$

signifying

$$\vdash (\mathrm{E}x).K(x).F(x).G(x): \supset :(\mathrm{E}x).K(x).F(x):(\mathrm{E}x).K(x).G(x).$$

This is easily proved since

$$\vdash K(x).F(x).G(x): \equiv :K(x).F(x):K(x).G(x).$$

From Part I one can get Part II in the same manner as for unrestricted quantifiers.

Thm.VI.7.5 would read $\vdash (\mathrm{E}\alpha)(\gamma)\ F(\alpha,\gamma). \supset .(\gamma)(\mathrm{E}\alpha)\ F(\alpha,\gamma)$, signifying

$$\vdash (\mathrm{E}x):K(x):(y).L(y) \supset F(x,y).: \supset :.(y):L(y) \supset .(\mathrm{E}x).K(x).F(x,y).$$

One proves in succession

$$(\mathrm{E}x):K(x):(y).L(y) \supset F(x,y),\ L(y) \vdash_C (\mathrm{E}x).K(x).F(x,y),$$

$$(\mathrm{E}x):K(x):(y).L(y) \supset F(x,y),\ L(y) \vdash (\mathrm{E}x).K(x).F(x,y),$$

$$(\mathrm{E}x):K(x):(y).L(y) \supset F(x,y) \vdash (y):L(y) \supset .(\mathrm{E}x).K(x).F(x,y).$$

Thm.VI.7.6 would read

$$\vdash (\alpha).F(\alpha) \supset G(\alpha): \supset :(\mathrm{E}\alpha)\ F(\alpha). \supset .(\mathrm{E}\alpha)\ G(\alpha),$$

signifying

$$\vdash (x):K(x) \supset .F(x) \supset G(x).: \supset :.(\mathrm{E}x).K(x).F(x): \supset :(\mathrm{E}x).K(x).G(x).$$

This is easily proved, following the pattern of proof of the original Thm. VI.7.6.

Similarly for Thm.VI.7.7.

We now raise the question of the significance of $F(\alpha)$, in which the occurrences of α are free. In deciding to take $(x).K(x) \supset F(x)$ and $(\mathrm{E}x).K(x).F(x)$ as the meanings of $(\alpha)\ F(\alpha)$ and $(\mathrm{E}\alpha)\ F(\alpha)$, we were guided by the intuitive meanings. In the case of $F(\alpha)$, the intuitive meaning does not furnish a satisfactory guide. In everyday mathematics, if it has been agreed that α stands for a quantity satisfying the restriction $K(\alpha)$, it is commonly the case that, if one is assuming $F(\alpha)$, then $K(\alpha)\&F(\alpha)$ is understood, but if one is trying to prove $F(\alpha)$, then $K(\alpha) \supset F(\alpha)$ is understood. It seems that in symbolic logic perhaps it is best not to give any especial significance to the α in $F(\alpha)$ when it occurs free. This does not cause any confusion, because it has the effect of associating the restriction with the quantifiers (α) and $(\mathrm{E}\alpha)$, rather than merely with the letter α. As the restriction is associated merely with the letter in everyday mathematics, we are using a different system from that used in everyday mathematics, and the reader who is accustomed to the procedures of everyday mathematics should note carefully the difference in treatment.

Accordingly, if a variable occurs both free and bound in a statement, the free occurrences are subject to no restriction, whereas the bound occurrences may be restricted. One can always deal with this situation by giving the restricted quantifiers their actual significance. Thus, by Thm.VI.5.1, we have

$$\vdash (x).K(x) \supset F(x) \colon \supset \colon K(x) \supset F(x).$$

Using restricted quantification, we can write this as

$$\vdash (\alpha)\ F(\alpha). \supset .K(x) \supset F(x).$$

This is then the form which Axiom scheme 6 takes with restricted quantification. A moment's thought will indicate that this is the only form it could take. Since $(\alpha)\ F(\alpha)$ means that $F(\alpha)$ is true for all α satisfying $K(\alpha)$, one could not expect to infer $F(x)$ without the prior hypothesis $K(x)$.

A similar situation holds with respect to Thm.VI.7.3. By the corollary to this we have

$$\vdash K(x).F(x) \colon \supset \colon (\mathrm{E}x).K(x).F(x).$$

That is,

$$\vdash K(x).F(x) \colon \supset \colon (\mathrm{E}\alpha)\ F(\alpha).$$

This is as close to Thm.VI.7.3 as one can come with restricted quantification, and it is as close as one would expect to come.

If one applies rule C to $(\mathrm{E}\alpha)\ F(\alpha)$, then, since this is really $(\mathrm{E}x).K(x).F(x)$, one gets not merely $F(y)$, but $K(y).F(y)$; again just what one would expect.

In connection with rule G, the situation is more difficult. If one has proved $\vdash F(\alpha)$, then one easily gets $\vdash K(\alpha) \supset F(\alpha)$, and so $\vdash (\alpha)\ F(\alpha)$ by Thm.VI.4.1. However, the more usual situation is that in which one has $P_1, P_2, \ldots, P_n, K(\alpha) \vdash_C F(\alpha)$ and wishes to progress to $P_1, P_2, \ldots, P_n \vdash_C (\alpha)\ F(\alpha)$; naturally one can hope to do this only in case α satisfies the various restrictions imposed on a use of rule G. If we were dealing with $\vdash$ instead of $\vdash_C$, the matter would be simple. First we proceed to $P_1, P_2, \ldots, P_n \vdash K(\alpha) \supset F(\alpha)$ by the deduction theorem, and then Thm.VI.4.2 gives $P_1, P_2, \ldots, P_n \vdash (\alpha)\ F(\alpha)$. As a matter of fact, except in the most complicated cases, one can proceed from $P_1, P_2, \ldots, P_n, K(\alpha) \vdash_C F(\alpha)$ to $P_1, P_2, \ldots, P_n, K(\alpha) \vdash F(\alpha)$, and then proceed as indicated. Our proof of the version of Thm.VI.7.5 with restricted quantification is an instance of this.

However, in very complicated cases, we shall have to keep the $\vdash_C$. In such cases, what we need is a generalized deduction theorem. If we could proceed from $P_1, P_2, \ldots, P_n, K(\alpha) \vdash_C F(\alpha)$ to $P_1, P_2, \ldots, P_n \vdash_C K(\alpha) \supset F(\alpha)$, then we could proceed from $K(\alpha) \supset F(\alpha)$ to $(\alpha)\ F(\alpha)$ by rule G (unless there were prohibitions on the use of rule G with α, in which case one wouldn't expect to be able to prove $P_1, P_2, \ldots, P_n \vdash_C (\alpha)\ F(\alpha)$). We now state and prove this generalized deduction theorem. Since we expect to follow the use of our generalized deduction theorem by a use of rule G, we shall need to have information on the uses of rule C, and this information is included in the theorem.

****Theorem VI.8.1.** Suppose there is a demonstration of $P_1, P_2, \ldots, P_n, Q \vdash_C R$ in which there are m uses of rule C. Moreover, let $F_1(y_1), F_2(y_2), \ldots, F_m(y_m)$ be the steps resulting from uses of rule C, and let $y_1, y_2, \ldots, y_m$ be the corresponding y's with which rule C is used. Then there is a demonstration of $P_1, P_2, \ldots, P_n \vdash_C Q \supset R$ in which there are m uses of rule C, and $Q \supset F_1(y_1), Q \supset F_2(y_2), \ldots, Q \supset F_m(y_m)$ are the steps resulting from these uses of rule C, and $y_1, y_2, \ldots, y_m$ are the corresponding y's.

Proof. The proof is quite like that of the original deduction theorem (Thm.IV.6.1). If $S_1, S_2, \ldots, S_s$ are the steps of the demonstration of $P_1, P_2, \ldots, P_n\ Q \vdash_C R$, then we take $Q \supset S_1, Q \supset S_2, \ldots, Q \supset S_s$ to be key steps in a demonstration of $P_1, P_2, \ldots, P_n \vdash_C Q \supset R$. We now show by induction on i that up to $Q \supset S_i$ one can fill in additional steps so that the demonstration is complete up to that point, and that any uses of rule C which have occurred up to this point are used to produce those of $Q \supset F_1(y_1), Q \supset F_2(y_2), \ldots$ which have occurred up to and including the step $Q \supset S_i$. We take care of those cases in which S_i is an axiom, or a P, or Q, or a repetition, or the result of modus ponens exactly as in the proof of Thm.IV.6.1. Incidentally, this takes care of the case $i = 1$, so that our induction is now started. Also, all the cases treated so far involve no uses of rule G or rule C.

Now consider the case where S_i arose from a use of rule G. Then S_i is $(x)\ S_j$ where $j < i$. Also, x must not occur free in any of $P_1, P_2, \ldots, P_n, Q, F_1(y_1), F_2(y_2), \ldots, F_\alpha(y_\alpha)$, where $F_1(y_1), F_2(y_2), \ldots, F_\alpha(y_\alpha)$ are the results of rule C which occur previous to S_i in the demonstration of $P_1, P_2, \ldots, P_n, Q \vdash_C R$. Then in the demonstration of $P_1, P_2, \ldots, P_n \vdash_C Q \supset R$, we have up to this point had the steps $Q \supset F_1(y_1), Q \supset F_2(y_2), \ldots, Q \supset F_\alpha(y_\alpha)$ produced by rule C. None of these contains free occurrences of x. Also $P_1, P_2, \ldots, P_n$ do not contain free occurrences of x. So the restrictions for the use of rule G are satisfied. Hence we apply rule G to $Q \supset S_j$, getting $(x).Q \supset S_j$. Now by Thm.VI.6.6, Part IX, there is a demonstration of $\vdash (x).Q \supset S_j : \supset :Q \supset (x)\ S_j$. So we insert the steps of this demonstration, and then the step $Q \supset (x)\ S_j$ follows by modus ponens. As $(x)\ S_j$ is S_i, we now have the step $Q \supset S_i$.

Now consider the case where S_i arose from a use of rule C. Then S_i is

$F_\alpha(y_\alpha)$ and there is an S_j with $j < i$ such that S_j is $(\mathrm{E}x_\alpha)\ F_\alpha(x_\alpha)$. Also, y_α does not occur free in any of $P_1, P_2, \ldots, P_n, Q, F_1(y_1), F_2(y_2), \ldots, F_{\alpha-1}(y_{\alpha-1})$. So y_α does not occur free in any of $P_1, P_2, \ldots, P_n, Q \supset F_1(y_1), Q \supset F_2(y_2), \ldots, Q \supset F_{\alpha-1}(y_{\alpha-1})$, and the restrictions on the use of rule C are satisfied. We already have $Q \supset (\mathrm{E}x_\alpha)\ F_\alpha(x_\alpha)$ in our demonstration. By Thm.VI.6.8, Part II, we can fill in steps to get $Q \supset (\mathrm{E}y_\alpha)\ F_\alpha(y_\alpha)$. Then by Thm.VI.6.6, Part X, we can fill in steps to get $(\mathrm{E}y_\alpha).Q \supset F_\alpha(y_\alpha)$. Then by rule C, we get $Q \supset F_\alpha(y_\alpha)$. This is $Q \supset S_i$.

With the aid of this theorem, we can operate with restricted quantifiers in a manner strictly analogous to the manner with which we can operate with unrestricted quantifiers. The only point to keep in mind is that no restrictions can be understood in connection with free occurrences of a letter, so that, if we are dealing with restricted quantification for the letter α, then we shall encounter $K(\alpha)\&F(\alpha)$ or $K(\alpha) \supset F(\alpha)$ in places where we would have only $F(\alpha)$ if we were using unrestricted quantification.

The use of restricted quantification casts some light on the question of unorthodox converses (see the end of Sec. 4 of Chapter II). It is natural to take $(x).Q \supset P$ as the converse of $(x).P \supset Q$. If we follow this same rule with restricted quantification, we get $(\alpha).G(\alpha) \supset F(\alpha)$ as the converse of $(\alpha).F(\alpha) \supset G(\alpha)$. That is, $(x){:}K(x). \supset .G(x) \supset F(x)$ is the converse of $(x){:}K(x). \supset .F(x) \supset G(x)$. If we leave off the initial (x), as is customary in everyday mathematics, we get $K(x). \supset .G(x) \supset F(x)$ as the converse of $K(x). \supset .F(x) \supset G(x)$. From this, it is but a step to considering $P \supset (R \supset Q)$ to be the converse of $P \supset (Q \supset R)$ in cases where P is noticeably simpler than Q or R.

Let us see how much simpler the definition of continuity becomes if we use restricted quantification. We shall agree for the moment that δ and ε denote positive real numbers. Then we can write the definition of "f is continuous at the point c" as

$$(\varepsilon)(\mathrm{E}\delta)(x){:}\,|\,x - c\,| < \delta. \supset .|\,f(x) - f(c)\,| < \varepsilon.$$

A similar simplification will ensue whenever we are dealing with quantities from an assigned range of values.

EXERCISES

VI.8.1. If α and β denote quantities subject to the restriction $K(\alpha)$ and γ denotes a quantity subject to the restriction $L(\gamma)$, prove:

(a) $\vdash (\alpha)\ P \supset (\mathrm{E}\alpha)\ P$.
(b) $\vdash (\mathrm{E}\alpha)\ F(\alpha). \equiv .(\mathrm{E}\alpha,\beta).F(\alpha)\mathbf{v}F(\beta)$.
(c) $\vdash (\mathrm{E}\alpha)\ P.(\alpha)\ Q. \supset .(\mathrm{E}\alpha).PQ$.
(d) $\vdash (\alpha,\gamma).P \supset Q{:} \supset {:}(\alpha,\gamma)\ P. \supset .(\alpha,\gamma)\ Q$.

(e) $\vdash (\alpha)(E\gamma).P \supset Q: \supset :(E\alpha)(\gamma)\ P. \supset .(E\alpha,\gamma)\ Q.$
(f) $\vdash (\alpha).P \mathbf{v} Q: \supset :(\alpha)\ P.\mathbf{v}.(E\alpha)\ Q.$
(g) $\vdash (\alpha)\ P.\mathbf{v}.(E\alpha)\ Q: \supset :(E\alpha).P \mathbf{v} Q.$
(h) $\vdash (E\alpha)\ P. \supset .(\alpha)\ Q: \supset :(\alpha).P \supset Q.$
(i) $\vdash (E\alpha)\ P. \supset .(E\alpha)\ Q: \supset :(E\alpha).P \supset Q.$
(j) $\vdash (\alpha)\ P. \supset .(\alpha)\ Q: \supset :(E\alpha).P \supset Q.$

VI.8.2. On November 22, 1948, in Pop's place, three consecutive song titles in the juke box were "Everybody loves somebody," "I never loved anyone," and "Somebody loves me." In order to avoid complications due to tenses, let us rewrite the second as "I do not love anyone." Let us refer to them, in the order given, as A, B, and C. Using "I" to stand for "I" or "me" according to grammatical position, and $L(x,y)$ to stand for "x loves y," translate each of the above song titles, using x, y, and z as variables with their ranges restricted to people. State and prove all provable implications of the form $\vdash W \supset V$, where each of W and V is one of A, $\sim A$, B, $\sim B$, C, or $\sim C$.

VI.8.3. Using restricted quantification translate "For every positive ε there is a positive integer m such that for every greater positive integer n, $| a_m - a_n | < \varepsilon$" into symbolic logic; also write the dual of this statement.

VI.8.4. Prove that $\vdash (\alpha_1, \alpha_2, \ldots, \alpha_n).P \supset Q: \supset :(\alpha_1, \alpha_2, \ldots, \alpha_n)\ P. \supset .$ $(\alpha_1, \alpha_2, \ldots, \alpha_n)\ Q$, regardless of whether any of the α's are restricted or whether the restricted α's have the same restriction or not.

VI.8.5. Let P have no free occurrences of any variable. Let Q be got from P by replacing all quantifiers of P by restricted quantifiers, all having identical restrictions. Show that, if P can be deduced from Axiom schemes 1 to 6 by modus ponens, then so can Q. (*Hint.* Let $S_1, S_2, \ldots, S_s$ be a demonstration of $\vdash P$, using only Axiom schemes 1 to 6. Let Σ_i be related to S_i as Q is related to P. Let $x_1, \ldots, x_n$ be all variables which occur free in any of $S_1, \ldots, S_s$. Using Ex.VI.8.4 at the points where modus ponens was used with the S's, prove $\vdash (x_1, \ldots, x_n)\ \Sigma_i$ for $1 \leq i \leq s$, where in $(x_1, \ldots, x_n)\ \Sigma_i$ all quantifiers have the same restrictions as in Q. Then get $\vdash Q$ from $\vdash (x_1, \ldots, x_n)\ Q$ by the generalized form of Thm.VI.6.6, Part I.)

VI.8.6. Indicate that the result of the preceding exercise would fail to hold generally if different quantifiers in Q are allowed to have different restrictions, and state where the proof in the preceding exercise would break down. (*Hint.* Take P to be $(x)\ F(x). \equiv .(y)\ F(y)$.)

9. Applications to Everyday Mathematics. At the end of Chapter II, we listed a number of rules of everyday logic which could be derived by truth tables. We are now in a position to extend the list of rules of everyday logic considerably by giving rules derived from results of the present chapter. Perhaps most important are the intuitive equivalents of rule G and rule C. However, we need not discuss them further here, since we have already discussed them at length in Secs. 4 and 7 of the present chapter.

The duality theorem is very useful, and indeed special cases of it are in common use in analysis. By means of the duality theorem, we can write variants of the principle "If $\sim Q \supset \sim P$, then $P \supset Q$," to wit:

If $Q^* \supset \sim P$, then $P \supset Q$.
If $\sim Q \supset P^*$, then $P \supset Q$.
If $Q^* \supset P^*$, then $P \supset Q$.

Here P^* and Q^* denote the duals of P and Q. Similarly (as noted earlier) we get variants of the principle of reductio ad absurdum, to wit:

Assume P^* and deduce $Q{\sim}Q$.
Assume $\sim P$ and deduce QQ^*.
Assume P^* and deduce QQ^*.

One can write similar variants of various other of the principles by replacing $\sim P$ by P^*, $\sim Q$ by Q^*, etc. We mention one particularly useful one, namely, the proof of $P \equiv Q$ by proving each of $P \supset Q$ and $P^* \supset Q^*$.

By the deduction theorem, we get $\vdash P \supset Q$ whenever we can show $P \vdash Q$. This is very useful when taken in conjunction with various powerful ways of inferring $P \vdash Q$, notably Thm.VI.7.2. The reader is reminded that he can also infer $\vdash P \supset Q$ from any of $\sim Q \vdash \sim P$, $Q^* \vdash \sim P$, $\sim Q \vdash P^*$, or $Q^* \vdash P^*$.

In this connection, there is an important consideration having to do with proofs by reductio ad absurdum. To prove $\vdash P$, it suffices to prove $\vdash \sim P \supset Q{\sim}Q$, and so it suffices to prove $\sim P \vdash Q{\sim}Q$, for which it suffices to prove $\sim P \vdash_C Q{\sim}Q$ if there are no free $y_1, y_2, \ldots, y_m$ in Q (where $y_1, y_2, \ldots, y_m$ are the y's used with rule C in the proof of $\sim P \vdash_C Q{\sim}Q$). The important point to note is that, in the special case under consideration, it is permissible that some or all of $y_1, y_2, \ldots, y_m$ occur free in Q. For from $\sim P \vdash_C Q{\sim}Q$, we get $\sim P \vdash_C R{\sim}R$ without additional uses of rule G or rule C by Thm.VI.6.1, Part LXV. This can be done regardless of what we take R to be, and so we can choose an R with no free occurrences of $y_1, y_2, \ldots, y_m$. For instance, we could take R to be $(y_1, y_2, \ldots, y_m)\ S$. So to infer $\vdash P$, it suffices to prove $\sim P \vdash_C Q{\sim}Q$ quite regardless of what variables occur free in Q.

The duality theorem and its corollary give a powerful means of proving equivalences, which are then useful either in their own right or in connection with the substitution theorem. One can often simplify the proof of a theorem by replacing some portion of it by an equivalent portion, which is permitted by the substitution theorem.

To prove statements of the form $(x)\ P$, we have Thm.VI.4.1 and Thm.VI.4.2. More generally, we can apply rule G and then use Thm.VI.7.1

or VI.7.2. An alternative, and not uncommon, procedure is to use reductio ad absurdum, of which the most common variation is to start with the dual of $(x)\ P$, namely, $(\mathrm{E}x)\ P^*$, use rule C, and then proceed to a contradiction.

With the axioms presently at our disposal, we cannot prove $(\mathrm{E}x)\ P$ for any P's of real interest. The only procedure we have as yet for proving statements of the form $(\mathrm{E}x)\ P$, except for general methods such as reductio ad absurdum, is that furnished by Thm.VI.7.3. Among the axioms which we shall later add will be some whose primary purpose is to prove additional statements of the form $(\mathrm{E}x)\ P$.

We now give a number of illustrations from everyday mathematics.

THEOREM. The derived set of a point set is closed.

We use restricted quantification, letting δ and ε denote positive real numbers, and x, y, and z denote points. We also use the notation $x \in \alpha$ to denote that x is a member of α. We recall some definitions.

"x is a limit point of α if for every positive ε there is a point of α different from x whose distance from x is less than ε."

In symbols:

$$(\varepsilon)(\mathrm{E}y).y \neq x.y \in \alpha.|\ x - y\ | < \varepsilon.$$

"α is a closed set if all limit points of α are in α."

In symbols:

$$(x):.(\varepsilon)(\mathrm{E}y).y \neq x.y \in \alpha.|\ x - y\ | < \varepsilon: \supset :x \in \alpha.$$

"β is the derived set of α if β consists of all limit points of α."

In symbols:

(1) $$(x):.(\varepsilon)(\mathrm{E}y).y \neq x.y \in \alpha.|\ x - y\ | < \varepsilon: \equiv :x \in \beta.$$

Proof. To prove our theorem, we must show that from (1) we can infer

$$(x):.(\varepsilon)(\mathrm{E}y).y \neq x.y \in \beta.|\ x - y\ | < \varepsilon: \supset :x \in \beta.$$

Let us first give the proof in words, as it might appear in a text on analysis.

Let x be a limit point of β. Let $\varepsilon > 0$. Then $\varepsilon/2 > 0$, and we can choose a point y in β different from x whose distance from x is less than $\varepsilon/2$. Since $y \neq x$, $|\ x - y\ | > 0$, and so since y is in β, and hence is a limit point of α, we can choose a point z in α different from y whose distance from y is less than $|\ x - y\ |$. Since $|\ y - z\ | < |\ x - y\ |$, we have $z \neq x$ and $|\ y - z\ | < \varepsilon/2$. So $|\ x - z\ | = |\ (x - y) + (y - z)\ | \leq |\ x - y\ | + |\ y - z\ | < \varepsilon/2 + \varepsilon/2 \leq \varepsilon$. So we have found a z in α different from x with $|\ x - z\ | < \varepsilon$. Hence x is a limit point of α, and so x is in β.

We now give a formal proof, filling in the full logical details. Insertion of the full details lengthens the proof considerably.

Let us assume that β is the derived set of α,

(1) $$(x):.(\varepsilon)(\mathrm{E}y).y \neq x.y \in \alpha.|x - y| < \varepsilon: \equiv :x \in \beta,$$

that x is a limit point of β,

(2) $$(\varepsilon)(\mathrm{E}y).y \neq x.y \in \beta.|x - y| < \varepsilon,$$

and that ε is positive,

(3) $$\varepsilon > 0.$$

By (3), we get

(4) $$\varepsilon/2 > 0.$$

By (2), Axiom scheme 6, and (4), we get

(5) $$(\mathrm{E}y).y \neq x.y \in \beta.|x - y| < \varepsilon/2.$$

The procedure which we carried out to get step (5) is standard, but as this is our first use of it we shall go through it again in slow motion.

Since we are using restricted quantification, (2) signifies

$$(w):w > 0. \supset .(\mathrm{E}y).y \neq x.y \in \beta.|x - y| < w.$$

Now, by Axiom scheme 6,

$$\vdash (w)\, F(w). \supset .F(\varepsilon/2),$$

and so we get

$$\varepsilon/2 > 0. \supset .(\mathrm{E}y).y \neq x.y \in \beta.|x - y| < \varepsilon/2.$$

Now by (4) and modus ponens we get (5).

Applying rule C to (5), and recalling that we are dealing with restricted quantification, we get

(6) y is a point,

(7) $$y \neq x,$$

(8) $$y \in \beta,$$

(9) $$|x - y| < \varepsilon/2.$$

From (1), we get

$$(x):.(\varepsilon)(\mathrm{E}z).z \neq x.z \in \alpha.|x - z| < \varepsilon: \equiv :x \in \beta.$$

From this by Axiom scheme 6 and (6) we get

$$(\varepsilon)(\mathrm{E}z).z \neq y.z \in \alpha.|y - z| < \varepsilon: \equiv :y \in \beta.$$

From this and (8), we get

(10) $$(\varepsilon)(\mathrm{E}z).z \neq y.z \in \alpha.|\, y - z\,| < \varepsilon.$$

From (7), we get

(11) $$|\, x - y\,| > 0.$$

From (10) by Axiom scheme 6 and (11), we get

(12) $$(\mathrm{E}z).z \neq y.z \in \alpha.|\, y - z\,| < |\, x - y\,|.$$

By rule C,

(13) z is a point,

(14) $$z \neq y,$$

(15) $$z \in \alpha,$$

(16) $$|\, y - z\,| < |\, x - y\,|.$$

By (16),

(17) $$z \neq x.$$

By (16) and (9)

(18) $$|\, y - z\,| < \varepsilon/2.$$

By (18) and (9),

(19) $$|\, x - z\,| < \varepsilon.$$

(Here we have skipped a couple of purely mathematical steps. See our verbal proof.) Collecting (13), (17), (15), and (19), we have

(20) z is a point $.z \neq x.z \in \alpha.|\, x - z\,| < \varepsilon.$

So by Thm.VI.7.3,

(21) $$(\mathrm{E}z).z \neq x.z \in \alpha.|\, x - z\,| < \varepsilon.$$

So by Thm.VI.6.8, Part II,

(22) $$(\mathrm{E}y).y \neq x.y \in \alpha.|\, x - y\,| < \varepsilon.$$

We have shown

$$(1), (2), (3) \vdash_C (22).$$

As neither y nor z occurs free in (22), we get

$$(1), (2), (3) \vdash (22).$$

That is,

$$(1), (2), \varepsilon > 0 \vdash (\mathrm{E}y).y \neq x.y \in \alpha.|\, x - y\,| < \varepsilon.$$

So by the deduction theorem and the generalization theorem

$$(1), (2), \vdash (\varepsilon)(\mathrm{E}y).y \neq x.y \in \alpha.|\, x - y \,| < \varepsilon.$$

However, by Axiom scheme 6,

$$(1), x \text{ is a point} \vdash (\varepsilon)(\mathrm{E}y).y \neq x.y \in \alpha.|\, x - y \,| < \varepsilon: \equiv :x \in \beta.$$

So

$$(1), x \text{ is a point}, (2) \vdash x \in \beta.$$

Then by the deduction theorem,

$$(1), x \text{ is a point} \vdash (2) \supset x \in \beta.$$

That is,

$$(1), x \text{ is a point} \vdash (\varepsilon)(\mathrm{E}y).y \neq x.y \in \beta.|\, x - y \,| < \varepsilon: \supset :x \in \beta.$$

Then by the deduction theorem and the generalization theorem,

$$(1) \vdash (x):.(\varepsilon)(\mathrm{E}y).y \neq x.y \in \beta.|\, x - y \,| < \varepsilon: \supset :x \in \beta.$$

Then our theorem follows by the deduction theorem.

We now give a more complicated instance.

THEOREM. If in a region R each f_n is continuous, and f_n converges uniformly to f in R, then f is continuous in R.

We use restricted quantification, letting δ and ε denote positive real numbers, x, y, and z denote points of R, and m and n denote positive integers. Then

$$(x,\varepsilon)(\mathrm{E}\delta)(y):|\, x - y \,| < \delta. \supset .|\, f(x) - f(y) \,| < \varepsilon$$

is the statement that f is continuous in R, and

$$(\varepsilon)(\mathrm{E}n)(m,x):m > n. \supset .|\, f(x) - f_m(x) \,| < \varepsilon$$

is the statement that f_n converges uniformly to f in R.

Proof. Let us first give the proof in words, as it might appear in a text on analysis or advanced calculus.

Given $\varepsilon > 0$, choose n so that, for $m > n$, $|\, f(x) - f_m(x) \,| < \varepsilon/3$. Then choose δ so that, for $|\, x - y \,| < \delta$, $|\, f_{n+1}(x) - f_{n+1}(y) \,| < \varepsilon/3$.

Then

$$\begin{aligned} |\, f(x) - f(y) \,| & \\ &= |\, (f(x) - f_{n+1}(x)) + (f_{n+1}(x) - f_{n+1}(y)) + (f_{n+1}(y) - f(y)) \,| \\ &\leq |\, f(x) - f_{n+1}(x) \,| + |\, f_{n+1}(x) - f_{n+1}(y) \,| + |\, f(y) - f_{n+1}(y) \,| \\ &< \varepsilon/3 + \varepsilon/3 + \varepsilon/3 \leq \varepsilon. \end{aligned}$$

So, whenever $|\, x - y \,| < \delta$, $|\, f(x) - f(y) \,| < \varepsilon$, and so f is continuous in R.

Let us now give a formal proof, filling in the full logical details, which considerably lengthens the proof. We let $n \epsilon PI$, $x \epsilon R$, and $\varepsilon > 0$ denote "n is a positive integer," "x is a point of R," and "ε is a positive real number." We first prove:

Lemma. $x \epsilon R,\ (x).|\ f(x) - f_{n+1}(x)\ | < \varepsilon/3,\ (y):|\ x - y\ | < \delta. \supset .\ |\ f_{n+1}(x) - f_{n+1}(y)\ | < \varepsilon/3 \vdash (y):|\ x - y\ | < \delta. \supset .|\ f(x) - f(y)\ | < \varepsilon.$

Proof. Assume

(i) $$x \epsilon R,$$

(ii) $$(x).|\ f(x) - f_{n+1}(x)\ | < \varepsilon/3,$$

(iii) $$(y):|\ x - y\ | < \delta. \supset .|\ f_{n+1}(x) - f_{n+1}(y)\ | < \varepsilon/3,$$

(iv) $$y \epsilon R,$$

(v) $$|\ x - y\ | < \delta.$$

By (ii), Axiom scheme 6, and (i), we get

(vi) $$|\ f(x) - f_{n+1}(x)\ | < \varepsilon/3.$$

By (ii), Axiom scheme 6, and (iv), we get

(vii) $$|\ f(y) - f_{n+1}(y)\ | < \varepsilon/3.$$

By (iii), Axiom scheme 6, and (iv), we get

$$|\ x - y\ | < \delta. \supset .|\ f_{n+1}(x) - f_{n+1}(y)\ | < \varepsilon/3,$$

so that by (v), we get

(viii) $$f_{n+1}(x) - f_{n+1}(y)\ | < \varepsilon/3.$$

By (vi), (vii), and (viii), together with certain mathematical theorems, we get

(ix) $$|\ f(x) - f(y)\ | < \varepsilon.$$

So we have shown

$$\text{(i), (ii), (iii)},\ y \epsilon R,\ |\ x - y\ | < \delta \vdash |\ f(x) - f(y)\ | < \varepsilon.$$

So two uses of the deduction theorem give

$$\text{(i), (ii), (iii)} \vdash y \epsilon R. \supset :|\ x - y\ | < \delta. \supset .|\ f(x) - f(y)\ | < \varepsilon.$$

Then we can use the generalization theorem to infer

$$\text{(i), (ii), (iii)} \vdash (y):|\ x - y\ | < \delta. \supset .|\ f(x) - f(y)\ | < \varepsilon.$$

This is our lemma.

Now assume that each f_n is continuous in R,

(1) $$(n,x,\varepsilon)(\mathrm{E}\delta)(y):|\, x - y \,| < \delta . \supset .|\, f_n(x) - f_n(y) \,| < \varepsilon,$$

that f_n converges uniformly to f in R,

(2) $$(\varepsilon)(\mathrm{E}n)(m,x):m > n . \supset .|\, f(x) - f_m(x) \,| < \varepsilon,$$

that x is a point of R,

(3) $$x \epsilon R,$$

and that ε is positive,

(4) $$\varepsilon > 0.$$

Then

(5) $$\varepsilon/3 > 0,$$

and so by (2),

(6) $$(\mathrm{E}n)(m,x):m > n . \supset .|\, f(x) - f_m(x) \,| < \varepsilon/3.$$

Then by rule C,

(7) $$n \epsilon PI,$$

(8) $$(m,x):m > n . \supset .|\, f(x) - f_m(x) \,| < \varepsilon/3.$$

From (8), by Thm.VI.6.6, Part IX,

(9) $$(m):m > n . \supset .(x).|\, f(x) - f_m(x) \,| < \varepsilon/3.$$

Now, by (7), we get $n + 1 \epsilon PI$, so that by (9) we have

(10) $$n + 1 > n . \supset .(x).|\, f(x) - f_{n+1}(x) \,| < \varepsilon/3.$$

Also by (7), $n + 1 > n$, so that

(11) $$(x).|\, f(x) - f_{n+1}(x) \,| < \varepsilon/3.$$

Since $n + 1 \epsilon PI$ by (7), we get by (1),

$$(x,\varepsilon)(\mathrm{E}\delta)(y):|\, x - y \,| < \delta . \supset .|\, f_{n+1}(x) - f_{n+1}(y) \,| < \varepsilon.$$

Then by (3),

$$(\varepsilon)(\mathrm{E}\delta)(y):|\, x - y \,| < \delta . \supset .|\, f_{n+1}(x) - f_{n+1}(y) \,| < \varepsilon.$$

Then by (5),

$$(\mathrm{E}\delta)(y):|\, x - y \,| < \delta . \supset .|\, f_{n+1}(x) - f_{n+1}(y) \,| < \varepsilon/3.$$

So by rule C

(12) $$\delta > 0,$$

(13) $$(y):|\, x - y \,| < \delta. \supset .|\, f_{n+1}(x) - f_{n+1}(y) \,| < \varepsilon/3.$$

Now by our lemma, (3), (11), and (13), we get (with no additional uses of rule G or rule C),

(14) $$(y):|\, x - y \,| < \delta. \supset .|\, f(x) - f(y) \,| < \varepsilon.$$

So by Thm.VI.7.3,

(15) $$(E\delta)(y):|\, x - y \,| < \delta. \supset .|\, f(x) - f(y) \,| < \varepsilon.$$

We have now shown

$$(1),\ (2),\ x \in R,\ \varepsilon > 0 \vdash_C (E\delta)(y):|\, x - y \,| < \delta. \supset .|\, f(x) - f(y) \,| < \varepsilon.$$

As neither n nor δ occurs free in the conclusion of this, we can replace $\vdash_C$ by $\vdash$. Then by the deduction theorem and the generalization theorem, we infer

$$(1),\ (2),\ x \in R \vdash (\varepsilon)(E\delta)(y):|\, x - y \,| < \delta. \supset .|\, f(x) - f(y) \,| < \varepsilon.$$

Using the deduction theorem and generalization theorem again gives

$$(1),\ (2) \vdash (x,\varepsilon)(E\delta)(y):|\, x - y \,| < \delta. \supset .|\, f(x) - f(y) \,| < \varepsilon.$$

Our theorem now follows by two more uses of the deduction theorem.

By using Thm.VI.8.1, we could have avoided having to prove a preliminary lemma in the previous proof. That is, by using Thm.VI.8.1, we could have kept the formal proof closer to the intuitive proof.

We have filled in full logical details in the above proofs to illustrate the logical principles involved. The reader should not suppose that it is necessary to fill in the full logical details in order to have a correct formal proof. All that is necessary is to furnish enough details so that the reader can reconstruct a proof with full details if called upon to do so. How many details are required for this purpose depends on the reader's experience. As the reader becomes more experienced, fewer details need to be supplied. It will be our policy to give fewer and fewer details as we proceed and the reader acquires experience. Thus, at first we wrote out demonstrations in full, then we quickly changed to merely indicating key steps, and we now give fewer and fewer of these. Even in the last two proofs, where we were supposedly giving full details, we have progressively diminished the amount of detail given. For example, in the first proof, we gave the full details of how to get from steps (2) and (4) to (5). In the second proof we make the analogous step from (2) and (5) to (6) without comment.

We now present one more illustration which is of particular logical interest. In his doctor's thesis, M. D. Donsker needed an upper bound for the Lebesgue measure of the set of all real numbers t such that

$$(\mathrm{E}x):.(m,n):1 \leq n \leq N.\left[\frac{M(n-1)}{N}\right] < m \leq \left[\frac{Mn}{N}\right].$$

$$\supset .\phi(x,m,n):.(\mathrm{E}m,n):1 \leq m \leq M.1 \leq n \leq N.$$

$$\frac{m-1}{M} < t \leq \frac{m}{M}.\frac{n-1}{N} < t \leq \frac{n}{N}.{\sim}\phi(x,m,n),$$

where we are using restricted quantification with x representing a point in many-dimensional space and m and n representing positive integers. M and N are fixed positive integers, $[w]$ denotes the greatest integer less than or equal to w, and $\phi(x,m,n)$ is a very complicated statement involving x, m, and n. The details of $\phi(x,m,n)$ need not concern us. Let us denote the above condition on t by $F(t)$, and denote the set of all t's such that $F(t)$ by T. Donsker got an upper bound on the measure of T by showing that T is a subset of a set T' of all real numbers t such that

$$(\mathrm{E}n).1 \leq n \leq N.\frac{n-1}{N} < t \leq \frac{n}{N}.\left[\frac{Mn}{N}\right] < Mt.$$

We denote this condition by $G(t)$. It is not particularly difficult to get an upper bound for the measure of T'. So the only difficulty is to show that T is indeed a subset of T'. For this it is sufficient (and necessary) to show $(t).F(t) \supset G(t)$. This is done by showing $(t).G^*(t) \supset F^*(t)$, where $G^*(t)$ and $F^*(t)$ are the duals of $F(t)$ and $G(t)$. Since t is a real number we can write $G(t)$ in the equivalent form

$$(\mathrm{E}n).1 \leq n \leq N.\frac{n-1}{N} < t \leq \frac{n}{N}.{\sim}\left(Mt \leq \left[\frac{Mn}{N}\right]\right).$$

Then $G^*(t)$ has the form

$$(n):1 \leq n \leq N.\frac{n-1}{N} < t \leq \frac{n}{N}. \supset .Mt \leq \left[\frac{Mn}{N}\right].$$

Then $(t).G^*(t) \supset F^*(t)$ has the form

$$(t)::(n):1 \leq n \leq N.\frac{n-1}{N} < t \leq \frac{n}{N}. \supset .Mt \leq \left[\frac{Mn}{N}\right].: \supset :.(x):.$$

$$(m,n):1 \leq n \leq N.\left[\frac{M(n-1)}{N}\right] < m \leq \left[\frac{Mn}{N}\right]. \supset .\phi(x,m,n): \supset :$$

$$(m,n):1 \leq m \leq M.1 \leq n \leq N.\frac{m-1}{M} < t \leq \frac{m}{M}.$$

$$\frac{n-1}{N} < t \leq \frac{n}{N}. \supset .\phi(x,m,n).$$

In spite of its apparent complication, this is very easy to prove. We assume

(1) $$(n):1 \leq n \leq N.\frac{n-1}{N} < t \leq \frac{n}{N}. \supset .Mt \leq \left[\frac{Mn}{N}\right],$$

(2) x is a point,

(3) $$(m,n):1 \leq n \leq N.\left[\frac{M(n-1)}{N}\right] < m \leq \left[\frac{Mn}{N}\right]. \supset .\phi(x,m,n),$$

(4) $m \epsilon PI,$

(5) $n \epsilon PI,$

(6) $1 \leq m \leq M,$

(7) $1 \leq n \leq N,$

(8) $$\frac{m-1}{M} < t \leq \frac{m}{M},$$

(9) $$\frac{n-1}{N} < t \leq \frac{n}{N},$$

and undertake to prove $\phi(x,m,n)$. By (8) and (9),

$$\frac{M(n-1)}{N} < Mt \leq m,$$

so that

(10) $$\left[\frac{M(n-1)}{N}\right] < m.$$

Also, by (1), (5), (7), and (9),

$$Mt \leq \left[\frac{Mn}{N}\right],$$

and so by (8),

$$m - 1 < \left[\frac{Mn}{N}\right].$$

Since m and $\left[\frac{Mn}{N}\right]$ are each integers, we get

(11) $$m \leq \left[\frac{Mn}{N}\right].$$

Now by (3), (4), (5), (7), (10), and (11), we get

(12) $\phi(x,m,n).$

Now $(t).G^*(t) \supset F^*(t)$ follows by repeated applications of the deduction theorem and the generalization theorem.

Actually, Donsker used the procedure above to discover what formula he should use for $G(t)$. In the proof outlined above, (1) is $G^*(t)$. To discover $G(t)$, Donsker merely chose a $G^*(t)$ which if combined with (2) to (9), inclusive, would enable him to prove $\phi(x,m,n)$. Then $G(t)$ resulted from dualizing.

EXERCISES

VI.9.1. Write out a formal version of a proof of the result that, if $\lim_{n\to\infty} a_n = a$ and $\lim_{n\to\infty} b_n = b$, then $\lim_{n\to\infty} (a_n + b_n) = a + b$. (For instance, the proof given in Hardy, 1947, pages 129 to 130.)

VI.9.2. In a certain paper, the author was discussing a certain function $S(F)$ whose value was always a positive integer. This author devoted several pages to an intricate proof that "$S(F)$ is odd is a sufficient condition that $(x)\ F(x)$." He then devoted several more pages to an intricate proof that "$S(F)$ is even is a necessary condition that $(\mathrm{E}x) \sim F(x)$." What should one say to this author?

10. Church's Theorem. There is a point in connection with the axioms given so far which is not relevant to the main purpose of this text, but which is of remarkable interest. It concerns the problem of deciding whether or not a given statement can be derived from the six axiom schemes by use of modus ponens.

When we had only the first three axiom schemes, the corresponding problem was readily solvable. We recall that the method of truth-value tables gave a systematic solution, namely, that if a statement P always takes the value T, then it can be derived from the first three axiom schemes by modus ponens, but if P ever takes the value F, then it cannot be so derived.

The problem of finding a systematic procedure which, for a given set of axioms and rules, will tell whether or not any particular arbitrarily chosen statement can be derived from the given set of axioms and rules is called the decision problem for the given set of axioms and rules. The method of truth-value tables gives a solution to the decision problem for the statement calculus (the first three axiom schemes with modus ponens). What about a solution to the decision problem for the predicate calculus (the first six axiom schemes with modus ponens)? So far none has been discovered.

Of course, given a statement P, one can search for a demonstration of it. If such a demonstration is found, then certainly P can be derived from the axioms by modus ponens. But suppose no demonstration is found? Then it might be the case that no demonstration exists, but it could equally well be the case that one had merely given up looking too soon. Thus, one may happen to settle the question of derivability for a particular statement P by finding a demonstration of it, but if one fails to find a demonstration one can conclude nothing about the derivability of P. As a solution of the decision problem must be a method which will infallibly decide the derivability of any arbitrarily chosen statement P, the method of looking for a demonstration does not constitute a solution of the decision problem, however successful one may be in finding demonstrations of particular statements.

As we said, no solution of the decision problem for the predicate calculus has yet been discovered.

We can say much more. There is no solution to be discovered! This result was proved by Alonzo Church (see Church, 1936).

Let there be no misunderstanding here. Church's theorem does not say merely that no solution has been found or that a solution is hard to find. It says that there simply is no solution at all. What is more, the theorem continues to hold as we add further axioms (unless by mischance we add axioms which lead to a contradiction, so that every statement becomes derivable). Applying Church's theorem to our complete set of axioms for mathematics, we conclude that there can never be a systematic or mechanical procedure for solving all mathematical problems. In other words, the mathematician will never be replaced by a machine.

11. A Convention Concerning Bound Variables. Although we permit such expressions as $(x)(x)\ P$, $(x)(\mathrm{E}x)\ P$, etc., for the sake of complete generality, they serve no useful purpose, and we shall encounter them almost not at all. So we shall agree that if we write a formula $(x)\ P$, then if any variables occur bound within P they shall be distinct from x unless we specifically state otherwise. In particular, if we write $(x,y)\ Q$, $(x)(\mathrm{E}z)\ Q$, $(x,y,z)\ Q$, $(\mathrm{E}y,z)\ Q$, etc., then it shall be understood that x and y, or x and z, or x, y, and z, or y and z, etc., are distinct variables unless explicitly stated otherwise.

CHAPTER VII

EQUALITY

1. General Properties. We introduce equality and use the familiar notation $x = y$. If we were attaching meanings to our statements, the meaning of $x = y$ would be that x and y are two names of the same identical object. We place no restrictions on the nature of the object, so that we shall have equality not only between numbers (names of numbers, really), as is common in mathematics, but between sets, or between functions, or indeed between the names of any logical object.

We utilize the familiar symbolism, $x \neq y$, for $\sim(x = y)$. In the matter of parentheses, we shall enclose $x = y$ or $x \neq y$ in parentheses whenever necessary to avoid confusion, but if no parentheses are written, one is to understand the parentheses with the smallest possible scope.

If x and y are variables, the indicated occurrences of x and y are free in $x = y$, and no other occurrences of any variable are free in $x = y$. The significance of these remarks will become clear when we introduce a definition of $x = y$ in Chapter IX.

The familiar property of equals is:

"A quantity may be substituted for its equal in any equation or inequality."

We take it in the more general form:

"A quantity may be substituted for its equal in any statement."

In symbols, this takes the form:

Axiom scheme 7A. Let $x_1, x_2, \ldots, x_n, x, y, z$ be variables, of which x, y, and z are distinct, but of which $x_1, x_2, \ldots, x_n$ need not be distinct either from each other or from x, y, or z. Let P be a statement which contains no bound occurrences of x or y. Let Q and R be the results of replacing all free occurrences of z in P by occurrences of x and y, respectively. Then

$$(x_1, x_2, \ldots, x_n)(x,y)\!:\!x = y. \supset .Q \supset R$$

is an axiom.

That is, if P is $F(x,y,z)$, then Axiom scheme 7A says:

$$(x,y)\!:\!x = y. \supset .F(x,y,x) \supset F(x,y,y).$$

In words, if $x = y$, then one may replace some (or none or all) of the x's of any statement $F(x,y,x)$ by y's (getting $F(x,y,y)$).

The requirement that P (or $F(x,y,z)$) contain no bound occurrences of x or y is not really restrictive. In any special case, one can replace some free x's of an arbitrary Q by y's by first using Thm.VI.6.8 to replace all bound x's and y's by other letters, then using Axiom scheme 7A to replace the free x's by free y's, and finally using Thm.VI.6.8 to change the bound letters back again.

The familiar wording, "A quantity may be substituted for its equal in any statement," as a paraphrase for Axiom scheme 7A is actually quite incorrect and thoroughly misleading. As we saw in Chapter III, a quantity cannot appear in a statement about the quantity, and if it could so appear, it would be ridiculous to speak of replacing the quantity by its equal because its equal could not conceivably be anything other than the quantity itself. Actually, not the quantity but a name of it appears in any statement about it, and Axiom scheme 7A merely says that we may replace that name by any other name of the same quantity. Needless to say, if we should have a statement about the name rather than a statement containing the name, Axiom scheme 7A would not permit replacement by some other name of the same quantity.

In other words, one is to put "=" between two names if and only if they are names of the same object. The resulting statement about the object, that it does not differ from itself in any way, is of an excessive degree of triviality. Nevertheless the statement does call our attention to the fact of the two names being names of the same object, and hence justifies our using the names interchangeably in statements about the object. This is the sole meaning of Axiom scheme 7A.

Thus if we write "$\frac{3}{4} = \frac{9}{12}$," we indicate that "3/4" and "9/12" are names of the same number. Then if we have any statement about this number containing one of the names, say "$\frac{3}{4} < 3$," we may use the other name in this statement, to wit: "$\frac{9}{12} < 3$." If, on the other hand, we have a statement about one of the names, we are not entitled to make the same statement about the other name. Thus "the denominator of '$\frac{3}{4}$' is not divisible by 3" is true whereas "the denominator of '$\frac{9}{12}$' is not divisible by 3" is false.

Besides Axiom scheme 7A, we need:

Axiom scheme 7B. Let $x_1, x_2, \ldots, x_n, x$ be variables, not necessarily distinct. Then

$$(x_1, x_2, \ldots, x_n)(x)\ x = x$$

is an axiom.

The property $x = x$ is called the reflexive property of equality.

Later, after further ideas have been introduced, we shall be able to define equality in terms of these further ideas. We shall then be able to replace Axiom scheme 7A and Axiom scheme 7B by a single Axiom scheme 7. This is why we are counting Axiom scheme 7A and 7B as parts of one axiom scheme instead of as two axiom schemes.

We now prove the symmetric property of equality:

***Theorem VII.1.1.** $\vdash (x,y).x = y \supset y = x.$

Proof. Take P to be $z = x$ in Axiom scheme 7A. Then Q is $x = x$ and R is $y = x$. So by Axiom scheme 7A, $\vdash x = y. \supset .x = x \supset y = x$. So $\vdash x = x. \supset .x = y \supset y = x$. So our theorem follows by Axiom scheme 7B.

By our convention stated at the end of Chapter VI, x and y denote distinct variables in this theorem. A similar remark applies to subsequent theorems.

We now prove the transitive property of equality:

****Theorem VII.1.2.** $\vdash (x,y,z):x = y.y = z. \supset .x = z.$

Proof. By Thm.VI.6.8, it suffices to prove

$$\vdash (w,x,y):w = x.x = y. \supset .w = y.$$

Take P to be $w = z$ in Axiom scheme 7A. Then Q is $w = x$ and R is $w = y$. So by Axiom scheme 7A,

$$\vdash x = y. \supset .w = x \supset w = y.$$

From this, our theorem follows.

This is commonly stated as "Things equal to the same thing are equal to each other." However, this is not quite an accurate rendering of the meaning of the theorem. A more accurate version would be "If x and y are names of the same object, and y and z are names of the same object, then x and z are names of the same object."

Theorem VII.1.3. $\vdash (x,y):x = y. \supset .F(x) \supset F(y).$

Proof. Let the x, y, and z of Axiom scheme 7A be taken to be three distinct variables u, v, w which do not occur at all in $F(x)$ or $F(y)$. Then $F(w)$, $F(u)$, and $F(v)$ play the role of P, Q, and R in Axiom scheme 7A. So by Axiom scheme 7A,

$$\vdash (u,v):u = v. \supset .F(u) \supset F(v).$$

From this our theorem follows by Thm.VI.6.8.

***Theorem VII.1.4.** If x, y, z, P, Q, and R are as in Axiom scheme 7A, then

$$\vdash (x,y):Q{\sim}R. \supset .x \neq y.$$

Proof. This follows from $\vdash (x,y):x = y. \supset .{\sim}(Q{\sim}R)$ by Thm.VI.6.1, Part XLV. In effect this theorem says

$$\vdash (x,y):F(x,y,x).{\sim}F(x,y,y). \supset .x \neq y.$$

This theorem is fairly important, since it is a generalized form of the useful result that, if one can find a statement which is true for x but false for y, then $x \neq y$.

Theorem VII.1.5.

$\star$I. $\vdash (y){:}F(y). \equiv .(\mathrm{E}x).x = y.F(x).$

$\star$II. $\vdash (y){:}F(y). \equiv .(x).x = y \supset F(x).$

Proof of Part I. By Thm.VI.7.3, $\vdash y = y.F(y). \supset .(\mathrm{E}x).x = y.F(x)$. So by Axiom scheme 7B,

$$\vdash F(y). \supset .(\mathrm{E}x).x = y.F(x).$$

Now by Thm.VII.1.3,

$$\vdash (x){:}x = y.F(x). \supset .F(y).$$

So by Thm.VI.6.6, Part VII

$$\vdash (\mathrm{E}x).x = y.F(x){:} \supset {:}F(y).$$

To prove Part II, we put $\sim F(x)$ for $F(x)$ in Part I.

EXERCISES

VII.1.1. Prove $\vdash (x,y){:}x = y. \equiv .y = x.$

VII.1.2. Prove:

(a) $\vdash (x,y,z){:.}x = y{:} \supset {:}x = z. \equiv .y = z.$

(b) $\vdash (x,y,z){:.}x = y{:} \supset {:}x \neq z. \equiv .y \neq z.$

VII.1.3. Prove $\vdash (x,y){:}x = y. \supset .F(x) \equiv F(y).$

VII.1.4. Prove:

(a) $\vdash (y,z){:.}y = z{:} \equiv {:}(x).y = x \supset x = z.$

(b) $\vdash (y,z){:.}y = z{:} \equiv {:}(x){:}y = x. \equiv .x = z.$

VII.1.5. Prove $\vdash (x,y,z){:}x = y.y \neq z. \supset .x \neq z.$

VII.1.6. Prove $\vdash (x)(\mathrm{E}y).y = x.$

VII.1.7. Let α and β be variables subject to the restriction $K(x)$. Prove:

(a) $\vdash K(y)F(y). \equiv .(\mathrm{E}\alpha).\alpha = y.F(\alpha).$

(b) $\vdash (\beta){:}F(\beta). \equiv .(\mathrm{E}\alpha).\alpha = \beta.F(\alpha).$

(c) $\vdash K(y) \supset F(y). \equiv .(\alpha).\alpha = y \supset F(\alpha).$

(d) $\vdash (\beta){:}F(\beta). \equiv .(\alpha).\alpha = \beta \supset F(\alpha).$

2. Enumerative Quantifiers. The statement $(\mathrm{E}x)\ F(x)$ is interpreted as meaning that there is at least one x such that $F(x)$ is true. We shall now show how, for a given positive integer n, we can write formulas whose interpretations would be:

(VII.2.1) "There are at least n different x's such that $F(x)$."
(VII.2.2) "There are at most n different x's such that $F(x)$."
(VII.2.3) "There are exactly n different x's such that $F(x)$."

These are not used sufficiently commonly to warrant a special notation for them. However, throughout the next few paragraphs we shall use the temporary notation $(\mathrm{E}^{(n)}x)\ F(x)$ to denote (VII.2.1). We easily define $(\mathrm{E}^{(n)}x)\ F(x)$ for successively greater n's as follows:

$$(\mathrm{E}^{(1)}x)\ F(x) \equiv (\mathrm{E}x)\ F(x),$$

$$(\mathrm{E}^{(2)}x)\ F(x) : \equiv :(\mathrm{E}x) : F(x) : (\mathrm{E}^{(1)}y) . x \neq y . F(y),$$

$$(\mathrm{E}^{(3)}x)\ F(x) : \equiv :(\mathrm{E}x) : F(x) : (\mathrm{E}^{(2)}y) . x \neq y . F(y),$$

$$(\mathrm{E}^{(4)}x)\ F(x) : \equiv :(\mathrm{E}x) : F(x) : (\mathrm{E}^{(3)}y) . x \neq y . F(y),$$

and so on.

Clearly $\sim(\mathrm{E}^{(n+1)}x)\ F(x)$ will denote (VII.2.2), and $(\mathrm{E}^{(n)}x)\ F(x) . \sim(\mathrm{E}^{(n+1)}x)\ F(x)$ will denote (VII.2.3).

Various other interesting combinations can be written. Thus $(\mathrm{E}^{(n)}x) \sim F(x) . \sim(\mathrm{E}^{(n+1)}x) \sim F(x)$ states that $F(x)$ is true for all but n different x's, and $(\mathrm{E}^{(m)}x)\ F(x) . \sim(\mathrm{E}^{(n-1)}x)\ F(x)$ states that $F(x)$ is true for at least m but at most n different x's.

Of these various notions, only two are sufficiently often used to merit a permanent notation, namely, "$F(x)$ is true for at least one x," for which we have the notation $(\mathrm{E}x)\ F(x)$, and "$F(x)$ is true for exactly one x," for which we shall adopt the notation $(\mathrm{E}_1x)\ F(x)$.

We shall define $(\mathrm{E}_1x)\ F(x)$ as the simplest of several statements equivalent to $(\mathrm{E}^{(1)}x)\ F(x) . \sim(\mathrm{E}^{(2)}x)\ F(x)$. In unabbreviated form, this is

$$(\mathrm{E}x) . F(x) : \sim(\mathrm{E}x) . F(x) . (\mathrm{E}y) . x \neq y . F(y).$$

We shall now show this equivalent to four other statements, the last (and simplest) of which we shall take as the definition of $(\mathrm{E}_1x)\ F(x)$.

***Theorem VII.2.1.**

$$\vdash (\mathrm{E}x) . F(x) : \sim(\mathrm{E}x) . F(x) . (\mathrm{E}y) . x \neq y . F(y) :.$$

$$\equiv :. (\mathrm{E}x) . F(x) : (x,y) : F(x) . F(y) . \supset . x = y :.$$

$$\equiv :. (\mathrm{E}x) : F(x) . (y) . F(y) \supset x = y :.$$

$$\equiv :. (\mathrm{E}x)(y) . x = y \equiv F(y) :.$$

$$\equiv :. (\mathrm{E}y)(x) . y = x \equiv F(x).$$

Proof. Let these five statements be denoted by A, B, C, D, E in the order named. We shall prove $\vdash A \equiv B$, $\vdash B \supset C$, $\vdash C \equiv D$, $\vdash D \supset B$, and $\vdash D \equiv E$, which suffice to prove our theorem.

Proof of $\vdash A \equiv B$. By Thm.VI.6.6, Part VI,

$$\vdash F(x).(\mathrm{E}y).x \neq y.F(y): \equiv :(\mathrm{E}y).F(x).x \neq y.F(y).$$

So

$$\vdash \sim(\mathrm{E}x).F(x).(\mathrm{E}y).x \neq y.F(y): \equiv :\sim(\mathrm{E}x,y).F(x).F(y).x \neq y.$$

By the duality theorem

$$\vdash \sim(\mathrm{E}x,y).F(x).F(y).x \neq y.: \equiv :.(x,y):F(x).F(y). \supset .x = y.$$

We now easily infer $\vdash A \equiv B$.

Proof of $\vdash B \supset C$. We first show $B \vdash_C C$. We assume B, whence we get $(\mathrm{E}x)\ F(x)$ and $(x,y):F(x).F(y). \supset .x = y$. So by rule C and Thm.VI.5.1, $F(x)$ and $(y):F(x).F(y). \supset .x = y$. So $(y):F(x). \supset .F(y) \supset x = y$. So $F(x). \supset .(y).F(y) \supset x = y$. Then by $F(x)$ and modus ponens, we get $(y).F(y) \supset x = y$. Then $F(x).(y).F(y) \supset x = y$. Finally by Thm.VI.7.3, $(\mathrm{E}x):F(x).(y).F(y) \supset x = y$. This is C. We can replace $\vdash_C$ by $\vdash$, and then $\vdash B \supset C$ follows.

Proof of $\vdash C \equiv D$. By Thm.VII.1.5, Part II,

$$\vdash F(x). \equiv .(y).x = y \supset F(y).$$

So by the equivalence theorem

$$\vdash C \equiv :.(\mathrm{E}x):.(y).x = y \supset F(y):(y).F(y) \supset x = y.$$

Then by Thm.VI.6.5, Part I, we get $\vdash C \equiv D$.

Proof of $\vdash D \supset B$. We first show $D \vdash_C B$. We assume D and get

(1) $$(y).x = y \equiv F(y)$$

by rule C. Then $x = x \equiv F(x)$ by Axiom scheme 6, and so $F(x)$ by Axiom scheme 7B, and so

(2) $$(\mathrm{E}x)\ F(x)$$

by Thm.VI.7.3. Let z be a variable different from x and y, which does not appear in $F(y)$. Then by Axiom scheme 6, with (1),

(3) $$x = y \equiv F(y),$$

(4) $$x = z \equiv F(z).$$

However, $\vdash x = z.x = y. \supset .z = y$. So by (3) and (4), $F(z)F(y) \supset z = y$ So by two uses of rule G, $(z,y):F(z).F(y). \supset .z = y$. Then by Thm.VI.6.8, $(x,y):F(x).F(y). \supset .x = y$. Finally by (2),

$$(\mathrm{E}x).F(x):(x,y):F(x).F(y). \supset .x = y.$$

This is B. We can replace $\vdash_C$ by $\vdash$, and then $\vdash D \supset B$ follows.

Proof of $\vdash D \equiv E$. Choose z a variable different from x and y and not appearing in $F(x)$. Then by Thm.VI.6.8,

$$\vdash D \equiv :(\mathrm{E}z)(y).z = y \equiv F(y):$$

$$\equiv :(\mathrm{E}z)(x).z = x \equiv F(x):$$

$$\equiv :(\mathrm{E}y)(x).y = x \equiv F(x).$$

This is $\vdash D \equiv E$.

Note that in A, B, and C, each of $F(x)$ and $F(y)$ occur, and so our convention says that $F(y)$ is the result of replacing all free occurrences of x in $F(x)$ by occurrences of y, and that $F(x)$ is the result of replacing all free occurrences of y in $F(y)$ by occurrences of x. Since only $F(y)$ appears in D and only $F(x)$ appears in E, it is perhaps necessary to state explicitly that our convention applies to D and E also. In particular, in E, there are no free occurrences of y in $F(x)$. Then by Thm.VI.6.8, we can change y to any other variable (except x) with no free occurrences in $F(x)$. This condition that y have no free occurrences in $F(x)$ needs to be stated when we give the definition of $(\mathrm{E}_1x)\ F(x)$.

Definition. If y is a variable distinct from x with no free occurrences in P, then we define $(\mathrm{E}_1x)\ P$ to be $(\mathrm{E}y)(x).y = x \equiv P$.

There are various ways of expressing $(\mathrm{E}_1x)\ F(x)$ in English. For instance:

"$F(x)$ is true for exactly one x."

"$F(x)$ is true for one and only one x."

"For precisely one x, $F(x)$."

"For one and only one x, $F(x)$."

Statement B of the statements proved equivalent in Thm.VII.2.1 is particularly suited to the phraseology "one and only one," since $(\mathrm{E}x)\ F(x)$ indicates that $F(x)$ is true for one x, and $(x,y):F(x).F(y). \supset .x = y$ indicates that $F(x)$ is true for only one x.

Theorem VII.2.2. $\vdash (z)(\mathrm{E}_1x)\ x = z$.

Proof. By Thm.VI.7.3, $\vdash z = z. \supset .(\mathrm{E}y)\ y = z$. So by Axiom scheme 7B, $\vdash (\mathrm{E}y)\ y = z$. Then by Ex.VII.1.4(b), $\vdash (\mathrm{E}y)(x):y = x. \equiv .x = z$. By definition, this is $\vdash (\mathrm{E}_1x)\ x = z$, and our theorem follows.

There is a question as to what $(\mathrm{E}_1\alpha)\ F(\alpha)$ shall denote when α is a variable subject to the restriction $K(\alpha)$. It was agreed that in such case $(\alpha)\ F(\alpha)$ should denote $(x).K(x) \supset F(x)$, and $(\mathrm{E}\alpha)\ F(\alpha)$ should denote $(\mathrm{E}x).K(x).F(x)$. So, by referring to the definition, $(\mathrm{E}_1\alpha)\ F(\alpha)$ denotes $(\mathrm{E}\beta)(\alpha).\beta = \alpha \equiv F(\alpha)$, namely,

$$(\mathrm{E}\beta)(x):K(x). \supset .\beta = x \equiv F(x).$$

The question is whether we should put a restriction on β, and if so what?

It turns out that we should put the same restriction on β that we put on α. So $(\mathrm{E}_1\alpha)\ F(\alpha)$ denotes

$$(\mathrm{E}y){:}K(y){:}(x){:}K(x).\supset .y = x \equiv F(x).$$

This seems awkward, but it enables us to prove the following theorem, which gives us a much simpler, and completely natural, interpretation for $(\mathrm{E}_1\alpha)\ F(\alpha)$.

Theorem VII.2.3. If we are using restricted quantification with α subject to the restriction $K(\alpha)$, then

$$\vdash (\mathrm{E}_1\alpha)\ F(\alpha){:} \equiv {:}(\mathrm{E}_1x).K(x).F(x).$$

Proof. We use two lemmas.

Lemma A.

$$K(y){:}(x){:}K(x).\supset .y = x \equiv F(x) \vdash (x){:}y = x. \equiv .K(x).F(x).$$

Proof. We first establish

$$K(y){:}(x){:}K(x).\supset .y = x \equiv F(x),\ y = x \vdash K(x).F(x),$$

by noting that if we have $K(y)$ and $y = x$, we get $K(x)$ by Thm.VII.1.3, and then from $K(x)$, $y = x$, and $(x){:}K(x).\supset .y = x \equiv F(x)$, we get $F(x)$. We next establish

$$K(y){:}(x){:}K(x).\supset .y = x \equiv F(x),\ K(x).F(x) \vdash y = x$$

for from $K(x)$, $F(x)$, and $(x){:}K(x).\supset .y = x \equiv F(x)$, we get $y = x$. From these two results, our lemma follows.

Lemma B.

$$(x){:}y = x. \equiv .K(x).F(x) \vdash (x){:}K(x).\supset .y = x \equiv F(x).$$

Proof. This follows easily from the two obvious results

$$y = x. \equiv .K(x).F(x),\ K(x),\ y = x \vdash F(x),$$

$$y = x. \equiv .K(x).F(x),\ K(x),\ F(x) \vdash y = x.$$

We now proceed with the proof of our theorem. First assume $(\mathrm{E}_1\alpha)\ F(\alpha)$. Then by rule C

$$K(y){:}(x){:}K(x).\supset .y = x \equiv F(x).$$

So by Lemma A

$$(x){:}y = x. \equiv .K(x).F(x).$$

So $(\mathrm{E}y)(x){:}y = x. \equiv .K(x).F(x)$. This is $(\mathrm{E}_1x).K(x).F(x)$.

Second assume $(\mathrm{E}_1x).K(x).F(x)$. Then by rule C

(1) $$(x){:}y = x. \equiv .K(x).F(x).$$

So by Lemma B,

(2) $$(x):K(x). \supset .y = x \equiv F(x).$$

Also, from (1) by Axiom scheme 6, we get

$$y = y. \equiv .K(y).F(y).$$

So $K(y)$ by Axiom scheme 7B. Hence by (2)

$$K(y):(x):K(x). \supset .y = x \equiv F(x).$$

So

$$(\mathrm{E}y):K(y):(x):K(x). \supset .y = x \equiv F(x).$$

This is $(\mathrm{E}_1\alpha)\ F(\alpha)$.

By making several uses of Thm.VI.8.1, we could avoid the necessity for using lemmas in the proof above.

Because of the theorem just proved, we need not use the strict interpretation for $(\mathrm{E}_1\alpha)\ F(\alpha)$ but can always use the more natural interpretation $(\mathrm{E}_1x).K(x).F(x)$.

EXERCISES

VII.2.1. Let α and β be variables subject to the restriction $K(x)$. Prove:

$$\vdash (\mathrm{E}\alpha).F(\alpha):\sim(\mathrm{E}\alpha).F(\alpha).(\mathrm{E}\beta).\alpha \neq \beta.F(\beta):.$$
$$\equiv :.(\mathrm{E}\alpha).F(\alpha):(\alpha,\beta):F(\alpha).F(\beta). \supset .\alpha = \beta:.$$
$$\equiv :.(\mathrm{E}\alpha):F(\alpha).(\beta).F(\beta) \supset \alpha = \beta:.$$
$$\equiv :.(\mathrm{E}\alpha)(\beta).\alpha = \beta \equiv F(\beta):.$$
$$\equiv :.(\mathrm{E}\beta)(\alpha).\beta = \alpha \equiv F(\alpha).$$

VII.2.2. Let x, y, and z be distinct variables, of which y and z do not occur in P. Prove:

(a) $\vdash (\mathrm{E}_1x)\ P. \supset :.\sim(\mathrm{E}y).Q.(x).y = x \equiv P: \supset :(\mathrm{E}y).\sim Q.(x).y = x \equiv P.$
(b) $\vdash (\mathrm{E}y).\sim Q.(x).y = x \equiv P: \supset :\sim(\mathrm{E}y).Q.(x).y = x \equiv P.$ (*Hint.* Use reductio ad absurdum.)
(c) $\vdash (z)(\mathrm{E}y).Q.(x).y = x \equiv P: \equiv :(\mathrm{E}y).(z)Q.(x).y = x \equiv P.$ (*Hint.* Prove the lemma $\vdash (z)(\mathrm{E}y).Q.(x).y = x \equiv P: \supset :(\mathrm{E}_1x)\ P.$)
(d) $\vdash (\mathrm{E}y).Q.R.(x).y = x \equiv P: \equiv :(\mathrm{E}y).Q.(x).y = x \equiv P:(\mathrm{E}y).R.(x).y = x \equiv P.$

VII.2.3. Prove $\vdash (x).P \equiv Q: \supset :(\mathrm{E}_1x)P \equiv (\mathrm{E}_1x)Q.$
VII.2.4. Prove $\vdash (\mathrm{E}_1x)P \supset (\mathrm{E}x)P.$
VII.2.5. Prove $\vdash (x,y):F(x).F(y). \supset .x = y.: \equiv :.(x,y):F(x).x \neq y. \supset .\sim F(y).$

3. Applications. We can prove the trivial equality $x = x$, and we can derive new equalities from given ones by the commutative and transitive laws of equality. However, we have as yet no direct way to prove any really useful equality, though we shall soon add axiom schemes which will enable us to prove useful equalities. Meanwhile, one can prove equalities by indirect means. Consider the following proof of equality by reductio ad absurdum.

THEOREM. A sequence can have at most one limit. That is, if $\lim_{n\to\infty} a_n = \alpha$ and $\lim_{n\to\infty} a_n = \beta$, then $\alpha = \beta$.

Proof. We use restricted quantification, with m and n denoting positive integers and ε denoting a positive real number. We give the same meaning to "$n \epsilon PI$" and "$\varepsilon > 0$" as before.

We assume $\lim_{n\to\infty} a_n = \alpha$, namely,

(1) $$(\varepsilon)(En)(m).m > n \supset |a_m - \alpha| < \varepsilon.$$

We also assume $\lim_{n\to\infty} a_n = \beta$, namely,

(2) $$(\varepsilon)(En)(m).m > n \supset |a_m - \beta| < \varepsilon.$$

Since we intend to prove $\alpha = \beta$ by reductio ad absurdum, we also assume

(3) $$\alpha \neq \beta.$$

From this we get

(4) $$|\alpha - \beta| > 0,$$

whence we get

(5) $$\tfrac{1}{2}|\alpha - \beta| > 0.$$

Then by (1) and (2)

(6) $$(En)(m).m > n \supset |a_m - \alpha| < \tfrac{1}{2}|\alpha - \beta|,$$

(7) $$(En)(m).m > n \supset |a_m - \beta| < \tfrac{1}{2}|\alpha - \beta|.$$

So by rule C,

(8) $$n \epsilon PI,$$

(9) $$(m).m > n \supset |a_m - \alpha| < \tfrac{1}{2}|\alpha - \beta|,$$

(10) $$N \epsilon PI,$$

(11) $$(m).m > N \supset |a_m - \beta| < \tfrac{1}{2}|\alpha - \beta|.$$

By (8) and (10),

$$n + N \in PI, \tag{12}$$

$$n + N > n, \tag{13}$$

$$n + N > N. \tag{14}$$

Then by (12) and (9)

$$n + N > n \supset |\, a_{n+N} - \alpha \,| < \tfrac{1}{2} \,|\, \alpha - \beta \,|,$$

and by (12) and (11)

$$n + N > N \supset |\, a_{n+N} - \beta \,| < \tfrac{1}{2} \,|\, \alpha - \beta \,|.$$

So by (13) and (14),

$$|\, a_{n+N} - \alpha \,| < \tfrac{1}{2} \,|\, \alpha - \beta \,|, \tag{15}$$

$$|\, a_{n+N} - \beta \,| < \tfrac{1}{2} \,|\, \alpha - \beta \,|. \tag{16}$$

From (15) and (16) by use of some theorems of mathematics, we get

$$\begin{aligned} |\, \alpha - \beta \,| &= |\, -(a_{n+N} - \alpha) + (a_{n+N} - \beta) \,| \\ &\leq |\, a_{n+N} - \alpha \,| + |\, a_{n+N} - \beta \,| \\ &< \tfrac{1}{2} \,|\, \alpha - \beta \,| + \tfrac{1}{2} \,|\, \alpha - \beta \,| \\ &= |\, \alpha - \beta \,|. \end{aligned}$$

So

$$|\, \alpha - \beta \,| < |\, \alpha - \beta \,|. \tag{17}$$

However, this contradicts

$$\sim(|\, \alpha - \beta \,| < |\, \alpha - \beta \,|) \tag{18}$$

which follows from (4) by a known theorem of mathematics.

Strictly speaking, our theorem should have the additional hypothesis that we are operating in a metric space and should read "In a metric space, a sequence can have at most one limit." The reader who is acquainted with metric spaces will recognize that this hypothesis justifies the step from (3) to (4) and the step from (15) and (16) to (17). Needless to say, it would be permissible to make stronger assumptions such as that α, β, and all the a's are real (or complex) numbers.

There is a subtle point in connection with the use of Axiom scheme 7A which is overlooked by all but the most careful writers. Suppose we have

$$\lim_{n \to \infty} a_n = \alpha$$

and $(n).a_n = b_n$. At first sight the step to

$$\lim_{n\to\infty} b_n = \alpha$$

appears to be a simple application of Axiom scheme 7A. However, the situation is more complex than this. By repeated applications of Axiom scheme 7A, we can replace each of a finite number of quantities by its equal. However, in the present situation, we have an infinite number of quantities, a_n, each to be replaced by its equal. This cannot be justified by a direct application of Axiom scheme 7A.

In general, each situation requiring an infinite number of uses of Axiom scheme 7A requires individual attention. We now give a valid proof which covers this situation. It will be noted that the method of procedure is fairly general and can easily be modified to handle other cases. Let us use restricted quantification, with the same conventions as in the preceding proof.

Assume

$$(n)\ a_n = b_n.$$

Then by Axiom scheme 6

$$m \epsilon PI \supset a_m = b_m.$$

So by Ex.VII.1.3,

$$m \epsilon PI{:} \supset {:}.m > n \supset | a_m - \alpha | < \varepsilon{:} \equiv {:}m > n \supset | b_m - \alpha | < \varepsilon.$$

Then by Thm.VI.6.1, Part XXVII,

$$m \epsilon PI. \supset .m > n \supset | a_m - \alpha | < \varepsilon{:} \equiv {:}m \epsilon PI. \supset .m > n \supset | b_m - \alpha | < \varepsilon.$$

So by three uses of Thm.VI.4.2,

$$(\varepsilon,n,m){:}.m \epsilon PI. \supset .m > n \supset | a_m - \alpha | < \varepsilon{:} \equiv {:}m \epsilon PI. \supset .m > n \supset | b_m - \alpha | < \varepsilon,$$

where here we temporarily suspend our convention that we are using restricted quantification with ε, n, and m. Then by Thm.VI.5.4,

$$(\varepsilon)(En)(m).m > n \supset | a_m - \alpha | < \varepsilon{:} \equiv {:}(\varepsilon)(En)(m).m > n \supset | b_m - \alpha | < \varepsilon,$$

where we are now using restricted quantification.

This is the statement

$$\lim_{n\to\infty} a_n = \alpha. \equiv .\lim_{n\to\infty} b_n = \alpha,$$

and we can now proceed from $\lim_{n\to\infty} a_n = \alpha$ to $\lim_{n\to\infty} b_n = \alpha$.

The transitive property of equality is commonly used in everyday mathematics, where it is commonly (and not altogether accurately) paraphrased as "Things equal to the same thing are equal to each other." For instance, to solve the two simultaneous equations $x + y = 5$ and $x + 2y = 7$, we reduce them to $x = 5 - y$ and $x = 7 - 2y$, whence we get $5 - y = 7 - 2y$ by the transitive law.

More commonly, Axiom scheme 7A is used in solving simultaneous equations. Thus, given $x + y = 5$ and $xy = 6$, we get $x = 6/y$ from the second and "substitute" into the first, getting

$$6/y + y = 5.$$

This substitution is merely a use of Axiom scheme 7A. To see this, let $F(z)$ be $z + y = 5$. Then $F(x)$ is $x + y = 5$ and $F(6/y)$ is $6/y + y = 5$. Then Axiom scheme 7A states

$$x = 6/y : \supset : x + y = 5 . \supset . 6/y + y = 5.$$

Another instance of the use of Axiom scheme 7A is in deriving such principles as

$$(x,y,X,Y) : x = y . X = Y . \supset . x + X = y + Y.$$

This is commonly (and not altogether accurately) paraphrased as "If equals are added to equals, the sums are equal." This is derived as follows. First take $F(x,y,z)$ to be $x + X = z + X$ in Axiom scheme 7A, and infer

(1) $$x = y : \supset : x + X = x + X . \supset . x + X = y + X.$$

Now take $F(X,Y,Z)$ to be $x + X = y + Z$ in Axiom scheme 7A, and infer

(2) $$X = Y : \supset : x + X = y + X . \supset . x + X = y + Y.$$

Now by Axiom scheme 7B, we have $x + X = x + X$. So by (1), we get

$$x = y . \supset . x + X = y + X.$$

Combining this with (2) gives

$$x = y . X = Y . \supset . x + X = y + Y.$$

Obviously this proof makes use of no properties of $+$ except that $x + y$ is an object. A precisely similar proof would show

$$(x,y,X,Y) : x = y . X = Y . \supset . xX = yY,$$

$$(x,y,X,Y) : x = y . X = Y . \supset . X^x = Y^y,$$

$$(x,y,X,Y) : x = y . X = Y . \supset . \log_x X = \log_y Y,$$

etc.

We have had an instance of the use of Thm.VII.1.4 on page 154. We had proved

(16) $$| y - z | < | x - y |.$$

We take Thm.VII.1.4 in the form

$$\vdash (z,x):F(z,x,z).\sim F(z,x,x). \supset .z \neq x.$$

We take $F(z,x,z)$ to be (16), and then $F(z,x,x)$ is

$$| y - x | < | x - y |.$$

However, a theorem of mathematics states

$$\sim(| y - x | < | x - y |).$$

So we have $F(z,x,z)$ and $\sim F(z,x,x)$, and hence infer

(17) $$z \neq x.$$

In connection with $(E_1x)\ P$ and related matters, we should like to consider two postulates and three theorems of plane geometry, as given by Wentworth and Smith. We shall use restricted quantification, letting capital roman letters denote points, and small greek letters denote straight lines. Further, we shall adopt the following shorthand notations for geometric ideas:

$\alpha \perp \beta$ . . . . α is perpendicular to β,
$\alpha \parallel \beta$ . . . . α is parallel to β,
A on α . . . . A is on α,
A on α . . . . α passes through A.

On page 23, Wentworth and Smith state Postulate 1:[1]
"One straight line and only one can be drawn through two given points."
In symbols:

$$(A,B):A \neq B. \supset .(E_1\alpha).A \text{ on } \alpha.B \text{ on } \alpha.$$

On page 46 is given the definition of parallel lines:[1]
"Lines that lie in the same plane and cannot meet however far produced are called *parallel lines*."
In symbols:

$$\alpha \parallel \beta: \equiv :\alpha \text{ and } \beta \text{ are in the same plane}:\sim(EA).A \text{ on } \alpha.A \text{ on } \beta.$$

Immediately below the definition of parallel lines is given the parallel postulate:[1]

[1] From "Plane and Solid Geometry" by George Wentworth and D. E. Smith, copyright 1913, courtesy of Ginn & Company.

"Through a given point only one line can be drawn parallel to a given line."

We recall that $(Ex)\,F(x)$ means that there is at least one x such that $F(x)$, and $(x,y){:}F(x).F(y). \supset .x = y$ means that there is only one x such that $F(x)$. So we can render the parallel postulate into symbols as follows:

$$(A,\gamma)(\alpha,\beta){:}\alpha \parallel \gamma.A \text{ on } \alpha.\beta \parallel \gamma.A \text{ on } \beta. \supset .\alpha = \beta.$$

Now let us look at Proposition VIII on page 39:[1]

"Only one perpendicular can be drawn to a given line from a given external point."

In symbols:

$$(A,\gamma){:}.\sim(A \text{ on } \gamma){:} \supset {:}(\alpha,\beta){:}\alpha \perp \gamma.A \text{ on } \alpha.\beta \perp \gamma.A \text{ on } \beta. \supset .\alpha = \beta.$$

Since, by truth values $\vdash PQ \supset R. \equiv .P{\sim}R \supset {\sim}Q$ (the P, Q, and R here denote statements, and not points), an alternative version of this is

$$(A,\gamma){:}.\sim(A \text{ on } \gamma){:} \supset {:}(\alpha,\beta){:}\alpha \perp \gamma.A \text{ on } \alpha.A \text{ on } \beta.\alpha \neq \beta. \supset .\sim(\beta \perp \gamma).$$

It is in this form that Wentworth and Smith prove the proposition. We give a condensed version of their proof (see Fig. VII.3.1).[1]

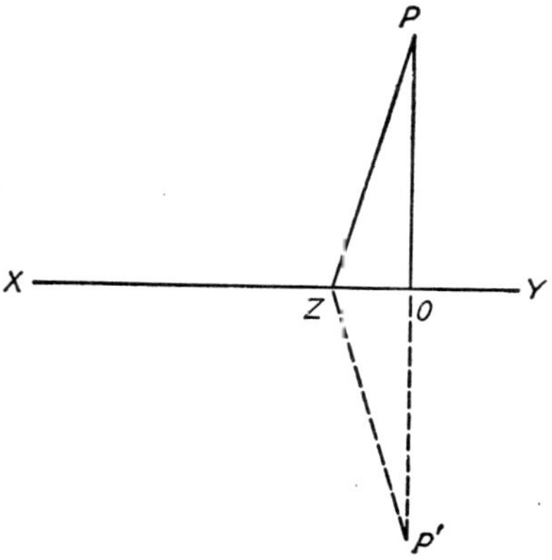

FIG. VII. 3.1.

Given: A line XY, P an external point, PO a perpendicular to XY from P, and PZ any other line from P to XY.

To prove: That PZ is not $\perp$ to XY.

(The reader will note that our A is their P, our γ is their XY, our α is their PO, and our β is their PZ. Then, in our notation, they are assuming $\sim(A \text{ on } \gamma)$, $\alpha \perp \gamma$, A on α, A on β, and $\alpha \neq \beta$, and are undertaking to prove $\sim(\beta \perp \gamma)$.)

Proof. Produce PO to P', making OP' equal PO, and draw $P'Z$. By construction, POP' is a straight line, and so by Postulate 1, PZP' is not a straight line. Hence $\angle P'ZP$ is not a straight angle. Now $PO = P'O$, $OZ = OZ$, and $\angle POZ = \angle P'OZ$ (since each is a right angle). Hence the triangles POZ and $P'OZ$ are congruent. So $\angle OZP = \angle OZP'$, so that $\angle OZP$ is half of $\angle PZP'$. As $\angle PZP'$ is not a straight angle, $\angle OZP$ is not a right angle, and so PZ is not $\perp$ to XY.

[1] *Ibid.*

We should like to pay special attention to the use of Postulate 1 in this proof, since it involves uses of Axiom scheme 7A. If we put in the details of the use of Postulate 1, they might run as follows: Suppose PZP' is a straight line. Then by Postulate 1, $PZP' = POP'$. But Z on PZP'. So by Axiom scheme 7A, Z on POP'. Then $Z = 0$, for if $Z \neq 0$, then POP' and XY would coincide by Postulate 1, since each passes through the distinct points Z and 0. However, if $Z = 0$, then $PZ = PO$ (apply Axiom scheme 7A to the statement $PZ = PZ$), contrary to assumption.

This completes the proof of Proposition VIII. We turn now to Proposition XIV on page 46:[1]

"Two lines in the same plane perpendicular to the same line cannot meet however far they are produced."

Actually, the proposition as stated is false, as one can see by considering in 3-space the configuration consisting of three mutually perpendicular lines through a common point. An accurate statement of the proposition would be:

"If each of two lines is perpendicular to a third, and there is a single plane in which all three lines lie, then the two original lines cannot meet however far they are produced."

Actually, since at this point Wentworth and Smith have not yet embarked on the study of solid geometry, it seems most appropriate to assume for all statements in this portion of the book that they apply only to figures which can be embedded in a plane. If this is not assumed, then the statement,[1] "From a given point in a given line only one perpendicular can be drawn to the line," which appears on page 23 of Wentworth and Smith is clearly false.

So we make the assumption that we are considering only figures in a plane, and simplify Proposition XIV to:

"Two lines perpendicular to the same line cannot meet however far they are produced."

In symbols:

$$(\alpha,\beta,\gamma):\alpha \neq \beta.\alpha \perp \gamma.\beta \perp \gamma. \supset .\sim(\mathrm{E}A).A \text{ on } \alpha.A \text{ on } \beta.$$

The proof is by reductio ad absurdum.[1] We assume $\alpha \neq \beta.\alpha \perp \gamma.\beta \perp \gamma$ and $(\mathrm{E}A).A$ on $\alpha.A$ on β and try to derive a contradiction. By rule C, we get A on $\alpha.A$ on β. Now if A on γ, we get a contradiction by the result which we quoted from page 23 of Wentworth and Smith (Wentworth and Smith overlook this possibility), and if $\sim(A$ on $\gamma)$ we get a contradiction by Proposition VIII (see above).

Incidentally, the above proof is an illustration of the advantage of formalizing statements and proofs. With the statements and proofs in

[1] *Ibid.*

words, it is very easy to overlook the case, A on γ, but when we are using symbols it would be very hard to overlook it.

We come now to the third (and most interesting) proposition, namely, Proposition XV on page 47:[1]

"If a line is perpendicular to one of two parallel lines, it is perpendicular to the other also."

This proposition would be false if we do not have the implicit assumption that the entire figure lies in a plane. However, we are assuming this.

In symbols, the proposition would read

$$(\alpha,\beta,\gamma):\alpha \neq \beta.\alpha \parallel \beta.\gamma \perp \alpha. \supset .\gamma \perp \beta.$$

Actually, the condition $\alpha \neq \beta$ is unnecessary, since Wentworth and Smith have framed their definition of $\alpha \parallel \beta$ so that one can prove

$$\vdash \alpha \parallel \beta \supset \alpha \neq \beta.$$

So we shall prove the theorem in the (apparently) stronger form

$$(\alpha,\beta,\gamma):\alpha \parallel \beta.\gamma \perp \alpha. \supset .\gamma \perp \beta,$$

using a proof adapted from Wentworth and Smith (see Fig. VII.3.2).[1]

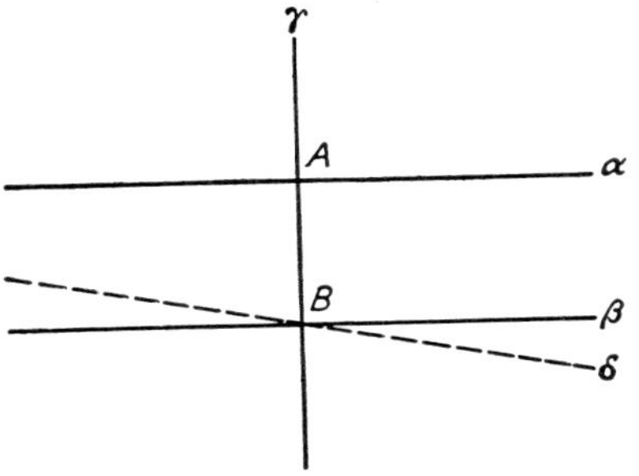

FIG. VII.3.2.

We assume $\alpha \parallel \beta$ and $\gamma \perp \alpha$, and the entire figure lying in some plane. By the definition of perpendicularity, α and γ have a point in common. By rule C, call it A. Now γ must intersect β, else (since γ and β are coplanar) we would have $\gamma \parallel \beta$, whence we would get $\alpha = \gamma$ by the parallel postulate, and this is impossible since $\gamma \perp \alpha$. By rule C, we can let B be the intersection of β and γ. Through B we draw δ (in the plane of our figure) with $\delta \perp \gamma$. Then $\delta \neq \alpha$, for if $\delta = \alpha$, then B on α by Axiom scheme 7A, so that α and β meet in B, contradicting $\alpha \parallel \beta$. (Wentworth and Smith overlook the necessity for proving $\delta \neq \alpha$.) Then δ and α never meet, by

[1] *Ibid.*

Proposition XIV (see above), since $\delta \neq \alpha . \delta \perp \gamma . \alpha \perp \gamma$. So, since δ and α are coplanar by construction, we have $\delta \parallel \alpha$. Now, with δ and β both parallel to α and both passing through B, we get $\delta = \beta$ by the parallel postulate. We now come to the most interesting step of the whole proof. We have just shown $\delta = \beta$. Also we have $\gamma \perp \delta$ by construction. So $\gamma \perp \beta$ by Axiom scheme 7A.

EXERCISES

VII.3.1. In the three geometric proofs which have just been given, point out uses of the logical principles listed in Sec. 5 of Chapter II.

VII.3.2. Find an illustration in the mathematical literature of the use of Axiom scheme 7A.

CHAPTER VIII

DESCRIPTIONS

1. Axioms for Descriptions. In Chapter III, and again in Chapter VII, when we spoke of names, we were using the term "name" in its most general sense as any word or symbol or arrangement of words and symbols which signifies some object and is used in statements to refer to that object. In general, there are many names for a given object. This is familiar in the case of names of persons. Thus we might find "Jack" and "Mr. John Murgatroyd Smith" as names for the same person. In a certain legal document "the party of the first part" may serve as an additional name for this same person. In army records he would be referred to by a number. On a ticket for overparking which a policeman leaves attached to the steering wheel of his car, he would be referred to as the "owner of a Nash 4-door sedan, registration TP 899, year 1949."

Of these various names, the last differs from the rest in one important particular, in that it identifies the person completely, even to someone with no previous acquaintance with him. The other names are names of this particular person only by agreement or usage, and if a newcomer is unaware of the agreement or usage he would have no way of identifying the person from his name.

A similar situation occurs in mathematics. By agreement and usage, "e" is the name of a certain number.

$$\lim_{n\to\infty}\left(1+\frac{1}{n}\right)^n$$

is another name of the same number. However, the second name identifies the number unequivocally, even to one who has never before heard of it, and so the second name could never become the name of a different number. On the other hand, a change in usage would suffice to make "e" the name of quite a different number.

We shall use the word "description" to indicate a name which by its own structure unequivocally identifies the object of which it is a name. It is not our intention to pursue further the distinction between definitions and more ordinary names, or to analyze the mechanism by which a name can be associated with an object if the name is not a description of the object. We proceed now to a formal treatment of descriptions.

The most commonly occurring form of description is constructed as follows. One finds somehow a statement $F(x)$ which is true exactly when x is the object in question. We then take as a description of our object "the x such that $F(x)$."

This is symbolized by "$\iota x\ F(x)$", which is read "the x such that $F(x)$", and which is called a description.

In connection with this notation, the following point rises immediately. If $(E_1x)\ F(x)$, then $\iota x\ F(x)$ is a name of the unique object which makes $F(x)$ true. However, suppose $\sim(E_1x)\ F(x)$, so that there is no unique object which makes $F(x)$ true. Shall we permit $\iota x\ F(x)$ in such cases, and what meaning shall we assign to it?

It will be recalled that we have not committed ourselves to using only formulas which have meaning. So we agree to use $\iota x\ F(x)$ in the case of any $F(x)$, and in case $\sim(E_1x)\ F(x)$, we shall simply consider $\iota x\ F(x)$ as a meaningless formula. In fact, we shall not even require that $F(x)$ contain x. Given an arbitrary statement P, we shall admit $\iota x\ P$ as a formula. This is to be a name and may properly occur as a constituent of statements, even though it may fail to be a name of anything.

If the reader is unhappy about using formulas without meaning, he can arrange for $\iota x\ P$ to have a meaning, regardless of what x and P are, by adopting the following convention. Choose some arbitrary, fixed object, say the number π, and agree that, if $(E_1x)\ P$, then $\iota x\ P$ is a name of the unique x such that P is true, and if $\sim(E_1x)\ P$, then $\iota x\ P$ is a name of the number π. Then for each x and P, $\iota x\ P$ is a name of a unique object. Our axioms for "ι" will be in agreement with such an interpretation.

Whitehead and Russell showed that any statement containing ι's is equivalent to a much more elaborate statement without ι's. Hence they dispensed with statements containing ι's, using instead the very elaborate equivalent statements. By this means they did not use ι's at all. Following their lead, many logicians do likewise. This has the advantage of saving one symbol, ι, and four axiom schemes. However, even the simplest statements of mathematics are transformed into very complicated circumlocutions by this procedure, and so we do not take advantage of it, despite its considerable usefulness in many logical studies. In a mathematical development, such as we are pursuing here, it is far more convenient to use ι's, and we shall do so.

Notice that in $\iota x\ F(x)$ it is quite immaterial what variable we use for x. Clearly $\iota y\ F(y)$ would denote the same object. So in $\iota x\ F(x)$, all occurrences of x are bound. However, if y is a variable different from x, then any occurrences of y which are free in $F(x)$ are also free in $\iota x\ F(x)$.

If $F(x)$ contains no free occurrences of any variable except x, then $\iota x\ F(x)$ contains no free occurrences of any variable, and so must be a constant. Examples are

$$\iota x\ (x \in R . x + x = x),$$

$$\iota x\ (x \in R :(y). y \in R \supset yx = y),$$

$$\iota x\ (x \in R :. (\varepsilon) :. \varepsilon > 0 : \supset :(\mathrm{E}y) : y \in R :(z). z > y \supset |\,(1 + 1/z)^z - x\,| < \varepsilon),$$

where "$x \in R$" denotes "x is a real number." The three formulas just written denote 0, 1, and e, respectively.

If $F(x)$ contains free occurrences of x and y only (where x and y are distinct variables), then $\iota x\ F(x)$ contains free occurrences of y only, and is a function of y. Thus

$$\iota x\ (x \in R . y \in R . x + y = 0),$$

$$\iota x\ (x \in R . y \in R . xy = 1)$$

denote $-y$ and $1/y$, respectively.

Similarly, if $F(x)$ contains free occurrences of x, y, and z, then $\iota x\ F(x)$ is a function of y and z.

All constants and functions of mathematics will arise in this manner.

We now have two ways to bind the occurrences of x in P, namely, to form $(x)\ P$ and $\iota x\ P$. Correspondingly, we now have more ways to produce confusion of bound variables. Even if our definition of confusion of bound variables (page 94) is not changed, it now covers more situations. Thus if P is $x = \iota y\ (y = x)$, and we replace all free occurrences of x by occurrences of y, we get $y = \iota y\ (y = y)$, which is quite a different statement about y. However, this is because we made a replacement which caused confusion of bound variables, in that the rightmost occurrence of x in P is free, but when we replace it by an occurrence of y, the resulting occurrence of y is bound.

We extend our conventions about $F(x,y)$ and $F(y,y)$ and $F(x)$ and $F(y)$ (see page 95) to cover the extension in the meaning of "confusion of bound variables" caused by the introduction of a new means of binding variables.

We must now take account of one essentially new method of causing confusion of bound variables. This arises from the possibility of replacing free occurrences of x in P by occurrences of $\iota z\ Q$ rather than by occurrences of another variable y. If we have a statement, for instance, $(\mathrm{E}y)\ y \neq x$, about a variable x, we may wish to make the corresponding statement about a name $\iota z\ Q$. In general, we would do so by replacing the free occurrences of x by occurrences of $\iota z\ Q$; thus in the present case we would write $(\mathrm{E}y)\ y \neq \iota z\ Q$. However, in certain circumstances this is not the corresponding statement about $\iota z\ Q$. Thus if Q is $z = y$, then $\iota z\ Q$ is $\iota z\ (z = y)$, which is merely another name for the quantity of which y is a name. So, whereas $(\mathrm{E}y)\ y \neq x$ is true for every x, $(\mathrm{E}y)\ y \neq \iota z\ (z = y)$ is the same as $(\mathrm{E}y)\ y \neq y$, and is false, and besides is not strictly speaking a statement about $\iota z\ (z = y)$.

We see that, if we try to substitute $\iota z\ (z = y)$ for x, in the above instance, we get the same sort of confusion of bound variables that we would get if we try to substitute y for x, and for the same reason.

Accordingly, we do have to generalize our definition of confusion of bound variables. We take the new definition as follows.

Let A denote either a variable or a description. Let P be a statement and Q be the result of replacing each free occurrence of x (if any) in P by an occurrence of A. Consider each variable y which has free occurrences in A. If some bound occurrence of y in Q is one of the free occurrences of y in an occurrence of A in Q which is the result of replacing a free occurrence of x in P by an occurrence of A, then we say that the replacement causes confusion. Otherwise, we say that the replacement causes no confusion.

To understand this definition, the reader must realize that occurrences of a variable may be free in a part of a statement and yet be bound in the entire statement. Thus in $(\mathrm{E}y)\ y \neq \iota z\ (z = y)$, the rightmost occurrence of y is free in $\iota z\ (z = y)$, but bound in the entire statement.

As our notations $F(x,y)$ and $F(y,y)$ and $F(x)$ and $F(y)$ refer to replacing occurrences of a variable by occurrences of a variable, we can continue to use them with the same meaning as before. However, we wish to supplement them by a new notation.

In case we refer to two statements as $F(x)$ and $F(\iota y\ Q)$, where x and y are variables which may or may not be distinct, it shall be assumed that $F(\iota y\ Q)$ is the result of replacing each free occurrence of x (if any) in $F(x)$ by an occurrence of $\iota y\ Q$, and this replacement causes no confusion. It is not assumed that there are not occurrences of $\iota y\ Q$ in $F(x)$, nor is it assumed that there are. It is not assumed that there are free occurrences of x in $F(x)$. No assumption is made as to the occurrence or nonoccurrence of variables and descriptions which have not been explicitly mentioned.

This new notation is not strictly analogous to our earlier notations. To be strictly analogous, we should write $F(x,\iota y\ Q)$ and $F(\iota y\ Q,\iota y\ Q)$. However, we have preferred a condensed notation to one which preserves a strict analogy.

We shall now state our axiom schemes for ι, using the conventions which we have been discussing to avoid explicit mention of necessary assumptions about the absence of confusion of bound variables.

Axiom scheme 8. Let $x_1, x_2, \ldots, x_n, x, y$ be variables, not necessarily distinct. Let $F(x)$, $F(\iota y\ Q)$, and Q be statements. Then

$$(x_1, x_2, \ldots, x_n):(x)\ F(x). \supset .F(\iota y\ Q)$$

is an axiom.

Axiom scheme 9. Let $x_1, x_2, \ldots, x_n, x$ be variables, not necessarily distinct. Let P and Q be statements. Then

$$(x_1, x_2, \ldots, x_n):(x).P \equiv Q. \supset .\iota x\ P = \iota x\ Q$$

is an axiom.

Axiom scheme 10. Let $x_1, x_2, \ldots, x_n, x, y$ be variables, not necessarily distinct. Let $F(x)$ and $F(y)$ be statements. Then

$$(x_1, x_2, \ldots, x_n).\iota x\ F(x) = \iota y\ F(y)$$

is an axiom.

Axiom scheme 11. Let $x_1, x_2, \ldots, x_n, x$ be variables, not necessarily distinct. Let P be a statement. Then

$$(x_1, x_2, \ldots, x_n):.(\mathrm{E}_1x)\ P: \supset :(x):\iota x\ P = x. \equiv .P$$

is an axiom.

The first of these says for descriptions what Axiom scheme 6 says for variables. Taken together, Axiom scheme 6 and Axiom scheme 8 say that, if A is an object (that is, a variable or a description), then $(x)\ F(x) \supset F(A)$. Since we place no restrictions on $\iota y\ Q$ in Axiom scheme 8, this means that we intend to treat $\iota y\ Q$ as an object even in the situation where $\sim(\mathrm{E}_1y)\ Q$, and where $\iota y\ Q$ has no meaning. The reader who objects to this can interpret $\iota y\ Q$ as a name for π in all such cases.

Axiom scheme 9 says that, if P and Q are equivalent for all x, then $\iota x\ P$ and $\iota x\ Q$ are names of the same object. The question of what sense this makes if $\sim(\mathrm{E}_1x)\ P$ can be raised as for Axiom scheme 8, and answered similarly.

Axiom scheme 10 enables us to change bound variables to other bound variables as long as no confusion of bound variables is caused. Because of this, we can extend the convention of Sec. 11 of Chapter VI to the following. If we write a formula $(x)\ P$ or $\iota x\ P$, then if any variables occur bound within P they shall be distinct from x unless we specifically indicate otherwise.

In effect, Axiom scheme 11 says that, if $(\mathrm{E}_1x)\ P$, then $\iota x\ P$ is the unique x which makes P true. To see that this is the case, write Axiom scheme 11 in the form

$$(\mathrm{E}_1x)\ F(x): \supset :(x):\iota x\ F(x) = x. \equiv F(x),$$

which we change to the equivalent form

$$(\mathrm{E}_1x)\ F(x): \supset :(y):\iota x\ F(x) = y. \equiv F(y).$$

Now assume $(\mathrm{E}_1x)\ F(x)$. Then $(y):\iota x\ F(x) = y. \equiv F(y)$. If there is any confusion of bound variables in $F(\iota x\ F(x))$, we can change the bound variables of $F(y)$ by Thm.VI.6.8 or Axiom scheme 10, so that there is no confusion of bound variables in $F(\iota x\ F(x))$. Then by Axiom scheme 8,

$$\iota x\ F(x) = \iota x\ F(x). \equiv F(\iota x\ F(x)).$$

So by Thm.VIII.2.1 below,

$$F(\iota x\ F(x)).$$

So $\iota x\ F(x)$ is one of the x's which make $F(x)$ true. We now show that it is the only such x. For suppose $F(z)$. By Axiom scheme 6, $\iota x\ F(x) = z . \equiv F(z)$, whence $F(z) . \supset . \iota x\ F(x) = z$, and so $z = \iota x\ F(x)$.

The reader will note that we now have essentially three ways of using variables (letters, that is). They may occur free, or they may occur bound by (x) or they may occur bound by ιx. These three uses are analogous to familiar usages in everyday mathematics, to wit:

A free use of x, say in $F(x)$, is analogous to an unknown as in

$$x^2 - 4x + 3 = 0.$$

A use of x bound by (x), say in $(x)\ F(x)$, is analogous to one kind of variable as in

$$x^2 - 1 \equiv (x + 1)(x - 1).$$

A use of x bound by ιx, say in $\iota x\ F(x)$, is analogous to another kind of variable as in

$$\int_0^3 x^2\, dx.$$

It will turn out that these three uses of variables (letters) suffice for all mathematical statements. Indeed, as shown by Whitehead and Russell, one can dispense with ιx, but only at the expense of using very elaborate circumlocutions.

EXERCISES

VIII.1.1. Let "$x \in \text{Nn}$" denote "x is a nonnegative integer" and let $+$ and $\times$ have their customary numerical significance. Using "$x \in \text{Nn}$", $+$, $\times$, and logical symbols write formulas for:

(a) The greatest prime factor of n.
(b) The least common multiple of m and n.
(c) The greatest integer less than or equal to $\sqrt{n}$, when n is a positive integer.
(d) The integer quotient got by dividing m by n when m and n are positive integers.
(e) The remainder left after dividing m by n when m and n are positive integers.
(f) $n - 1$.

VIII.1.2. Let "$x \in R$" denote "x is a real number" and let $+$ and

$\times$ have their customary numerical significance. Using "$x \epsilon R$," $+$, $\times$, and logical symbols write formulas for:

(a) $\frac{x}{2}$.
(b) $+ \sqrt{x}$.
(c) $| x - y |$.

2. Definition by Cases. We first establish a few properties of ι.

Theorem VIII.2.1. $\vdash \iota x\ P = \iota x\ P$.

Proof. By Axiom scheme 8, $\vdash (x)\ x = x. \supset .\iota x\ P = \iota x\ P$. So our theorem follows by Axiom scheme 7B.

Theorem VIII.2.2. If $F(x)$ is a statement such that there is no confusion of bound variables in $F(\iota x\ F(x))$, then $\vdash (E_1 x)\ F(x) \supset F(\iota x\ F(x))$.

Proof. By Axiom scheme 8, $\vdash (x){:}\iota x\ F(x) = x. \equiv F(x){:} \supset {:}\iota x\ F(x) = \iota x\ F(x). \equiv F(\iota x\ F(x))$.

So, by Thm.VIII.2.1 and the statement calculus,

$$\vdash (x){:}\iota x\ F(x) = x. \equiv F(x){:} \supset {:}F(\iota x\ F(x)).$$

Our theorem now follows by Axiom scheme 11.

Theorem VIII.2.3. $\vdash (y).\iota x\ (x = y) = y$.

Note that our conventions require that x and y be distinct variables.

Proof. Choose y a variable distinct from x and take $F(x)$ to be $x = y$. Then by Thm.VII.2.2, $\vdash (E_1 x)\ F(x)$, and so by Thm.VIII.2.2, $\vdash F(\iota x\ F(x))$. That is, $\vdash \iota x\ (x = y) = y$.

The question now arises whether we can prove $\vdash y = \iota x\ (x = y)$. One is tempted to try to use Axiom scheme 8 to replace x by $\iota x\ (x = y)$ in $\vdash (x,y).x = y \supset y = x$, but unfortunately the prohibition against confusion of bound variables in Axiom scheme 8 prevents this. To take care of this sort of difficulty, we prove the following theorem, in which it is permitted that there be free occurrences of y in $\iota x\ P$.

Theorem VIII.2.4.

$$\vdash (y){:}\iota x\ P = y. \equiv .y = \iota x\ P.$$

Proof. Choose a z which does not occur in $\iota x\ P$. Then by Ex.VII.1.1,

$$\vdash (x,z){:}x = z. \equiv .z = x.$$

So by Axiom scheme 8,

$$\vdash (z){:}\iota x\ P = z. \equiv .z = \iota x\ P.$$

Then by Axiom scheme 6,

$$\vdash \iota x\ P = y. \equiv .y = \iota x\ P.$$

In a similar manner we prove:

Theorem VIII.2.5.

I. $\vdash (y,z){:}\iota x\ P = y.y = z. \supset .\iota x\ P = z.$
II. $\vdash (x,z){:}x = \iota y\ Q.\iota y\ Q = z. \supset .x = z.$
III. $\vdash (z){:}\iota x\ P = \iota y\ Q.\iota y\ Q = z. \supset .\iota x\ P = z.$
IV. $\vdash (y){:}\iota x\ P = y.y = \iota z\ R. \supset .\iota x\ P = \iota z\ R.$

If we are going to be able to substitute $\iota x\ (x = y)$ for y or vice versa, we need a similar generalized form of Axiom scheme 7A, which we now prove.

Theorem VIII.2.6. Let $F(x,y)$ be a statement, and let $F(\iota x\ P,y)$ and $F(y,y)$ be the results of replacing all free occurrences of x in $F(x,y)$ by occurrences of $\iota x\ P$ and y, respectively, and suppose these replacements cause no confusion of bound variables. Then

$$\vdash (y){:}\iota x\ P = y. \supset .F(\iota x\ P,y) \equiv F(y,y).$$

Proof. Let z be a variable which does not occur in $F(x,y)$ or $\iota x\ P$, and let $F(x,z)$ and $F(z,z)$ denote the results of replacing all free occurrences of y in $F(x,y)$ and $F(y,y)$ by occurrences of z. Also let $F(\iota x\ P,z)$ be the result of replacing all free occurrences of x in $F(x,z)$ by occurrences of $\iota x\ P$. Clearly there is no confusion of bound variables in $F(\iota x\ P,z)$ since there is none in $F(\iota x\ P,y)$. By Axiom scheme 7A,

$$\vdash (x,z){:}x = z. \supset .F(x,z) \supset F(z,z).$$

So by Axiom scheme 8

$$\vdash (z){:}\iota x\ P = z. \supset .F(\iota x\ P,z) \supset F(z,z).$$

So by Axiom scheme 6

$$\vdash \iota x\ P = y. \supset .F(\iota x\ P,y) \supset F(y,y).$$

By Thm.VII.1.1 and Axiom scheme 7A, we have

$$\vdash (x,z){:}x = z. \supset .F(z,z) \supset F(x,z).$$

So, by Axiom scheme 8 and Axiom scheme 6,

$$\vdash \iota x\ P = y. \supset .F(y,y) \supset F(\iota x\ P,y).$$

Then

$$\vdash \iota x\ P = y. \supset .F(\iota x\ P,y) \equiv F(y,y)$$

and our theorem follows.

****Theorem VIII.2.7.** $\vdash F(\iota y\ P) \supset (\text{E}x)\ F(x).$

Proof. Analogous to the proof of Thm.VI.7.3.

The reader should note carefully our conventions about the use of $F(\iota y\ P)$ and $F(x)$, which are such that an instance of this theorem would be

$$\vdash \iota y\, P = \iota y\, P. \supset .(\mathrm{E}x).x = \iota y\, P$$

if there are no free occurrences of x in P.

We are now about ready to prove the theorem which permits us to make a definition by cases. Such definitions are very common in mathematics, and we cite two familiar cases:

$$f(x) = \begin{cases} +1 & \text{if } x \text{ is rational} \\ 0 & \text{if } x \text{ is irrational} \end{cases}$$

$$f(x) = \begin{cases} -1 & \text{if } x < 0, \\ 0 & \text{if } x = 0, \\ +1 & \text{if } x > 0. \end{cases}$$

Note that these definitions do not define $f(x)$ for each x; both leave $f(\sqrt{-1})$ undefined. One could always add an additional clause defining $f(x)$ in all circumstances not already covered, but it is useful not to have to do so. The typical circumstance for a definition by cases is that we have some mutually exclusive conditions, for instance, "$x < 0$", "$x = 0$", "$x > 0$", and we wish to define $f(x)$ for each x covered by one of our conditions, and with different definitions according to which condition x satisfies.

A condition on x will in general be a statement involving x. The assertion that two conditions P_i and P_j be mutually exclusive is that $\sim(P_iP_j)$. The assertion that several conditions, $P_1, P_2, \ldots, P_n$ be mutually exclusive is the logical product of all statements $\sim(P_iP_j)$ with $1 \le i < j \le n$. So the first sentence of each of the next two theorems merely defines Q as the assertion that the conditions P are mutually exclusive.

Theorem VIII.2.8. Let $P_1, P_2, \ldots, P_n$ be statements and let Q be the logical product of all statements $\sim(P_iP_j)$ with $1 \le i < j \le n$. Let y be a variable. For each i, $1 \le i \le n$, let A_i be a variable different from y or a description not containing free occurrences of y. Then for $1 \le k \le n$:

I. $\vdash (y).QP_k\mathbf{:} \supset \mathbf{:}(\mathrm{E}_1y)\mathbf{:}y = A_1.P_1.\mathbf{v}.y = A_2.P_2.\mathbf{v}. \cdots .\mathbf{v}.y = A_n.P_n.$

II. $\vdash (y).QP_k\mathbf{:} \supset \mathbf{:}\iota y\, (y = A_1.P_1.\mathbf{v}.y = A_2.P_2.\mathbf{v}. \cdots .\mathbf{v}.y = A_n.P_n) = A_k.$

Proof. By truth values

$$\vdash QP_k\mathbf{:} \supset \mathbf{:}R_1P_1\mathbf{v}R_2P_2\mathbf{v} \cdots \mathbf{v}R_nP_n. \equiv .R_k.$$

So, if we take R_i to be $y = A_i$ and take $F(y)$ to be

$$y = A_1.P_1.\mathbf{v}.y = A_2.P_2.\mathbf{v}. \cdots .\mathbf{v}.y = A_n.P_n,$$

we have

$$\vdash QP_k\mathbf{:} \supset \mathbf{:}F(y). \equiv .y = A_k.$$

So by rule G and Axiom scheme 4, we get

$$\vdash (y).QP_k\colon \supset :(y):F(y). \equiv .y = A_k.$$

Now by Ex.VII.2.3,

$$\vdash (y):F(y). \equiv .y = A_k.\colon \supset :.(\mathrm{E}_1y)\ F(y). \equiv .(\mathrm{E}_1y)\ y = A_k.$$

If A_k is a variable, then we get $\vdash (\mathrm{E}_1y)\ y = A_k$ from Thm.VII.2.2 by Axiom scheme 6. If A_k is a description, then we get $\vdash (\mathrm{E}_1y)\ y = A_k$ from Thm. VII.2.2 by Axiom scheme 8. In either case, we get $\vdash (\mathrm{E}_1y)\ y = A_k$, and so infer

$$\vdash (y):F(y). \equiv .y = A_k.\colon \supset :.(\mathrm{E}_1y)\ F(y).$$

So

$$\vdash (y).QP_k\colon \supset :(\mathrm{E}_1y)\ F(y),$$

which is Part I of our theorem. By Axiom scheme 9,

$$\vdash (y):F(y). \equiv .y = A_k.\colon \supset :.\iota y\ F(y) = \iota y\ (y = A_k).$$

However, by Thm.VIII.2.3 and whichever of Axiom schemes 6 or 8 is appropriate, we have $\vdash \iota y\ (y = A_k) = A_k$. So we can combine the various results given above and get

$$\vdash (y).QP_k\colon \supset :\iota y\ F(y) = A_k,$$

which is Part II of our theorem.

The theorem which we have just proved is a little too general for most purposes. In general, if we are making a definition by cases, the P's will be conditions on x, and so must contain free occurrences of x, but we shall be able to take y to be a variable which does not occur in the P's. This gives us a special case of the above theorem, which special case is the one in common use.

****Theorem VIII.2.9.** Let $P_1, P_2, \ldots, P_n$ be statements and let Q be the logical product of all statements $\sim(P_iP_j)$ with $1 \leq i < j \leq n$. Let y be a variable not occurring in any of the P's. For each i, $1 \leq i \leq n$, let A_i be a variable different from y or a description not containing free occurrences of y. Then:

I. $\vdash Q(P_1 \mathbf{v} P_2 \mathbf{v} \cdots \mathbf{v} P_n)\colon \supset :(\mathrm{E}_1y):y = A_1.P_1.\mathbf{v}.y = A_2.P_2.\mathbf{v}. \cdots .\mathbf{v}. y = A_n.P_n.$

Also, for $1 \leq k \leq n$,

II. $\vdash QP_k\colon \supset :\iota y\ (y = A_1.P_1.\mathbf{v}.y = A_2.P_2.\mathbf{v}. \cdots .\mathbf{v}.y = A_n.P_n) = A_k.$

Proof. Let $F(y)$ be as in the preceding proof. Then by the preceding theorem,

$$\vdash (y).QP_k : \supset :(\mathrm{E}_1 y)\ F(y),$$

$$\vdash (y).QP_k : \supset :\iota y\ F(y) = A_k.$$

Since there are no occurrences of y in any P_i, there are no occurrences of y in QP_k. So by Thm.VI.6.6, Part I,

$$\vdash (y).QP_k : \equiv :QP_k.$$

Hence

$$\vdash QP_k : \supset :(\mathrm{E}_1 y)\ F(y),$$

$$\vdash QP_k : \supset :\iota y\ F(y) = A_k.$$

The second of these is Part II of our theorem. From the first, we get for $k = 1, 2, \ldots, n$

$$\vdash P_k \supset :Q. \supset .(\mathrm{E}_1 y)\ F(y)$$

by Thm.VI.6.1, Part LXIII. Then by repeated applications of Ex.IV.4.6, Part (d), we get

$$\vdash P_1 \mathbf{v} P_2 \mathbf{v} \cdots \mathbf{v} P_n : \supset :Q. \supset .(\mathrm{E}_1 y)\ F(y).$$

So

$$\vdash Q(P_1 \mathbf{v} P_2 \mathbf{v} \cdots \mathbf{v} P_n). \supset .(\mathrm{E}_1 y)\ F(y).$$

Let us now see how we can use this theorem to define the functions discussed earlier.

We can take P_1 to be "x is rational" and P_2 to be "x is irrational". Then Q is $\sim(P_1P_2)$, and we have $\vdash Q$. Also we have $\vdash x$ is real. $\supset .P_1 \mathbf{v} P_2$. So by the theorem just proved

$$\vdash x \text{ is real.} \supset .(\mathrm{E}_1 y) : y = 0.x \text{ is rational.} \mathbf{v}. y = 1.x \text{ is irrational},$$

$$\vdash x \text{ is rational.} \supset .\iota y\ (y = 0.x \text{ is rational.} \mathbf{v}. y = 1.x \text{ is irrational}) = 0,$$

$$\vdash x \text{ is irrational.} \supset .\iota y\ (y = 0.x \text{ is rational.} \mathbf{v}. y = 1.x \text{ is irrational}) = 1.$$

So if we take $f(x)$ to be $\iota y\ (y = 0.x$ is rational.$\mathbf{v}.y = 1.x$ is irrational), we have

$$\vdash x \text{ is rational.} \supset .f(x) = 0,$$

$$\vdash x \text{ is irrational.} \supset .f(x) = 1.$$

Similarly, to define the other function mentioned, we take P_1, P_2, and P_3 to be "$x < 0$", "$x = 0$", and "$x > 0$". In this case Q is $\sim(P_1P_2)\sim(P_1P_3)\sim(P_2P_3)$. By theorems of mathematics

$$\vdash Q$$

$$\vdash x \text{ is real.} \supset .P_1 \mathbf{v} P_2 \mathbf{v} P_3.$$

So by Part I of our theorem

$$\vdash x \text{ is real}: \supset :(E_1 y):y = -1.x < 0.\mathbf{v}.y = 0.x = 0.\mathbf{v}.y = 1.x > 0.$$

Also, if we take $f(x)$ to be $\iota y\ (y = -1.x < 0.\mathbf{v}.y = 0.x = 0.\mathbf{v}.y = 1.x > 0)$, then by Part II of our theorem we have

$$\vdash x < 0. \supset .f(x) = -1,$$

$$\vdash x = 0. \supset .f(x) = 0,$$

$$\vdash x > 0. \supset .f(x) = 1.$$

Notice that it is permitted that the A_i contain free occurrences of x. Thus, let P_1 be $x < 0$, P_2 be $x \geq 0$, A_1 be $-x$, A_2 be x. Then if we define $f(x)$ to be $\iota y\ (y = -x.x < 0.\mathbf{v}.y = x.x \geq 0)$, we have

$$\vdash x < 0. \supset .f(x) = -x,$$

$$\vdash x \geq 0. \supset .f(x) = x.$$

For another example of definition by cases, see Titchmarsh, 1939, Sec. 1.63, page 31.

We now raise the question of the interpretation of $\iota\alpha\ F(\alpha)$ when α is restricted to the range $K(\alpha)$. The obvious interpretation would be $\iota x\ (K(x).F(x))$. However, in case $\sim(E_1 x).K(x).F(x)$, this definition would not permit us to prove $\vdash K(\iota\alpha\ F(\alpha))$. For this reason, we adopt a definition by cases. First of all we choose some fixed object A satisfying our restriction $K(x)$, so that we have $\vdash K(A)$. Now we define $\iota\alpha\ F(\alpha)$ to be $\iota x\ (K(x).F(x))$ in case $(E_1 x).K(x).F(x)$, and to be A in case $\sim(E_1 x).K(x).F(x)$. That is, we define $\iota\alpha\ F(\alpha)$ to be

$$\iota y\ (y = \iota x\ (K(x).F(x)):(E_1 x).K(x).F(x).:\mathbf{v}:.y = A.\sim(E_1 x).K(x).F(x)),$$

being careful to choose y a variable that does not occur in A or $K(x)F(x)$.

Theorem VIII.2.10. If α is subject to the restriction $K(\alpha)$ and A is the fixed object chosen for use in defining $\iota\alpha\ F(\alpha)$, then:

I. $\vdash (E_1\alpha)\ F(\alpha). \supset .\iota\alpha\ F(\alpha) = \iota x\ (K(x)F(x))$.
II. $\vdash \sim(E_1\alpha)\ F(\alpha). \supset .\iota\alpha\ F(\alpha) = A$.

Proof. This follows from Thm.VIII.2.9, Part II, and the definition of $\iota\alpha\ F(\alpha)$, since by Thm.VII.2.3,

$$\vdash (E_1\alpha)\ F(\alpha): \equiv :(E_1 x).K(x).F(x).$$

We now wish to prove $\vdash K(\iota\alpha\ F(\alpha))$. However, we can prove this only when there is no confusion of bound variables in $K(\iota\alpha\ F(\alpha))$, and indeed it does not mean what we intend in case there is confusion of bound variables.

We shall prove instead $\vdash (\mathrm{E}z).\iota\alpha\, F(\alpha) = z.K(z)$, where z does not occur in $\iota\alpha\, F(\alpha)$. Then, if there is no confusion of bound variables in $K(\iota\alpha\, F(\alpha))$, we would have

$$\vdash K(\iota\alpha\, F(\alpha)) : \equiv :(\mathrm{E}z).\iota\alpha\, F(\alpha) = z.K(z)$$

by Thm.VII.1.5, Part I, and Axiom scheme 8. So, since we can always choose z so as to avoid confusion of bound variables, $(\mathrm{E}z).\iota\alpha\, F(\alpha) = z.K(z)$ serves as a substitute for $K(\iota\alpha\, F(\alpha))$.

Theorem VIII.2.11. If α is subject to the restriction $K(\alpha)$ and z does not occur in $\iota\alpha\, F(\alpha)$, then $\vdash (\mathrm{E}z).\iota\alpha\, F(\alpha) = z.K(z)$.

Proof. By $\vdash \iota\alpha\, F(\alpha) = \iota\alpha\, F(\alpha)$, we get $\vdash (\mathrm{E}z).\iota\alpha\, F(\alpha) = z$ by Thm. VIII.2.7. So by rule C, $\iota\alpha\, F(\alpha) = z$. We now proceed by cases (see 6 in Sec. 5 of Chapter II).

Case 1. $(\mathrm{E}_1\alpha)\, F(\alpha)$. Then $\iota\alpha\, F(\alpha) = \iota x\, (K(x)F(x))$ by Thm.VIII.2.10, Part I. So $\iota x\, (K(x)F(x)) = z$. Now from $(\mathrm{E}_1\alpha)\, F(\alpha)$, we get $(\mathrm{E}_1 x)\, K(x) F(x)$ by Thm.VII.2.3, and so get $(x):\iota x\, (K(x)F(x)) = x. \equiv .K(x)F(x)$ by Axiom scheme 11. So $\iota x\, (K(x)F(x)) = z. \equiv .K(z).F(z)$. So $K(z)$, and hence $\iota\alpha\, F(\alpha) = z.K(z)$, and so $(\mathrm{E}z).\iota\alpha\, F(\alpha) = z.K(z)$.

Case 2. $\sim(\mathrm{E}_1\alpha)\, F(\alpha)$. Then $\iota\alpha\, F(\alpha) = A$ by Thm.VIII.2.10, Part II. So $A = z$. However, we chose A so that $\vdash K(A)$, and so $K(z)$. Then $(\mathrm{E}z).\iota\alpha\, F(\alpha) = z.K(z)$.

Corollary. If α is subject to the restriction $K(\alpha)$ and there is no confusion of bound variables in $K(\iota\alpha\, F(\alpha))$, then $\vdash K(\iota\alpha\, F(\alpha))$.

Theorem VIII.2.12. If α and β are subject to the restriction $K(\alpha)$, then:

I. $\vdash (\alpha)\, F(\alpha). \supset .F(\iota\beta\, G(\beta))$.
II. $\vdash (\alpha).F(\alpha) \equiv G(\alpha): \supset :\iota\alpha\, F(\alpha) = \iota\alpha\, G(\alpha)$.
III. $\vdash \iota\alpha\, F(\alpha) = \iota\beta\, F(\beta)$.
IV. If there are no free occurrences of x in $\iota\alpha\, F(\alpha)$, then $\vdash (\mathrm{E}_1\alpha)\, F(\alpha) : \supset : (x):\iota\alpha\, F(\alpha) = x. \equiv .K(x).F(x)$.
V. If there are no free occurrences of β in $\iota\alpha\, F(\alpha)$, then $\vdash (\mathrm{E}_1\alpha)\, F(\alpha): \supset : (\beta):\iota\alpha\, F(\alpha) = \beta. \equiv .F(\beta)$.

Proof of I. By Thm.VIII.2.11 and rule C, $\iota\beta\, G(\beta) = z.K(z)$. By Axiom scheme 6, $\vdash (\alpha)\, F(\alpha): \supset :K(z) \supset F(z)$. So $(\alpha)\, F(\alpha). \supset .F(z)$, and from this by $z = \iota\beta\, G(\beta)$ we get $(\alpha)\, F(\alpha). \supset .F(\iota\beta\, G(\beta))$.

Proof of II. $(\alpha).F(\alpha) \equiv G(\alpha)$ is $(x):K(x). \supset .F(x) \equiv G(x)$, from which we quickly get $(x):K(x).F(x). \equiv .K(x).G(x)$.

Case 1. $(\mathrm{E}_1\alpha)\, F(\alpha)$. That is, $(\mathrm{E}_1 x).K(x).F(x)$. Then by Ex.VII.2.3, $(\mathrm{E}_1 x).K(x).G(x)$. So by Thm.VIII.2.10, Part I, $\iota\alpha\, F(\alpha) = \iota x\, (K(x).F(x))$ and $\iota\alpha\, G(\alpha) = \iota x\, (K(x).G(x))$. However, by Axiom scheme 9, $\iota x\, (K(x).F(x)) = \iota x\, (K(x).G(x))$. So $\iota\alpha\, F(\alpha) = \iota\alpha\, G(\alpha)$.

Case 2. $\sim(\mathrm{E}_1\alpha)\, F(\alpha)$. Then $\sim(\mathrm{E}_1\alpha)\, G(\alpha)$ by Ex.VII.2.3. So by

Thm.VIII.2.10, Part II, $\iota\alpha\, F(\alpha) = A$ and $\iota\alpha\, G(\alpha) = A$. So $\iota\alpha\, F(\alpha) = \iota\alpha\, G(\alpha)$.

Proof of III. There is really nothing to prove, since in general the variable α does not actually occur in the expanded form of $\iota\alpha\, F(\alpha)$. However, to justify using for $\iota\alpha\, F(\alpha)$ a formula in which some other variable occurs bound, we need to know that (aside from avoiding confusion of bound variables) the choice of this other variable is immaterial. On this point we are assured by Axiom scheme 10.

Proof of IV. Assume $(\mathrm{E}_1\alpha).F(\alpha)$. Then by Thm.VIII.2.10, $\iota\alpha\, F(\alpha) = \iota x\, (K(x).F(x))$. However, by Axiom scheme 11 we have $(x){:}\iota x\, (K(x).F(x)) = x. \equiv .K(x).F(x)$. So we get $(x){:}\iota\alpha\, F(\alpha) = x. \equiv .K(x)F(x)$.

Proof of V. Assume $(\mathrm{E}_1\alpha).F(\alpha)$. Then by Part IV, $(x){:}\iota\alpha\, F(\alpha) = x. \equiv . K(x)F(x)$. So $(x){:}.K(x){:} \supset {:}\iota\alpha\, F(\alpha) = x. \equiv .F(x)$. That is, $(\beta){:}\iota\alpha\, F(\alpha) = \beta. \equiv .F(\beta)$.

Note that in I, III, and V it is necessary that α and β be subject to the same restriction. In the case of I and V, this is clear from the proof, and in the case of III it turns out that $\iota\alpha\, F(\alpha)$ and $\iota\beta\, F(\beta)$ are abbreviations of quite different statements if α and β are subject to different restrictions.

EXERCISES

VIII.2.1. Prove:

(a) $\vdash \iota x\, P = \iota y\, Q. \equiv .\iota y\, Q = \iota x\, P.$
(b) $\vdash \iota x\, P = \iota y\, Q.\iota y\, Q = \iota z\, R. \supset .\iota x\, P = \iota z\, R.$
(c) $\vdash F(\iota x\, P). \equiv .(\mathrm{E}x).x = \iota x\, P.F(x).$
(d) $\vdash F(\iota x\, P){:} \equiv {:}(x){:}x = \iota x\, P. \supset .F(x).$

VIII.2.2. Prove that, if y does not occur free in $\iota x\, P$, then

$$\vdash F(\iota x\, P). \equiv .(\mathrm{E}y).y = \iota x\, P.F(y),$$

and explain where the proof would break down if there were free occurrences of y in $\iota x\, P$.

VIII.2.3. Taking $F(y)$ to be $y = y$, find a mathematical statement P such that $(\mathrm{E}_1x)\, P$ is true and $F(\iota x\, P). \equiv .(\mathrm{E}y).y = \iota x\, P.F(y)$ is false.

VIII.2.4. If $F(x)$, $F(\iota x\, P)$, and $F(\iota y\, Q)$ are interpreted by our conventions, prove $\vdash \iota x\, P = \iota y\, Q. \supset .F(\iota x\, P) \equiv F(\iota y\, Q)$.

VIII.2.5. Prove

$$\vdash (y){:}(x).y = x \equiv P. \supset .y = \iota x\, P.$$

VIII.2.6. Prove that, if there are no free occurrences of y in P, then

$$\vdash (\mathrm{E}_1x)\, P{:} \supset {:}F(\iota x\, P). \equiv .(\mathrm{E}y).F(y).(x).y = x \equiv P.$$

VIII.2.7. In the preceding exercise, indicate why none of our conventions ensures that there are no free occurrences of y in P, and show where the proof breaks down if we permit P to contain some free occurrences of y.

VIII.2.8. Prove that, if α and β are subject to the restriction $K(\alpha)$, then $\vdash (\beta).\iota\alpha\ (\alpha = \beta) = \beta$. State where the proof would break down if α and β were not subject to the same restriction.

VIII.2.9. Prove that, if α is subject to the restriction $K(\alpha)$, then

$$\vdash F(\iota\alpha\ G(\alpha)). \supset .(\mathrm{E}x).K(x).F(x).$$

VIII.2.10. Prove that in Thm.VIII.2.9, if we replace y by a variable α subject to the restriction $K(\alpha)$, the conclusions still hold if we insert the additional hypothesis $K(A_1).K(A_2). \cdots .K(A_n)$ into each conclusion.

VIII.2.11. Let "$x \in R$" denote "x is a real number" and let $<$ have its customary numerical significance. Using "$x \in R$", $<$, and logical symbols write a formula for "the least of x, y, and z."

VIII.2.12. Supply the conditions on free and bound variables needed to make the following statement valid, and prove the resulting valid statement.

$$\vdash (x,y).F_1(x,y) \equiv F_2(x,y).: \supset :.(z).G_1(z) \equiv G_2(z): \supset :\iota y\ G_1(\iota x\ F_1(x,y)) = \iota y\ G_2(\iota x\ F_2(x,y)).$$

3. Uses of Descriptions in Everyday Mathematics. The uses of descriptions in everyday mathematics are so numerous that we shall just point to a few instances to indicate this widespread use. Some notion of the extensive use of descriptions can be got from the fact that "the" is the most common word in the English language and that most uses of "the" occur in descriptions. When we speak of "the line through two points," "the set of all primes," "the derivative of $f(x)$," etc., we are using descriptions. All particular constants or functions of mathematics are given by descriptions.

In proving theorems about descriptions, most of the results do not follow from any special axioms about descriptions, but from the description itself. In all practical cases where we are dealing with $\iota x\ F(x)$, we can prove $(\mathrm{E}_1x)\ F(x)$, and hence infer $F(\iota x\ F(x))$ (unless there is confusion of bound variables, which there never is in any practical case), and practically all theorems about $\iota x\ F(x)$ are derived from the result $F(\iota x\ F(x))$. We occasionally use Axiom scheme 9 to prove important equalities between different descriptions, and indeed some of the most useful equalities in mathematics come from Axiom scheme 9. A typical use of Axiom scheme 9 occurred in the proof of Thm.VIII.2.8.

We have encountered descriptions many times already in various of our examples. Since we had not yet explained the theory of descriptions, we tried to find examples with as few descriptions as possible, and when we could not avoid descriptions, we treated them as part of the mathematics. Let us now go back and clear up the use of descriptions in one of our examples. On pages 136 to 139 we formalized Bôcher's proof that the sum of two continuous functions is continuous. The first use of a description occurs in the notation $f(x)$. We cannot now give any further details, but the entire question of the treatment of functions will be taken up later and will be seen to depend greatly on the use of descriptions. Our next description is the quantity $\varepsilon/2$. This might be defined as $\iota w\ (w > 0.w + w = \varepsilon)$ or in various other ways according to how many of the symbols $+$, $\times$, 2, etc., are then available. However it is defined, it is a description, and our use of Axiom scheme 6 on page 137 must really be a use of Axiom scheme 8.

On page 138, our definition of δ as the smaller of δ_1 and δ_2 is a definition by cases. That is, we take δ to be

$$\iota w\ (w = \delta_1 . \delta_1 \leq \delta_2 . \mathbf{v} . w = \delta_2 . \delta_1 > \delta_2).$$

Then by Thm.VIII.2.9, Part II, we get

$$\vdash \delta_1 \leq \delta_2 . \supset . \delta = \delta_1 .$$

$$\vdash \delta_1 > \delta_2 . \supset . \delta = \delta_2 .$$

From these, we can infer $\delta > 0$, $\delta \leq \delta_1$, $\delta \leq \delta_2$ as follows. Since $\delta_1 > 0$ and $\delta_2 > 0$, we have $\delta_1 \leq \delta_2 \mathbf{v} \delta_1 > \delta_2$ by a theorem of mathematics. We now give a proof by cases (see 5 of Sec. 5 of Chapter II).

Case 1. $\delta_1 \leq \delta_2$. Then $\delta = \delta_1$ so that $\delta \leq \delta_1$ and $\delta \leq \delta_2$ and $\delta > 0$ (since $\delta_1 > 0$).

Case 2. $\delta_1 > \delta_2$. Then $\delta = \delta_2$ so that $\delta \leq \delta_2$ and $\delta < \delta_1$ (giving $\delta \leq \delta_1$) and $\delta > 0$.

Since δ is a description, our reference to Thm.VI.7.3 on page 139 should actually be a reference to Thm.VIII.2.7.

CHAPTER IX

CLASS MEMBERSHIP

1. The Notion of a Class. The notion of a class, or set, or aggregate, or ensemble is familiar and widely used. The theory of point sets has received especial attention, but many other types of classes are of common occurrence, for instance, the class of differentiable functions, the set of prime numbers, the cosets of a subgroup, etc. Some sets are ordered, for instance, the Fourier coefficients of a periodic integrable function. We shall later consider ordered sets but for the present shall confine our attention to unordered sets. For us, the word "class" or "set" will always mean an unordered class or set, unless explicitly stated otherwise. We make no distinction at all between "class" and "set."

We shall use "ϵ" for the relation of membership between an object and a class, so that "$x \epsilon \alpha$" shall denote that the object denoted by "x" is in the class denoted by "α." That is, x is a member of α. Thus, if "DF" denotes the class of differentiable functions, "$f \epsilon$ DF" shall denote that f is a differentiable function. Likewise, if "PN" denotes the set of prime numbers, then "$3 \epsilon PN$" shall denote that 3 is a prime number.

The notation $x_1, x_2, \ldots, x_n \epsilon \alpha$ shall denote $(x_1 \epsilon \alpha)(x_2 \epsilon \alpha) \cdots (x_n \epsilon \alpha)$. When necessary to avoid ambiguity, we shall enclose $x \epsilon \alpha$ in parentheses. If no parentheses are used, $x \epsilon \alpha$ is to have the minimum possible scope. We shall commonly write $\sim(x \epsilon \alpha)$ as $\sim x \epsilon \alpha$. This is possible because x will never be a statement, and as $\sim$ can be applied only to statements, it must be applied to the complete statement $x \epsilon \alpha$, and not to the portion x, which is not a statement. Many logicians write $x \sim \epsilon \alpha$ or $x \not\epsilon \alpha$ for $\sim(x \epsilon \alpha)$.

Intuitively there seems to be a vast distinction between the notions of finite and infinite class. In theory, one could always collect together the members of a finite class and thus have explicitly before one a totality comprising the class in question. No such procedure is even theoretically possible with an infinite class. Thus, in dealing with an infinite class, one is laboring under a handicap of intangibility which is supposedly not present when one is dealing with a finite class. Of course, many finite classes arising in scientific problems are quite as intangible as any infinite class. The classes of stars in this galaxy or atoms in this sheet of paper or animals on this planet are as incapable of comprehension as a totality as is the class of prime numbers. So the notion of a class as an assembled totality will not be useful for us. Although one may think of the simple aggregates encountered in daily life (*e.g.*, family, wardrobe, etc.) as assembled totalities, this will not do for the infinite or very numerous finite classes needed in mathematical discourse.

How, then, shall we treat these classes? Perhaps the first conscious effort to deal with infinite classes came with the study of geometrical loci. A geometrical locus is the set of points satisfying some condition. Though it is past the power of the human mind to conceive of the totality of all points in the usual geometrical locus, the defining condition can be easily grasped. Consequently, in trying to treat geometrical loci, it was found expedient to operate with the defining condition rather than to attempt to manipulate the intangible infinite totality which actually constitutes the locus. This worked so well that it has been extended to all infinite classes, so that now the standard procedure for treating an infinite class is to find a defining condition for it and to deal with the defining condition.

A condition on x is just a statement containing free occurrences of x. Thus the statement, "x is equidistant from the points A and B" is a condition on x. This condition determines a class of points, namely, the perpendicular bisector of the line joining A and B. When we say that a condition determines a class, we mean that exactly those objects are members of the class which satisfy the condition. That is, if $F(x)$ is a condition and α is a class, we say that $F(x)$ determines α if and only if $(x).x \epsilon \alpha \equiv F(x)$.

This is familiar from the treatment of geometrical loci. To show that the perpendicular bisector of the line joining A and B is the locus of points equidistant from A and B we must show two things:

(1) If x is on the bisector, it is equidistant from A and B.
(2) If x is equidistant from A and B, it is on the bisector.

If α is the class of points constituting the bisector, so that $x \epsilon \alpha$ means that x is on the bisector, and if $F(x)$ is the statement that x is equidistant from A and B, then (1) and (2) above are, respectively:

(1) $(x).x \epsilon \alpha \supset F(x)$.
(2) $(x).F(x) \supset x \epsilon \alpha$.

When one has proved both (1) and (2), one has

$$(x).x \epsilon \alpha \equiv F(x).$$

As another instance of a class being defined by a condition $F(x)$, recall that the derived set, β, of a set, α, is defined by the condition that the members of β shall be limit points of α. In this case $F(x)$ would be $(\varepsilon)(\mathrm{E}y).$ $y \neq x.y \epsilon \alpha.|x - y| < \varepsilon$ and we recall that the definition of β was given by

$$(x):.x \epsilon \beta : \equiv :(\varepsilon)(\mathrm{E}y).y \neq x.y \epsilon \alpha.|x - y| < \varepsilon.$$

In quite analogous fashion, if we wish α to be the set of points of discontinuity of a function, f, we write

$$(x):.x \epsilon \alpha : \equiv :(\mathrm{E}\varepsilon)(\delta)(\mathrm{E}y).\ |\ y - x\ | < \delta . \sim(|\ f(y) - f(x)\ | < \varepsilon).$$

Other instances of classes which are determined by conditions are the class of prime divisors of an integer, the class of nth roots of unity, a circle (all points at a distance r from a point c), etc.

Clearly conditions can define finite classes; for instance, the condition "x is an even prime" defines a class with the single member 2. Conversely, every finite class is determined by some condition. In particular, if $a_1, a_2, \ldots, a_n$ are the members of the finite class, then

$$x = a_1 \mathbf{v} x = a_2 \mathbf{v} \cdots \mathbf{v} x = a_n$$

is a condition determining the class. Thus the procedure of defining classes by conditions is valid for finite classes as well as for infinite classes and so has won general acceptance as a suitable procedure for defining all kinds of classes. There is also general acceptance of the principle that every condition determines a class, and every class has a determining condition. As it happens, this principle is false. Nevertheless, belief in it is so strong that proofs of its falsity are called paradoxes and are widely ignored.

To show that not every class has a determining condition, we give the following proof, known as Skolem's paradox (see Skolem, 1929). For each real number, we can determine at least one class of real numbers; for instance, the class of all smaller real numbers, or the class of all larger real numbers (the two classes of a Dedekind cut), or the class whose sole member is the given real number, etc. Thus, the set of all classes of real numbers is not denumerable, since the set of real numbers is not denumerable. Then the set of all classes whatsoever is certainly not denumerable. So, if every class has a determining condition, the set of conditions must be nondenumerable. As every condition is a statement, the set of statements must accordingly also be nondenumerable. However, the set of statements is denumerable. For English statements, this is easily shown, since each statement is a finite sequence of letters of the English alphabet, and there are only a finite number of letters in the alphabet. Even with a denumerable alphabet, such as most symbolic logics have, the number of statements would still be denumerable.

The fairly obvious suggestions have been made that one might either use a nondenumerable alphabet or else permit statements which are infinite sequences of letters (see Helmer, 1938). We cannot conceive how to do this without violating our basic consideration that all our dealings with statements must be of a constructive sort. Moreover, an increase in the number of statements would not necessarily eliminate the Skolem paradox.

If one has as many statements as there are real numbers, for instance, one still can derive the Skolem paradox by starting with some still more numerous class, such as the class of all functions of real numbers.

Some people propose to side-step the Skolem paradox by saying that we have prescribed wrongly what a condition is. We have said that a condition on x is a statement with free occurrences of x. If, instead, one defines a condition as a proposition with free occurrences of x, and if one is sufficiently vague as to what a proposition is, then one cannot prove that the set of conditions is denumerable. Thus one avoids the Skolem paradox, but one must then admit the existence of propositions which cannot be expressed by any statement.

We fail to see that this means of avoiding the Skolem paradox is of any value. The advantage of having a determining condition for a class is that, while one cannot deal directly with the class because it has an infinity of members, one can deal with the condition, because it is a finite statement. If, however, we allow the condition to become a vague thing called a proposition, about which we know essentially no more than we do about the class we wish to deal with, then we lose the advantage that should accrue from having a determining condition for our class.

Moreover, it really doesn't matter that there should be classes with no determining conditions because no one will ever exhibit such a class. As soon as one exhibits some particular class, one can then find a condition which determines that class, for if no better condition is available, one can take the condition of being a member of that class. Since we are dealing with an explicit class, this will give an explicit condition for that class.

The above argument shows that there must be some classes which can never be explicitly exhibited, and that it is among these classes that the classes will occur for which there are no determining conditions.

So we stand by our original prescription that a condition on x shall be a statement with free occurrences of x, and accept the fact that there must therefore be some classes (which can never be exhibited) for which there is no determining condition.

We now turn to a much more painful point, namely, the proof that there are conditions which determine no class. At least three such proofs are known. They are called the Russell paradox, the Cantor paradox, and the Burali-Forti paradox. The Cantor paradox depends upon the theory of cardinal numbers, and the Burali-Forti paradox depends upon the theory of ordinal numbers, and so discussion of these two paradoxes will be postponed until we have developed these theories.

However, the Russell paradox is very simple. The condition $F(x)$ which Russell considered is the condition $\sim x \epsilon x$. This seems a perfectly respectable condition. In fact, it is satisfied by most objects x. If x is not a class, it can have no members, and in such case certainly $\sim x \epsilon x$. Even for many classes x, we have $\sim x \epsilon x$. For instance, let x be the class of prime numbers, PN. This class is certainly not a prime number, so that $\sim PN \epsilon PN$, and PN satisfies our condition. Similarly for the class of differentiable functions, and many other classes. As many classes and all nonclasses satisfy our condition, it must be a respectable condition. Nevertheless, it determines no class. For suppose it does; then there is an α such that

$$(x)\ (x \epsilon \alpha \equiv \ \sim x \epsilon x).$$

In symbols

$$(\text{E}\alpha)(x)\ (x \epsilon \alpha \equiv \ \sim x \epsilon x).$$

However, by Axiom scheme 6,

$$\vdash (x)\ (x \epsilon \alpha \equiv \ \sim x \epsilon x) \supset (\alpha \epsilon \alpha \equiv \ \sim \alpha \epsilon \alpha).$$

We recollect that $\sim \alpha \epsilon \alpha$ is just $\sim(\alpha \epsilon \alpha)$. So we have

$$\vdash (x)\ (x \epsilon \alpha \equiv \ \sim x \epsilon x) \supset (\alpha \epsilon \alpha \equiv \ \sim(\alpha \epsilon \alpha)).$$

However, by truth tables, $\vdash (P \equiv \sim P) \supset Q{\sim}Q$. So

$$\vdash (x)\ (x \epsilon \alpha \equiv \ \sim x \epsilon x) \supset Q{\sim}Q.$$

Hence by rule G and Thm.VI.6.6, Part VII,

$$\vdash (\text{E}\alpha)(x)\ (x \epsilon \alpha \equiv \ \sim x \epsilon x) \supset Q{\sim}Q.$$

Hence, if the condition $\sim x \epsilon x$ could determine a class, one could derive a contradiction.

The Cantor and Burali-Forti paradoxes were discovered around the same time as the Russell paradox but they are quite complex, enough so to permit plausible doubt of their validity on various grounds. Not so the Russell paradox, which uses only simple and well-established logical principles. Accordingly, it was mainly because of the appearance of the Russell paradox that a serious doubt was raised against the validity of the principle that every condition should determine a class.

We have carefully led up to this point in such a manner as to suggest that the appropriate reaction to Russell's (and Cantor's and Burali-Forti's) paradox is to abandon the principle that every condition should determine a class; indeed, such is our opinion. Nevertheless, resistance to such a reaction has been persistent and prolonged. Various alternative measures have been proposed to preserve the principle that every condition shall determine a class.

We give a brief survey of the better known of these measures. Let us list the key steps in the proof of the Russell paradox.

1. $\sim x \epsilon x$ is a statement.
2. $\sim x \epsilon x$ contains free occurrences of x.
3. Hence $\sim x \epsilon x$ is a condition.
4. $(x)\ (x \epsilon \alpha \equiv \sim x \epsilon x)$ is the statement that the condition $\sim x \epsilon x$ determines the class α.
5. $(x)\ (x \epsilon \alpha \equiv \sim x \epsilon x) \supset (\alpha \epsilon \alpha \equiv \sim \alpha \epsilon \alpha)$.
6. $(P \equiv \sim P) \supset Q \sim Q$.
7. Every condition determines a class.

Anyone who would seek to preserve the validity of step 7 must perforce deny one of the other steps. Step 2 seems unexceptionable, and step 3 merely embodies the definition of a condition. Step 5 uses the principle that a statement which is true for all objects x must be true for α, and can hardly be denied. This leaves only steps 1, 4, and 6 that can plausibly be denied if one wishes to preserve the validity of step 7.

Various proposals for eliminating the Russell paradox involve denial of one or more of steps 1, 4, or 6.

Step 6 depends upon the system of truth values set up in Chapter II. To deny step 6 would necessitate devising a new system to replace the statement and predicate calculus. This is a large undertaking. It has been attempted by a few people but not yet completed by anyone. A favorite starting point is to assume three truth values instead of the two truth values of Chapter II, and thus get a "three-valued" logic. This eliminates step 6, but unless the three-valued logic is set up with a great deal of care, alternative forms of the Russell paradox can still be derived. A particular three-valued system set up by Bočvar (see Bočvar, 1939) does appear to avoid the Russell paradox. However, Bočvar's system is only very partially developed, and it still remains to be seen if Bočvar's system avoids the Cantor and Burali-Forti paradoxes. Even if it does, it represents a violent departure from accepted mathematical reasoning and so is not likely to become popular any time in the near future.

On the whole, attempts to deny step 6 have not been very successful.

There are systems of logic in widespread use which deny step 4. These developed from a system invented by Zermelo and are often called systems of Zermelo set theory, or just "set theory" for short (see Zermelo, 1908, second paper; Gödel, 1940; and Quine, 1951). In set theory, a substitute for step 4 is based on the following notion. Let us consider that there is a distinction between sets and classes. All sets are classes, but some classes are nonsets. Often the term "individual" is used instead of "set," so that some classes are individuals, and some are nonindividuals, while all individuals are classes. The distinction between a set and a nonset is that sets can be members of classes but nonsets cannot be members of anything.

It turns out that every set actually is a member of some class. In other words, x is a set if and only if $(\text{E}\beta)\ x \in \beta$.

As nonsets cannot be members of anything, the members for any class must necessarily be chosen from among sets only. Hence, the class determined by any condition $F(x)$ shall consist not of all objects x which satisfy $F(x)$, but only of all sets x which satisfy $F(x)$. In other words, we express the statement "$F(x)$ determines the class α" by

$$(x).x \in \alpha \equiv F(x)\ (x \text{ is a set}),$$

which is equivalent to

$$(x).x \in \alpha \equiv F(x)(\text{E}\beta)\ x \in \beta.$$

Then step 4 is replaced by

"$(x).x \in \alpha \equiv (\sim x \in x)\ (\text{E}\beta)\ x \in \beta$ is the statement that the condition $\sim x \in x$ determines the class α".

If one assumes that there is a class α determined by $\sim x \in x$, one can then infer $\alpha \in \alpha \equiv (\sim \alpha \in \alpha)\ (\text{E}\beta)\ \alpha \in \beta$. Applying truth values to this leads to no contradiction, but only to the conclusion $\sim(\text{E}\beta)\ \alpha \in \beta$. That is, α is a nonset.

So in Zermelo set theory, the condition $\sim x \in x$ determines a class but this class is a nonset. Similarly both the Cantor and Burali-Forti paradoxes depend at a critical point on some class being a set and so will fail to go through because the class in question can be and apparently is a nonset.

There is still a difficulty to be surmounted. Most of the classes arising in mathematics have to be members of something in one proof or another and hence must be sets. So one must devise a criterion for deciding which classes are sets, and this criterion must admit as sets most classes of mathematics without admitting as sets the critical classes arising in the Russell, Cantor, and Burali-Forti paradoxes. One basic criterion often used is roughly that classes with an excessively large number of members are nonsets. For details, we refer the reader to Gödel, 1940, or Quine, 1951, in which distinct criteria are employed.

On the whole, denial of step 4 in the manner just indicated works reasonably well. Alternatively, a considerable number of mathematicians deny step 1. The two best-known schools of thought in this doctrine are those of Brouwer and Russell, who have contrived definitions of being a statement according to which $\sim x \in x$ is not a statement.

Brouwer (see Heyting, 1934) seems to say that a collection of words, $F(x)$, is a statement only in case there is a constructive method whereby for each x one can determine definitely whether $F(x)$ is true or false. Thus "x is a prime" is a statement because one can test the primality of x by dividing it by all integers $\leq\sqrt{x}$. On the other hand, "x is an integer exponent such that there are nonzero integers a, b, and c with $a^x + b^x = c^x$" is perhaps not a statement, because there is no way known to decide for a given x whether the statement is false or true. Brouwer's restriction is drastic but effective. There is no constructive method whereby for each x one can determine definitely whether $\sim x \epsilon x$, and so $\sim x \epsilon x$ is not a statement. In fact, step 6 is also thrown out, since it is not a statement either.

Brouwer has got some followers, but since his criterion apparently rules that most of the theorems of mathematics are not statements, there has been no general acceptance of his views.

Russell was much more moderate in his proposal. He recognized that one should set up the criterion for what a statement is in such a way that most theorems of mathematics would remain statements, but $\sim x \epsilon x$ would fail to be a statement. He proposed his famous theory of types to provide such a criterion. According to this, one conceives of the objects of discourse arranged into types. The objects of type n shall be members only of objects of type $n + 1$, and objects of type $n + 1$ shall have as members only objects of type n. Any sentence violating these conditions is to be outlawed, and not considered a statement.

Clearly $x \epsilon x$ violates the conditions, because whatever type x is in, any member of x must belong to the next lower type and so cannot be x. So $x \epsilon x$ is outlawed, and with it $\sim x \epsilon x$. Russell pointed out that certain sentences in the derivations of Cantor's paradox and Burali-Forti's paradox would likewise be outlawed by his theory of types, so that use of the theory of types would eliminate these paradoxes also.

One can reduce Russell's theory of types to a mechanical rule. Consider any sentence P and consider the parts of it of the form $x \epsilon \alpha$. If P is not to violate the type restrictions, x must be in a type exactly one lower than α for every part of the form $x \epsilon \alpha$ in P. Suppose we attach as subscripts to the x's and α's the numbers of the types to which they belong. Then we have attached numerical subscripts to the variables in such a way that, in every part of the form $x \epsilon \alpha$, the α has a subscript exactly one greater than the subscript on the x.

Quine (see Quine, 1937) has suggested that any sentence for which such an assignment of subscripts is possible be called stratified. Thus we see that the theory of types would outlaw every sentence which is not stratified and leave only stratified sentences as statements.

Actually the theory of types would outlaw many other sentences besides those which are not stratified. The original theory of types, as set forth by Whitehead and Russell in "Principia Mathematica," was a wondrously complex affair involving multiple subscripts not only on variables but on statements also. Ramsey (see Ramsey, 1926) later introduced the so-called "simplified theory of types." In this system, single subscripts are attached to variables, and to variables only, but they are permanently attached. Then a sentence is a statement if and only if for every part of the form $x \epsilon \alpha$, the subscript permanently attached to α is exactly one greater than the subscript permanently attached to x.

Quine (see Quine, 1937) has suggested as a still simpler theory of types that one simply admit as statements all sentences which are stratified. This is appreciably more liberal than Ramsey's system. Quine would admit both $x \epsilon y$ and $y \epsilon x$ as statements, because each is (separately) stratified. Thus, to stratify $x \epsilon y$, we attach subscripts so: $x_1 \epsilon y_2$. Similarly, to stratify $y \epsilon x$, we attach subscripts so: $y_1 \epsilon x_2$. However, Ramsey has subscripts permanently attached to each variable, and so in both $x \epsilon y$ and $y \epsilon x$ there would already be subscripts on x and y, and it would be the values of these permanently attached subscripts which would determine whether $x \epsilon y$ or $y \epsilon x$ should be statements. For $x \epsilon y$ to be a statement, the subscript on x must be one less than the subscript on y. If $y \epsilon x$ is to be a statement, then the subscript on y must be one less than the subscript on x. Accordingly, for Ramsey, it could never be that both $x \epsilon y$ and $y \epsilon x$ are statements, and often neither would be a statement. However $x \epsilon x$, and hence $\sim x \epsilon x$, would not be a statement for either Quine or Ramsey.

Quine's theory of types seems adequate to avoid the known paradoxes, and is much less cumbersome than the Russell or Ramsey theory of types. However, there is one disconcerting feature of the Quine theory of types. Both $x \epsilon y$ and $y \epsilon x$ are stratified, as we saw, so that neither is outlawed. However, their logical product, $(x \epsilon y)(y \epsilon x)$, is not stratified, and so must be outlawed. When x's occur in different statements, as $x \epsilon y$ and $y \epsilon x$, they may have different subscripts attached for the purposes of stratification, since separate sentences are to be stratified separately. However, throughout a single sentence, such as $(x \epsilon y)(y \epsilon x)$, one must attach the same subscript to all the x's that occur. The same applies to y, and so one easily sees that $(x \epsilon y)(y \epsilon x)$ cannot be stratified, though its parts can be stratified separately.

All in all, denial of step 1 is feasible, but not wholly satisfactory.

There still remains the possibility of denying step 7, which appeals to us as the most natural of all. We adopt this procedure.

As we are not denying step 1, we have no need to outlaw various types of sentences. We shall consider any declarative sentence to be a statement. In particular, $\sim x \epsilon x$ is to be considered a perfectly legitimate statement and hence is a condition. However, we do not claim that every condition shall determine a class. In fact, from our point of view, the Russell paradox is merely a proof that $\sim x \epsilon x$ does not determine a class. Similarly, the Cantor and Burali-Forti paradoxes are merely proofs that a couple of other statements do not determine classes.

We now wish a criterion for deciding which conditions shall determine classes. Clearly this criterion must exclude the statements arising in the paradoxes, while including all the conditions commonly used in mathematics to determine classes. Our problem is analogous to the problem in Zermelo set theory of finding a criterion which would classify most classes of mathematics as sets, but which would classify as nonsets the classes arising in connection with the paradoxes. So far, no means of adapting the solution of the set-theory problem to our problem has been suggested. Instead, we have adopted a suggestion of Quine (see Quine, 1937) that stratification could be used as the criterion. This criterion is to be used in a positive rather than a negative sense. That is, we require that, if a condition is stratified, then it shall determine a class, but we do not insist that, if a condition is unstratified, then it may not determine a class. It will turn out in fact that many unstratified conditions do determine classes. Fortunately, this is not true of the critical statements arising in the known paradoxes, as far as can be determined, and so the known paradoxes merely serve to prove that certain unstratified conditions fail to determine classes.

The resulting system, which is used in the present text, is known as "Quine's New Foundations," after the title of the paper in which it was proposed (see Quine, 1937).

It will perhaps have occurred to the reader that, since stratification seems to provide us with an answer to our problem of deciding which conditions shall determine classes, it might provide an answer to the analogous problem in Zermelo set theory of deciding which classes shall be sets and which nonsets. This was suggested by Quine (see Quine, 1940), who proposed that all classes determined by stratified conditions be admitted as sets. Actually, this is too liberal. It seems to avoid the Russell and Cantor paradoxes, but permits the Burali-Forti paradox (see Rosser, 1942). However, by adding one additional very minor restriction, Quine's proposal appears to work quite well (see Quine, 1951).

There is a warning in this. The problem of the exact relationship between classes and statements is a difficult and subtle one and must be approached quite warily. Undoubtedly the last word on the subject has not yet been said. All the present suggestions for avoiding the paradoxes retain a tinge of artificiality. Certainly the theory of types is artificial. In the Zermelo set theory, the distinction between sets and nonsets is irksome, and the various criteria for deciding between sets and nonsets are not intuitively very natural.

In the system of the present text, Quine's New Foundations, it is irksome that not all conditions determine classes, and the criterion of stratification for deciding which conditions shall determine classes is not intuitively natural.

Both set theory and Quine's New Foundations reproduce mathematical reasoning with a remarkably close approximation to the unhampered methods in use before the discovery of the paradoxes. Certain regions of the theory of cardinals and ordinals are too near the paradoxes to survive unchanged, but it has been possible to amputate the known paradoxes with remarkably little injury to the main body of mathematics.

Still other means of avoiding the paradoxes have been suggested. Church and Curry agree with us in denying that every condition must determine a class, but their suggestions are very drastic. In effect, they propose dispensing with classes altogether, and dealing only with the conditions themselves. In order to succeed in such an endeavor, they must allow that one operate on conditions in a way which is usually not allowed (and usually not necessary, because one can ordinarily use operations on classes instead). In their first attempt, Church and Curry were too liberal in allowing operations on conditions and became involved in a rather intricate and unforeseen contradiction (see Kleene and Rosser). Their present suggestions (see Church, 1941, and Curry, 1942) are more conservative and are probably free from contradictions. However, these suggestions have not yet been thoroughly developed.

In summary, if one wishes something as like classical mathematics as possible, one has at present the option of choosing either a Zermelo set theory or Quine's New Foundations or a version of type theory.

In view of the fact that the paradoxes arose from logical principles which had been generally accepted for thousands of years, one might wonder if one does not run a risk with any of the presently proposed systems that a contradiction may appear after the system has been generally accepted and in use for a long time. Apparently one does. According to a theorem of Gödel (see Gödel, 1931), if a system of logic is adequate for even a reasonable facsimile of present-day mathematics, then there can be no adequate assurance that it is free of contradiction. Failure to derive the known paradoxes is very negative assurance at best and may merely indicate lack of skill on our part. Thus it would be very unwise to adopt a firm belief in the validity of any of the better-known systems of logic. One should always remain aware of the possibility that someone may discover a contradiction in the system to which one has become accustomed and compel a change to some other system. In fact, there is the awkward possibility that present-day mathematics is actually in serious error, so that any formal system which gives a reasonable facsimile of present-day mathematics must contain a contradiction. We do not believe this to be the case, but we can offer no reason why it should not be the case.

2. Axioms for Classes. One of our axioms for classes will have to state that stratified conditions shall determine classes. To state this axiom precisely, we shall need a precise definition of stratification and of what a statement is. Up to now, we have not been able to give a precise definition of what a statement is, because we had not yet introduced all the constituents of statements. Now, with the introduction of the notion of class membership, we have available all constituents of statements and can give a precise definition of what a statement is. Also, we can now define equality and replace Axiom schemes 7A and 7B by a single weaker axiom scheme. Accordingly, this seems a good place to restate our former axioms as well as stating the new axioms for classes.

We now start from scratch. The constituents which we shall allow for building up statements are:

(,), $\sim$, &, ι, ϵ, variables.

With regard to the use of "(" and ")," we should make it clear that our former carefree and indiscriminate use of "( )", "{ }", and "[ ]" is not permitted in a strict formulation such as we now present. Nevertheless, when we have finished presenting the strict formulation, we shall revert to our former practice of omitting parentheses when it can be done unambiguously, and of using different styles of parentheses, or brackets, or braces, or dots, whenever it will help the eye.

The supply of variables is supposed to be inexhaustible. As we never need more than a finite number at a time, it suffices to have a denumerable set of variables.

We now define "term", "statement", "free", and "bound".

(a) Each variable is a term; in this term the occurrence of the variable in question is free.

(b) If A and B are terms, then $(A \epsilon B)$ is a statement; the occurrences of variables in the parts A and B, respectively, are free or bound in $(A \epsilon B)$ according as they are free or bound in A and B, respectively.

(c) If x is a variable and P is a statement, then $(x)\ P$ is a statement and $\iota x\ P$ is a term; in these all occurrences of x are bound, but for each variable different from x the occurrences in the part P are free or bound in $(x)\ P$ and $\iota x\ P$ according as they are free or bound in P.

(d) If P and Q are statements, then $\sim P$ and $(P\&Q)$ are statements; the occurrences of variables in $\sim P$ are free or bound according as they are free or bound in P, and the occurrences of variables in the parts P and Q, respectively, are free or bound in $(P\&Q)$ according as they are free or bound in P and Q, respectively.

It is intended that those combinations of symbols, and only those combinations of symbols, are terms or statements which can be shown to be terms or statements by repeated use of (a), (b), (c), and (d).

Unless otherwise specified, it will be taken for granted in any context that whenever $(A \epsilon B)$ is written A and B are terms; whenever $(x)\ P$ or $\iota x\ P$

is written x is a variable and P is a statement; whenever $\sim P$ is written P is a statement; and whenever $(P \& Q)$ is written P and Q are statements. This convention is to be automatically extended to abbreviations, such as $P \vee Q$, $(\mathrm{E}x)\ P$, etc.

Any occurrence of $(x)\ P$ or $\iota x\ P$ as a part of S will be called an x-bound part of S, and P will be called the scope of (x) or ιx. One can prove by induction on the number of symbols of S that, if x is a variable and S is a statement, then those occurrences (if any) of x in an x-bound part of S are bound in S, and all other occurrences (if any) of x in S are free in S.

If $x_1, x_2, \ldots, x_n$ are distinct variables, then {Sub in S: A_1 for x_1, A_2 for $x_2, \ldots, A_n$ for x_n} shall denote the result of simultaneously replacing each free occurrence (if any) of x_i in S by A_i $(i = 1, 2, \ldots, n)$.

One can prove by induction on the number of symbols of S that, if $A_1, A_2, \ldots, A_n$ are each terms, and S is a term or a statement, then {Sub in S: A_1 for x_1, A_2 for $x_2, \ldots, A_n$ for x_n} is correspondingly a term or a statement.

Whenever we use the notation, it is to be understood that S is a term or statement and $A_1, A_2, \ldots, A_n$ are each terms.

We say that the substitution indicated by {Sub in S: A_1 for x_1, A_2 for x_2, $\ldots$, A_n for x_n} causes confusion of bound variables if there is a variable y and an i $(1 \leq i \leq n)$ such that there is a free occurrence of y in A_i and there is an occurrence of x_i in S which is free in S and occurs in some y-bound part of S; otherwise we say that the substitution causes no confusion of bound variables.

This is merely a precise formulation of our earlier definition of "confusion of bound variables."

We shall commonly use more convenient notations in place of {Sub in S: A_1 for x_1, A_2 for $x_2, \ldots, A_n$ for x_n} in those cases in which the substitution indicated causes no confusion of bound variables. Thus we often write $F(x,y)$ for S and $F(y,y)$ for {Sub in S: y for x}. Also we often write $F(x)$ for S and $F(\iota y\ Q)$ for {Sub in S: $\iota y\ Q$ for x}.

A formula S is said to be stratified if one can attach an integer subscript to each occurrence of each variable in S in such a way that:

(a) If x is a variable and P a statement which is part of S, then all occurrences of x which are free in P shall have the same subscript attached.

(b) If x is a variable which occurs free in a statement P, then in each particular occurrence (if any) of $(x)\ P$ or $\iota x\ P$ as a part of S, the explicitly indicated occurrence of x in the prefix (x) or ιx shall have the same subscript attached as the free occurrences of x in that particular occurrence of P.

(c) In each occurrence in S of a part of the form $(x \in y)$, $(\iota x\ P \in y)$, $(x \in \iota y\ Q)$, or $(\iota x\ P \in \iota y\ Q)$ in which x and y are variables and P and Q are statements, the subscript attached to the occurrence of y which is explicitly indicated shall be exactly one greater than the subscript attached to the occurrence of x which is explicitly indicated.

A discussion of this definition is in order. As indicated in the previous section, stratification is to be a mechanical equivalent of the simple theory of types as applied to any particular formula. Throughout any given formula, all free occurrences of a given variable would be understood as having reference to the same object (this is the standard procedure in mathematics with regard to the use of variables) and hence would all have to be in the same type and hence should have the same subscript attached. This we require in part (a) of the above definition where we interpret "part" in the liberal sense which considers S a part of itself. However, bound occurrences of x in one part of S would generally have no connection with free occurrences of x elsewhere in S, and so could have different subscripts attached. This is permitted by part (b). However, throughout any x-bound part of S, uniformity of type for x is required, and this is the meaning of part (b). One might be tempted to state part (b) in the simpler form:

(b*) All occurrences of x in any particular occurrence of $(x)\ P$ or $\iota x\ P$ shall have the same subscript attached.

However, this is too stringent. P may contain some free occurrences of x, all with the subscript i, and some bound occurrences of x, all with the subscript j. Then the x which goes on the front as part of (x) or ιx should also have the subscript i, but one would not require equality of i and j. Hence we use (b) rather than (b*).

Part (c) is the crux of the definition. It says that a member of a class shall be of type exactly one lower than the class. Moreover, part (c) has the consequence that $\iota x\ P$ shall be considered to have the same type as any free x's occurring in P. This last is quite to be expected if one recalls the meaning of $\iota x\ P$.

Sometimes it is stated as a requirement for stratification that all subscripts should be positive. This is quite a trivial requirement, for if one has an assignment of subscripts satisfying (a), (b), and (c), one can add some integer uniformly to all subscripts and get another assignment of subscripts satisfying (a), (b), and (c). So if a formula can be stratified, it can be stratified with all subscripts positive.

One can readily make a direct test for stratification of any particular formula S. Choose a variable occurring in S and choose a subscript, zero perhaps. Attach this subscript to an occurrence of the variable. Then (a) and (b) will perhaps require attaching the same subscript to other occurrences of the variable. If already (c) is violated, our formula is not stratified. If (c) is not violated, then (c) will usually require attaching appropriate subscripts to further occurrences of variables. Then (a) and (b) may require still further attachments. These may perhaps violate (c), in which case the formula is not stratified. Otherwise, use (c) to determine still other attachments. Ordinarily this process will proceed until one has either stratified the formula or proved it unstratified. However, occasionally the process will terminate and there will still remain occurrences of variables with no subscripts attached. One merely attaches a subscript to one of them and starts the process going again. If one repeats this sort of thing enough, one eventually will either stratify the formula or prove that it cannot be stratified.

Although we are not using the theory of types at all, nevertheless stratification had its origin in the theory of types, and it is convenient to speak of the subscript attached to a variable as the type of the variable. In this connection, we also speak of the type of $\iota x\ P$, by which we mean the subscript attached to the explicitly indicated occurrence of x in the prefix ιx.

The reader is perhaps troubled by the fact that, no matter what the terms A and B are, we permit formation of the statement $(A \in B)$, which would make sense only if B is a class. That is, we have made no provision for nonclasses. To put it otherwise, we admit as statements only sentences concerned exclusively with classes. It might be argued with good reason that this is an unnecessarily restricted definition of a statement. However, it is sufficiently broad for the development of mathematics, which is our sole aim at present, and so we take it as our definition. It is certainly possible for anyone to extend the definition of a statement by allowing as statements additional sentences besides those prescribed by our definition above. Such a person would then have to choose appropriate axioms to go with his new definition of a statement. However, we leave such matters to someone else and proceed with statements which speak only of classes.

Since all our objects of discourse are classes, we can take as the criterion of equality of two objects just the criterion of equality of two classes. Two classes are equal if and only if they have the same members. Some philosophers would not accept this, but mathematicians generally would, and we shall. Thus $\alpha = \beta$ if and only if

$$(x)\ (x \in \alpha \equiv x \in \beta).$$

Accordingly, we adopt the definition:

If x is a variable and A and B are terms and x does not occur in either A or B, then

$$(x)\ (x \in A \equiv x \in B)$$

shall be abbreviated to

$$A = B$$

or occasionally to

$$A =_x B$$

in case we wish to indicate just which x we are using. On occasion we write

$$A = B = C \quad \text{for} \quad (A = B)(B = C),$$

$$A = B = C = D \quad \text{for} \quad (A = B)(B = C)(C = D),$$

etc.

Clearly the free occurrences of variables in $A = B$ are just the free occurrences in A or B, and the bound occurrences are all occurrences of x plus the bound occurrences in A or B.

If one is trying to stratify a formula containing

$$A =_x B,$$

one can see by referring to the definition that both A and B would have to have a type one higher than the type of x. That is, in

$$A = B,$$

A and B would have to have the same type. Conversely, if they can be simultaneously stratified in such a way that they have the same type, then $A = B$ can be stratified. This can be put in more exact form. Suppose we are trying to determine if S is stratified, and S contains a part $A = B$. To apply the definition of stratification as stated, one would expect to have to replace $A = B$ by its definition. However, this is not necessary, since it suffices to assign the same types to A and B. In effect then, we are avoiding the necessity of replacing $A = B$ by its definition by adding to the specifications for stratification another part:

(d) In each occurrence in S of a part of the form $x = y$, $\iota x\ P = y$, $x = \iota y\ Q$, or $\iota x\ P = \iota y\ Q$ in which x and y are variables and P and Q are statements, the same subscript shall be attached to the explicitly indicated occurrences of x and y.

We now list our rules and axioms, including the new ones for class membership.

Modus Ponens: If P and $P \supset Q$, then Q, where P and Q are statements.

The axioms are any of the statements listed below, with as many universal quantifiers as desired attached on the front (in particular, none need be attached, and a given one can be attached more than once if desired). It is understood that P, Q, and R denote statements and x, y, and z denote variables, and the statements need not be distinct and the variables need not be distinct unless explicitly stated.

1. $P \supset PP.$
2. $PQ \supset P.$
3. $(P \supset Q) \supset (\sim(QR) \supset \sim(RP)).$
4. $(x).P \supset Q : \supset :(x)\ P \supset (x)\ Q.$

5. $P \supset (x)\ P$, in case there are no free occurrences of x in P.

6. $(x)\ P \supset \{\text{Sub in } P\text{: } y \text{ for } x\}$, in case there is no confusion of bound variables in the substitution indicated by $\{\text{Sub in } P\text{: } y \text{ for } x\}$.

7. $(x,y,z){:}x = y. \supset .x \in z \supset y \in z$, in case x, y, and z are distinct.

8. $(x)\ P \supset \{\text{Sub in } P\text{: } \iota y\ Q \text{ for } x\}$, in case there is no confusion of bound variables in the substitution indicated by $\{\text{Sub in } P\text{: } \iota y\ Q \text{ for } x\}$.

9. $(x).P \equiv Q{:} \supset {:}\iota x\ P = \iota x\ Q$.

10. $\iota x\ P = \iota y\ Q$, in case Q is the result of replacing each free occurrence of x in P by an occurrence of y, and P is the result of replacing each free occurrence of y in Q by an occurrence of x.

11. $(\mathrm{E}_1 x)\ P{:} \supset {:}(x).\iota x\ P = x \equiv P$.

12. $(\mathrm{E}y)(x).x \in y \equiv P$, in case x and y are distinct, there are no occurrences of y in P, and P is stratified.

Our convention stated at the end of Chapter VI would assure the distinctness of x, y, and z in Axiom scheme 7 and the distinctness of x and y in Axiom scheme 12. However, in stating our axioms, it seemed safest to be overly explicit in order to emphasize that distinctness is required only when it is stated.

We see that we have added only one new axiom scheme, namely, Axiom scheme 12. However, we have replaced Axiom schemes 7A and 7B by the single Axiom scheme 7. More importantly, we have taken $A = B$ to be

$$(x).x \in A \equiv x \in B.$$

This gives us immediately the theorem

$$(y,z){:}.(x).x \in y \equiv x \in z{:} \supset {:}y = z.$$

If we should wish to keep $A = B$ as an undefined concept, we should have to retain Axiom schemes 7A and 7B and add the theorem above as an Axiom scheme 13.

It might be thought that in Axiom scheme 12 we should specify that x should occur free in P, so that P will be a condition on x. However, since

$$\vdash P \equiv (x = x)P$$

for each P, one can easily deduce our form of Axiom scheme 12 from a form in which P is required to have free occurrences of x, and so we take our form, since it is simpler.

The first order of business is the proof of Axiom schemes 7A and 7B.

***Theorem IX.2.1.** $\vdash (x).x = x$.

Proof. By the definition of equality, this is just

$$\vdash (x,y).y \in x \equiv y \in x,$$

which is an easy consequence of $\vdash P \equiv P$.

****Theorem IX.2.2.** $\vdash (x,y).x = y \equiv y = x.$

Proof. This is just

$$\vdash (x,y):.(z).z \in x \equiv z \in y: \equiv :(z).z \in y \equiv z \in x.$$

Theorem IX.2.3. $\vdash (x,y,z):x = y. \supset .x \in z \equiv y \in z.$

Proof. By Axiom scheme 7,

(1) $$\vdash x = y. \supset .x \in z \supset y \in z.$$

(2) $$\vdash y = x. \supset .y \in z \supset x \in z.$$

By (2) and Thm.IX.2.2,

(3) $$\vdash x = y. \supset .y \in z \supset x \in z.$$

Our theorem follows from (1) and (3).

Axiom scheme 7A says that

$$(x,y):x = y. \supset .F(x,y,x) \supset F(x,y,y)$$

with certain restrictions on bound variables. We now prove a slightly stronger statement.

****Theorem IX.2.4.** If x, y, and z are distinct variables, and $F(x,y,z)$ is a statement, and $F(x,y,x)$ and $F(x,y,y)$ are the results of replacing each free occurrence of z in $F(x,y,z)$ by occurrences of x and y, respectively, and if this replacement causes no confusion of bound variables, then

$$\vdash (x,y):x = y. \supset .F(x,y,x) \equiv F(x,y,y).$$

Proof. Proof by induction on the number of symbols in $F(x,y,z)$.

If $F(x,y,z)$ contains only one symbol, it is not a statement, and the theorem holds. Assume the theorem for all $F(x,y,z)$ with n or fewer symbols, and let $F(x,y,z)$ have $n + 1$ symbols. By the definition of a statement, there are four main cases.

Case 1. $F(x,y,z)$ is $A \in B$.

Lemma. $\vdash x = y. \supset .\{\text{Sub in } A : x \text{ for } z\} = \{\text{Sub in } A : y \text{ for } z\}.$

(i) Let A contain no free z's. Then the lemma takes the form $\vdash x = y \supset A = A$, which is easily proved.

(ii) Let A be z. Then the lemma takes the form $\vdash x = y \supset x = y$, which is easily proved.

(iii) Let A contain free occurrences of z, and be $\iota v\, G(x,y,z)$. Then v is distinct from z, since A contains free occurrences of z. Also v is distinct from both x and y, since otherwise there would be confusion of bound variables in forming $F(x,y,x)$ or $F(x,y,y)$. By the hypothesis of the induction

$$\vdash x = y. \supset .G(x,y,x) \equiv G(x,y,y).$$

By rule G and Thm.VI.6.6, Part IX,

$$\vdash x = y\!:\ \supset\ :(v).G(x,y,x)\ \equiv\ G(x,y,y).$$

By Axiom scheme 9,

$$\vdash x = y \supset \iota v\ G(x,y,x) = \iota v\ G(x,y,y),$$

which is the lemma, since v is distinct from z.

In the same manner exactly, we prove

(1) $$\vdash x = y.\ \supset .\{\text{Sub in } B\!: x \text{ for } z\} = \{\text{Sub in } B\!: y \text{ for } z\}.$$

By Thm.IX.2.3 and our lemma,

(2) $$\vdash x = y.\ \supset .\{\text{Sub in } A\!: x \text{ for } z\} \in \{\text{Sub in } B\!: x \text{ for } z\}$$
$$\equiv \{\text{Sub in } A\!: y \text{ for } z\} \in \{\text{Sub in } B\!: x \text{ for } z\}.$$

By the definition of equality, (1) is

$$\vdash x = y\!:\ \supset\ :(w).w \in \{\text{Sub in } B\!: x \text{ for } z\}$$
$$\equiv w \in \{\text{Sub in } B\!: y \text{ for } z\}.$$

Hence by Axiom scheme 6 or 8

$$\vdash x = y.\ \supset .\{\text{Sub in } A\!: y \text{ for } z\} \in \{\text{Sub in } B\!: x \text{ for } z\}$$
$$\equiv \{\text{Sub in } A\!: y \text{ for } z\} \in \{\text{Sub in } B\!: y \text{ for } z\}.$$

From this and (2), we get

$$\vdash x = y.\ \supset .\{\text{Sub in } A\!: x \text{ for } z\} \in \{\text{Sub in } B\!: x \text{ for } z\}$$
$$\equiv \{\text{Sub in } A\!: y \text{ for } z\} \in \{\text{Sub in } B\!: y \text{ for } z\}.$$

This is just

$$\vdash x = y.\ \supset .F(x,y,x) \equiv F(x,y,y).$$

Case 2. $F(x,y,z)$ is $(v)\ G(x,y,z)$.

Subcase 1. Let $(v)\ G(x,y,z)$ contain no free z's. Then our theorem takes the form $\vdash x = y.\ \supset .(v)\ G(x,y,z) \equiv (v)\ G(x,y,z)$.

Subcase 2. Let $(v)\ G(x,y,z)$ contain free z's. Then v is distinct from z. Also v must be distinct from both x and y, else there would be confusion of bound variables in forming $F(x,y,x)$ or $F(x,y,y)$.

By the hypothesis of the induction,

$$\vdash x = y.\ \supset .G(x,y,x) \equiv G(x,y,y).$$

By rule G and Thm.VI.6.6, Part IX,

$$\vdash x = y\!:\ \supset\ :(v).G(x,y,x) \equiv G(x,y,y).$$

By Thm.VI.5.3,

$$\vdash x = y. \supset .F(x,y,x) \equiv F(x,y,y).$$

Case 3. $F(x,y,z)$ is $\sim G(x,y,z)$.
By the hypothesis of the induction,

$$\vdash x = y. \supset .G(x,y,x) \equiv G(x,y,y).$$

By $\vdash P \equiv Q. \supset .\sim P \equiv \sim Q$, we get

$$\vdash x = y. \supset .F(x,y,x) \equiv F(x,y,y).$$

Case 4. $F(x,y,z)$ is $G(x,y,z)\&H(x,y,z)$. Proof analogous to that of case 3.

****Theorem IX.2.5.** If x, y, and z are distinct variables, and $A(x,y,z)$ is a term, and $A(x,y,x)$ and $A(x,y,y)$ are the results of replacing each free occurrence of z in $A(x,y,z)$ by occurrences of x and y, respectively, and if this replacement causes no confusion of bound variables, then $\vdash (x,y){:}x = y. \supset . A(x,y,x) = A(x,y,y)$.

Proof. Taking $F(x,y,z)$ to be $A(x,y,x) = A(x,y,z)$ in Thm.IX.2.4 gives

$$\vdash x = y{:} \supset {:}A(x,y,x) = A(x,y,x). \equiv .A(x,y,x) = A(x,y,y).$$

However, by Thm.IX.2.1 and Axiom scheme 6 or 8,

$$\vdash A(x,y,x) = A(x,y,x).$$

Note. Thm.IX.2.4 allows us to substitute a quantity for its equal (more precisely, to substitute one name of a quantity for another name of the same quantity) in a statement. Thm.IX.2.5 allows us to make a similar substitution in a formula. Thus, from Thm.IX.2.4, we could get such results as

$$x = y, x < z \vdash y < z,$$

$$P = Q, P \text{ in circle } C \vdash Q \text{ in circle } C.$$

On the other hand, from Thm.IX.2.5, we get such results as

$$x = y \vdash x^2 = y^2,$$

$$x = y \vdash e^x = e^y.$$

We can easily get generalizations such as

$$x = y, u = v \vdash x + u = y + v$$

by using Thm.IX.2.5 twice to get

$$x = y \vdash x + u = y + u,$$

$$u = v \vdash y + u = y + v.$$

When we proved the substitution theorem, we said that we were proving only a special case and would later prove the theorem in full generality. The time has come to do so.

As before, we have a complicated hypothesis if we wish to state the theorem with precision.

Hypothesis H_2. $P_1, P_2, \ldots, P_n, Q, R$ are statements, $A_1, A_2, \ldots, A_m$ are terms, $x_1, x_2, \ldots, x_a$ are variables, and y is a variable distinct from all the x's, and not occurring in any of $P_1, P_2, \ldots, P_n, Q, R, A_1, A_2, \ldots, A_m$. U is a statement built up out of some or all of $y \in y, P_1, P_2, \ldots, P_n, Q, R, A_1, A_2, \ldots, A_m, x_1, x_2, \ldots, x_a$ by means of (,), $\sim$, &, ι, and ϵ, where each part listed may be used as often as desired. W and V are the results of replacing all occurrences of $y \in y$ in U by Q and R, respectively.

Theorem IX.2.6. Assume Hypothesis H_2. Let $y_1, y_2, \ldots, y_b$ be variables such that there are no free occurrences of any of the x's in $(y_1, y_2, \ldots, y_b).Q \equiv R$. Then $\vdash (y_1, y_2, \ldots, y_b).Q \equiv R{:} \supset {:}W \equiv V$.

Proof. Proof by induction on the number of symbols in U. Temporarily let X denote $(y_1, y_2, \ldots, y_b).Q \equiv R$.

If U has only one symbol, it is not a statement, and the theorem is true.

Assume the theorem if U has n or fewer symbols, and let U have $n + 1$ symbols. The first five cases, namely:

1. U is $y \in y$.
2. U does not contain $y \in y$.
3. U is $\sim Y$.
4. U is $Y \& Z$.
5. U is $(x)\ Y$.

are handled just like the cases in the proof of Thm.VI.5.4. There remains:

Case 6. U is $B \in C$. Then W and V are $D \in E$ and $F \in G$, where D and E are the results of replacing all occurrences of $y \in y$ in B and C by Q, and F and G are the results of replacing all occurrences of $y \in y$ in B and C by R.

Lemma 1. $\vdash X. \supset .D = F$.

In case there are no occurrences of $y \in y$ in B, this follows from Thm.IX.2.1. So let B contain some occurrences of $y \in y$. Then B must have the form $\iota x\ Y_1$, and D and F must be $\iota x\ Y_2$ and $\iota x\ Y_3$, where Y_2 and Y_3 are the results of replacing all occurrences of $y \in y$ in Y_1 by Q and R, respectively. By the hypothesis of the induction, $\vdash X. \supset .Y_2 \equiv Y_3$. But there are no free occurrences of x in X, so that by rule G and Thm.VI.6.6, Part IX, $\vdash X. \supset .(x).Y_2 \equiv Y_3$. So by Axiom scheme 9, $\vdash X. \supset .\iota x\ Y_2 = \iota x\ Y_3$. That is, $\vdash X. \supset .D = F$.

Lemma 2. $\vdash X. \supset .E = G$.

Proof. Proof similar to that of Lemma 1.

By Lemma 1 and Thm.IX.2.3,

(1) $$\vdash X: \supset :D \epsilon E \equiv F \epsilon E.$$

By Lemma 2 and the definition of equality $\vdash X: \supset :(w).w \epsilon E \equiv w \epsilon G$. So $\vdash X: \supset :F \epsilon E \equiv F \epsilon G$. Hence by (1), $\vdash X: \supset :D \epsilon E \equiv F \epsilon G$. That is, $\vdash X: \supset :W \equiv V$.

Theorem IX.2.7. Assume Hypothesis H_2. If $\vdash Q \equiv R$, then $\vdash W \equiv V$.

Proof. Proof like that of Thm.VI.5.5.

Theorem IX.2.8. Assume Hypothesis H_2. If $\vdash Q \equiv R$ and $\vdash W$, then $\vdash V$.

In this connection, there are two other useful results. We first define Hypothesis H_3.

Hypothesis H_3. Same as Hypothesis H_2 except that U, V, and W are terms.

Theorem IX.2.9. Assume Hypothesis H_3. Let $y_1, y_2, \ldots, y_b$ be variables such that there are no free occurrences of any x's in $(y_1, y_2, \ldots, y_b)$. $Q \equiv R$. Then $\vdash (y_1, y_2, \ldots, y_b).Q \equiv R: \supset :W = V$.

Proof. Choose w a variable distinct from each of the x's and distinct from y and not occurring in any of $P_1, P_2, \ldots, P_n, Q, R, A_1, A_2, \ldots, A_m$. Then by Thm.IX.2.6, $\vdash (y_1, y_2, \ldots, y_b).Q \equiv R: \supset :w \epsilon W \equiv w \epsilon V$. So by rule G and Thm.VI.6.6, Part IX,

$$\vdash (y_1, y_2, \ldots, y_b).Q = R: \supset :(w).w \epsilon W \equiv w \epsilon V.$$

This is

$$\vdash (y_1, y_2, \ldots, y_b).Q \equiv R: \supset :W = V.$$

Theorem IX.2.10. Assume Hypothesis H_3. If $\vdash Q \equiv R$, then $\vdash W = V$.

By use of the substitution theorem and either Thm.VI.6.8 or Axiom scheme 10, one can in any statement S replace any x-bound part $(x)\ F(x)$ or $\iota x\ F(x)$ by $(y)\ F(y)$ or $\iota y\ F(y)$, where y is a new variable not previously appearing in S. If one repeats this for all x-bound parts of S for the various x's for which there are x-bound parts of S, one will eventually arrive at an equivalent form of S in which no bound variable is the same as a free variable, and no x-bound part will contain the same bound variables as any other nonoverlapping part which is bound by a variable. Likewise, given any term A, we can find another term B such that $\vdash A = B$ and in B no bound variable is the same as any free variable, and no x-bound part will contain the same bound variables as any other nonoverlapping part which is bound by a variable.

These possibilities greatly widen the applicability of theorems such as Thm.IX.3.5 below, since preparatory to the use of such a theorem we can change all bound variables to something else and afterward change back again, subject always to avoiding confusion of bound variables.

EXERCISES

IX.2.1. Test for stratification:

(a) $\iota\alpha\ ((x)\ x \epsilon \alpha) \epsilon \iota\alpha\ ((x)\ x \epsilon \alpha)$.
(b) $\iota\alpha\ ((x).x \epsilon \alpha \equiv \sim x \epsilon \beta) \epsilon \iota\alpha\ ((x).x \epsilon \alpha \equiv \sim x \epsilon \beta)$.
(c) $y \epsilon \iota\alpha\ (x){:}x \epsilon \alpha. \equiv .x = y$.
(d) $x \epsilon \alpha. \equiv .x \epsilon \beta \& x \epsilon \gamma$.
(e) $x \epsilon \beta. \equiv .x \epsilon \iota\alpha\ (y).y \epsilon \alpha \equiv \beta \epsilon y$.

IX.2.2. Let α and β be restricted variables, both subject to the restriction $K(\alpha)$. State what conditions must be satisfied if $(\beta).\beta = \iota\alpha\ (\alpha = \beta)$ is to be stratified.

3. Formalism for Classes. The notion of the class (if any) determined by a condition $F(x)$ is basic in all of mathematics. As we indicated above, if α is such a class, then

$$(x).x \epsilon \alpha \equiv F(x).$$

Clearly such a class is unique, for if also

$$(x).x \epsilon \beta \equiv F(x),$$

then we infer

$$(x).x \epsilon \alpha \equiv x \epsilon \beta,$$

which is $\alpha = \beta$.

Under the circumstances, a suitable notation for the class (if any) determined by a condition $F(x)$ is

$$\iota\alpha\ (x).x \epsilon \alpha \equiv F(x).$$

We shall denote the class determined by $F(x)$ by $\hat{x}F(x)$. Specifically, we set forth the following definition.

If x is a variable and P is a statement, then $\hat{x}P$ shall denote

$$\iota\alpha\ (x).x \epsilon \alpha \equiv P,$$

where α is a variable which is distinct from x and does not occur at all in P.

$\hat{x}P$ is to be considered as the class of all x's which make P true. That is, $\hat{x}P$ is the class determined by P. Clearly $\hat{x}P$ can function as this class only in case there is such a class. If there is no class determined by P, then we may consider $\hat{x}P$ as meaningless. Actually, if P determines no class, then we have $\sim(E_1\alpha)(x).x \epsilon \alpha \equiv P$, and $\hat{x}P$ would have whatever meaning we have agreed to give to $\iota\alpha\ (x).x \epsilon \alpha \equiv P$ under such a circumstance. One possibility is that no meaning at all is assigned, but this does not prevent us from making formal use of $\hat{x}P$.

Note that P need not contain any occurrences of x in order to give a meaning to $\hat{x}P$. If P contains no free occurrences of x, then $\hat{x}P$ is the class of all objects in case P is true and the class of no objects in case P is false.

$\hat{x}P$ is commonly read "x hat P" or "x roof P." In a rough way, it symbolizes the idea of collecting under one roof all x's which make P true.

All occurrences of x and α in $\hat{x}P$ are bound. Occurrences of other variables are free or bound in $\hat{x}P$ according as they are free or bound in the part P.

$\hat{x}P$ is stratified if and only if P is. If $\hat{x}P$ is stratified and P contains free occurrences of x, the type of $\hat{x}P$ must be exactly one higher than the type of the free occurrences of x in P. This accords with the basic tenet of the theory of types, according to which a class should be of type exactly one higher than its members. If there are no free occurrences of x in P, then in stratifying $\hat{x}P$ the type of $\hat{x}P$ is quite unrelated to the type of any constituent of P.

As we indicated earlier, not every condition determines a class. More generally, given an arbitrary x and P, there may or may not exist the class which we would like to denote by $\hat{x}P$. Note that we are entitled to use $\hat{x}P$ in our symbolic logic even if there is no class which it denotes, since we do not require that our formulas have meaning. In order for there to be a class denoted by $\hat{x}P$, it is necessary and sufficient that

$$(\mathrm{E}\alpha)(x).x \in \alpha \equiv P$$

where α does not occur in P (our conventions ensure that x and α are distinct variables). We shall abbreviate this to $\exists(\hat{x}P)$ or $\exists\hat{x}P$, which we read as "$\hat{x}P$ exists."

In mathematics, one often finds $\underset{x}{\mathrm{E}}\,P$ or $\{x \mid P\}$ written to denote $\hat{x}P$.

Another widely used notion is a generalization of the class of all x's determined by a condition $F(x)$. In the generalization, we have some function $f(x)$ and we ask for the class of all objects $f(x)$ got by using x's which satisfy the condition $F(x)$. If α is this class, then

$$(x){:}x \in \alpha. \equiv .(\mathrm{E}y).x = f(y).F(y).$$

So the class in question would be

$$\hat{x}(\mathrm{E}y).x = f(y).F(y).$$

A typical example might be the class of all squares of primes. Here $f(x)$ is x^2 and $F(x)$ is "x is a prime."

One can generalize still further and have a function $f(x,y)$ of two variables and a condition $F(x,y)$ on two variables. Then one can ask for the class of all objects $f(x,y)$ got by using pairs of x and y which satisfy the condition $F(x,y)$. If α is this class, then

$$(x){:}x \in \alpha. \equiv .(\mathrm{E}y,z).x = f(y,z).F(y,z).$$

So the class in question is

$$\hat{x}(\mathrm{E}y,z).x = f(y,z).F(y,z).$$

A typical example might be the class of all sums of two odd primes. Here $f(x,y)$ is $x + y$ and $F(x,y)$ is "x and y are each odd primes." The famous Goldbach conjecture is that the class in question consists of all even numbers greater than four.

In general, we might have a function $f(y_1, \ldots, y_n)$ and a condition $F(y_1, \ldots, y_n)$, and we might ask for the class of all objects $f(y_1, \ldots, y_n)$ got by using n-tuples $y_1, \ldots, y_n$ which satisfy the condition $F(y_1, \ldots, y_n)$. In symbolic logic, the role of the function $f(y_1, \ldots, y_n)$ would be played by a term A with free occurrences of $y_1, \ldots, y_n$ and the role of the condition $F(y_1, \ldots, y_n)$ would be played by a statement P with free occurrences of $y_1, \ldots, y_n$. Then if α is the class of all objects A got by using n-tuples $y_1, \ldots, y_n$ which satisfy the condition P, we would have

$$(x){:}x \in \alpha. \equiv .(\mathrm{E}y_1, \ldots, y_n).x = A.P.$$

Then $\hat{x}(\mathrm{E}y_1, \ldots, y_n).x = A.P$ is the class in question.

Mathematicians have a convenient notation for this class, to wit

$$\{A \mid P\}.$$

We shall adopt this notation, but we have to add certain additional qualifications to give the notation a unique significance. This comes about as follows. If we write

$$\{x + y \mid F(x,y)\},$$

this means the class of all sums of pairs of numbers x and y satisfying the condition $F(x,y)$. However, if we write

$$\{x + y \mid F(x)\}$$

we then mean the class of all sums formed by adding to the fixed number y each x which satisfies the condition $F(x)$.

The point is that one can consider $x + y$ as a function of two variables x and y, or as a function of x dependent on the parameter y. If we write

$$\{ x + y \mid P\},$$

it is quite necessary to know which interpretation of $x + y$ is intended, since in the one case we get a unique class, and in the other case we get a class dependent on a parameter y.

There seems to be no established mathematical convention to cover this point. However, common usage seems to accord generally with the following convention (which we hereby adopt):

Let $y_1, y_2, \ldots, y_n$ be distinct variables constituting exactly all variables which have free occurrences in both of A and P. Then A is to be considered as a function of $y_1, y_2, \ldots, y_n$ and P is to be considered as a condition on $y_1, y_2, \ldots, y_n$. Any other variables which may have free occurrences in either of A or P are to be construed as parameters upon which the class $\{A \mid P\}$ depends. That is, we consider $\{A \mid P\}$ as an abbreviation for

$$\hat{x}(\mathrm{E}y_1, y_2, \ldots, y_n).x = A.P,$$

where $y_1, y_2, \ldots, y_n$ are as stated above and x is a variable not occurring in either of A or P (this ensures that x is not one of $y_1, y_2, \ldots, y_n$). Whenever we use the notation $\{A \mid P\}$, the y's are understood to be as stated above.

Clearly $\{A \mid P\}$ is stratified if and only if $(\mathrm{E}y_1, y_2, \ldots, y_n).x = A.P$ is stratified, and if stratified, $\{A \mid P\}$ must have type one higher than A. Hence $\{A \mid P\}$ is stratified if and only if $A = A.P$ is stratified.

In $\{A \mid P\}$, all the y's are bound as also are the x and α implicit in the definition (not to mention the bound variable implicit in the $=$ of $x = A$). Other variables are free or bound in $\{A \mid P\}$ according as they are free or bound in A and P. There is nothing in the notation $\{A \mid P\}$ to remind the reader that all the y's are bound. It will simply be necessary to cultivate the habit of considering the $\{\ \mid\ \}$ notation as binding those variables which appear to occur free on each side of the vertical bar.

If P contains no free variables except x, then $\hat{x}P$ has no free variables; in case it is stratified, it can be assigned an arbitrary type, and two occurrences of it in the same formula may be assigned different types. If $y_1, y_2, \ldots, y_n$ are all the variables which occur free in either of A or P, then $\{A \mid P\}$ contains no free variables; in case it is stratified, it can be assigned an arbitrary type, and two occurrences of it in the same formula may be assigned different types.

****Theorem IX.3.1.** If P is stratified, then $\vdash \exists\hat{x}P$.

Proof. Use Axiom scheme 12.

****Corollary.** If $A = A.P$ is stratified, then $\vdash \exists\{A \mid P\}$.

Theorem IX.3.2. If β has no free occurrences in P, then $\vdash \exists\hat{x}P.{:}\supset{:}.(\beta){:}\beta = \hat{x}P. \equiv .(x).x \in \beta \equiv P$.

Proof. Temporarily, let $F(\alpha)$ denote $(x).x \in \alpha \equiv P$. Then we easily show

$$\vdash F(\alpha)F(\beta). \supset .(x).x \in \alpha \equiv x \in \beta.$$

By the definition of equality, this is

$$\vdash F(\alpha)F(\beta) \supset \alpha = \beta.$$

Noting that $\exists\hat{x}P$ is just $(\mathrm{E}\alpha)\ F(\alpha)$, we see that if we assume $\exists\hat{x}P$ we get

$$(\mathrm{E}\alpha)\ F(\alpha){:}(\alpha,\beta).F(\alpha)F(\beta) \supset \alpha = \beta.$$

So by Thm.VII.2.1, $(E_1\alpha)\ F(\alpha)$. So by Axiom scheme 11,

$$(\alpha){:}\,\iota\alpha\ F(\alpha) = \alpha. \equiv .F(\alpha).$$

Hence

$$(\beta){:}\,\iota\alpha\ F(\alpha) = \beta. \equiv .F(\beta).$$

That is,

$$(\beta){:}\hat{x}P = \beta. \equiv .F(\beta),$$

which is the desired conclusion.

****Corollary 1.** $\vdash \exists \hat{x}P{:} \supset {:}(x).x \in \hat{x}P \equiv P.$

Corollary 2. If x and β have no free occurrences in either of A or P, then $\vdash \exists\{A \mid P\}{::} \supset {::}(\beta){:}.\beta = \{A \mid P\}{:} \equiv {:}(x){:}x \in \beta. \equiv .(Ey_1, y_2, \ldots, y_n). x = A.P.$

****Corollary 3.** If x has no free occurrences in either of A or P, then $\vdash \exists\{A \mid P\}.{:} \supset {:}.(x){:}x \in \{A \mid P\}. \equiv .(Ey_1, y_2, \ldots, y_n).x = A.P.$

Corollary 4. $\vdash \exists\{A \mid P\}{:} \supset {:}P. \supset .A \in \{A \mid P\}.$

****Theorem IX.3.3.** $\vdash (x).P \equiv Q{:} \supset {:}\hat{x}P = \hat{x}Q.$

Proof. Choose α a variable which does not occur in either P or Q. Then by Thm.VI.5.4,

$$\vdash (x).P \equiv Q.{:} \supset {:}.(x).x \in \alpha \equiv P{:} \equiv {:}(x).x \in \alpha \equiv Q.$$

So by rule G and Thm.VI.6.6, Part IX,

$$\vdash (x).P \equiv Q{::} \supset {::}(\alpha){:}.(x).x \in \alpha \equiv P{:} \equiv {:}(x).x \in \alpha \equiv Q.$$

Then by Axiom scheme 9,

$$\vdash (x).P \equiv Q.{:} \supset {:}.\iota\alpha\ (x).x \in \alpha \equiv P{:} = {:}\iota\alpha\ (x).x \in \alpha \equiv Q.$$

Corollary 1. $\vdash (y_1, y_2, \ldots, y_n).P \equiv Q{:} \supset {:}\{A \mid P\} = \{A \mid Q\}.$

Corollary 2. If there are free occurrences of x in P, then $\vdash \hat{x}P = \{x \mid P\}$.

Corollary 3. $\vdash \hat{x}P = \{x \mid x = x.P\}.$

****Theorem IX.3.4.** $\vdash \hat{x}P = \hat{y}Q$ in case Q is the result of replacing each free occurrence of x in P by an occurrence of y, and P is the result of replacing each free occurrence of y in Q by an occurrence of x.

Proof. We note that the theorem to be proved can be written $\vdash \hat{x}F(x) = \hat{y}F(y)$. Choose a variable α which does not occur in either $F(x)$ or $F(y)$. Then by Thm.VI.6.8, Part I,

$$\vdash (x).x \in \alpha \equiv F(x){:} \equiv {:}(y).y \in \alpha \equiv F(y).$$

So

$$\vdash (\alpha){:}.(x).x \in \alpha \equiv F(x){:} \equiv {:}(y).y \in \alpha \equiv F(y).$$

By Axiom scheme 9, $\vdash \hat{x}F(x) = \hat{y}F(y)$.

Theorem IX.3.5. Let $y_1, y_2, \ldots, y_n$ be distinct variables which constitute exactly all the variables which have free occurrences in each of A and

P. Let $u_1, u_2, \ldots, u_n$ be distinct variables which do not occur in either of A or P. Let B denote {Sub in A: u_1 for y_1, u_2 for y_2, . . . , u_n for y_n} and Q denote {Sub in P: u_1 for y_1, u_2 for y_2, . . . , u_n for y_n}. Then $\vdash \{A \mid P\} = \{B \mid Q\}$.

Proof like that of Thm.IX.3.4.

Clearly, our theorem will give such useful results as

$$\vdash \{x + y \mid F(x,y)\} = \{u + v \mid F(u,v)\}.$$

It can be made to give

$$\vdash \{x + y \mid F(x,y)\} = \{x + z \mid F(x,z)\}$$

by using it a second time to give

$$\vdash \{u + v \mid F(u,v)\} = \{x + z \mid F(x,z)\}.$$

Similarly, by using the theorem twice, we can get

$$\vdash \{x + y \mid F(x,y)\} = \{y + x \mid F(y,x)\}.$$

The extension of these to other functions than $x + y$ and to several variables is obvious.

Theorem IX.3.6. $\vdash (\beta,x){:}x \in \hat{x}(x \in \beta). \equiv .x \in \beta$.

Proof. $\vdash (x).x \in \beta \equiv x \in \beta$. Hence by Thm.VI.7.3, $\vdash (\mathrm{E}\alpha)(x).x \in \alpha \equiv x \in \beta$. That is, $\vdash \exists\hat{x}(x \in \beta)$. Then the theorem follows by Thm.IX.3.2, Cor. 1.

Corollary 1. $\vdash (\beta).\hat{x}(x \in \beta) = \beta$.

Corollary 2. $\vdash (\alpha){:}.(x).x \in \alpha \equiv P{:} \supset {:}\alpha = \hat{x}P$.

Proof. By Thm.IX.3.3, $\vdash (x).x \in \alpha \equiv P{:} \supset {:}\hat{x}(x \in \alpha) = \hat{x}P$.

***Theorem IX.3.7.** Suppose that y is the only variable which occurs free in both A and P and u and v are two variables not occurring in A or P. Then $\vdash (u,v){:}\{\text{Sub in } A{:}\ u \text{ for } y\} = \{\text{Sub in } A{:}\ v \text{ for } y\}. \supset .u = v{::} \supset {::} \exists\{A \mid P\}.{:} \supset {:}.(y){:}A \in \{A \mid P\}. \equiv .P$.

Proof. Denote A by $B(y)$, {Sub in A: u for y} by $B(u)$, etc. Similarly denote P by $F(y)$. Assume

(1) $$(u,v){:}B(u) = B(v). \supset .u = v$$

and

(2) $$\exists\{A \mid P\}.$$

Then by (1) and Thm.IX.2.5,

(3) $$(u,v){:}B(u) = B(v). \equiv .u = v.$$

Now by (2) and Thm.IX.3.2, Cor. 3,

$$(x){:}x \in \{A \mid P\}. \equiv .(\mathrm{E}v).x = B(v).F(v).$$

So

$$B(u) \epsilon \{A \mid P\}. \equiv .(\mathrm{E}v).B(u) = B(v).F(v).$$

Then by (3) and Thm.VI.5.4,

$$B(u) \epsilon \{A \mid P\}. \equiv .(\mathrm{E}v).u = v.F(v).$$

So by Thm.VII.1.5, Part I,

$$B(u) \epsilon \{A \mid P\}. \equiv .F(u).$$

So

$$(u){:}B(u) \epsilon \{A \mid P\}. \equiv .F(u),$$

$$(y){:}B(y) \epsilon \{A \mid P\}. \equiv .F(y).$$

This latter is

$$(y){:}A \epsilon \{A \mid P\}. \equiv .P.$$

Theorem IX.3.8. Suppose that y_1 and y_2 are the only variables which occur free in both A and P and that u_1, u_2, v_1, v_2 are variables not occurring in A or P. If we denote {Sub in A: u_1 for y_1, u_2 for y_2} by $B(u_1,u_2)$ and similarly for $B(v_1,v_2)$, then $\vdash (u_1,u_2,v_1,v_2){:}B(u_1,u_2) = B(v_1,v_2). \supset .u_1 = v_1. u_2 = v_2{::} \supset {::}\exists\{A \mid P\}.{:} \supset {:}.(y_1,y_2){:}A \epsilon \{A \mid P\}. \equiv .P.$

Proof similar to that of Thm.IX.3.7.

EXERCISES

IX.3.1. Prove

$$\vdash \exists\hat{x}P.\exists\hat{x}Q{:} \supset {:}\hat{x}P = \hat{x}Q. \supset .(x).P \equiv Q.$$

IX.3.2. Give an example from mathematics for which $\exists\{A \mid P\}$ is true, but $A \epsilon \{A \mid P\} \equiv P$ is false.

IX.3.3. Prove that if $y_1, y_2, \ldots, y_n$ are distinct variables which constitute all the variables which have free occurrences in both A and P and if the y's are all the variables which occur free in A, then

(a) $\vdash \exists\{A \mid P\} \supset \exists\{A \mid A \epsilon \{A \mid P\}\}.$
(b) $\vdash \exists\{A \mid P\}. \supset .\{A \mid A \epsilon \{A \mid P\}\} = \{A \mid P\}.$

IX.3.4. Prove $\vdash \hat{x}(x \epsilon \hat{x}P) = \hat{x}P.$

IX.3.5. Prove that $\hat{x}P$ is stratified if and only if P is.

IX.3.6. Prove Thm.IX.3.3, Cor. 2.

IX.3.7. Prove $\vdash \sim\exists\hat{x}(\sim x \epsilon x).$

IX.3.8. Prove $\vdash (\mathrm{E}_1\alpha).\alpha = \hat{x}(\sim(x \epsilon x)).$ Explain why we cannot derive the Russell paradox from this theorem. Give a statement from which the Russell paradox can be derived and which, from a careless, intuitive point of view, might seem to say about the same thing as the statement given above.

IX.3.9. Prove:

(a) $\vdash (x)\exists\hat{z}(x = z)$.
(b) $\vdash (x,y){:}x = y. \equiv .y \in \hat{z}(x = z)$.
(c) $\vdash (x,y){:}x = y. \equiv .\hat{z}(z = x) = \hat{z}(z = y)$.

IX.3.10. Prove:

(a) $\vdash (\beta)\exists\hat{z}((\alpha){:}\alpha \in \beta. \supset .z \in \alpha)$.
(b) $\vdash (\beta,x){:.}x \in \hat{z}((\alpha){:}\alpha \in \beta. \supset .z \in \alpha){:} \equiv {:}(\alpha){:}\alpha \in \beta. \supset .x \in \alpha$.
(c) $\vdash (x){:}x = \hat{z}((\alpha){:}\alpha \in \hat{z}(z = x). \supset .z \in \alpha)$.

4. The Calculus of Classes. We define

V	for	$\hat{x}(x = x)$.
Λ	for	$\hat{x}(x \neq x)$.
$A \cap B$	for	$\hat{x}(x \in A \& x \in B)$.
$A \cup B$	for	$\hat{x}(x \in A \vee x \in B)$.
$\overline{A}$	for	$\hat{x}(\sim x \in A)$.
$A - B$	for	$A \cap \overline{B}$.

where in the definitions we take x as a variable not occurring in A or B.

We read V as "Vee", Λ as "lambda", $A \cap B$ as "A cap B", $A \cup B$ as "A cup B", $\overline{A}$ as "A bar", and $A - B$ as "A minus B". We refer to V as the universal class, Λ as the null class, $A \cap B$ as the product (or logical product, or common part, or cross cut, or meet, or intersection, or product class) of A and B, $A \cup B$ as the sum (or logical sum, or union, or join, or sum class) of A and B, and $\overline{A}$ as the complement (or negate, or complementary class) of A. All objects are members of V, no objects are members of Λ, the members of $A \cap B$ are just those objects which are in both of A and B, the members of $A \cup B$ are just those objects which are in at least one of A and B, and the members of $\overline{A}$ are just those objects which are not in A. Rather commonly one writes AB, $A + B$, and $-A$ for $A \cap B$, $A \cup B$, and $\overline{A}$. We favor this notation ourselves but have not felt free to use it because we shall have to use class sums and products in the same context with cardinal and ordinal sums and products, and confusion would arise if we were not using the cap and cup notation. Other notations which are occasionally encountered are 1 for V, 0 for Λ, and $C(A)$ for $\overline{A}$.

V and Λ contain no free variables. The free variables of $A \cap B$ and $A \cup B$ are just those of A and B separately. Certain bound variables are inherent in the $\hat{x}$ used to define $A \cap B$ and $A \cup B$, but these variables are distinct from any variables of A or B. Any other bound variables are those of A and B. Similar remarks hold for $\overline{A}$.

One may think of V as the initial letter of "Universal class" in the classic roman alphabet. Whitehead and Russell point to the appropriateness of reversing the symbol for the universal class to get the symbol, Λ, for the null class. Also they call attention to the fact that, when the symbol is denoting the universal class, it is turned so as to hold the maximum amount, whereas when it is denoting the null class, it is turned so as to hold nothing. Also they note that the cup used in forming the sum of two classes is turned so as to hold the maximum amount, which agrees with the definition of the sum class.

V and Λ are stratified and, since they contain no free variables at all, can be assigned any types whatever. Two V's in the same formula can be given different types if desired. Similarly for two Λ's, or a Λ and a V. To stratify a statement containing $A \cap B$, it will turn out that A and B have to have the same type, which must be taken as the type of $A \cap B$. Moreover, to stratify $A \cap B$ it is necessary and sufficient that we can stratify each of A and B separately in such a way that the subscripts attached to free occurrences of any variable in A are the same as the subscripts attached to free occurrences of this same variable in B. That is, $A \cap B$ is stratified if and only if $A = B$ is stratified. Similar remarks hold for $A \cup B$. Finally, $\overline{A}$ is stratified if and only if A is, and if $\overline{A}$ is stratified, it has the same type as A.

In trying to picture the relations of the class calculus, it is helpful to use Venn diagrams. Figure IX.4.1 is such a diagram. The points in the inte-

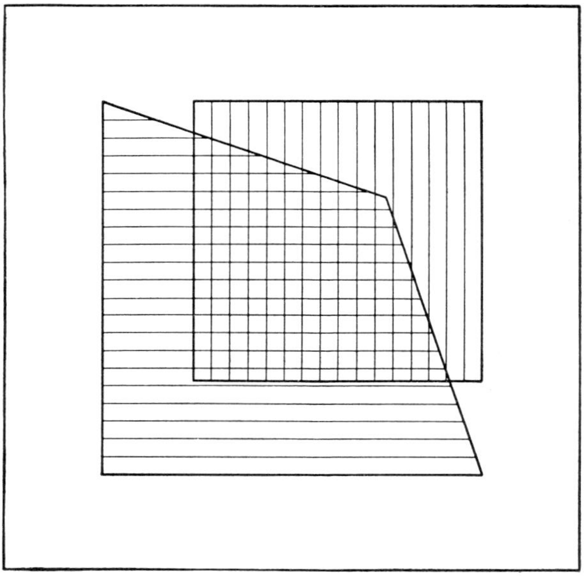

FIG. IX.4.1.

rior of the large square are supposed to represent the universe of discourse; the members of V, in other words. The points in the region with horizontal shading represent members of A, and the points in the region with vertical shading represent members of B. The points in the region with both kinds of shading represent members of $A \cap B$. The points in the entire region which has the shading of some kind represent members of $A \cup B$. The points in the region with no horizontal shading represent members of $\bar{A}$, and the points in the region with no vertical shading represent $\bar{B}$.

By drawing a Venn diagram with three classes, A, B, and C, one can verify the commutative, associative, distributive, and other principles which we shall shortly prove. Also the Venn diagram is a useful device in recalling these various principles.

Theorem IX.4.1.

I. $\vdash \exists \hat{x}(x = x)$.

II. $\vdash \exists \hat{x}(x \neq x)$.

III. $\vdash (\alpha,\beta).\exists \hat{x}(x \in \alpha \& x \in \beta)$.

IV. $\vdash (\alpha,\beta).\exists \hat{x}(x \in \alpha \mathbf{v} x \in \beta)$.

V. $\vdash (\alpha).\exists \hat{x}(\sim x \in \alpha)$.

Proof. Use Thm.IX.3.1.

Note that our conventions ensure the distinctness of α, β, and x in Parts III and IV, and of α and x in Part V.

Theorem IX.4.2.

*I. $\vdash (x){:}x \in \mathrm{V}. \equiv .x = x$.

*II. $\vdash (x){:}x \in \Lambda. \equiv .x \neq x$.

**III. $\vdash (\alpha,\beta,x){:}x \in \alpha \cap \beta. \equiv .x \in \alpha \& x \in \beta$.

**IV. $\vdash (\alpha,\beta,x){:}x \in \alpha \cup \beta. \equiv .x \in \alpha \mathbf{v} x \in \beta$.

**V. $\vdash (\alpha,x){:}x \in \bar{\alpha}. \equiv .\sim x \in \alpha$.

Proof. Use Thm.IX.4.1 and Thm.IX.3.2, Cor. 1.

Using Thm.IX.4.1, Part III, one can prove the existence of classes determined by unstratified conditions. For instance, use Axiom scheme 8 to replace α by $\hat{y}(\delta \in y)$, and then use Axiom scheme 6 to replace β by δ. There results

(1) $$\vdash \exists \hat{x}(x \in \hat{y}(\delta \in y) \& x \in \delta).$$

Now

(2) $$x \in \hat{y}(\delta \in y) \& x \in \delta$$

is unstratified; for suppose we attach the subscript unity to the two occurrences of δ. Then in $x \in \delta$ we must attach the subscript zero to x. In $\delta \in y$ we must attach the subscript 2 to y. Then we must consider $\hat{y}(\delta \in y)$ of type 3 (see the definition of $\hat{x}P$). Hence in the part $x \in \hat{y}(\delta \in y)$, we have a type difference of 3 instead of unity.

Nevertheless, though (2) is not stratified, (1) asserts that (2) determines a class.

It might be feared that this possibility of determining classes by certain types of unstratified conditions would lead to a contradiction of some sort, but apparently it does not.

One could avoid this means of determining classes by means of unstratified conditions by putting additional restrictions on Axiom scheme 6 and Axiom scheme 8. For instance, one could require that {Sub in P: y for x} in Axiom scheme 6 and {Sub in P: $\iota y\ Q$ for x} in Axiom scheme 8 should be stratified. A less stringent requirement would be to require in Axiom scheme 6 that {Sub in P: y for x} be stratified if P is, and in Axiom scheme 8 that {Sub in P: $\iota y\ Q$ for x} be stratified if P is.

As long as we get into no difficulties by allowing the determination of classes by special unstratified conditions, we welcome the flexibility which this allows us. We hold in reserve the additional requirements on Axiom schemes 6 and 8 in case they are ever needed to prevent a contradiction.

****Theorem IX.4.3.** Let x, α_1, α_2, . . . , α_n be distinct variables. Let A be built up out of the α's by use of $\cap$, $\cup$, and $\overline{}$. Let P be the result of replacing α_i by $x \epsilon \alpha_i$, $\cap$ by &, $\cup$ by $\mathbf{v}$, and $\overline{}$ by $\sim$ in A. Then $\vdash (\alpha_1, \alpha_2, \ldots, \alpha_n)(x).x \epsilon A \equiv P$.

Proof. We note that Thm.IX.4.2, Parts III, IV, and V are special cases of this theorem, and furnish just the lemmas needed to prove the theorem by induction on the number of symbols in A.

When A and P are related as in this theorem, we say that P is the statement analogous to the class A and A is the class analogous to the statement P.

Thm.IX.4.3 gives us a very potent means of proving equalities between classes. Let A and B be built up out of some or all of the distinct variables α_1, α_2, . . . , α_n by use of $\cap$, $\cup$, and $\overline{}$. Let P and Q be the analogous statements. P and Q will then be statements of the statement calculus, whose constituent parts are of the form $x \epsilon \alpha_i$. If one can prove $\vdash P \equiv Q$, then by Thm.IX.4.3 we shall have $\vdash x \epsilon A \equiv x \epsilon B$, whence we get $\vdash A = B$. In case $\vdash P \equiv Q$ is proved by truth values, we shall say that $\vdash A = B$ is proved by truth values.

Theorem IX.4.4.

**I. $\vdash (\alpha)\ \alpha = \bar{\bar{\alpha}}$.

**II. $\vdash (\alpha)\ \alpha = \alpha \cap \alpha$.

**III. $\vdash (\alpha)\ \alpha = \alpha \cup \alpha$.

IV. $\vdash (\alpha,\beta)\ \alpha = \alpha \cap (\alpha \cup \beta)$.

V. $\vdash (\alpha,\beta)\ \alpha = \alpha \cup (\alpha \cap \beta)$.

VI. $\vdash (\alpha,\beta)\ \alpha = (\alpha \cap \beta) \cup (\alpha \cap \bar{\beta})$.

VII. $\vdash (\alpha,\beta)\ \alpha = (\alpha \cup \beta) \cap (\alpha \cup \bar{\beta})$.

**VIII. $\vdash (\alpha,\beta)\ \alpha \cap \beta = \beta \cap \alpha$.

$$\star\star\text{IX.}\ \vdash (\alpha,\beta)\ \alpha \cup \beta = \beta \cup \alpha.$$
$$\star\star\text{X.}\ \vdash (\alpha,\beta,\gamma)\ \alpha \cap (\beta \cap \gamma) = (\alpha \cap \beta) \cap \gamma.$$
$$\star\star\text{XI.}\ \vdash (\alpha,\beta,\gamma)\ \alpha \cup (\beta \cup \gamma) = (\alpha \cup \beta) \cup \gamma.$$
$$\star\star\text{XII.}\ \vdash (\alpha,\beta,\gamma)\ \alpha \cap (\beta \cup \gamma) = (\alpha \cap \beta) \cup (\alpha \cap \gamma).$$
$$\star\star\text{XIII.}\ \vdash (\alpha,\beta,\gamma)\ \alpha \cup (\beta \cap \gamma) = (\alpha \cup \beta) \cap (\alpha \cup \gamma).$$
$$\text{XIV.}\ \vdash (\alpha,\beta)\ \alpha \cup \beta = \overline{\bar\alpha \cap \bar\beta}.$$
$$\text{XV.}\ \vdash (\alpha,\beta)\ \alpha \cap \beta = \overline{\bar\alpha \cup \bar\beta}.$$
$$\text{XVI.}\ \vdash (\alpha,\beta)\ \overline{\alpha \cup \beta} = \bar\alpha \cap \bar\beta.$$
$$\text{XVII.}\ \vdash (\alpha,\beta)\ \overline{\alpha \cap \beta} = \bar\alpha \cup \bar\beta.$$
$$\text{XVIII.}\ \vdash (\alpha,\beta)\ \alpha \cap \beta = (\alpha \cup \bar\beta) \cap \beta.$$
$$\star\text{XIX.}\ \vdash (\alpha,\beta)\ \alpha \cup \beta = (\alpha \cap \bar\beta) \cup \beta.$$
$$\text{XX.}\ \vdash (\alpha,\beta)\ \alpha \cup \beta = (\alpha \cap \beta) \cup (\alpha \cap \bar\beta) \cup (\bar\alpha \cap \beta).$$
$$\text{XXI.}\ \vdash (\alpha,\beta)\ \alpha \cap \beta = (\alpha \cup \beta) \cap (\alpha \cup \bar\beta) \cap (\bar\alpha \cup \beta).$$
$$\text{XXII.}\ \vdash (\alpha,\beta)\ \overline{\alpha \cap \beta} = (\alpha \cap \bar\beta) \cup (\bar\alpha \cap \beta) \cup (\bar\alpha \cap \bar\beta).$$
$$\text{XXIII.}\ \vdash (\alpha,\beta)\ \overline{\alpha \cup \beta} = (\alpha \cup \bar\beta) \cap (\bar\alpha \cup \beta) \cap (\bar\alpha \cup \bar\beta).$$
$$\star\star\text{XXIV.}\ \vdash (\alpha)\ \alpha \cap \bar\alpha = \Lambda.$$
$$\star\star\text{XXV.}\ \vdash (\alpha)\ \alpha \cup \bar\alpha = \text{V}.$$
$$\star\star\text{XXVI.}\ \vdash \Lambda = \bar{\text{V}}.$$
$$\star\star\text{XXVII.}\ \vdash \text{V} = \bar\Lambda.$$
$$\star\star\text{XXVIII.}\ \vdash (\alpha)\ \alpha \cap \text{V} = \alpha.$$
$$\star\star\text{XXIX.}\ \vdash (\alpha)\ \alpha \cup \text{V} = \text{V}.$$
$$\star\star\text{XXX.}\ \vdash (\alpha)\ \alpha \cap \Lambda = \Lambda.$$
$$\star\star\text{XXXI.}\ \vdash (\alpha)\ \alpha \cup \Lambda = \alpha.$$

Proof. All except the last eight parts are proved by truth values. To illustrate a proof by truth values, we give the proof of Part XX.

The statements analogous to $\alpha \cup \beta$ and $(\alpha \cap \beta) \cup (\alpha \cap \bar\beta) \cup (\bar\alpha \cap \beta)$ are

$$x \in \alpha \mathbf{v} x \in \beta$$

and

$$x \in \alpha . x \in \beta : \mathbf{v} : x \in \alpha . \sim x \in \beta : \mathbf{v} : \sim x \in \alpha . x \in \beta .$$

By truth values

$$\vdash x \in \alpha \mathbf{v} x \in \beta .: \equiv :. x \in \alpha . x \in \beta : \mathbf{v} : x \in \alpha . \sim x \in \beta : \mathbf{v} : \sim x \in \alpha . x \in \beta$$

(see Thm.VI.6.1, Part XXXVII).

So by Thm.IX.4.3,

$$\vdash x \in \alpha \cup \beta . \equiv . x \in (\alpha \cap \beta) \cup (\alpha \cap \bar\beta) \cup (\bar\alpha \cap \beta).$$

So

$$\vdash \alpha \cup \beta = (\alpha \cap \beta) \cup (\alpha \cap \bar\beta) \cup (\bar\alpha \cap \beta).$$

By Parts XXIV and XXV we can write the last six parts in the forms

$$\text{XXVI.}\ \vdash (\alpha)\ \alpha \cap \bar\alpha = \overline{\alpha \cup \bar\alpha}.$$
$$\text{XXVII.}\ \vdash (\alpha)\ \alpha \cup \bar\alpha = \overline{\alpha \cap \bar\alpha}.$$

XXVIII. $\vdash (\alpha,\beta)\ \alpha \cap (\beta \cup \bar{\beta}) = \alpha.$
XXIX. $\vdash (\alpha,\beta)\ \alpha \cup (\beta \cup \bar{\beta}) = \beta \cup \bar{\beta}.$
XXX. $\vdash (\alpha,\beta)\ \alpha \cap (\beta \cap \bar{\beta}) = \beta \cap \bar{\beta}.$
XXXI. $\vdash (\alpha,\beta)\ \alpha \cup (\beta \cap \bar{\beta}) = \alpha.$

In these forms, they can be proved by truth values. This leaves us with only Parts XXIV and XXV to prove. For these we need merely

$$\vdash x \in \alpha . \mathbf{v} . \sim x \in \alpha : \equiv : x = x$$

and

$$\vdash x \in \alpha . \sim x \in \alpha : \equiv : x \neq x,$$

which follow easily by Thm.VI.6.1, Parts LXXI and LXXIV.

Because we now have the associative law for $\cap$ and $\cup$, we can and will hereafter write $\alpha \cap \beta \cap \gamma$ for either of $(\alpha \cap \beta) \cap \gamma$ and $\alpha \cap (\beta \cap \gamma)$; similarly for $\alpha \cup \beta \cup \gamma$, $\alpha \cap \beta \cap \gamma \cap \delta$, $\alpha \cup \beta \cup \gamma \cup \delta$, etc.

Let A be built up out of V, Λ, and the distinct variables $\alpha_1, \alpha_2, \ldots, \alpha_n$ by use of $\cap$, $\cup$, and $\overline{}$. Then the dual of A, A^*, is got from A by simultaneously performing the following changes:

1. If an occurrence of α_i has no bar over it, place one over it (*i.e.*, replace α_i by $\overline{\alpha_i}$).
2. If an occurrence of α_i has a bar over it, replace the entire occurrence of $\overline{\alpha_i}$ by α_i.
3. Replace each $\cap$ by $\cup$ and each $\cup$ by $\cap$.
4. Replace each V by Λ and each Λ by V.

****Theorem IX.4.5.** If A is built up out of V, Λ, and the distinct variables $\alpha_1, \alpha_2, \ldots, \alpha_n$ by use of $\cap$, $\cup$, and $\overline{}$, and A^* is the dual of A, then $\vdash (\alpha_1, \alpha_2, \ldots, \alpha_n) A^* = \bar{A}$.

Proof. Choose β a variable distinct from any of the α's and replace all V's and Λ's of A and A^* by $\beta \cup \bar{\beta}$ and $\beta \cap \bar{\beta}$, and call the results B and B^*. Clearly B^* is the dual of B. Also, by Thm.IX.4.4, Parts XXIV and XXV, $\vdash A = B$ and $\vdash A^* = B^*$. As B and B^* are built up entirely from variables, we can form the analogous statements, P and P^*. Clearly P^* is the dual of P. So

$$\vdash P^* \equiv \sim P.$$

Hence by Thm.IX.4.3,

$$\vdash x \in B^* \equiv \sim(x \in B).$$

So

$$\vdash x \in A^* \equiv \sim(x \in A).$$

Accordingly, by Thm.IX.4.2, Part V,

$$\vdash x \in A^* \equiv x \in \bar{A}.$$

So

$$\vdash A^* = \overline{A}.$$

Several parts of Thm.IX.4.4 are special cases of this duality theorem.

From this duality theorem, one easily has another type of duality theorem. Let A and B be built up out of V, Λ, and the distinct variables $\alpha_1, \alpha_2, \ldots, \alpha_n$ by use of $\cap$, $\cup$, and $\overline{}$, and suppose we have $\vdash A = B$. Then we have $\vdash C = D$, where C and D are got from A and B by replacing $\cap$ by $\cup$, $\cup$ by $\cap$, V by Λ, and Λ by V. For from $\vdash A = B$, we have $\vdash \overline{A} = \overline{B}$. Then by the duality theorem $\vdash A^* = B^*$. So by rule G, $\vdash (\alpha_1, \alpha_2, \ldots, \alpha_n)A^* = B^*$. Now by Axiom scheme 8 replace each α_i by $\overline{\alpha_i}$. With a few applications of $\vdash \alpha_i = \overline{\overline{\alpha_i}}$, we get $\vdash C = D$.

Many pairs of parts of Thm.IX.4.4 will be seen to be related by this type of duality.

Theorem IX.4.6. $\vdash (\alpha)\ \alpha \neq \bar{\alpha}$.

Proof. By the definition of equality

$$\vdash \alpha = \bar{\alpha}. \supset .x \in \alpha \equiv x \in \bar{\alpha}.$$

So

$$\vdash \alpha = \bar{\alpha}: \supset :x \in \alpha. \equiv .\sim x \in \alpha.$$

However, by truth values

$$\vdash P \supset .Q \equiv \sim Q: \supset :\sim P.$$

So $\vdash \sim(\alpha = \bar{\alpha})$.

***Corollary.** $\vdash \Lambda \neq \text{V}$.

Theorem IX.4.7. $\vdash (\alpha,\beta):\bar{\alpha} = \bar{\beta}. \supset .\alpha = \beta.$

Proof. By Thm.IX.2.5, $\vdash \bar{\alpha} = \bar{\beta}. \supset .\bar{\bar{\alpha}} = \bar{\bar{\beta}}$.

Theorem IX.4.8. If P contains free occurrences of α, then $\vdash \exists\{\bar{\alpha} \mid P\}.: \supset :.(\alpha):\bar{\alpha} \in \{\bar{\alpha} \mid P\}. \equiv .P.$

Proof. Use Thm.IX.3.7 and Thm.IX.4.7.

Corollary. If P is stratified and contains free occurrences of α, then $\vdash (\alpha):\bar{\alpha} \in \{\bar{\alpha} \mid P\}. \equiv .P.$

Theorem IX.4.9. $\vdash (\alpha,\beta,\gamma):\alpha \cup \beta = \gamma.\alpha \cap \beta = \Lambda. \supset .\alpha = \gamma - \beta.$

Proof. Assume $\alpha \cup \beta = \gamma$ and $\alpha \cap \beta = \Lambda$. By Thm.IX.4.4, Part XIX, $\vdash \alpha \cup \bar{\beta} = (\alpha \cap \beta) \cup \bar{\beta}$. So by our assumption, $\alpha \cup \bar{\beta} = \Lambda \cup \bar{\beta}$, and so by Thm.IX.4.4, Part XXXI, $\alpha \cup \bar{\beta} = \bar{\beta}$. So by Thm.IX.4.4, Part VII, $\alpha = (\alpha \cup \beta) \cap (\alpha \cup \bar{\beta}) = \gamma \cap \bar{\beta} = \gamma - \beta$.

Corollary 1. $\vdash (\alpha,\beta):\alpha \cup \beta = \text{V}.\alpha \cap \beta = \Lambda. \supset .\alpha = \bar{\beta}.$

Proof. Put $\gamma = \text{V}$.

Corollary 2. $\vdash (\alpha,\beta):\alpha \cap \beta = \Lambda. \supset .\alpha = (\alpha \cup \beta) - \beta.$

Proof. Put $\gamma = \alpha \cup \beta$.

Corollary 3. $\vdash (\alpha,\beta,\gamma):\alpha \cup \beta = \gamma \cup \beta.\alpha \cap \beta = \Lambda.\gamma \cap \beta = \Lambda. \supset .\alpha = \gamma.$

Proof. By Cor. 2, $\alpha = (\alpha \cup \beta) - \beta = (\gamma \cup \beta) - \beta = \gamma$.

One can also prove Thm.IX.4.9 by use of truth values as follows.

By truth values,

$$\vdash P\mathbf{v}Q \equiv R.PQ \equiv S{\sim}S. \supset .P \equiv R{\sim}Q.$$

Replacing P by $x \epsilon \alpha$, Q by $x \epsilon \beta$, R by $x \epsilon \gamma$, and S by $x \epsilon \delta$, we get

$$\vdash x \epsilon \alpha \cup \beta \equiv x \epsilon \gamma.x \epsilon \alpha \cap \beta \equiv x \epsilon \delta \cap \bar{\delta}. \supset .x \epsilon \alpha \equiv x \epsilon \gamma - \beta.$$

Then by rule G, Axiom scheme 4, and Thm.VI.6.5, Part I

$$\vdash (x).x \epsilon \alpha \cup \beta \equiv x \epsilon \gamma{:}(x).x \epsilon \alpha \cap \beta \equiv x \epsilon \Lambda{:} \supset {:}(x).x \epsilon \alpha \equiv x \epsilon \gamma - \beta.$$

Our theorem now follows by the definition of equality.

Theorem IX.4.10.

I. $\vdash (x)\ x \epsilon \mathrm{V}$.

★II. $\vdash (x) \sim x \epsilon \Lambda$.

Proof. Use Thm.IX.4.2, Parts I and II.

Theorem IX.4.11.

I. $\vdash (x)\ Q{:} \supset {:}(x).x \epsilon \mathrm{V} \equiv Q$.

II. $\vdash (x) \sim Q{:} \supset {:}(x).x \epsilon \Lambda \equiv Q$.

Proof of I. By putting $x \epsilon \mathrm{V}$ for P in Thm.VI.6.1, Part LXXI, we get $\vdash Q{:} \supset {:}x \epsilon \mathrm{V} \equiv Q$. So $\vdash (x)\ Q{:} \supset {:}(x).x \epsilon \mathrm{V} \equiv Q$.

Proof of Part II is similar, using Thm.VI.6.1, Part LXXIV.

Corollary 1.

I. $\vdash (x)\ Q. \supset .\exists\hat{x}Q$.

II. $\vdash (x) \sim Q. \supset .\exists\hat{x}Q$.

Corollary 2.

I. $\vdash (x)\ Q. \supset .\mathrm{V} = \hat{x}Q$.

II. $\vdash (x) \sim Q. \supset .\Lambda = \hat{x}Q$.

Theorem IX.4.12.

I. $\vdash (\alpha){:}.(x).x \epsilon \alpha{:} \equiv {:}\alpha = \mathrm{V}$.

II. $\vdash (\alpha){:}.(x).\sim x \epsilon \alpha{:} \equiv {:}\alpha = \Lambda$.

Proof of I. By Thm.IX.4.10, Part I, and Thm.IX.2.4,

$$\vdash \alpha = \mathrm{V}{:} \supset {:}(x).x \epsilon \alpha.$$

Conversely, putting $x \epsilon \alpha$ for Q in Thm.IX.4.11, Part I, gives

$$\vdash (x).x \epsilon \alpha{:} \supset {:}\alpha = \mathrm{V}.$$

Proof of Part II is similar.

Corollary.

I. $\vdash (\alpha){:}.(\mathrm{E}x).\sim x \epsilon \alpha{:} \equiv {:}\alpha \neq \mathrm{V}$.

★II. $\vdash (\alpha){:}.(\mathrm{E}x).x \epsilon \alpha{:} \equiv {:}\alpha \neq \Lambda$.

We introduce the definitions:

$$A \subseteq B \quad \text{for} \quad (x).x \in A \supset x \in B,$$

$$A \subset B \quad \text{for} \quad A \subseteq B \& A \neq B,$$

$$A \subseteq B \subseteq C \quad \text{for} \quad A \subseteq B \& B \subseteq C,$$

$$A \subset B \subseteq C \quad \text{for} \quad A \subset B \& B \subseteq C,$$

$$A \subseteq B = C \quad \text{for} \quad A \subseteq B \& B = C,$$

etc.

In the first of these we require that x be a variable which does not occur in A or B. Clearly, except for the bound x, all free occurrences of variables of $A \subseteq B$ are the free occurrences in A and B, and similarly for the bound occurrences.

We read $A \subseteq B$ as "A is included in B" or "B includes A" or "A is a subset of B." We read $A \subset B$ as "A is a proper subset of B."

Many logicians use the symbol $\subset$ to mean what we denote by $\subseteq$. This leaves them no simple notation for what we denote by $\subset$. Our notation has general mathematical sanction.

In the Venn diagram, $A \subseteq B$ would mean that all the area denoted by A is comprised within the area denoted by B, and $A \subset B$ would mean that moreover some of B is not a part of A.

$A \subseteq B$ and $A \subset B$ are stratified if and only if $A = B$ is stratified. In particular, for stratification of $A \subseteq B$ or $A \subset B$, A and B must have the same type.

We now prove a theorem which is very important because it allows us to replace the inclusion of two classes by the equality of two other classes, and in fact in four different ways. Thus all our means of proving equalities between classes become available for proving inclusions between classes.

Theorem IX.4.13.

**I. $\vdash (\alpha,\beta){:}\alpha \subseteq \beta. \equiv .\alpha \cap \beta = \alpha.$

II. $\vdash (\alpha,\beta){:}\alpha \subseteq \beta. \equiv .\alpha \cap \bar{\beta} = \Lambda.$

*III. $\vdash (\alpha,\beta){:}\alpha \subseteq \beta. \equiv .\alpha \cup \beta = \beta.$

IV. $\vdash (\alpha,\beta){:}\alpha \subseteq \beta. \equiv .\bar{\alpha} \cup \beta = V.$

Proof of Part I. By Thm.VI.6.1, Part XLIX, and Thm.IX.4.2, Part III, $\vdash (x).x \in \alpha \supset x \in \beta{:} \equiv {:}(x).x \in \alpha \equiv x \in \alpha \cap \beta$. By the definitions of equality and of $\subseteq$, this is Part I.

Proof of Part III is similar, using Thm.VI.6.1, Part L, and Thm.IX.4.2, Part IV.

Proof of Part II. By Parts I and III, it suffices to prove

(1) $$\vdash \alpha \cap \beta = \alpha. \supset .\alpha \cap \bar{\beta} = \Lambda,$$

(2) $$\vdash \alpha \cap \bar{\beta} = \Lambda. \supset .\alpha \cup \beta = \beta.$$

To prove (1), assume $\alpha \cap \beta = \alpha$. Then $\alpha \cap \bar{\beta} = (\alpha \cap \beta) \cap \bar{\beta} = \alpha \cap (\beta \cap \bar{\beta}) = \alpha \cap \Lambda = \Lambda$. To prove (2), assume $\alpha \cap \bar{\beta} = \Lambda$. Then by Thm.IX.4.4, Part XIX, $\alpha \cup \beta = (\alpha \cap \bar{\beta}) \cup \beta = \Lambda \cup \beta = \beta$.

Proof of Part IV. By Part II, it suffices to prove

$$(3) \qquad \vdash \alpha \cap \bar{\beta} = \Lambda. \equiv .\bar{\alpha} \cup \beta = V.$$

Assume $\alpha \cap \bar{\beta} = \Lambda$. Then $\overline{\alpha \cap \bar{\beta}} = \bar{\Lambda}$. That is, $\bar{\alpha} \cup \beta = V$. Conversely, if $\bar{\alpha} \cup \beta = V$, then by reversing our steps, we get $\alpha \cap \bar{\beta} = \Lambda$.

Corollary 1. $\vdash (\beta){:}V \subseteq \beta. \equiv .\beta = V.$

Proof. Put $\alpha = V$ in Part I.

Corollary 2. $\vdash (\alpha){:}\alpha \subseteq \Lambda. \equiv .\Lambda = \alpha.$

Corollary 3. $\vdash (\alpha).\alpha \subseteq \alpha.$

Corollary 4. $\vdash (\alpha).\alpha \subseteq V.$

Corollary 5. $\vdash (\beta).\Lambda \subseteq \beta.$

★Corollary 6. $\vdash (\alpha,\beta).\alpha \cap \beta \subseteq \beta.$

★Corollary 7. $\vdash (\alpha,\beta).\alpha \subseteq \alpha \cup \beta.$

★★Theorem IX.4.14. $\vdash (\alpha,\beta){:}\alpha \subseteq \beta.\beta \subseteq \alpha. \equiv .\alpha = \beta.$

Proof. By Thm.VI.6.5, Part I, $\vdash (x).x \in \alpha \supset x \in \beta{:}(x).x \in \beta \supset x \in \alpha.{:} \equiv {:}.\ (x){:}x \in \alpha \supset x \in \beta.x \in \beta \supset x \in \alpha$. By the definitions of equality and inclusion, this is our theorem.

This theorem is very commonly used to prove the equality of two classes.

★★Theorem IX.4.15. $\vdash (\alpha,\beta,\gamma){:}\alpha \subseteq \beta.\beta \subseteq \gamma. \supset .\alpha \subseteq \gamma.$

Proof. Assume $\alpha \subseteq \beta$ and $\beta \subseteq \gamma$. Then by Thm.IX.4.13, Part I, $\alpha \cap \beta = \alpha$ and $\beta \cap \gamma = \beta$. So $\alpha \cap \gamma = (\alpha \cap \beta) \cap \gamma = \alpha \cap (\beta \cap \gamma) = \alpha \cap \beta = \alpha$.

For an alternative proof, one can put $x \in \alpha$, $x \in \beta$, and $x \in \gamma$ for P, Q, and R in

$$\vdash P \supset Q.Q \supset R. \supset .P \supset R.$$

Theorem IX.4.16.

I. $\vdash (\alpha,\beta,\gamma){:}\alpha \subseteq \beta. \supset .\alpha \cap \gamma \subseteq \beta \cap \gamma.$

II. $\vdash (\alpha,\beta,\gamma){:}\alpha \subseteq \beta. \supset .\alpha \cup \gamma \subseteq \beta \cup \gamma.$

Proof of Part I. Assume $\alpha \subseteq \beta$. Then by Thm.IX.4.13, Part I, $\alpha \cap \beta = \alpha$. So $(\alpha \cap \beta) \cap (\gamma \cap \gamma) = \alpha \cap \gamma$. So $(\alpha \cap \gamma) \cap (\beta \cap \gamma) = \alpha \cap \gamma$. Accordingly, $\alpha \cap \gamma \subseteq \beta \cap \gamma$.

Proof of Part II is similar using Thm.IX.4.13, Part III.

Alternatively one can derive Parts I and II from $\vdash P \supset Q. \supset .PR \supset QR$ and $\vdash P \supset Q. \supset .P{\vee}R \supset Q{\vee}R$, respectively.

Corollary 1. $\vdash (\alpha,\beta,\gamma,\delta){:}\alpha \subseteq \beta.\gamma \subseteq \delta. \supset .\alpha \cap \gamma \subseteq \beta \cap \delta.$

For $\alpha \subseteq \beta$ gives $\alpha \cap \gamma \subseteq \beta \cap \gamma$ and $\gamma \subseteq \delta$ gives $\beta \cap \gamma \subseteq \beta \cap \delta$.

Corollary 2. $\vdash (\alpha,\beta,\gamma,\delta){:}\alpha \subseteq \beta.\gamma \subseteq \delta. \supset .\alpha \cup \gamma \subseteq \beta \cup \delta.$

Theorem IX.4.17. $\vdash (\alpha,\beta){:}\alpha \subseteq \beta. \equiv .\bar{\beta} \subseteq \bar{\alpha}.$

Proof. Assume $\alpha \subseteq \beta$. Then $\alpha \cap \beta = \alpha$. So $\overline{\alpha \cap \beta} = \bar{\alpha}$. That is,

$\bar{\alpha} \cup \bar{\beta} = \bar{\alpha}$. So $\bar{\beta} \subseteq \bar{\alpha}$. Since these steps are reversible, we get our theorem.

Alternatively one can derive the theorem from $\vdash P \supset Q. \equiv .\sim Q \supset \sim P$.

Theorem IX.4.18.

$\star$I. $\vdash (\alpha,\beta,\gamma):.\alpha \subseteq \beta \cap \gamma: \equiv :\alpha \subseteq \beta.\alpha \subseteq \gamma$.

$\star$II. $\vdash (\alpha,\beta,\gamma):.\alpha \cup \beta \subseteq \gamma: \equiv :\alpha \subseteq \gamma.\beta \subseteq \gamma$.

Proof of Part I. Assume $\alpha \subseteq \beta \cap \gamma$. Combining this with $\beta \cap \gamma \subseteq \beta$ and $\beta \cap \gamma \subseteq \gamma$ (which we get by Thm.IX.4.13, Cor. 6), we get $\alpha \subseteq \beta$ and $\alpha \subseteq \gamma$. Conversely, assume $\alpha \subseteq \beta$ and $\alpha \subseteq \gamma$. Then $\alpha \subseteq \beta \cap \gamma$ by Thm. IX.4.16, Cor. 1.

Proof of Part II is similar.

Alternatively one can derive Parts I and II from $\vdash P \supset QR: \equiv :P \supset Q. P \supset R$ and $\vdash P \mathbf{v} Q \supset R: \equiv :P \supset R.Q \supset R$, respectively.

Corollary 1. $\vdash (\beta,\gamma):.\mathrm{V} = \beta \cap \gamma: \equiv :\mathrm{V} = \beta.\mathrm{V} = \gamma$.

Corollary 2. $\vdash (\alpha,\beta):.\alpha \cup \beta = \Lambda: \equiv :\alpha = \Lambda.\beta = \Lambda$.

Theorem IX.4.19. $\vdash (\alpha,\beta):\alpha \subset \beta. \supset .\sim(\beta \subseteq \alpha)$.

Proof. By Thm.IX.4.14, $\vdash \alpha \subseteq \beta: \supset :\beta \subseteq \alpha. \supset .\alpha = \beta$. So $\vdash \alpha \subseteq \beta: \supset : \alpha \neq \beta. \supset .\sim(\beta \subseteq \alpha)$. Then $\vdash \alpha \subseteq \beta.\alpha \neq \beta. \supset .\sim(\beta \subseteq \alpha)$, which is our theorem.

Theorem IX.4.20. $\vdash (\alpha,\beta):.\alpha \subset \beta: \equiv :\alpha \subseteq \beta.\sim(\beta \subseteq \alpha)$.

Proof. By Thm.IX.4.19,

(1) $$\vdash \alpha \subset \beta: \supset :\alpha \subseteq \beta.\sim(\beta \subseteq \alpha).$$

By Thm.IX.4.14, $\vdash \alpha = \beta. \supset .\beta \subseteq \alpha$. So $\vdash \sim(\beta \subseteq \alpha). \supset .\alpha \neq \beta$. So $\vdash \alpha \subseteq \beta.\sim(\beta \subseteq \alpha). \supset .\alpha \subset \beta$. Combining with (1) gives our theorem.

Theorem IX.4.21. $\vdash (\alpha,\beta):.\alpha \subset \beta: \equiv :\alpha \subseteq \beta.(\mathrm{E}x).x \in \beta.\sim x \in \alpha$.

Proof. By the duality theorem, $\vdash \sim(\beta \subseteq \alpha): \equiv :(\mathrm{E}x).x \in \beta.\sim x \in \alpha$.

Theorem IX.4.22.

I. $\vdash (\alpha,\beta,\gamma):\alpha \subset \beta.\beta \subseteq \gamma. \supset .\alpha \subset \gamma$.

II. $\vdash (\alpha,\beta,\gamma):\alpha \subseteq \beta.\beta \subset \gamma. \supset .\alpha \subset \gamma$.

III. $\vdash (\alpha,\beta,\gamma):\alpha \subset \beta.\beta \subset \gamma. \supset .\alpha \subset \gamma$.

Proof of Part I. Assume $\alpha \subset \beta$ and $\beta \subseteq \gamma$. Then $\alpha \subseteq \beta$, $\alpha \neq \beta$, and $\beta \subseteq \gamma$. By $\alpha \subseteq \beta$ and $\beta \subseteq \gamma$, we get $\alpha \subseteq \gamma$. It remains to prove $\alpha \neq \gamma$, which we do by reductio ad absurdum. Assume $\alpha = \gamma$. Then by substituting in $\beta \subseteq \gamma$, we get $\beta \subseteq \alpha$, which with $\alpha \subseteq \beta$ gives $\alpha = \beta$, which is our contradiction.

Proofs of Parts II and III are similar.

Theorem IX.4.23. $\vdash (\alpha,\beta):\alpha \subset \beta. \equiv .\bar{\beta} \subset \bar{\alpha}$.

Proof. Combine Thm.IX.4.17 with the result $\vdash \alpha \neq \beta. \equiv .\bar{\alpha} \neq \bar{\beta}$, which follows from $\vdash \alpha = \beta. \equiv .\bar{\alpha} = \bar{\beta}$, which follows from Thm.IX.4.7.

Theorem IX.4.24.

I. $\vdash (\alpha,\beta,\gamma):.\alpha \subset \beta \cap \gamma: \supset :\alpha \subset \beta.\alpha \subset \gamma$.

II. $\vdash (\alpha,\beta,\gamma):.\alpha \cup \beta \subset \gamma: \supset :\alpha \subset \gamma.\beta \subset \gamma$.

Proof. Analogous to the corresponding portions of the proof of Thm. IX.4.18.

EXERCISES

IX.4.1. Construct Venn diagrams to show that each of the following is false:

(a) $(\alpha,\beta,\gamma):.\alpha \subset \beta: \supset :\alpha \cap \gamma \subset \beta \cap \gamma.$
(b) $(\alpha,\beta,\gamma):.\alpha \subset \beta: \supset :\alpha \cup \gamma \subset \beta \cup \gamma.$
(c) $(\alpha,\beta,\gamma):.\alpha \subset \beta.\alpha \subset \gamma: \supset :\alpha \subset \beta \cap \gamma.$
(d) $(\alpha,\beta,\gamma):.\alpha \subset \gamma.\beta \subset \gamma: \supset :\alpha \cup \beta \subset \gamma.$

IX.4.2. Illustrate Thm.IX.4.13 by a Venn diagram.

IX.4.3. Illustrate Parts VI, XVI, XIX, and XX of Thm.IX.4.4. by Venn diagrams.

IX.4.4. Prove:

(a) $\vdash \exists\hat{x}P.\exists\hat{x}Q: \supset :(x):x \in \hat{x}P \cap \hat{x}Q. \equiv .PQ.$
(b) $\vdash \exists\hat{x}P.\exists\hat{x}Q: \supset :(x):x \in \hat{x}P \cup \hat{x}Q. \equiv .P\mathbf{v}Q.$
(c) $\vdash \exists\hat{x}P: \supset :(x):x \in \overline{\hat{x}P}. \equiv .\sim P.$

IX.4.5. Prove:

(a) $\vdash \exists\hat{x}P.\exists\hat{x}Q: \supset :\exists\hat{x}(PQ).$
(b) $\vdash \exists\hat{x}P.\exists\hat{x}Q: \supset :\exists\hat{x}(P\mathbf{v}Q).$
(c) $\vdash \exists\hat{x}P. \supset .\exists\hat{x}(\sim P).$

IX.4.6. Prove:

(a) $\vdash \exists\hat{x}P.\exists\hat{x}Q: \supset :\hat{x}P \cap \hat{x}Q = \hat{x}(PQ).$
(b) $\vdash \exists\hat{x}P.\exists\hat{x}Q: \supset :\hat{x}P \cup \hat{x}Q = \hat{x}(P\mathbf{v}Q).$
(c) $\vdash \exists\hat{x}P. \supset .\overline{\hat{x}P} = \hat{x}(\sim P).$

IX.4.7. Prove:

(a) $\vdash (\alpha,\beta,\gamma).\alpha \cap (\beta - \gamma) = (\alpha \cap \beta) - (\alpha \cap \gamma).$
(b) $\vdash (\alpha,\beta,\gamma).(\alpha - \beta) \cup (\alpha - \gamma) = \alpha - (\beta \cap \gamma).$
(c) $\vdash (\alpha,\beta).(\alpha - \beta) \cup (\beta - \alpha) = (\alpha \cup \beta) - (\alpha \cap \beta).$
(d) $\vdash (\alpha,\beta).\alpha - (\alpha - \beta) = \alpha \cap \beta.$
(e) $\vdash (\alpha,\beta,\gamma).(\alpha \cup \gamma) \cap (\beta \cup \bar{\gamma}) = (\alpha \cap \bar{\gamma}) \cup (\beta \cap \gamma).$

IX.4.8. Prove:

(a) $\vdash (\alpha,\beta):\alpha \cup \beta = \alpha \cap \beta. \equiv .\alpha = \beta.$
(b) $\vdash (\alpha,\beta):\alpha \cap \beta = \Lambda. \equiv .(\alpha \cup \beta) - \alpha = \beta. \equiv .(\alpha \cup \beta) - \beta = \alpha.$
(c) $\vdash (\alpha,\beta):\alpha \subseteq \beta. \supset .\alpha \cup (\beta - \alpha) = \beta.$
(d) $\vdash (\alpha,\beta,\gamma):.\beta \subseteq \alpha.\alpha - \beta = \gamma: \supset :\alpha - \gamma = \beta.$
(e) $\vdash (\alpha,\beta,\gamma):\alpha \cap \gamma = \Lambda. \supset .(\alpha \cup \gamma) - (\beta \cup \gamma) = \alpha - \beta.$
(f) $\vdash (\alpha,\beta,\gamma):.\gamma \subseteq \alpha \cup \beta: \supset :(E\theta,\phi):\theta \subseteq \alpha.\phi \subseteq \beta.\gamma = \theta \cup \phi.$

IX.4.9. Prove:

$$\vdash (\alpha,\beta):.\alpha \subseteq \beta: \equiv :\alpha \subset \beta.\mathbf{v}.\alpha = \beta.$$

IX.4.10. The quantity $(\alpha - \beta) \cup (\beta - \alpha)$ is sometimes called the symmetric difference of α and β or the sum of α and β (modulo 2). Denote it by $\alpha * \beta$. Prove:

(a) $\vdash (\alpha,\beta).\alpha * \beta = \beta * \alpha.$
(b) $\vdash (\alpha,\beta,\gamma).(\alpha * \beta) * \gamma = \alpha * (\beta * \gamma).$
(c) $\vdash (\alpha,\beta,\gamma).(\alpha * \beta) \cap \gamma = (\alpha \cap \gamma) * (\beta \cap \gamma).$
(d) $\vdash (\alpha).\alpha * \Lambda = \alpha.$
(e) $\vdash (\alpha).\alpha * \alpha = \Lambda.$
(f) $\vdash (\alpha,\beta,\gamma):\alpha * \gamma = \beta * \gamma. \supset .\alpha = \beta.$
(g) $\vdash (\alpha,\beta):\alpha = \beta. \equiv .\alpha * \beta = \Lambda.$

IX.4.11. Illustrate $\alpha * \beta$ by a Venn diagram.

IX.4.12. Prove:

(a) $\vdash (\alpha,\beta):\beta = (\alpha \cap \beta) \cup ((\alpha \cup \beta) - \alpha).$
(b) $\vdash (\alpha,\beta,\gamma):\alpha \cup \beta = \alpha \cup \gamma.\alpha \cap \beta = \alpha \cap \gamma. \supset .\beta = \gamma.$

IX.4.13. Name parts of Thm.IX.4.4 which are illustrations of the duality theorem (Thm.IX.4.5).

IX.4.14. Name pairs of parts of Thm.IX.4.4 which are duals of the sort described after the proof of Thm.IX.4.5.

IX.4.15. Write a 250-word essay on the distinction between "member of" and "subclass of".

5. Manifold Products and Sums. We wish to generalize the product $A \cap B$ to

$$A \cap B \cap C \cap \cdots$$

where the product is extended over all $A, B, C, \ldots$ which are members of some class K. We denote this product by $\bigcap(K)$, or often simply $\bigcap K$. To make $\bigcap K$ have the desired properties we define it as

$$\hat{x}(\alpha).\alpha \in K \supset x \in \alpha,$$

where x and α are distinct variables not occurring in K. The reader can easily verify that this definition makes $\bigcap K$ consist of all objects which are members of each member of K at once; that is, of all objects in the product of all members of K. This definition is valid whether K is a finite or an infinite class. If K were finite, with members $A_1, A_2, \ldots, A_n$, one could use

$$A_1 \cap A_2 \cap \cdots \cap A_n$$

in place of $\bigcap K$. So the notation $\bigcap K$ is useful mainly in those cases where K is an infinite class. For this reason, $\bigcap K$ is often called an infinite product. However, the term "manifold product" is more accurate and is the name which we shall use for $\bigcap K$.

In analogous fashion, we wish to generalize the sum $A \cup B$ to

$$A \cup B \cup C \cup \cdots$$

where the sum is extended over all A, B, C, . . . which are members of K. The definition $\bigcup(K)$, or $\bigcup K$, for

$$\hat{x}(\mathrm{E}\alpha){:}\alpha \in K.x \in \alpha$$

(where x and α are distinct variables not occurring in K) will give us a notation for the class in question, since it will make $\bigcup K$ consist of all objects which are in at least one member of K. We shall refer to $\bigcup K$ as a manifold sum, though it is sometimes referred to as an infinite sum.

In $\bigcap K$ and $\bigcup K$, we refer to $\bigcap$ and $\bigcup$ as "large cap" and "large cup", respectively.

Except for α and the bound variables implicit in $\hat{x}$, which are all bound, a variable is free or bound in $\bigcap K$ or $\bigcup K$ according as it is free or bound in K.

$\bigcap K$ and $\bigcup K$ are stratified if and only if K is stratified. Moreover, for stratification, one must assign to $\bigcap K$ and $\bigcup K$ types one less than the type of K. That is, the sum or product of the members of K should have the same type as the members of K, namely, one less than the type of K.

If A contains free occurrences of x, but A and B have no free variables in common, then $\bigcap\{A \mid x \in B\}$ and $\bigcup\{A \mid x \in B\}$ are commonly denoted by

$$\prod_{x \in B} A \qquad \text{and} \qquad \sum_{x \in B} A$$

respectively. Other notations for the same thing are to be found in Bourbaki, 1939, pages 20 to 25, and Hausdorff, 1927, page 18.

The notions indicated by $\bigcap\{A \mid x \in B\}$ and $\bigcup\{A \mid x \in B\}$ are of frequent occurrence in the theory of sets. As an example, $\bigcap\{\bar{\alpha} \mid \alpha \in K\}$ is the product of all complements of members of K. A generalization of the law

$$\bar{\alpha} \cap \bar{\beta} = \overline{\alpha \cup \beta}$$

would be

$$\bigcap\{\bar{\alpha} \mid \alpha \in K\} = \overline{\bigcup K}.$$

Similarly, a generalization of

$$\bar{\alpha} \cup \bar{\beta} = \overline{\alpha \cap \beta}$$

would be

$$\bigcup\{\bar{\alpha} \mid \alpha \in K\} = \overline{\bigcap K},$$

a generalization of

$$\alpha \cap (\beta \cup \gamma) = (\alpha \cap \beta) \cup (\alpha \cap \gamma)$$

would be

$$\alpha \cap \bigcup K = \bigcup\{\alpha \cap \beta \mid \beta \in K\},$$

and so on. Indeed, many properties of $\bigcap K$ and $\bigcup K$ are generalizations of properties of finite products and sums. Most theorems of this section are analogues of theorems of the preceding section.

Analogous to Thm.IX.4.1, we have:

Theorem IX.5.1.

I. $\vdash (\lambda)\ \exists\bigcap\lambda.$

II. $\vdash (\lambda)\ \exists\bigcup\lambda.$

Analogous to Thm.IX.4.2, we have:

Theorem IX.5.2.

**I. $\vdash (\lambda,x){:}.x \in \bigcap\lambda{:} \equiv {:}(\alpha).\alpha \in \lambda \supset x \in \alpha.$

**II. $\vdash (\lambda,x){:}.x \in \bigcup\lambda{:} \equiv {:}(E\alpha).\alpha \in \lambda.x \in \alpha.$

Analogous to the associative laws, Thm.IX.4.4, Parts X and XI, we have:

Theorem IX.5.3.

I. $\vdash (\lambda,\mu).\bigcap\lambda \cap \bigcap\mu = \bigcap(\lambda \cup \mu).$

II. $\vdash (\lambda,\mu).\bigcup\lambda \cup \bigcup\mu = \bigcup(\lambda \cup \mu).$

Proof of Part I.

$$\begin{aligned}\vdash x \in \bigcap\lambda \cap \bigcap\mu{:}.\\ &\equiv {:}.x \in \bigcap\lambda.x \in \bigcap\mu{:}.\\ &\equiv {:}.(\alpha).\alpha \in \lambda \supset x \in \alpha{:}(\alpha).\alpha \in \mu \supset x \in \alpha{:}.\\ &\equiv {:}.(\alpha){:}\alpha \in \lambda \supset x \in \alpha.\alpha \in \mu \supset x \in \alpha{:}.\\ &\equiv {:}.(\alpha){:}\alpha \in \lambda \vee \alpha \in \mu. \supset .x \in \alpha{:}.\\ &\equiv {:}.(\alpha){:}\alpha \in \lambda \cup \mu. \supset .x \in \alpha{:}.\\ &\equiv {:}.x \in \bigcap(\lambda \cup \mu).\end{aligned}$$

Proof of Part II.

$$\begin{aligned}\vdash x \in \bigcup\lambda \cup \bigcup\mu{:}.\\ &\equiv {:}.(E\alpha){:}\alpha \in \lambda.x \in \alpha{:}\vee{:}(E\alpha){:}\alpha \in \mu.x \in \alpha{:}.\\ &\equiv {:}.(E\alpha){:}\alpha \in \lambda.x \in \alpha.\vee.\alpha \in \mu.x \in \alpha{:}.\\ &\equiv {:}.(E\alpha){:}\alpha \in \lambda \vee \alpha \in \mu.x \in \alpha{:}.\\ &\equiv {:}.(E\alpha){:}\alpha \in \lambda \cup \mu.x \in \alpha{:}.\\ &\equiv {:}.x \in \bigcup(\lambda \cup \mu).\end{aligned}$$

Analogous to Thm.IX.4.4, Parts XXX and XXIX, we have:

Theorem IX.5.4.

I. $\vdash (\lambda){:}\Lambda \in \lambda. \supset .\bigcap\lambda = \Lambda.$

II. $\vdash (\lambda){:}V \in \lambda. \supset .\bigcup\lambda = V.$

Proof of Part I. Assume $\Lambda \epsilon \lambda$. Putting $\Lambda \epsilon \lambda$ and $x \epsilon \Lambda$ for P and Q in $\vdash P \supset :\sim Q. \supset .\sim(P \supset Q)$, we get $\sim(\Lambda \epsilon \lambda \supset x \epsilon \Lambda)$. So $(E\alpha)\sim(\alpha \epsilon \lambda \supset x \epsilon \alpha)$. So $\sim(\alpha).\alpha \epsilon \lambda \supset x \epsilon \alpha$, and hence $\sim x \epsilon \bigcap\lambda$. So $(x).\sim x \epsilon \bigcap\lambda$. By Thm.IX.4.12, Part II, $\bigcap\lambda = \Lambda$.

Proof of Part II is similar.

Analogous to Thm.IX.4.13, Cor. 6 and Cor. 7, we have:

Theorem IX.5.5.

I. $\vdash (\lambda,\alpha):\alpha \epsilon \lambda. \supset .\bigcap\lambda \subseteq \alpha.$

II. $\vdash (\lambda,\alpha):\alpha \epsilon \lambda. \supset .\alpha \subseteq \bigcup\lambda.$

Proof of Part I. By Axiom scheme 6, $\vdash x \epsilon \bigcap\lambda: \supset :\alpha \epsilon \lambda. \supset .x \epsilon \alpha$. So $\vdash \alpha \epsilon \lambda: \supset :x \epsilon \bigcap\lambda. \supset .x \epsilon \alpha$. So by rule G and Thm.VI.6.6, Part IX, $\vdash \alpha \epsilon \lambda: \supset :(x):x \epsilon \bigcap\lambda. \supset .x \epsilon \alpha$.

Proof of Part II. By Thm.VI.7.3, $\vdash \alpha \epsilon \lambda.x \epsilon \alpha. \supset .x \epsilon \bigcup\lambda$. So $\vdash \alpha \epsilon \lambda: \supset : x \epsilon \alpha. \supset .x \epsilon \bigcup\lambda$, and so $\vdash \alpha \epsilon \lambda: \supset :(x):x \epsilon \alpha. \supset .x \epsilon \bigcup\lambda$.

Corollary. $\vdash (\lambda):\lambda \neq \Lambda. \supset .\bigcap\lambda \subseteq \bigcup\lambda.$

Proof. Use Thm.IX.4.12, corollary, Part II, and Thm.IX.4.15.

A different generalization of Thm.IX.4.13, Cor. 6 and Cor. 7, is given by the statements that a product of several classes includes a product of still more classes, and a sum of several classes is included in a sum of still more classes. These are expressed in:

Theorem IX.5.6.

I. $\vdash (\lambda,\mu):\lambda \subseteq \mu. \supset .\bigcap\mu \subseteq \bigcap\lambda.$

II. $\vdash (\lambda,\mu):\lambda \subseteq \mu. \supset .\bigcup\lambda \subseteq \bigcup\mu.$

Proof of Part I. Assume $\lambda \subseteq \mu$. Then $\alpha \epsilon \lambda \supset \alpha \epsilon \mu$. So $\alpha \epsilon \mu \supset x \epsilon \alpha. \supset .\alpha \epsilon \lambda \supset x \epsilon \alpha$. So $(\alpha).\alpha \epsilon \mu \supset x \epsilon \alpha: \supset :(\alpha).\alpha \epsilon \lambda \supset x \epsilon \alpha$. This is $x \epsilon \bigcap\mu. \supset .x \epsilon \bigcap\lambda$.

Proof of Part II. Assume $\lambda \subseteq \mu$. Then $\alpha \epsilon \lambda \supset \alpha \epsilon \mu$. So $\alpha \epsilon \lambda.x \epsilon \alpha. \supset . \alpha \epsilon \mu.x \epsilon \alpha$. So $(E\alpha).\alpha \epsilon \lambda.x \epsilon \alpha: \supset :(E\alpha).\alpha \epsilon \mu.x \epsilon \alpha$.

The generalizations of Thm.IX.4.16, Cor. 1 and Cor. 2, would be that, if one can make the members of λ and μ correspond in such a way that every member of λ is included in the corresponding member of μ, then $\bigcap\lambda \subseteq \bigcap\mu$ and $\bigcup\lambda \subseteq \bigcup\mu$. One can prove slightly stronger results, which we express in the following theorem.

Theorem IX.5.7.

I. $\vdash (\lambda,\mu)::(\beta):\beta \epsilon \mu. \supset .(E\alpha).\alpha \epsilon \lambda.\alpha \subseteq \beta.: \supset :.\bigcap\lambda \subseteq \bigcap\mu.$

II. $\vdash (\lambda,\mu)::(\alpha):\alpha \epsilon \lambda. \supset .(E\beta).\beta \epsilon \mu.\alpha \subseteq \beta.: \supset :.\bigcup\lambda \subseteq \bigcup\mu.$

Proof of Part I. Assume

(1) $$(\beta):\beta \epsilon \mu. \supset .(E\alpha).\alpha \epsilon \lambda.\alpha \subseteq \beta,$$

(2) $$x \epsilon \bigcap\lambda,$$

(3) $$\beta \epsilon \mu.$$

By (3) and (1), $(E\alpha).\alpha \epsilon \lambda.\alpha \subseteq \beta$, so that by rule C

(4) $$\alpha \epsilon \lambda,$$

(5) $$\alpha \subseteq \beta.$$

By (4) and (2), $x \epsilon \alpha$. Then by (5), $x \epsilon \beta$. So we have proved

$$(1),\ x \epsilon \bigcap\lambda,\ \beta \epsilon \mu \vdash x \epsilon \beta.$$

By the deduction theorem

$$(1),\ x \epsilon \bigcap\lambda \vdash \beta \epsilon \mu \supset x \epsilon \beta.$$

By rule G

$$(1),\ x \epsilon \bigcap\lambda \vdash x \epsilon \bigcap\mu.$$

Proof of Part II. Assume

(1) $$(\alpha):\alpha \epsilon \lambda. \supset .(E\beta).\beta \epsilon \mu.\alpha \subseteq \beta,$$

(2) $$x \epsilon \bigcup\lambda.$$

Then, by (2) and rule C

(3) $$\alpha \epsilon \lambda,$$

(4) $$x \epsilon \alpha.$$

So by (3) and (1), $(E\beta).\beta \epsilon \mu.\alpha \subseteq \beta$.
By rule C

(5) $$\beta \epsilon \mu,$$

(6) $$\alpha \subseteq \beta.$$

By (4) and (6), $x \epsilon \beta$. Using this and (5), we have $(E\beta).\beta \epsilon \mu.x \epsilon \beta$. That is, $x \epsilon \bigcup\mu$.

Analogous to Thm.IX.4.18, we have:

Theorem IX.5.8.

I. $\vdash (\lambda,\alpha):.\alpha \subseteq \bigcap\lambda: \equiv :(\beta):\beta \epsilon \lambda. \supset .\alpha \subseteq \beta.$

$\star$II. $\vdash (\lambda,\gamma):.\bigcup\lambda \subseteq \gamma: \equiv :(\beta):\beta \epsilon \lambda. \supset .\beta \subseteq \gamma.$

Proof of Part I.

$$\begin{aligned}\vdash \alpha \subseteq \bigcap\lambda:.\ & \\ &\equiv :.(x):x \epsilon \alpha. \supset .x \epsilon \bigcap\lambda:. \\ &\equiv :.(x):x \epsilon \alpha. \supset .(\beta).\beta \epsilon \lambda \supset x \epsilon \beta:. \\ &\equiv :.(x,\beta):x \epsilon \alpha. \supset .\beta \epsilon \lambda \supset x \epsilon \beta:. \\ &\equiv :.(\beta,x):\beta \epsilon \lambda. \supset .x \epsilon \alpha \supset x \epsilon \beta:. \\ &\equiv :.(\beta):\beta \epsilon \lambda. \supset .(x).x \epsilon \alpha \supset x \epsilon \beta:. \\ &\equiv :.(\beta):\beta \epsilon \lambda. \supset .\alpha \subseteq \beta.\end{aligned}$$

Proof of Part II.

$$\vdash \bigcup\lambda \subseteq \gamma :.$$
$$\equiv :.(x):x \in \bigcup\lambda. \supset .x \in \gamma :.$$
$$\equiv :.(x):(E\beta).\beta \in \lambda.x \in \beta. \supset .x \in \gamma :.$$
$$\equiv :.(x,\beta):\beta \in \lambda.x \in \beta. \supset .x \in \gamma :.$$
$$\equiv :.(\beta,x):\beta \in \lambda. \supset .x \in \beta \supset x \in \gamma :.$$
$$\equiv :.(\beta):\beta \in \lambda. \supset .(x).x \in \beta \supset x \in \gamma :.$$
$$\equiv :.(\beta):\beta \in \lambda. \supset .\beta \subseteq \gamma.$$

Analogous to Thm.IX.4.24, we have:

Theorem IX.5.9.

I. $\vdash (\lambda,\alpha):.\alpha \subset \bigcap\lambda: \supset :(\beta):\beta \in \lambda. \supset .\alpha \subset \beta.$

II. $\vdash (\lambda,\gamma):.\bigcup\lambda \subset \gamma: \supset :(\beta):\beta \in \lambda. \supset .\beta \subset \gamma.$

Proof of Part I. Assume

(1) $$\alpha \subset \bigcap\lambda,$$

(2) $$\beta \in \lambda.$$

By (2) and Thm.IX.5.5, $\bigcap\lambda \subseteq \beta$. By this and (1), $\alpha \subset \beta$.

Proof of Part II is similar.

We have already indicated what are the generalizations of Thm.IX.4.4, Parts XVI and XVII. To prove these, we need certain preliminary results.

Theorem IX.5.10.

I. $\vdash (\lambda)\exists\{\bar{\alpha} \mid \alpha \in \lambda\}.$

II. $\vdash (\lambda,\beta):\beta \in \{\bar{\alpha} \mid \alpha \in \lambda\}. \equiv .\beta \in \lambda.$

III. $\vdash (\lambda,\beta):\beta \in \{\bar{\alpha} \mid \alpha \in \lambda\}. \equiv .(E\alpha).\alpha \in \lambda.\beta = \bar{\alpha}.$

Proof of Part I. Use Thm.IX.3.1.

Proof of Part II. Use Thm.IX.4.8.

Proof of Part III. Use Thm.IX.3.2, Cor. 3.

We now get the generalizations of Thm.IX.4.4, Parts XVI and XVII.

Theorem IX.5.11.

I. $\vdash (\lambda).\bigcap\{\bar{\alpha} \mid \alpha \in \lambda\} = \overline{\bigcup\lambda}.$

II. $\vdash (\lambda).\bigcup\{\bar{\alpha} \mid \alpha \in \lambda\} = \overline{\bigcap\lambda}.$

Proof of Part I. Using Thm.IX.5.10, Part III, and Thm.VII.1.5, Part II, we get

$$\vdash x \in \bigcap\{\bar{\alpha} \mid \alpha \in \lambda\} :.$$
$$\equiv :.(\beta):\beta \in \{\bar{\alpha} \mid \alpha \in \lambda\}. \supset .x \in \beta :.$$
$$\equiv :.(\beta):(E\alpha).\alpha \in \lambda.\beta = \bar{\alpha}. \supset .x \in \beta :.$$
$$\equiv :.(\beta,\alpha):\alpha \in \lambda.\beta = \bar{\alpha}. \supset .x \in \beta :.$$
$$\equiv :.(\alpha,\beta):\alpha \in \lambda. \supset .\beta = \bar{\alpha} \supset x \in \beta :.$$
$$\equiv :.(\alpha):\alpha \in \lambda. \supset .(\beta).\beta = \bar{\alpha} \supset x \in \beta :.$$
$$\equiv :.(\alpha):\alpha \in \lambda. \supset .x \in \bar{\alpha} :.$$

$$
\begin{aligned}
&\equiv :.(\alpha):\alpha \in \lambda. \supset .\sim x \in \alpha:. \\
&\equiv :.\sim(\mathrm{E}\alpha).\alpha \in \lambda.x \in \alpha:. \\
&\equiv :.\sim x \in \bigcup\lambda:. \\
&\equiv :.x \in \overline{\bigcup\lambda}.
\end{aligned}
$$

Proof of Part II. Using Thm.IX.5.10, Part III, and Thm.VII.1.5, Part I, we get

$$
\begin{aligned}
\vdash x \in \bigcup\{\bar{\alpha} \mid \alpha \in \lambda\}&:. \\
&\equiv :.(\mathrm{E}\beta):\beta \in \{\bar{\alpha} \mid \alpha \in \lambda\}.x \in \beta:. \\
&\equiv :.(\mathrm{E}\beta):(\mathrm{E}\alpha).\alpha \in \lambda.\beta = \bar{\alpha}:x \in \beta:. \\
&\equiv :.(\mathrm{E}\beta,\alpha):\alpha \in \lambda.\beta = \bar{\alpha}.x \in \beta:. \\
&\equiv :.(\mathrm{E}\alpha):\alpha \in \lambda.(\mathrm{E}\beta).\beta = \bar{\alpha}.x \in \beta:. \\
&\equiv :.(\mathrm{E}\alpha):\alpha \in \lambda.x \in \bar{\alpha}:. \\
&\equiv :.(\mathrm{E}\alpha):\alpha \in \lambda.\sim x \in \alpha:. \\
&\equiv :.\sim(\beta).\beta \in \lambda. \supset .x \in \beta:. \\
&\equiv :.\sim x \in \bigcap\lambda:. \\
&\equiv :.x \in \overline{\bigcap\lambda}.
\end{aligned}
$$

We have by no means listed all possible generalizations of theorems of Sec. 4, but we have listed those of importance.

One particularly important use of manifold products is in defining the closure of a class with respect to an operation or a set of operations. For example, when we wish to adjoin a root θ of an algebraic equation $P(\theta) = 0$ with rational coefficients to the field of rational numbers, we wish the least class $R(\theta)$ such that:

(A) $R(\theta)$ includes θ and all rationals.

(B) $R(\theta)$ is closed under each of the operations of adding together two members of $R(\theta)$, multiplying together two members of $R(\theta)$, and multiplying any member of $R(\theta)$ by a rational.

If we let R denote the class of rationals, we can rewrite (A) and (B) as follows.

(A1) $R \subseteq R(\theta)$.

(A2) $\theta \in R(\theta)$.

(B1) $(x,y):x,y \in R(\theta). \supset .x + y \in R(\theta)$.

(B2) $(x,y):x,y \in R(\theta). \supset .xy \in R(\theta)$.

(B3) $(x,y):x \in R(\theta).y \in R. \supset .xy \in R(\theta)$.

We express (B1), (B2), and (B3) by saying that $R(\theta)$ is closed with respect to the operations "plus," "times," and "multiplication by a rational."

Closure with respect to a relation often occurs and is more general. Thus, if we let $S_1(x,y,z)$, $S_2(x,y,z)$, and $S_3(x,z)$ denote, respectively, $x + y = z$, $xy = z$, and $(\mathrm{E}y).y \in R.xy = z$, then we can rewrite (B1), (B2), and (B3) as:

(B1) $(x,y,z):x,y \in R(\theta).S_1(x,y,z). \supset .z \in R(\theta).$
(B2) $(x,y,z):x,y \in R(\theta).S_2(x,y,z). \supset .z \in R(\theta).$
(B3) $(x,z):x \in R(\theta).S_3(x,z). \supset .z \in R(\theta).$

In this form, we express (B1), (B2), and (B3) by saying that $R(\theta)$ is closed with respect to the relations S_1, S_2, and S_3.

Finally, we can write $S(x,y,z)$ for

$$S_1(x,y,z) \vee S_2(x,y,z) \vee S_3(x,z),$$

and then (B1), (B2), and (B3) can be telescoped to:

(B) $(x,y,z):x,y \in R(\theta).S(x,y,z). \supset .z \in R(\theta).$

This is expressed by saying that $R(\theta)$ is closed with respect to the relation S.

The discussion above should make it clear that closure with respect to any set of operations or any set of relations can be reduced to closure with respect to a single relation. In general, this might be a relation between many things, so that one would wish to write it as $S(x_1, \ldots, x_n, z)$. Even more generally, it might involve various parameters $r_1, \ldots, r_m$, so that one would write it as $S(x_1, \ldots, x_n, z, r_1, \ldots, r_m)$. The closure of a class A with respect to S will be denoted by

$$\mathrm{Clos}(A, S(x_1, \ldots, x_n, z, r_1, \ldots, r_m)).$$

More precisely, we shall make the following definition, due essentially to Frege (see Frege, 1879).

When accompanied by a specification as to which free variables of P are to be considered as $x_1, \ldots, x_n, z, r_1, \ldots, r_m$, respectively, and provided that there are no free occurrences of $x_1, \ldots, x_n, z$ in A,

$$\mathrm{Clos}(A,P)$$

shall denote

$$\bigcap\hat{\beta}(A \subseteq \beta:.(x_1, \ldots, x_n, z):x_1, \ldots, x_n \in \beta.P. \supset .z \in \beta),$$

where β is a variable not appearing in A or P.

In $\mathrm{Clos}(A,P)$, the variables $x_1, \ldots, x_n, z$ are bound, as also are the bound variables implicit in $\bigcap\hat{\beta}$ and $A \subseteq \beta$; other than these, variables occur free or bound in $\mathrm{Clos}(A,P)$ according as they occur free or bound in A or P.

A set of general rules for determining if $\mathrm{Clos}(A,P)$ is stratified without writing it out would be too complicated to be worth stating. If the question of stratification of $\mathrm{Clos}(A,P)$ arises, the best procedure is to write out the definition. However, one should note that, if it is stratified, it must have the same type as A.

Temporarily throughout the next five theorems, let $H(A,\beta,P)$ denote

$$A \subseteq \beta :. (x_1, \ldots, x_n, z) : x_1, \ldots, x_n \in \beta . P . \supset . z \in \beta,$$

where β is distinct from $x_1, \ldots, x_n, z$ and does not occur in A or P, so that $\mathrm{Clos}(A,P) = \bigcap \hat{\beta} H(A,\beta,P)$.

The meaning of $H(A,\beta,P)$ is that β includes A and is closed with respect to the relation P. Such β's exist, for example, $\beta = \mathrm{V}$. It is less obvious that $\mathrm{Clos}(A,P)$ is such a β, but we shall prove this. As $\mathrm{Clos}(A,P)$ is the logical product of all such β's, it is necessarily the least, by Thm.IX.5.5, Part I.

By putting $\hat{\beta} H(A,\beta,P)$ for λ in Thm.IX.5.1, Part I, we get $\vdash \exists \mathrm{Clos}(A,P)$. Surprisingly enough, this fact is not particularly useful. What is required to prove our theorems about $\mathrm{Clos}(A,P)$ is the hypothesis $\exists \hat{\beta} H(A,\beta,P)$. Actually, $\hat{\beta} H(A,\beta,P)$ is stratified whenever $\mathrm{Clos}(A,P)$ is stratified, so that the hypothesis $\exists \hat{\beta} H(A,\beta,P)$ will be available in all those cases in which one would expect to be able to do anything significant with $\mathrm{Clos}(A,P)$.

Theorem IX.5.12. $\vdash (\alpha) :. \exists \hat{\beta} H(\alpha,\beta,P) : \supset : (x) : x \in \mathrm{Clos}(\alpha,P) . \equiv . (\beta) . H(\alpha,\beta,P) \supset x \in \beta$.

Proof. By Thm.IX.5.2, Part I, $\vdash (x) : x \in \mathrm{Clos}(\alpha,P) . \equiv . (\beta) . \beta \in \hat{\beta}(H(\alpha,\beta,P)) \supset x \in \beta$. However, by Thm.IX.3.2, Cor. 1, $\vdash \exists \hat{\beta} H(\alpha,\beta,P) : \supset : (\beta) . \beta \in \hat{\beta}(H(\alpha,\beta,P)) \equiv H(\alpha,\beta,P)$.

Theorem IX.5.13. $\vdash (\alpha) : \exists \hat{\beta} H(\alpha,\beta,P) . \supset . \alpha \subseteq \mathrm{Clos}(\alpha,P)$.

Proof. Assume $\exists \hat{\beta} H(\alpha,\beta,P)$. Then by Thm.IX.3.2, Cor. 1, and the definition of $H(\alpha,\beta,P)$, $(\beta) : \beta \in \hat{\beta}(H(\alpha,\beta,P)) . \supset . \alpha \subseteq \beta$. So, putting $\hat{\beta} H(\alpha,\beta,P)$ for λ in Thm.IX.5.8, Part I, we get our theorem.

Theorem IX.5.14. $\vdash (\alpha) :. \exists \hat{\beta} H(\alpha,\beta,P) : \supset : (x_1, \ldots, x_n, z) : x_1, \ldots, x_n \in \mathrm{Clos}(\alpha,P) . P . \supset . z \in \mathrm{Clos}(\alpha,P)$.

Proof. Assume

(1) $$\exists \hat{\beta} H(\alpha,\beta,P),$$

(2) $$x_1, \ldots, x_n \in \mathrm{Clos}(\alpha,P) . P,$$

(3) $$H(\alpha,\beta,P).$$

By (1), (2), (3), and Thm.IX.5.12,

(4) $$x_1, \ldots, x_n \in \beta . P.$$

Using (4), (3), and the definition of $H(\alpha,\beta,P)$, we infer $z \in \beta$. So we have shown

$$(1), (2), H(\alpha,\beta,P) \vdash z \in \beta.$$

So

$$(1), (2) \vdash (\beta) . H(\alpha,\beta,P) \supset z \in \beta.$$

So by Thm.IX.5.12,

$$(1), (2) \vdash z \in \mathrm{Clos}(\alpha,P).$$

Thm.IX.5.13 says that α is included in Clos(α,P), and Thm.IX.5.14 says that Clos(α,P) is closed with respect to the relation P. We wish to verify also that Clos(α,P) is the least class which includes α and is closed with respect to P. However, this is given to us by Thm.IX.5.12. For let β include α and be closed with respect to P. That is, assume $H(\alpha,\beta,P)$. Then, by Thm.IX.5.12, $(x).x \in \mathrm{Clos}(\alpha,P) \supset x \in \beta$. So $\mathrm{Clos}(\alpha,P) \subseteq \beta$, and β is no smaller than Clos(α,P).

Actually, we need a stronger version of the result that Clos(α,P) is the least class which includes β and is closed with respect to P. This result we now prove.

Theorem IX.5.15. $\vdash (\alpha)::\exists\hat{\beta}H(\alpha,\beta,P).:\supset:.(\beta):.\alpha \subseteq \beta:(x_1, \ldots, x_n, z): x_1, \ldots, x_n \in \beta.x_1, \ldots, x_n \in \mathrm{Clos}(\alpha,P).P. \supset .z \in \beta: \supset :\mathrm{Clos}(\alpha,P) \subseteq \beta.$

Proof. Assume

$$\exists\hat{\beta}H(\alpha,\beta,P), \tag{1}$$

$$\alpha \subseteq \beta:(x_1, \ldots, x_n, z):x_1, \ldots, x_n \in \beta.x_1, \ldots, x_n \in \mathrm{Clos}(\alpha,P).P. \supset .z \in \beta, \tag{2}$$

$$x \in \mathrm{Clos}(\alpha,P). \tag{3}$$

Temporarily write A for $\beta \cap \mathrm{Clos}(\alpha,P)$. Then by Thm.IX.4.2, Part III,

$$\vdash (w):w \in A. \equiv .w \in \beta.w \in \mathrm{Clos}(\alpha,P). \tag{4}$$

Then by (2),

$$(x_1, \ldots, x_n, z):x_1, \ldots, x_n \in A.P. \supset .z \in \beta.$$

So by (1) and Thm.IX.5.14,

$$(x_1, \ldots, x_n, z):x_1, \ldots, x_n \in A.P. \supset .z \in A. \tag{5}$$

Also by (2), we get $\alpha \subseteq \beta$ and by (1) and Thm.IX.5.13 we get $\alpha \subseteq \mathrm{Clos}(\alpha,P)$. So by Thm.IX.4.18, Part I,

$$\alpha \subseteq A. \tag{6}$$

Then by (5) and (6), we have $H(\alpha,A,P)$. Using this and (3) and (1) with Thm.IX.5.12, we get $x \in A$. So by (4), we get finally $x \in \beta$. Since we derived this from (1), (2), and (3), our theorem follows.

One may think of Clos(α,P) as being generated as follows. Start with α. As a first step toward achieving closure with respect to P, add to α all z's such that $x_1, \ldots, x_n$ are in α and P holds. If we call the resulting enlarged class β_1, we enlarge again by adding to β_1 all z's such that $x_1, \ldots, x_n$ are in β_1 and P holds. We can call the resulting class β_2 and enlarge again and again to get $\beta_3, \beta_4, \ldots$. Then

$$\mathrm{Clos}(\alpha,P) = \alpha \cup \beta_1 \cup \beta_2 \cup \ldots.$$

We cannot prove this result exactly until we are in a position to define the sequence β_1, β_2, . . . in the symbolic logic. However, the next theorem makes the result look plausible. One can interpret the next theorem as saying that, if z is in Clos(α,P), then either z was in α to begin with or else z was put in because some $x_1, \dots, x_n$ had already been put in and $x_1, \dots, x_n$ had the relation P to z.

Theorem IX.5.16. $\vdash (\alpha)::\exists\hat{\beta}H(\alpha,\beta,P):\exists\hat{z}(z \in \alpha.\mathbf{v}.(\mathrm{E}x_1, \dots, x_n).x_1, \dots, x_n \in \mathrm{Clos}(\alpha,P).P).:\supset:.(z):.z \in \mathrm{Clos}(\alpha,P):\equiv:z \in \alpha.\mathbf{v}.(\mathrm{E}x_1, \dots, x_n).x_1, \dots, x_n \in \mathrm{Clos}(\alpha,P).P.$

Proof. By Thm.IX.5.13 and Thm.IX.5.14, we easily infer

(1) $\vdash \exists\hat{\beta}H(\alpha,\beta,P).:\supset:.(z):.z \in \alpha.\mathbf{v}.(\mathrm{E}x_1, \dots, x_n).x_1, \dots, x_n \in \mathrm{Clos}(\alpha,P).P:\supset:z \in \mathrm{Clos}(\alpha,P).$

Now assume

(2) $$\exists\hat{\beta}H(\alpha,\beta,P),$$

(3) $$\exists\hat{z}(z \in \alpha.\mathbf{v}.(\mathrm{E}x_1, \dots, x_n).x_1, \dots, x_n \in \mathrm{Clos}(\alpha,P).P).$$

Temporarily let A denote

$$\hat{z}(z \in \alpha.\mathbf{v}.(\mathrm{E}x_1, \dots, x_n).x_1, \dots, x_n \in \mathrm{Clos}(\alpha,P).P).$$

Then by (3) and Thm.IX.3.2, Cor. 1,

(4) $(z):.z \in A:\equiv:z \in \alpha.\mathbf{v}.(\mathrm{E}x_1, \dots, x_n).x_1, \dots, x_n \in \mathrm{Clos}(\alpha,P).P.$

From this, we readily infer

(5) $$\alpha \subseteq A,$$

(6) $(x_1, \dots, x_n, z):x_1, \dots, x_n \in A.x_1, \dots, x_n \in \mathrm{Clos}(\alpha,P).P.\supset.z \in A.$

Then, by (2), (5), (6), and Thm.IX.5.15,

(7) $$\mathrm{Clos}(\alpha,P) \subseteq A.$$

By (4), we have then shown

(2), (3) $\vdash (z):.z \in \mathrm{Clos}(\alpha,P):\supset:z \in \alpha.\mathbf{v}.(\mathrm{E}x_1, \dots, x_n).x_1, \dots, x_n \in \mathrm{Clos}(\alpha,P).P.$

Combining this result with (1) gives our theorem.

EXERCISES

IX.5.1. Prove:

(a) $\vdash \bigcap\Lambda = \mathrm{V}$.
(b) $\vdash \bigcup\Lambda = \Lambda$.
(c) $\vdash \bigcap\mathrm{V} = \Lambda$.
(d) $\vdash \bigcup\mathrm{V} = \mathrm{V}$.

IX.5.2. State and prove the generalization of Thm.IX.4.4, Part XII.

IX.5.3. State and prove the generalization of Thm.IX.4.4, Part XIII.

IX.5.4. Suppose that 0 is stratified and has no free variables, and $x + 1$ is stratified and has the same type as x and has only x as a free variable, and we define Nn as

$$\hat{x}((\beta):.0 \in \beta:(y).y \in \beta \supset y + 1 \in \beta: \supset :x \in \beta).$$

Prove:

(a) $\vdash 0 \in \mathrm{Nn}$.
(b) $\vdash (x):x \in \mathrm{Nn}. \supset .x + 1 \in \mathrm{Nn}$.
(c) $\vdash (\beta)::0 \in \beta:.(y):y \in \beta.y \in \mathrm{Nn}. \supset .y + 1 \in \beta.: \supset :.\mathrm{Nn} \subseteq \beta$.
(d) $\vdash (x):.x \in \mathrm{Nn}: \equiv :x = 0.\mathsf{v}.(\mathrm{E}y).y \in \mathrm{Nn}.x = y + 1$.

(*Hint.* Take α to be $\hat{z}(z = 0)$ and P to be $x + 1 = z$.)

IX.5.5. Identify the class Nn of the previous exercise as a class familiar in mathematics.

IX.5.6. Identify part (c) of Ex.IX.5.4 as a familiar principle of mathematics.

IX.5.7. Let us say that α is the least member of λ if

$$\alpha \in \lambda:(\beta).\beta \in \lambda \supset \alpha \subseteq \beta.$$

Prove the following results about least members of λ.

(a) $\vdash (\lambda,\alpha):.\alpha \in \lambda:(\beta).\beta \in \lambda \supset \alpha \subseteq \beta: \supset :\alpha = \bigcap\lambda$.
(b) $\vdash (\lambda,\alpha):.\alpha \in \lambda.\alpha = \bigcap\lambda: \equiv :\alpha \in \lambda:(\beta).\beta \in \lambda \supset \alpha \subseteq \beta$.
(c) $\vdash (\lambda):. \bigcap\lambda \in \lambda: \equiv :(\mathrm{E}\alpha):\alpha \in \lambda:(\beta).\beta \in \lambda \supset \alpha \subseteq \beta$.
(d) $\vdash (\lambda)::(\mathrm{E}\alpha):\alpha \in \lambda:(\beta).\beta \in \lambda \supset \alpha \subseteq \beta.: \supset :.(\mathrm{E}_1\alpha):\alpha \in \lambda:(\beta).\beta \in \lambda \supset \alpha \subseteq \beta$.

IX.5.8. Give an illustration of a class λ which has no least member in the sense of Ex.IX.5.7.

IX.5.9. Prove $\vdash \bigcup\{\bigcup\alpha \mid \alpha \in \lambda\} = \bigcup(\bigcup\lambda)$.

6. Unit Classes and Subclasses. The unit class of A, $\{A\}$, is the class whose sole member is A. That is, we define

$$\{A\} \quad \text{for} \quad \hat{x}(x = A)$$

where x is a variable not occurring in A. The class whose sole members are A and B will be

$$\{A\} \cup \{B\},$$

which we shall denote by

$$\{A,B\}.$$

Clearly A and B need not be distinct. However, when A and B are the same, one easily proves that $\{A,B\}$ and $\{A\}$ are the same.

More generally, the class whose sole members are $A_1, \ldots, A_n$ is

$$\{A_1\} \cup \cdots \cup \{A_n\},$$

which we shall denote by

$$\{A_1, \ldots, A_n\}.$$

Except for bound variables implicit in $\hat{x}$ and $\cup$, variables are free or bound in $\{A_1, \ldots, A_n\}$ according as they are free or bound in $A_1, \ldots, A_n$. $\{A\}$ is stratified if and only if A is stratified, and if $\{A\}$ is stratified, its type is one higher than the type of A. $\{A_1, \ldots, A_n\}$ is stratified if and only if $A_1 = A_2 = \cdots = A_n$ is stratified. In particular, for stratification of $\{A_1, \ldots, A_n\}$, each of $A_1, \ldots, A_n$ must have the same type, and the type of $\{A_1, \ldots, A_n\}$ must be one higher than this.

Theorem IX.6.1.

I. $\vdash (x)\ \exists\{x\}$.

II. $\vdash (x_1, \ldots, x_n)\ \exists\{x_1, \ldots, x_n\}$.

Theorem IX.6.2.

**I. $\vdash (x,y){:}y \in \{x\}. \equiv .y = x$.

II. $\vdash (x,y,z){:}z \in \{x,y\}. \equiv .z = x \vee z = y$.

III. $\vdash (x_1, \ldots, x_n, y){:}y \in \{x_1, \ldots, x_n\}. \equiv .y = x_1 \vee \cdots \vee y = x_n$.

***Corollary 1.** $\vdash (x).x \in \{x\}$.

Corollary 2. $\vdash (x,y).x,y \in \{x,y\}$.

Corollary 3. $\vdash (x_1, \ldots, x_n).x_1, \ldots, x_n \in \{x_1, \ldots, x_n\}$.

***Theorem IX.6.3.** $\vdash (x,y){:}\{x\} = \{y\}. \supset .x = y$.

Proof. Assume $\{x\} = \{y\}$. Then, since $x \in \{x\}$ by Thm.IX.6.2, Cor. 1, we get $x \in \{y\}$, whence we get $x = y$ by Thm.IX.6.2, Part I.

Corollary 1. $\vdash (x,y){:}\{x\} = \{y\}. \equiv .x = y$.

Corollary 2. $\vdash \exists\{\{x\} \mid P\}.{:} \supset {:}.(x){:}\{x\} \in \{\{x\} \mid P\}. \equiv .P$.

Historically, it has been popular to define $x = y$ as

(1) $$(\alpha){:}x \in \alpha. \supset .y \in \alpha.$$

The justification for this is based on the following argument. The basic characteristic of equality is that expressed in Axiom scheme 7A, namely, that if $x = y$, then any statement which is true of x shall be true of y. As each statement determines a class α (?), Axiom scheme 7A is equivalent to saying that y is in every class α which contains x, which is just the condition (1) given above. In the present system, not every statement determines a class, which somewhat spoils the above argument and makes (1) less intuitive as a definition of equality. However, it could be used, as is shown by the next theorem.

In the Zermelo set theory, (1) could not be used at all because of the existence of nonsets (or nonindividuals) which cannot be members of anything. Thus, if x is a nonset, $x \in \alpha$ is false for all α and so (1) would be true for all y.

Thus in Zermelo set theory, one is forced to use our definition of equality or else to take equality as undefined. Our definition of equality is suitable only in case all objects are classes.

If we wish to enlarge the present system by the addition of nonclasses, we would wish to change to (1) as a definition of equality. If we wish to have both nonclasses and nonmembers, then we probably have to take equality as undefined, with appropriate axiom schemes, such as Axiom schemes 7A and 7B, for instance.

Theorem IX.6.4. $\vdash (x,y){:.}x = y{:} \equiv {:}(\alpha).x \in \alpha \supset y \in \alpha.$

Proof. By Axiom scheme 7, we have

(1) $$\vdash x = y{:} \supset {:}(\alpha).x \in \alpha \supset y \in \alpha.$$

Assume $(\alpha).x \in \alpha \supset y \in \alpha$. Then by Axiom scheme 8, $x \in \{x\} \supset y \in \{x\}$. Then by Thm.IX.6.2, Cor. 1, $y \in \{x\}$, and so by Thm.IX.6.2, Part I, $y = x$.

Corollary. $\vdash (x,y){:.}x = y{:} \equiv {:}(\alpha).x \in \alpha \equiv y \in \alpha.$

***Theorem IX.6.5.** $\vdash (\alpha,x){:}x \in \alpha. \equiv .\{x\} \subseteq \alpha.$

Proof. By Thm.VII.1.5, Part II, $\vdash x \in \alpha{:} \equiv {:}(y).y = x \supset y \in \alpha$. Then by Thm.IX.6.2, Part I, $\vdash x \in \alpha{:} \equiv {:}(y).y \in \{x\} \supset y \in \alpha$. This is our theorem.

Corollary 1. $\vdash (\alpha,x){:}x \in \alpha. \equiv .\{x\} \cap \alpha = \{x\}.$

Corollary 2. $\vdash (\alpha,x){:}x \in \alpha. \equiv .\{x\} \cup \alpha = \alpha.$

Corollary 3. $\vdash (\alpha,x){:}x \in \alpha. \equiv .(\alpha - \{x\}) \cup \{x\} = \alpha.$

Proof. Use Thm.IX.4.13 and Thm.IX.4.4, Part XIX.

Theorem IX.6.6. $\vdash (\alpha,x){:}\sim x \in \alpha. \equiv .\alpha \subseteq \overline{\{x\}}.$

Proof. $\vdash \sim x \in \alpha{:} \equiv {:}x \in \bar{\alpha}{:} \equiv {:}\{x\} \subseteq \bar{\alpha}{:} \equiv {:}\alpha \subseteq \overline{\{x\}}$, by Thm.IX.6.5 and Thm.IX.4.17.

***Corollary 1.** $\vdash (\alpha,x){:}\sim x \in \alpha. \equiv .\{x\} \cap \alpha = \Lambda.$

Corollary 2. $\vdash (\alpha,x){:}x \in \alpha. \equiv .\{x\} \cap \alpha \neq \Lambda.$

Theorem IX.6.7. $\vdash (\alpha,x){:}\{x\} \cap \alpha = \Lambda. \vee .\{x\} \cap \alpha = \{x\}.$

Proof. By Thm.IX.6.6, Cor. 2 and Thm.IX.6.5, Cor. 1, $\vdash \{x\} \cap \alpha \neq \Lambda. \equiv .\{x\} \cap \alpha = \{x\}$. So $\vdash \{x\} \cap \alpha \neq \Lambda. \supset .\{x\} \cap \alpha = \{x\}$. This is our theorem.

Corollary. $\vdash (\alpha,x){:}\alpha \subseteq \{x\}. \supset .\alpha = \Lambda \vee \alpha = \{x\}.$

For if $\alpha \subseteq \{x\}$, then $\alpha = \{x\} \cap \alpha$.

Theorem IX.6.8. $\vdash (x,y){:}x \neq y. \equiv .\{x\} \cap \{y\} = \Lambda.$

Proof. By Thm.IX.6.2, Part I, $\vdash x \neq y. \equiv .\sim y \in \{x\}$, and by Thm. IX.6.6, Cor. 1, $\vdash \sim y \in \{x\}. \equiv .\{y\} \cap \{x\} = \Lambda$.

Theorem IX.6.9.

I. $\vdash (\alpha).\bigcap\{\alpha\} = \alpha.$

II. $\vdash (\alpha,\beta).\bigcap\{\alpha,\beta\} = \alpha \cap \beta.$

III. $\vdash (\alpha_1, \ldots, \alpha_n).\bigcap\{\alpha_1, \ldots, \alpha_n\} = \alpha_1 \cap \cdots \cap \alpha_n.$

IV. $\vdash (\lambda,\alpha).\bigcap(\{\alpha\} \cup \lambda) = \alpha \cap \bigcap\lambda.$

V. $\vdash (\alpha).\bigcup\{\alpha\} = \alpha.$

VI. $\vdash (\alpha,\beta).\bigcup\{\alpha,\beta\} = \alpha \cup \beta.$
VII. $\vdash (\alpha_1, \ldots, \alpha_n).\bigcup\{\alpha_1, \ldots, \alpha_n\} = \alpha_1 \cup \cdots \cup \alpha_n.$
VIII. $\vdash (\lambda,\alpha).\bigcup(\{\alpha\} \cup \lambda) = \alpha \cup \bigcup\lambda.$

Proof of Part I.

$$\begin{aligned}\vdash x \in \bigcap\{\alpha\}:& \\ &\equiv :(\beta).\beta \in \{\alpha\} \supset x \in \beta: \\ &\equiv :(\beta).\beta = \alpha \supset x \in \beta: \\ &\equiv :x \in \alpha.\end{aligned}$$

Proof of Parts II, III, *and* IV. Use Part I with Thm.IX.5.3, Part I.

Proof of Part V.

$$\begin{aligned}\vdash x \in \bigcup\{\alpha\}:& \\ &\equiv :(\mathrm{E}\beta).\beta \in \{\alpha\}.x \in \beta: \\ &\equiv :(\mathrm{E}\beta).\beta = \alpha.x \in \beta: \\ &\equiv :x \in \alpha.\end{aligned}$$

Proof of Parts VI, VII, *and* VIII. Use Part V with Thm.IX.5.3, Part II.

We now introduce the class of unit subclasses of A, which we denote by USC(A). In this, the letters U, S, and C stand for "unit," "sub," and "classes," respectively. Specifically we define

$$\mathrm{USC}(A) \quad \text{for} \quad \{\{x\} \mid x \in A\}$$

where x is a variable that does not occur in A. We also define

$$\begin{array}{lll}\mathrm{USC}^2(A) & \text{for} & \mathrm{USC}(\mathrm{USC}(A)) \\ \mathrm{USC}^3(A) & \text{for} & \mathrm{USC}(\mathrm{USC}^2(A)) \\ \text{etc.} & & \end{array}$$

We also define the cardinal numbers 0 and 1 as follows:

$$\begin{array}{lll}0 & \text{for} & \{\Lambda\} \\ 1 & \text{for} & \mathrm{USC}(V).\end{array}$$

Except for x (which is bound) and other bound variables implicit in the notation $\{\{x\} \mid x \in A\}$, variables are bound or free in USC(A) according as they are bound or free in A. Correspondingly for $\mathrm{USC}^2(A)$, $\mathrm{USC}^3(A)$, etc. There are no free variables in 0 or 1.

USC(A) is stratified if and only if A is stratified, and similarly for $\mathrm{USC}^2(A)$, $\mathrm{USC}^3(A)$, etc. For stratification, USC(A) must be one type higher than A, $\mathrm{USC}^2(A)$ must be two types higher, etc. 0 and 1 are stratified and may be assigned any types whatever, even to being assigned different types in the same context.

Theorem IX.6.10.

I. $\vdash (\alpha)\ \exists(\mathrm{USC}(\alpha)).$
*II. $\vdash (\alpha,x):\{x\} \in \mathrm{USC}(\alpha). \equiv .x \in \alpha.$

$\star$III. $\vdash (\alpha,x):.x \in \mathrm{USC}(\alpha): \equiv :(\mathrm{E}y).y \in \alpha.x = \{y\}.$

Proof of Part I. Use Thm.IX.3.1.

Proof of Part II. Use Thm.IX.6.3, Cor. 2.

Proof of Part III. Use Thm.IX.3.2, Cor. 3.

Corollary 1. $\vdash (\alpha)\ \exists(\mathrm{USC}^2(\alpha)).$

Proof. Use Part I twice.

Corollary 2. $\vdash (\alpha,x):\{\{x\}\} \in \mathrm{USC}^2(\alpha). \equiv .x \in \alpha.$

Proof. Use Part II twice.

Corollary 3. $\vdash (\alpha,x):.x \in \mathrm{USC}^2(\alpha): \equiv :(\mathrm{E}y).y \in \alpha.x = \{\{y\}\}.$

Proof. Use Part III twice.

Corollary 4. $\vdash (x).\{x\} \in 1.$

Proof. Put $\alpha = \mathrm{V}$ in Part II.

Corollary 5. $\vdash (x):x \in 1. \equiv .(\mathrm{E}y).x = \{y\}.$

Proof. Put $\alpha = \mathrm{V}$ in Part III.

Theorem IX.6.11. $\vdash (\alpha).\bigcup(\mathrm{USC}(\alpha)) = \alpha.$

Proof.

$$\begin{aligned}
&\vdash x \in \bigcup(\mathrm{USC}(\alpha)):.\\
&\quad\equiv :.(\mathrm{E}\beta):\beta \in \mathrm{USC}(\alpha).x \in \beta:.\\
&\quad\equiv :.(\mathrm{E}\beta):x \in \beta:(\mathrm{E}y).y \in \alpha.\beta = \{y\}:.\\
&\quad\equiv :.(\mathrm{E}\beta,y):x \in \beta.y \in \alpha.\beta = \{y\}:.\\
&\quad\equiv :.(\mathrm{E}y):y \in \alpha:(\mathrm{E}\beta).\beta = \{y\}.x \in \beta:.\\
&\quad\equiv :.(\mathrm{E}y):y \in \alpha.x \in \{y\}:.\\
&\quad\equiv :.(\mathrm{E}y):y = x.y \in \alpha:.\\
&\quad\equiv :.x \in \alpha.
\end{aligned}$$

Corollary 1. $\vdash (\alpha,\beta):\mathrm{USC}(\alpha) = \mathrm{USC}(\beta). \equiv .\alpha = \beta.$

Proof. If $\mathrm{USC}(\alpha) = \mathrm{USC}(\beta)$, then $\alpha = \bigcup(\mathrm{USC}(\alpha)) = \bigcup(\mathrm{USC}(\beta)) = \beta.$

Corollary 2. $\vdash \exists\{\mathrm{USC}(\alpha) \mid P\}.: \supset :.(\alpha):\mathrm{USC}(\alpha) \in \{\mathrm{USC}(\alpha) \mid P\}. \equiv .P.$

Theorem IX.6.12.

I. $\vdash (\alpha,\beta):\mathrm{USC}(\alpha \cap \beta) = \mathrm{USC}(\alpha) \cap \mathrm{USC}(\beta).$

$\star$II. $\vdash (\alpha,\beta):\mathrm{USC}(\alpha \cup \beta) = \mathrm{USC}(\alpha) \cup \mathrm{USC}(\beta).$

III. $\vdash (\alpha,\beta):\mathrm{USC}(\alpha - \beta) = \mathrm{USC}(\alpha) - \mathrm{USC}(\beta).$

$\star$IV. $\vdash \mathrm{USC}(\Lambda) = \Lambda.$

V. $\vdash (\alpha,\beta):\alpha \subseteq \beta. \equiv .\mathrm{USC}(\alpha) \subseteq \mathrm{USC}(\beta).$

VI. $\vdash (\alpha,\beta):\alpha \subset \beta. \equiv .\mathrm{USC}(\alpha) \subset \mathrm{USC}(\beta).$

Proof of Part I. Assume $x \in \mathrm{USC}(\alpha \cap \beta)$. Then $(\mathrm{E}y).y \in \alpha \cap \beta.x = \{y\}$. So by rule C, $y \in \alpha$, $y \in \beta$, $x = \{y\}$. So $x \in \mathrm{USC}(\alpha)$ and $x \in \mathrm{USC}(\beta)$. Hence

(1) $$\vdash x \in \mathrm{USC}(\alpha \cap \beta). \supset .x \in \mathrm{USC}(\alpha) \cap \mathrm{USC}(\beta).$$

Now assume $x \in \mathrm{USC}(\alpha) \cap \mathrm{USC}(\beta)$. Then $x \in \mathrm{USC}(\alpha)$ and $x \in \mathrm{USC}(\beta)$. So by rule C, $y \in \alpha$, $x = \{y\}$, $z \in \beta$, $x = \{z\}$. This gives $\{y\} = \{z\}$, $y = z$, $y \in \beta$. So $y \in \alpha \cap \beta.x = \{y\}$. So $x \in \mathrm{USC}(\alpha \cap \beta)$.

Proof of Part II.

$$\vdash x \in \mathrm{USC}(\alpha \cup \beta) :. \equiv :. (\mathrm{E}y).y \in \alpha \cup \beta . x = \{y\} :. \equiv :. (\mathrm{E}y) : y \in \alpha . x = \{y\} . \mathbf{v} . y \in \beta . x = \{y\} :. \equiv :. (\mathrm{E}y).y \in \alpha . x = \{y\} : \mathbf{v} : (\mathrm{E}y).y \in \beta . x = \{y\} :. \equiv :. x \in \mathrm{USC}(\alpha) . \mathbf{v} . x \in \mathrm{USC}(\beta).$$

Proof of Part IV. It suffices to prove $\vdash (x) \sim x \in \mathrm{USC}(\Lambda)$. That is, $\vdash (x,y).x = \{y\} \supset \sim y \in \Lambda$. This is a ready consequence of Thm.IX.4.10, Part II.

Proof of Part III. Assume $x \in \mathrm{USC}(\alpha - \beta)$. Then by Part I, $x \in \mathrm{USC}(\alpha)$ and $x \in \mathrm{USC}(\bar{\beta})$. Then we need to prove $\sim x \in \mathrm{USC}(\beta)$, which we do by reductio ad absurdum. Assume further $x \in \mathrm{USC}(\beta)$. Then by Part I, $x \in \mathrm{USC}(\beta \cap \bar{\beta})$. By Part IV, this is a contradiction. So

(1) $$\vdash \mathrm{USC}(\alpha - \beta) \subseteq \mathrm{USC}(\alpha) - \mathrm{USC}(\beta).$$

Now assume $x \in \mathrm{USC}(\alpha)$, $\sim x \in \mathrm{USC}(\beta)$. Then $(\mathrm{E}y).y \in \alpha . x = \{y\}$ and $(y).x = \{y\} \supset \sim y \in \beta$. Then by rule C, $y \in \alpha$, $x = \{y\}$, so that $\sim y \in \beta$, $y \in \bar{\beta}$. Then $y \in \alpha - \beta . x = \{y\}$. So $x \in \mathrm{USC}(\alpha - \beta)$.

Proof of Part V. $\vdash \alpha \subseteq \beta : \equiv : \alpha \cap \beta = \alpha : \equiv : \mathrm{USC}(\alpha \cap \beta) = \mathrm{USC}(\alpha) : \equiv : \mathrm{USC}(\alpha) \cap \mathrm{USC}(\beta) = \mathrm{USC}(\alpha) : \equiv : \mathrm{USC}(\alpha) \subseteq \mathrm{USC}(\beta)$.

Part VI follows readily from Part V.

Corollary 1. $\vdash (\beta).\mathrm{USC}(\bar{\beta}) = 1 - \mathrm{USC}(\beta)$.

Proof. Put $\alpha = \mathrm{V}$ in Part III.

Corollary 2. $\vdash (\alpha).\mathrm{USC}(\alpha) \subseteq 1$.

Proof. Put $\beta = \mathrm{V}$ in Part V.

Theorem IX.6.13.

I. $\vdash (\alpha)\ \exists \hat{x}(\{x\} \in \alpha)$.

II. $\vdash (\alpha,x) : x \in \hat{x}(\{x\} \in \alpha) . \equiv . \{x\} \in \alpha$.

Theorem IX.6.14. $\vdash (\alpha,\beta) :. \alpha \subseteq \mathrm{USC}(\beta) : \supset : \hat{x}(\{x\} \in \alpha) \subseteq \beta . \alpha = \mathrm{USC}(\hat{x}(\{x\} \in \alpha))$.

Proof. Assume

(1) $$\alpha \subseteq \mathrm{USC}(\beta).$$

Let $x \in \hat{x}(\{x\} \in \alpha)$. Then $\{x\} \in \alpha$. So $\{x\} \in \mathrm{USC}(\beta)$. So $x \in \beta$. Hence

(2) $$\hat{x}(\{x\} \in \alpha) \subseteq \beta.$$

Now let $x \in \alpha$. Then $x \in \mathrm{USC}(\beta)$. So by rule C, $y \in \beta$, $x = \{y\}$. So successively, $\{y\} \in \alpha$, $y \in \hat{x}(\{x\} \in \alpha)$, $\{y\} \in \mathrm{USC}(\hat{x}(\{x\} \in \alpha))$, $x \in \mathrm{USC}(\hat{x}(\{x\} \in \alpha))$. Thus

(3) $$\alpha \subseteq \mathrm{USC}(\hat{x}(\{x\} \in \alpha)).$$

Finally, let $x \epsilon \text{USC}(\hat{x}(\{x\} \epsilon \alpha))$. Then by rule C, $y \epsilon \hat{x}(\{x\} \epsilon \alpha), x = \{y\}$. From $y \epsilon \hat{x}(\{x\} \epsilon \alpha)$ we get $\{y\} \epsilon \alpha$ and so $x \epsilon \alpha$. Thus

$$\text{USC}(\hat{x}(\{x\} \epsilon \alpha)) \subseteq \alpha. \tag{4}$$

Corollary 1. $\vdash (\alpha){:}\alpha \subseteq 1. \supset .\alpha = \text{USC}(\hat{x}(\{x\} \epsilon \alpha))$.

Proof. Put $\beta = \text{V}$.

***Corollary 2.** $\vdash (\alpha,\beta){:.}\alpha \subseteq \text{USC}(\beta){:} \equiv {:}(\text{E}\gamma).\gamma \subseteq \beta.\alpha = \text{USC}(\gamma)$.

Proof. Combine with Thm.IX.6.12, Part V.

Theorem IX.6.15. $\vdash (\alpha).\sim \Lambda \epsilon \text{USC}(\alpha)$.

Proof. Assume $\Lambda \epsilon \text{USC}(\alpha)$. Then by rule C, $y \epsilon \alpha$, $\Lambda = \{y\}$. Hence $y \epsilon \Lambda$. This gives a contradiction.

Corollary 1. $\vdash (\alpha).\text{USC}(\alpha) \neq 0$.

Corollary 2. $\vdash 1 \neq 0$.

***Theorem IX.6.16.** $\vdash (x).\text{USC}(\{x\}) = \{\{x\}\}$.

Proof.

$$\begin{aligned} \vdash y \epsilon \text{USC}(\{x\})&{:} \\ &\equiv {:}(\text{E}z).z \epsilon \{x\}.y = \{z\}{:} \\ &\equiv {:}(\text{E}z).z = x.y = \{z\}{:} \\ &\equiv {:}y = \{x\}{:} \\ &\equiv {:}y \epsilon \{\{x\}\}. \end{aligned}$$

We have occasional use for the class of all subclasses of A. We call this $\text{SC}(A)$, the S and C standing for "sub" and "classes," respectively. Specifically, we put

$\text{SC}(A)$	for	$\hat{\beta}(\beta \subseteq A)$,
$\text{SC}^2(A)$	for	$\text{SC}(\text{SC}(A))$,
$\text{SC}^3(A)$	for	$\text{SC}(\text{SC}^2(A))$,
etc.,		

where in the definition of $\text{SC}(A)$, β is a variable which does not occur in A. Some people refer to $\text{SC}(A)$ as the power class of A.

Except for the bound variables implicit in $\hat{\beta}$ and $\subseteq$, a variable is free or bound in $\text{SC}(A)$ according as it is free or bound in A.

$\text{SC}(A)$ is stratified if and only if A is stratified, and similarly for $\text{SC}^2(A)$, $\text{SC}^3(A)$, etc. If A is stratified, then the type of A is one less than the type of $\text{SC}(A)$, two less than the type of $\text{SC}^2(A)$, etc.

One will commonly read $A \epsilon \text{SC}(B)$ as "A is a subclass of B."

Theorem IX.6.17.

I. $\vdash (\alpha).\exists(\text{SC}(\alpha))$.

*II. $\vdash (\alpha,\beta){:}\beta \epsilon \text{SC}(\alpha). \equiv .\beta \subseteq \alpha$.

Theorem IX.6.18.

I. $\vdash (\alpha).\alpha \epsilon \text{SC}(\alpha)$.

II. $\vdash (\alpha).\Lambda \epsilon \text{SC}(\alpha)$.

III. $\vdash (\alpha,\beta).\alpha \cap \beta \in \mathrm{SC}(\alpha)$.
IV. $\vdash (\alpha,x):x \in \alpha. \equiv .\{x\} \in \mathrm{SC}(\alpha)$.

Corollary 1. $\vdash (\alpha).\mathrm{USC}(\alpha) \subseteq \mathrm{SC}(\alpha)$.

Proof. Use Part IV.

Corollary 2. $\vdash (\alpha).\mathrm{USC}(\alpha) \subset \mathrm{SC}(\alpha)$.

Proof. Use Part II, Thm.IX.4.21, and Thm.IX.6.15.

Theorem IX.6.19.

I. $\vdash \mathrm{SC}(\Lambda) = 0$.
II. $\vdash \mathrm{SC}(\mathrm{V}) = \mathrm{V}$.

Theorem IX.6.20. $\vdash (\alpha).\bigcup(\mathrm{SC}(\alpha)) = \alpha$.

Proof. Assume $x \in \bigcup(\mathrm{SC}(\alpha))$. Then by rule C, $\beta \in \mathrm{SC}(\alpha)$ and $x \in \beta$. So $\beta \subseteq \alpha$ and $x \in \beta$. So $x \in \alpha$. Conversely, let $x \in \alpha$. Then $\alpha \in \mathrm{SC}(\alpha).x \in \alpha$. So $(\mathrm{E}\beta).\beta \in \mathrm{SC}(\alpha).x \in \beta$. Hence $x \in \bigcup(\mathrm{SC}(\alpha))$.

Corollary 1. $\vdash (\alpha,\beta):\mathrm{SC}(\alpha) = \mathrm{SC}(\beta). \equiv .\alpha = \beta$.

Corollary 2. $\vdash \exists\{\mathrm{SC}(\alpha) \mid P\}.: \supset :.(\alpha):\mathrm{SC}(\alpha) \in \{\mathrm{SC}(\alpha) \mid P\}. \equiv .P$.

EXERCISES

IX.6.1. State what are the members of $\mathrm{SC}(\{x\})$ and $\mathrm{SC}(\{x,y\})$.

IX.6.2. Prove $\vdash (x,y,u,v):\{\{x\}, \{x,y\}\} = \{\{u\}, \{u,v\}\}. \equiv .x = u.y = v$. (*Hint.* $\vdash \bigcap(\{\{x\}, \{x,y\}\}) = \{x\}$ and $\vdash \bigcup(\{\{x\}, \{x,y\}\}) = \{x,y\}$.)

IX.6.3. Prove $\vdash (\lambda).\lambda \subseteq \mathrm{SC}(\bigcup\lambda)$.

IX.6.4. Prove $\vdash (\alpha).\bigcap(\mathrm{SC}(\alpha)) = \Lambda$.

IX.6.5. Prove:

(a) $\vdash (\alpha,\beta):\alpha \subseteq \beta. \equiv .\mathrm{SC}(\alpha) \subseteq \mathrm{SC}(\beta)$.
(b) $\vdash (\alpha,\beta):\alpha \subset \beta. \equiv .\mathrm{SC}(\alpha) \subset \mathrm{SC}(\beta)$.

IX.6.6. Prove:

(a) $\vdash (\lambda,\mu).\mathrm{SC}(\lambda \cap \mu) = \mathrm{SC}(\lambda) \cap \mathrm{SC}(\mu)$.
(b) $\vdash (\lambda,\mu).\mathrm{SC}(\lambda \cup \mu) = \{\alpha \cup \beta \mid \alpha \in \mathrm{SC}(\lambda).\beta \in \mathrm{SC}(\mu)\}$.

IX.6.7. Prove:

(a) $\vdash (\lambda):\lambda \neq \Lambda. \supset .\mathrm{USC}(\bigcap\lambda) = \bigcap\{\mathrm{USC}(\alpha) \mid \alpha \in \lambda\}$.
(b) $\vdash (\lambda).\mathrm{USC}(\bigcup\lambda) = \bigcup\{\mathrm{USC}(\alpha) \mid \alpha \in \lambda\}$.

IX.6.8. Indicate why one needs the hypothesis $\lambda \neq \Lambda$ in Ex.IX.6.7(a) but not in (b).

7. Variables over the Range Σ. We have discussed restricted quantification in Chapter VI, Sec. 8, and elsewhere. We now discuss a more inclusive concept, namely, variables of restricted range.

Suppose we are particularly interested in members of some class Σ, and we choose certain variables, x, y, z, which shall denote only members of Σ.

Common instances would be where Σ is the class of integers, or the class of real numbers, or the class of complex numbers, or the class of vectors, etc.

This situation is by all odds the most commonly occurring one in mathematics. Almost never, except in cases of the most extreme generality, is there need for completely unrestricted variables, such as we have been using so far in this chapter. Accordingly, to put our class calculus in a form suitable for use in most mathematical disciplines, we must develop carefully the technique of variables of restricted range.

A part of the technique is the use of restricted quantification. If x is restricted to be a member of Σ, then our conventions on restricted quantification provide that $(x)\ F(x)$ and $(\mathrm{E}x)\ F(x)$ shall denote $(u).u \in \Sigma \supset F(u)$ and $(\mathrm{E}u).u \in \Sigma.F(u)$, respectively.

Still further conventions are needed in order to handle the class calculus effectively, particularly a convention as to the meaning of $\hat{x}F(x)$. To investigate these conventions, we assume throughout the rest of this section that x, y, and z are restricted to the range Σ, so that $(x)\ F(x)$ and $(\mathrm{E}x)\ F(x)$ are to be interpreted as above.

For the present discussion, Σ may be a variable or a term of the form $\iota w\ P$. Clearly, since the range of x, y, and z is to depend upon Σ, it would not do for the variables x, y, or z to have free occurrences in the term Σ. Otherwise Σ is completely at our disposal.

Theorem IX.7.1. $\vdash (x).x \in \alpha \equiv x \in \alpha \cap \Sigma$.

Proof. By Thm.VI.6.1, Part LXVII,

$$\vdash u \in \Sigma. \supset .u \in \alpha \equiv u \in \alpha \cap \Sigma.$$

Hence we see that $x \in \alpha$ might as well be replaced by $x \in \alpha \cap \Sigma$ everywhere.

We may think of $\alpha \cap \Sigma$ as the residue of α (modulo Σ). We shall say that α is congruent to β (modulo Σ) if $\alpha \cap \Sigma = \beta \cap \Sigma$.

Theorem IX.7.2. $\vdash (x).x \in \alpha \equiv x \in \beta: \equiv :\alpha \cap \Sigma = \beta \cap \Sigma$.

Proof. By Thm.VI.6.1, Part LXVII,

$$\vdash u \in \Sigma. \supset .u \in \alpha \equiv u \in \alpha \cap \Sigma,$$

$$\vdash u \in \Sigma. \supset .u \in \beta \equiv u \in \beta \cap \Sigma.$$

So

$$\vdash u \in \Sigma. \supset .u \in \alpha \equiv u \in \beta: \equiv :u \in \alpha \cap \Sigma \equiv u \in \beta \cap \Sigma.$$

Hence

$$\vdash (u):u \in \Sigma. \supset .u \in \alpha \equiv u \in \beta.: \equiv :.(u):u \in \alpha \cap \Sigma \equiv u \in \beta \cap \Sigma.$$

This is our theorem.

This theorem substantiates our earlier conclusion, based on Thm.IX.7.1, that, when we are dealing with variables, x, y, z, restricted to Σ, we might as well use $\alpha \cap \Sigma$ in place of α whenever one has $x \epsilon \alpha$. That is, one can deal with classes modulo Σ as far as membership of x, y, z in those classes is concerned.

We note that $\alpha \cap \Sigma$ is a subclass of Σ. So if we are replacing α by $\alpha \cap \Sigma$ for certain classes, we are essentially restricting attention to subclasses of Σ. Accordingly, if we are dealing with x, y, and z restricted to Σ, it would be natural to restrict α, β, and γ to SC(Σ), and we do so for the rest of this section. This is a further part of the technique of variables restricted to Σ. So now $(\alpha)\ F(\alpha)$ and $(\mathrm{E}\alpha)\ F(\alpha)$ denote $(\delta).\delta \subseteq \Sigma \supset F(\delta)$ and $(\mathrm{E}\delta).\delta \subseteq \Sigma.F(\delta)$, respectively. With α, β, and γ serving as restricted variables, we can now prove a theorem which looks like our definition of "=".

Theorem IX.7.3. $\vdash (\alpha,\beta):.(x).x \epsilon \alpha \equiv x \epsilon \beta: \equiv :\alpha = \beta.$

Proof. Written with unrestricted class variables, our theorem takes the form $(\theta,\phi)::\theta \subseteq \Sigma.\phi \subseteq \Sigma.: \supset :.(x).x \epsilon \theta \equiv x \epsilon \phi: \equiv :\theta = \phi$. Assume $\theta \subseteq \Sigma$ and $\phi \subseteq \Sigma$. Then $\theta = \theta \cap \Sigma$ and $\phi = \phi \cap \Sigma$. So by Thm.IX.7.2, $(x).x \epsilon \theta \equiv x \epsilon \phi: \equiv :\theta = \phi$.

In accordance with our conventions in Chapter VIII, Sec. 2, in order to interpret $\iota\alpha\ F(\alpha)$ we must choose an A such that $A \subseteq \Sigma$. We choose Λ for this A, and then $\iota\alpha\ F(\alpha)$ is to denote

$$\iota\delta\ (\delta = \iota\phi(\phi \subseteq \Sigma.F(\phi)).(\mathrm{E}_1\phi).\phi \subseteq \Sigma.F(\phi):\mathbf{v}:\delta = \Lambda.\sim(\mathrm{E}_1\phi).\phi \subseteq \Sigma.F(\phi)).$$

In view of this, and recalling that $\hat{x}F(x)$ is an abbreviation for $\iota\alpha\ (x).x \epsilon \alpha \equiv F(x)$, we see that $\hat{x}F(x)$ denotes

$$\iota\delta\ (\delta = \iota\phi(\phi \subseteq \Sigma:(u):u \epsilon \Sigma. \supset .u \epsilon \phi \equiv F(u)):.(\mathrm{E}_1\phi):\phi \subseteq \Sigma:(u):u \epsilon \Sigma. \supset . u \epsilon \phi \equiv F(u).:\mathbf{v}:.\delta = \Lambda:.\sim(\mathrm{E}_1\phi):\phi \subseteq \Sigma:(u):u \epsilon \Sigma. \supset .u \epsilon \phi \equiv F(u)).$$

Actually, from the intuitive interpretation that one would wish to give $\hat{x}F(x)$ when x denotes a member of Σ, one would wish $\hat{x}F(x)$ to mean $\hat{u}(u \epsilon \Sigma.F(u))$. We shall prove that, if the class denoted by $\hat{x}F(x)$ exists, then indeed $\hat{x}F(x) = \hat{u}(u \epsilon \Sigma.F(u))$.

Theorem IX.7.4. $\vdash (\Sigma,\phi)::\phi \subseteq \Sigma:(u):u \epsilon \Sigma. \supset .u \epsilon \phi \equiv F(u).: \equiv :.(u) :u \epsilon \phi. \equiv .u \epsilon \Sigma.F(u).$

Proof. Straightforward.

Theorem IX.7.5. If α is a variable which does not occur in $F(x)$, then $\vdash (\mathrm{E}\alpha)(x).x \epsilon \alpha \equiv F(x): \equiv :\exists\hat{u}(u \epsilon \Sigma.F(u))$.

Proof. Note that $(\mathrm{E}\alpha)(x).x \epsilon \alpha \equiv F(x)$ is $(\mathrm{E}\phi):\phi \subseteq \Sigma:(u):u \epsilon \Sigma. \supset . u \epsilon \phi \equiv F(u)$, and $\exists\hat{u}(u \epsilon \Sigma.F(u))$ is $(\mathrm{E}\phi)(u):u \epsilon \phi. \equiv .u \epsilon \Sigma.F(u)$.

Note that $(\mathrm{E}\alpha)(x).x \epsilon \alpha \equiv F(x)$ is just the formula which we would abbreviate to $\exists\hat{x}F(x)$ if the variables x and α were unrestricted. So essentially the theorem just proved says $\vdash \exists\hat{x}F(x) \equiv \exists\hat{u}(u \epsilon \Sigma.F(u))$.

Theorem IX.7.6. $\vdash \exists\hat{u}(u \epsilon \Sigma.F(u)): \supset :\hat{x}F(x) = \hat{u}(u \epsilon \Sigma.F(u))$.

Proof. Assume $\exists\hat{u}(u \in \Sigma.F(u))$. Then by Thm.IX.3.2 and Thm.IX.7.4, $(\phi)::\hat{u}(u \in \Sigma.F(u)) = \phi.: \equiv :.\phi \subseteq \Sigma:(u):u \in \Sigma. \supset .u \in \phi \equiv F(u)$. So $(\mathrm{E}\delta)::$ $\delta = \phi.: \equiv :.\phi \subseteq \Sigma:(u):u \in \Sigma. \supset .u \in \phi \equiv F(u)$. That is, $(\mathrm{E}_1\phi):.\phi \subseteq \Sigma:(u):$ $u \in \Sigma. \supset .u \in \phi \equiv F(u)$. Then by Thm.VIII.2.10, Part I, and Thm.VII.2.3, $\hat{x}F(x) = \iota\phi(\phi \subseteq \Sigma:(u):u \in \Sigma. \supset .u \in \phi \equiv F(u))$. However, by Axiom scheme 9 and Thm.IX.7.4, $\vdash \iota\phi(\phi \subseteq \Sigma:(u):u \in \Sigma. \supset .u \in \phi \equiv F(u)) =$ $\hat{u}(u \in \Sigma.F(u))$.

Corollary. $\vdash (\mathrm{E}\alpha)(x).x \in \alpha \equiv F(x): \supset :\hat{x}F(x) = \hat{u}(u \in \Sigma.F(u))$ if α is a variable which does not occur in $F(x)$.

We notice that in our interpretation of $\hat{x}F(x)$ we are applying to the implicit occurrence of α the rule that any variable which is to be associated with x, y, or z in a relation of membership is to be restricted to $\mathrm{SC}(\Sigma)$. If α occurs as a member of some λ, then the same rule would call for restricting λ to $\mathrm{SC}^2(\Sigma)$. Then by Thm.IX.7.6, we would have

$$\vdash \exists\hat{\delta}(\delta \subseteq \Sigma.G(\delta)): \supset :\hat{\alpha}G(\alpha) = \hat{\delta}(\delta \subseteq \Sigma.G(\delta)).$$

Similarly, if λ occurs as a member of some class, that class should be restricted to $\mathrm{SC}^3(\Sigma)$. Thus we find that there arises a natural sort of hierarchy of types.

By Thm.IX.7.3, our definition of equality of α and β is valid in terms of variables of restricted range. This suggests that the previous theorems of this chapter remain true if interpreted as involving variables of restricted range. This is true with reservations. As we noted above, in combinations like $x \in \alpha$, the ranges of x and α have to be properly adjusted. If x is restricted to Σ, then α should be restricted to $\mathrm{SC}(\Sigma)$. More generally, if there occurs such a formula as $(x):.x \in \bigcap\lambda: \equiv :(\alpha).\alpha \in \lambda \supset x \in \alpha$, then if we wish x restricted to Σ, we must not only have α restricted to $\mathrm{SC}(\Sigma)$ but λ restricted to $\mathrm{SC}^2(\Sigma)$.

Thus, in dealing with variables over a restricted range, we have imposed upon us a sort of natural hierarchy of types. Consequently, in dealing with variables over restricted ranges, we can hope to carry over only those theorems which would fit into such a hierarchy of types. Subject to this condition, however, the theorems not involving restricted variables carry over into theorems involving restricted variables. Certain other minor changes are needed. One such change is that, if a certain variable is restricted to Σ, then Σ serves as the universal class for that variable. This follows from Thm.IX.7.1, which with Thm.IX.7.3 tells us that

$$\vdash (\alpha).\alpha = \alpha \cap \Sigma,$$

which is analogous to the property

$$\vdash (\delta).\delta = \delta \cap \mathrm{V}.$$

Another change is that complementation must be replaced by complementation with respect to Σ. That is, analogous to $\bar{\delta}$ for unrestricted variables, we must use $\Sigma - \delta$ for variables of restricted range.

One should note how the type hierarchy is working here. If we have $x \epsilon \alpha$ and $\alpha \epsilon \lambda$ occurring and x restricted to Σ, then the universal class for x is Σ, the universal class for α is $\mathrm{SC}(\Sigma)$, and the universal class for λ is $\mathrm{SC}^2(\Sigma)$. However in such formulas as $\alpha \cap \mathrm{V}$, the V which must be used is the V of the same type as α, which is the V for the members of α, namely, Σ. However, if one has $\lambda \cap \mathrm{V}$, then one must use the V of the same type as λ, and for this V we would have to use the class to which α is restricted, namely, $\mathrm{SC}(\Sigma)$. Accordingly, in performing restricted complementation, the restricted complement of α would be $\Sigma - \alpha$, but the restricted complement of λ would be $\mathrm{SC}(\Sigma) - \lambda$.

In other words, the type distinctions of our hierarchy of types must be very carefully adhered to.

It does not noticeably complicate the formulas to use the appropriate one of Σ, $\mathrm{SC}(\Sigma)$, etc., for V at the proper places when dealing with variables of restricted ranges, and it helps us keep the range in mind. However, we shall simplify $\Sigma - \alpha$, $\mathrm{SC}(\Sigma) - \lambda$, etc., to just $\bar{\alpha}$, $\bar{\lambda}$, etc., and expect the reader to remember that complementation for variables of restricted ranges is restricted complementation.

It is not completely trivial to show that the previous theorems of the present chapter are valid when so interpreted, and we devote the rest of the section to verifying this fact.

We start with the axioms. All but Axiom scheme 12 have been covered by earlier discussions dealing with restricted quantification.

Theorem IX.7.7. $\vdash (\Sigma).\exists\hat{u}P \supset \exists\hat{u}(u \epsilon \Sigma.P)$.

Proof. Assume $\exists\hat{u}P$. Then by Thm.IX.3.2, Cor. 1, $u \epsilon \hat{u}P. \equiv .P$. So $u \epsilon \Sigma.u \epsilon \hat{u}P: \equiv :u \epsilon \Sigma.P$. Thus, $u \epsilon \Sigma \cap \hat{u}P: \equiv :u \epsilon \Sigma.P$. So $(\mathrm{E}\phi)(u)$: $u \epsilon \phi. \equiv .u \epsilon \Sigma.P$. That is, $\exists\hat{u}(u \epsilon \Sigma.P)$.

Theorem IX.7.8. If P is stratified and x and α are distinct variables and α does not occur in P, then $\vdash (\mathrm{E}\alpha)(x).x \epsilon \alpha \equiv P$.

Proof. Use Thm.IX.7.7 and Thm.IX.7.5.

We may as well agree that, when the variable x is restricted to Σ, then $\exists\hat{x}P$ shall denote $(\mathrm{E}\alpha)(x).x \epsilon \alpha \equiv P$ where α is a variable which does not occur in P and is restricted to $\mathrm{SC}(\Sigma)$. Then our analogue of Axiom scheme 12 says that, if P is stratified, then $\exists\hat{x}P$.

The theorems in Sec. 2 of the present chapter are readily proved when written with restricted variables. Indeed, the restricted form is a ready consequence of the unrestricted form.

Turning to Sec. 3, we note that we have taken care of Thm.IX.3.1 by Thm.IX.7.8. A useful lemma for later theorems is:

Theorem IX.7.9. $\vdash \exists \hat{x}P. \supset .\hat{x}P \subseteq \Sigma.$

Proof. Assume $\exists \hat{x}F(x)$. Then by Thm.IX.7.5, $\exists \hat{u}(u \in \Sigma.F(u))$. So by Thm.IX.3.2, Cor. 1, $u \in \hat{u}(u \in \Sigma.F(u)). \supset .u \in \Sigma$. So $\hat{u}(u \in \Sigma.F(u)) \subseteq \Sigma$. Accordingly, by Thm.IX.7.6, $\hat{x}F(x) \subseteq \Sigma$.

Corollary. $\vdash \exists \hat{x}P. \supset .\hat{x}P = \hat{x}P \cap \Sigma.$

Theorem IX.7.10. $\vdash \exists \hat{x}P: \supset :(x).x \in \hat{x}P \equiv P.$

Proof. Assume $\exists \hat{x}F(x)$. Then $\exists \hat{u}(u \in \Sigma.F(u))$. So $u \in \hat{u}(u \in \Sigma.F(u)). \equiv . u \in \Sigma.F(u)$. So $(u):u \in \Sigma. \supset .u \in \hat{u}(u \in \Sigma.F(u)) \equiv F(u)$. That is, $(x). x \in \hat{u}(u \in \Sigma.F(u)) \equiv F(x)$. However, $\hat{u}(u \in \Sigma.F(u)) = \hat{x}F(x)$.

By use of this theorem and Thm.IX.7.3 (with an assist from Thm. IX.7.9), we can prove that, if there is no free β in P, then $\vdash \exists \hat{x}P.: \supset :. (\beta):\beta = \hat{x}P. \equiv .(x).x \in \beta \equiv P$. This takes care of Thm.IX.3.2.

With regard to $\{A \mid P\}$, it seems clear that, if some of the y's which occur free in both A and P are subject to certain restrictions, one has merely to subject these y's to the same restrictions in the definition $\hat{u}(\mathrm{E}y_1, y_2, \ldots, y_n).u = A.P$ in order to make $\{A \mid P\}$ have the desired characteristics. In case A is such a function of $y_1, y_2, \ldots, y_n$ that we have $\vdash (y_1, y_2, \ldots, y_n).A \in \Sigma$, then one can prove $\vdash \exists\{A \mid P\}. \supset .\hat{u}((\mathrm{E}y_1, y_2, \ldots, y_n).u = A.P) = \hat{x}((\mathrm{E}y_1, y_2, \ldots, y_n).x = A.P)$. In such case one has the option of writing $\hat{x}(\mathrm{E}y_1, y_2, \ldots, y_n).x = A.P$ for $\{A \mid P\}$ if it serves any useful purpose (such as uniformity of notation).

With this understanding about $\{A \mid P\}$, the reader can check the proofs of the remaining theorems of Sec. 3 and verify that the proofs given for unrestricted variables generalize to the case of restricted variables. We might just remark with regard to Thm.IX.3.6, Cor. 1, that one would have

$$\vdash (\delta).\hat{x}(x \in \delta) = \delta \cap \Sigma$$

but

$$\vdash (\alpha).\hat{x}(x \in \alpha) = \alpha.$$

As a lemma for the theorems of Sec. 4, we prove:

Theorem IX.7.11.

I. $\vdash (x).x \in \Sigma \equiv x = x.$

II. $\vdash (x).x \in \Lambda \equiv x \neq x.$

III. $\vdash (\alpha,\beta,x):x \in \alpha \cap \beta. \equiv .x \in \alpha.x \in \beta.$

IV. $\vdash (\alpha,\beta,x):x \in \alpha \cup \beta. \equiv .x \in \alpha.\mathbf{v}.x \in \beta.$

V. $\vdash (\alpha,x):x \in \bar{\alpha}. \equiv .\sim x \in \alpha.$

Proof of Part I. We note that it is just $\vdash (u):u \in \Sigma. \supset .u \in \Sigma \equiv x = x$, which is easily proved.

Parts II, III, and IV are trivial. To prove Part V, note that it is $\vdash (\delta):.\delta \subseteq \Sigma: \supset :(x):x \in \Sigma - \delta. \equiv .x \in \bar{\delta}$, which follows by Thm.IX.7.1.

With the help of this result, we can carry through the proofs for restricted variables of the theorems of Secs. 4, 5, and 6 with no great difficulty. We must remember to replace V by Σ in all places.

In the proof of Thm.IX.4.6, we hit a slight snag. The use of free x's in the proof involves the assumption $x \epsilon \Sigma$. Hence, we conclude not $\vdash \alpha \neq \bar{\alpha}$, but $\vdash x \epsilon \Sigma \supset \alpha \neq \bar{\alpha}$. That is, Thm.IX.4.6 becomes $\vdash \Sigma \neq \Lambda . \supset .(\alpha).\alpha \neq \bar{\alpha}$.

The reader will recollect that, in dealing with restricted quantification, one needed to know that $(Ex)\ K(x)$; analogously in dealing with variables over the range Σ we shall need to know $(Ex)\ x \epsilon \Sigma$ or $\Sigma \neq \Lambda$. If we always use a Σ such that $\vdash \Sigma \neq \Lambda$, then we can carry out all theorems of Secs. 4, 5, and 6 for restricted quantification.

The $\{\alpha\}$ of Thm.IX.6.9 denotes $\hat{\delta}(\delta \subseteq \Sigma . \delta = \alpha)$ rather than $\hat{\delta}(\delta \epsilon \Sigma . \delta = \alpha)$, of course. This is a consequence of adhering to our type hierarchy. Correspondingly, we would have to write Thm.IX.6.10, Part III, in the form

$$\vdash (\alpha,\beta):.\beta \epsilon \mathrm{USC}(\alpha): \equiv :(Ey).y \epsilon \alpha.\beta = \{y\}$$

so that it would be interpreted as

$$\vdash (\phi,u)::\phi \subseteq \Sigma.u \subseteq \Sigma.: \supset :.u \epsilon \mathrm{USC}(\phi): \equiv :(Ev).v \epsilon \Sigma.v \epsilon \phi.u = \{v\}$$

rather than as

$$\vdash (\phi,u)::\phi \subseteq \Sigma.u \epsilon \Sigma.: \supset :.u \epsilon \mathrm{USC}(\phi): \equiv :(Ev).v \epsilon \Sigma.v \epsilon \phi.u = \{v\}.$$

So far as we know, the latter is not provable.

In Cor. 3 of Thm.IX.6.10, one must write a λ in place of x for similar reasons.

This illustrates what we said earlier, that use of restricted variables forces upon us a hierarchy of types which must be rigidly adhered to.

Likewise in Thms.IX.6.13 and IX.6.14, one should write λ in place of α to ensure the right sort of restrictions being implied in the use of the variable.

EXERCISES

IX.7.1. Prove $\vdash (\Sigma,\phi)::\phi \subseteq \Sigma:(u):u \epsilon \Sigma. \supset .u \epsilon \phi \equiv P.: \equiv :.(u):u \epsilon \phi. \equiv . u \epsilon \Sigma.P$.

IX.7.2. Criticize the following proof.

$$\vdash u \epsilon \Sigma. \supset .u \epsilon \phi \supset u \epsilon \Sigma.$$

So

$$\vdash (x).x \epsilon \phi \supset x \epsilon \Sigma.$$

So

$$\vdash \phi \subseteq \Sigma.$$

IX.7.3. Prove $\vdash \hat{x}P \subseteq \Sigma$.

IX.7.4. Prove $\vdash (\delta):\hat{x}(x \epsilon \delta) = \delta \cap \Sigma$.

8. Applications. As an illustration of the use of classes in mathematics, we shall consider Hausdorff spaces.

A Hausdorff space is a set, Σ, of points such that, with each point, x, of Σ is associated a set of neighborhoods, $H(x)$, of x, the neighborhoods being needed to satisfy certain requirements known as the Hausdorff axioms. The Hausdorff axioms are:

0a. $(x,\alpha):x \epsilon \Sigma.\alpha \epsilon H(x). \supset .\alpha \subseteq \Sigma.$
0b. $\Sigma \neq \Lambda.$
1a. $(x):x \epsilon \Sigma. \supset .H(x) \neq \Lambda.$
1b. $(x,\alpha):x \epsilon \Sigma.\alpha \epsilon H(x). \supset .x \epsilon \alpha.$
2. $(x,\alpha,\beta):x \epsilon \Sigma.\alpha,\beta \epsilon H(x). \supset .(\mathrm{E}\gamma).\gamma \epsilon H(x).\gamma \subseteq \alpha \cap \beta.$
3. $(x,y,\alpha):x,y \epsilon \Sigma.\alpha \epsilon H(x).y \epsilon \alpha. \supset .(\mathrm{E}\beta).\beta \epsilon H(y).\beta \subseteq \alpha.$
4. $(x,y):x,y \epsilon \Sigma.x \neq y. \supset .(\mathrm{E}\alpha,\beta).\alpha \epsilon H(x).\beta \epsilon H(y).\alpha \cap \beta = \Lambda.$

We agree that $H(x)$ shall be considered as stratified and have type two higher than x. Then the axioms given above are stratified. If one wishes to write a definition of $H(x)$ in some special case, these conditions of stratification must be adhered to.

We can consider that x is the only variable which has free occurrences in $H(x)$. In some applications, it may be desirable to let $H(x)$ contain free occurrences of other variables which would serve as parameters. If these additional variables are distinct from all variables which appear in the developments of this chapter, the effect for these developments would be the same as though x were the only free variable in $H(x)$. Thus it is quite possible for such extra variables to be used as parameters, which are effectively unchanging throughout the developments of the present chapter.

Of these seven axioms, Axioms 0a and 0b are never stated, though they are always implicitly assumed. Axioms 1a and 1b are usually not stated separately, but their logical product is stated as a single axiom, the "first Hausdorff axiom." Thus it comes about that one usually refers to the "four Hausdorff axioms" for a Hausdorff space.

There is no agreement as to just how general a Hausdorff space should be. Actually spaces of differing degrees of generality are often considered, the different degrees of generality being achieved by stating Axiom 4 in different forms with varying degrees of restrictiveness. In this connection, see Hausdorff, 1927, especially Sec. 40, page 229.

The form of Axiom 4 which we give here is one of the more commonly used forms.

In order to put the axioms easily into our symbolism, we have deviated slightly from the usual mode of statement. We use $H(x)$ for the set of all neighborhoods of a point, whereas in the usual formulation N_x is used to denote an unspecified neighborhood. N_x would then be a member of $H(x)$.

For comparison we quote a presentation of the Hausdorff axioms (see Bohnenblust, 1937, Chapter 4, Sec. 4.1).[1]

"According to Hausdorff, a space is a set of elements, in which certain subsets will play a distinguished role. These are called *neighborhoods*. To be regarded as neighborhoods, a class of subsets must satisfy the following axioms.

"(1) Any element x has at least one neighborhood N_x, and is an element of any one of its neighborhoods.

"(2) If there are two neighborhoods of x, then there exists a neighborhood of x which is contained in each of these.

"(3) If y lies in N_x, then there exists a neighborhood N_y of y which is contained in N_x.

"(4) If x and y are distinct, there exist an N_x and an N_y with no common element."

We note the following examples of Hausdorff spaces.

A. Σ is the set of rational points between zero and one. The neighborhoods are the open intervals, going from n/m to $(n + 1)/m$ for all pairs of integers n and m with $0 \leq n < m$.

The neighborhoods of a point x are just those neighborhoods which contain x. So

$$H(x) = \hat{\alpha}(\mathrm{E}m,n){:}0 \leq n < m.\frac{n}{m} < x < \frac{n+1}{m}.\alpha = \hat{y}\left(\frac{n}{m} < y < \frac{n+1}{m}\right).$$

Here we are using restricted ranges on m, n, and y with m and n restricted to integers and y to rational numbers.

B. Σ is the set of all real points on the line. The neighborhoods of a point x are all open intervals which contain x. So

$$H(x) = \hat{\alpha}(\mathrm{E}\varepsilon,\delta)\ \alpha = \hat{y}(x - \varepsilon < y < x + \delta).$$

Here we are using restricted ranges on ε and δ, namely, the usual ones, that ε and δ are real and positive. It is not necessary to use a restricted range for y, since the condition $x - \varepsilon < y < x + \delta$ implies that y is real.

C. Σ is the set of all complex points in the complex plane. The neighborhoods of a point z are all open circles with center at z. So

$$H(z) = \hat{\alpha}(\mathrm{E}R)\ \alpha = \hat{w}(|\ w - z\ | < R).$$

Here we are using restricted ranges on R and w, with R restricted to positive real numbers and w to complex numbers.

We now prove a few of the fundamental theorems about Hausdorff spaces. To simplify notation, we use x, y, and z with a restricted range,

[1] From "Theory of Functions of Real Variables" by H. F. Bohnenblust, published 1937 at Princeton University, quoted by permission.

namely, the range Σ. Then α, β, and γ are restricted to SC(Σ). Also the universal class of the type of α is Σ. Further, to avoid collision with the notation for the closure of a set, we use $-\alpha$ for $\hat{x}(\sim x \epsilon \alpha)$.

With variables of restricted ranges, the Hausdorff axioms take the form:

0a. $(x).H(x) \subseteq \mathrm{SC}(\Sigma)$.
0b. $\Sigma \neq \Lambda$.
1a. $(x).H(x) \neq \Lambda$.
1b. $(x).x \epsilon \bigcap H(x)$.
2. $(x,\alpha,\beta):\alpha,\beta \epsilon H(x). \supset .(\mathrm{E}\gamma).\gamma \epsilon H(x).\gamma \subseteq \alpha \cap \beta$.
3. $(x,y,\alpha):\alpha \epsilon H(x).y \epsilon \alpha. \supset .(\mathrm{E}\beta).\beta \epsilon H(y).\beta \subseteq \alpha$.
4. $(x,y):x \neq y. \supset .(\mathrm{E}\alpha,\beta).\alpha \epsilon H(x).\beta \epsilon H(y).\alpha \cap \beta = \Lambda$.

We quote some definitions from Bohnenblust, 1937.[1]

"*Definition.* Any subset S of the given space will be called *open* with respect to a set of neighborhoods if for any element x in S there exists an N_x contained in S."

"*Definition.* A subset of a space is said to be *closed* if its complement is open in the space."

"*Definition.* We call x a *limit point* of the set S if every open set containing x, whether x belongs to S or not, contains at least one element of S different from x."

"*Definition.* The set of limit points of S is called the *derived set* of S and is designated by S'."

"*Definition.* $S + S'$ is called the *closure* of S and is denoted by $\overline{S}$."

In translating these into symbolic logic, we define not the term "open set" but the class of open sets. If we let "OS" stand for the class of open sets, then the English statement "x is an open set" can be translated as "$x \epsilon$ OS". That is, in symbolic logic, we do not have available both of the two alternative, but synonymous, statements:

"x is an open set."

"x is a member of the class of open sets."

We have only the second. Clearly this will suffice for mathematical purposes, though it makes our symbolic logic statements rather stilted if translated literally.

Our earlier use of $H(x)$ instead of N_x is another instance of the same thing. Instead of saying that α (or N_x) is a neighborhood of x, we say that α is a member of the class of neighborhoods of x ($\alpha \epsilon H(x)$).

Similarly we define the class "CS" of closed sets. Further, where Bohnenblust defines both "limit point" and class of limit points (derived set), we get along with only the latter, and write "x is a limit point of S" as "$x \epsilon S'$".

[1] *Ibid.*

Our definitions, using α instead of Bohnenblust's S, are:

OS	for	$\hat{\alpha}(x){:}x \in \alpha. \supset .(\mathrm{E}\beta).\beta \in H(x).\beta \subseteq \alpha.$
CS	for	$\hat{\alpha}(-\alpha \in \mathrm{OS}).$
α'	for	$\hat{x}(\beta){:}x \in \beta.\beta \in \mathrm{OS}. \supset .(\mathrm{E}y).y \neq x.y \in \beta.y \in \alpha.$
$\bar{\alpha}$	for	$\alpha \cup \alpha'.$

Clearly OS, CS, and α' are defined by stratified statements, so that we may apply Thms.IX.7.8 and IX.7.10 and infer:

$(\alpha){:}.\alpha \in \mathrm{OS}{:} \equiv {:}(x){:}x \in \alpha. \supset .(\mathrm{E}\beta).\beta \in H(x).\beta \subseteq \alpha.$
$(\alpha){:}.\alpha \in \mathrm{CS}. \equiv .-\alpha \in \mathrm{OS}.$
$(x){:}.x \in \alpha'{:} \equiv {:}(\beta){:}x \in \beta.\beta \in \mathrm{OS}. \supset .(\mathrm{E}y).y \neq x.y \in \beta.y \in \alpha.$

In the hierarchy of types which accompanies the use of a restricted range of values for the variables, OS and CS must have the same type as $\mathrm{SC}(\Sigma)$, and α' and $\bar{\alpha}$ must have the same type as Σ. Adherence to this type hierarchy ensures stratification.

Theorem IX.8.1. $(\alpha,\beta){:}\alpha,\beta \in \mathrm{OS}. \supset .\alpha \cap \beta \in \mathrm{OS}.$

In words, "The intersection of two open sets is open".

Proof. Assume $\alpha,\beta \in \mathrm{OS}$ and $\alpha \subseteq \Sigma$ and $\beta \subseteq \Sigma$. Now let $x \in \Sigma$ and $x \in \alpha \cap \beta$. Then $x \in \alpha$ and $x \in \beta$. Then by rule C and the definition of OS, $\gamma \subseteq \Sigma$, $\gamma \in H(x).\gamma \subseteq \alpha$, $\delta \subseteq \Sigma$, and $\delta \in H(x).\delta \subseteq \beta$. So by Axiom 2 and rule C, $\phi \subseteq \Sigma$ and $\phi \in H(x).\phi \subseteq \gamma \cap \delta$. Then $\phi \subseteq \alpha \cap \beta$.

Theorem IX.8.2. $(\lambda){:}\lambda \subseteq \mathrm{OS}. \supset .\bigcup\lambda \in \mathrm{OS}.$

In words, "The sum of any number, finite or infinite, of open sets is open".

Proof. Assume $\lambda \subseteq \mathrm{SC}(\Sigma)$ and $\lambda \subseteq \mathrm{OS}$. Now let $x \in \Sigma$ and $x \in \bigcup\lambda$. Then by rule C, $\alpha \subseteq \Sigma.\alpha \in \lambda.x \in \alpha$. Hence $\alpha \in \mathrm{OS}$. So by the definition of CS, $(\mathrm{E}\beta).\beta \in H(x).\beta \subseteq \alpha$. So by Thm.IX.5.5, Part II, $(\mathrm{E}\beta).\beta \in H(x).\beta \subseteq \bigcup\lambda$.

Theorem IX.8.3. $(\alpha,\beta){:}\alpha,\ \beta \in \mathrm{CS}. \supset .\alpha \cup \beta \in \mathrm{CS}.$

In words, "The sum of two closed sets is closed".

Proof. Assume $\alpha \subseteq \Sigma$, $\beta \subseteq \Sigma$, and $\alpha,\beta \in \mathrm{CS}$. Then $-\alpha$, $-\beta \in \mathrm{OS}$ by the definition of CS. So by Thm.IX.8.1, $-\alpha \cap -\beta \in \mathrm{OS}$. So $-(\alpha \cup \beta) \in \mathrm{OS}$. That is, $\alpha \cup \beta \in \mathrm{CS}$.

Theorem IX.8.4. $(\lambda){:}\lambda \subseteq \mathrm{CS}. \supset .\bigcap\lambda \in \mathrm{CS}.$

In words, "The intersection of any number, finite or infinite, of closed sets is closed".

Proof. Assume $\lambda \subseteq \mathrm{SC}(\Sigma)$ and $\lambda \subseteq \mathrm{CS}$. Then $\{-\alpha \mid \alpha \in \lambda\} \subseteq \mathrm{OS}$. So by Thm.IX.8.2, $\bigcup\{-\alpha \mid \alpha \in \lambda\} \in \mathrm{OS}$. So by Thm.IX.5.11, Part II, $-\bigcap\lambda \in \mathrm{OS}$. So $\bigcap\lambda \in \mathrm{CS}$.

Theorem IX.8.5. $(x,\alpha){:}\alpha \in H(x). \supset .\alpha \in \mathrm{OS}.$

In words, "Any neighborhood of any point is open".

Proof. Rewrite Axiom 3 in the form $(x,\alpha){:}.\alpha \in H(x){:} \supset {:}(y){:}y \in \alpha. \supset .$ $(\mathrm{E}\beta).\beta \in H(y).\beta \subseteq \alpha.$

Theorem IX.8.6. $(\alpha){:}\alpha \in \mathrm{CS}. \supset .\alpha' \subseteq \alpha.$

In words, "A closed set contains all its limit points".

Proof. Assume $\alpha \subseteq \Sigma$ and $\alpha \in \mathrm{CS}$. Then $-\alpha \in \mathrm{OS}$. To prove $\alpha' \subseteq \alpha$, we assume $x \in \Sigma$ and $x \in \alpha'$ and prove $x \in \alpha$ by reductio ad absurdum, to which end we assume $\sim x \in \alpha$. Then $x \in -\alpha$. Since $-\alpha \in \mathrm{OS}$, we have by rule C that $\beta \subseteq \Sigma$, $\beta \in H(x)$, and $\beta \subseteq -\alpha$. Then by Axiom 1b and Thm. IX.8.5, $x \in \beta.\beta \in \mathrm{OS}$. So, since $x \in \alpha'$, we have by rule C, $y \in \Sigma$, $y \neq x$, $y \in \beta$, and $y \in \alpha$. But $\beta \subseteq -\alpha$, so that $y \in -\alpha$, so that $\sim y \in \alpha$. This is the desired contradiction.

Theorem IX.8.7. $(\alpha){:}\alpha' \subseteq \alpha. \supset .\alpha \in \mathrm{CS}.$

In words, "Any set is closed if it contains all its limit points".

Proof. We first prove:

Lemma. $\alpha \subseteq \Sigma,\ x \in -\alpha,\ (\beta){:}\beta \in H(x). \supset .\sim(\beta \subseteq -\alpha) \vdash x \in \alpha'.$

Proof. Assume

(1) $$\alpha \subseteq \Sigma,$$

(2) $$x \in -\alpha,$$

(3) $$(\beta){:}\beta \in H(x). \supset .\sim(\beta \subseteq -\alpha),$$

(4) $$\gamma \subseteq \Sigma,$$

(5) $$x \in \gamma.\gamma \in \mathrm{OS}.$$

By (4), (5), and rule C, $\beta \subseteq \Sigma$, $\beta \in H(x)$, and

(6) $$\beta \subseteq \gamma.$$

Then by (3), $\sim(\beta \subseteq -\alpha)$, which is equivalent to $(\mathrm{E}y).y \in \beta.y \in \alpha$ by the duality theorem. So by rule C,

(7) $$y \in \Sigma,$$

(8) $$y \in \beta,$$

(9) $$y \in \alpha.$$

From (2), we get $\sim x \in \alpha$, so that by (9) and Thm.VII.1.4,

(10) $$y \neq x.$$

Also by (6) and (8)

(11) $$y \in \gamma.$$

Then by (7), (10), (11), and (9),

$$(\mathrm{E}y).y \neq x.y \in \gamma.y \in \alpha.$$

Since this is derived from (1), (2), (3), (4), and (5), we infer

$$(1), (2), (3) \vdash x \epsilon \alpha'$$

which is our lemma.

We now prove the theorem by reductio ad absurdum, to which end we assume $\alpha \subseteq \Sigma$, $\alpha' \subseteq \alpha$, and $\sim \alpha \epsilon \mathrm{CS}$. The last gives $\sim(-\alpha \epsilon \mathrm{OS})$, from which we get $(\mathrm{E}x):x \epsilon -\alpha:(\beta):\beta \epsilon H(x). \supset .\sim(\beta \subseteq -\alpha)$. Then by rule C and our lemma, we get $x \epsilon -\alpha$ and $x \epsilon \alpha'$. That is, $\sim x \epsilon \alpha$ and $x \epsilon \alpha'$. But from $x \epsilon \alpha'$ and $\alpha' \subseteq \alpha$, we get $x \epsilon \alpha$, which is a contradiction.

Corollary 1. $(\alpha):\alpha \epsilon \mathrm{CS}. \equiv .\alpha' \subseteq \alpha.$

This agrees with the definition of closed set which is often given and which we quoted in Sec. 9 of Chapter VI, namely: "A set is said to be closed if it contains all its limit points."

Corollary 2. $(\alpha):\alpha \epsilon \mathrm{CS}. \equiv .\alpha = \bar{\alpha}.$

In words, "A set is closed if and only if it is identical with its closure".

By using Thm.VI.8.1, we could avoid the necessity of proving the lemma preparatory to proving our theorem

We are now able to prove that the derived set of a set is closed. However, this result requires use of Axiom 4, and as we have not yet used Axiom 4 we shall postpone this result until after we have proved a few other results which can be proved without Axiom 4.

Theorem IX.8.8. $(\alpha,\beta):\alpha \subseteq \beta. \supset .\alpha' \subseteq \beta'.$

Proof. From $\alpha \subseteq \beta$, we readily get

$$(\mathrm{E}y).y \neq x.y \epsilon \theta.y \epsilon \alpha: \supset :(\mathrm{E}y).y \neq x.y \epsilon \theta.y \epsilon \beta.$$

From this, we readily get

$$(\theta):x \epsilon \theta.\theta \epsilon \mathrm{OS}. \supset .(\mathrm{E}y).y \neq x.y \epsilon \theta.y \epsilon \alpha.: \supset :.(\theta):x \epsilon \theta.\theta \epsilon \mathrm{OS}. \supset .(\mathrm{E}y). y \neq x.y \epsilon \theta.y \epsilon \beta.$$

Hence $\alpha' \subseteq \beta'$.

Corollary. $(\alpha,\beta):\alpha \subseteq \beta. \supset .\bar{\alpha} \subseteq \bar{\beta}.$

Up to now, we have carefully inserted all hypotheses and conclusions of the form $x \epsilon \Sigma$, $\alpha \subseteq \Sigma$, etc., which are needed to take account properly of the fact that we are using restricted variables. However, since the proofs are getting rather long, we shall shorten them by omitting these. Strictly speaking, such omissions are not proper, but the omitted steps can readily be supplied by the reader.

Theorem IX.8.9. $(\alpha,\beta).(\alpha \cup \beta)' = \alpha' \cup \beta'.$

In words, "The derivative of a sum is the sum of the derivatives".

Proof. By Thm.IX.8.8, $\alpha' \subseteq (\alpha \cup \beta)'$ and $\beta' \subseteq (\alpha \cup \beta)'$. So by Thm.IX.4.18, Part II,

(1) $$\alpha' \cup \beta' \subseteq (\alpha \cup \beta)'.$$

Now assume

(2) $$x \epsilon (\alpha \cup \beta)'.$$

Case 1. $x \epsilon \alpha'$. Then $x \epsilon \alpha' \cup \beta'$.
Case 2. $x \epsilon \beta'$. Then $x \epsilon \alpha' \cup \beta'$.
Case 3. $(\sim x \epsilon \alpha')\&(\sim x \epsilon \beta')$. By the duality theorem and rule C, we get

(3) $$x \epsilon \gamma.\gamma \epsilon \text{OS}$$

(4) $$(y):y \neq x.y \epsilon \gamma. \supset .\sim y \epsilon \alpha$$

from $\sim x \epsilon \alpha'$ and

(5) $$x \epsilon \delta.\delta \epsilon \text{OS}$$

(6) $$(y):y \neq x.y \epsilon \delta. \supset .\sim y \epsilon \beta$$

from $\sim x \epsilon \beta'$. By (3), (5), and Thm.IX.8.1, $x \epsilon \gamma \cap \delta.\gamma \cap \delta \epsilon \text{OS}$. So by rule C,

(7) $$\phi \epsilon H(x),$$

(8) $$\phi \subseteq \gamma \cap \delta.$$

Then by Axiom 1b and Thm.IX.8.5, $x \epsilon \phi.\phi \epsilon \text{OS}$. Then by rule C and the assumption $x \epsilon (\alpha \cup \beta)'$, we get

(9) $$y \neq x$$

(10) $$y \epsilon \phi$$

(11) $$y \epsilon \alpha \cup \beta.$$

From (10) and (8), we get $y \epsilon \gamma \cap \delta$, and so $y \epsilon \gamma$ and $y \epsilon \delta$. Then by (4), (6), and (9), we get $\sim y \epsilon \alpha$ and $\sim y \epsilon \beta$. So

(12) $$(\sim y \epsilon \alpha)\&(\sim y \epsilon \beta).$$

However, from (11), $(y \epsilon \alpha)\mathbf{v}(y \epsilon \beta)$. This gives

(13) $$\sim((\sim y \epsilon \alpha)\&(\sim y \epsilon \beta)).$$

By truth values, $\vdash P{\sim}P \supset Q$. Taking P to be $(\sim y \epsilon \alpha)\&(\sim y \epsilon \beta)$ and Q to be $x \epsilon \alpha' \cup \beta'$, and using (12) and (13), we get $x \epsilon \alpha' \cup \beta'$.

Corollary. $(\alpha,\beta).\overline{\alpha \cup \beta} = \bar{\alpha} \cup \bar{\beta}$.

Theorem IX.8.10. $(x,\alpha):.x \epsilon \bar{\alpha}: \equiv :(\beta):x \epsilon \beta.\beta \epsilon \text{OS}. \supset .(\text{E}y).y \epsilon \beta.y \epsilon \alpha.$

In words, "We say that x is in the closure of α if every open set containing x contains at least one element of α".

Proof. Assume $x \epsilon \bar{\alpha}$. Then $x \epsilon \alpha \mathbf{v} x \epsilon \alpha'$.

Case 1. $x \epsilon \alpha'$. Then the right side follows easily.

Case 2. $x \epsilon \alpha$. Then the right side again follows easily by taking y to be x.

Conversely, assume

(1) $$(\beta):x \epsilon \beta.\beta \epsilon \text{OS}. \supset .(\text{E}y).y \epsilon \beta.y \epsilon \alpha.$$

Case 1. $x \epsilon \alpha'$. Then $x \epsilon \bar{\alpha}$.

Case 2. $\sim x \epsilon \alpha'$. Then by the duality theorem and rule C,

(2) $$x \epsilon \beta.\beta \epsilon \text{OS},$$

(3) $$(y):y \epsilon \beta.y \epsilon \alpha. \supset .y = x.$$

By (1) and (2) and rule C, $y \epsilon \beta.y \epsilon \alpha$. So by (3), $y = x$. Combining this with $y \epsilon \alpha$ gives $x \epsilon \alpha$. So $x \epsilon \bar{\alpha}$.

Corollary. $(x,\alpha):.x \epsilon \bar{\alpha}: \equiv :(\beta):x \epsilon \beta.\beta \epsilon \text{OS}. \supset .\alpha \cap \beta \neq \Lambda.$

We now prove that every open set is a sum of neighborhoods. That is, if α is an open set, then there is a λ, each of whose members is a neighborhood of some point, such that $\alpha = \bigcup\lambda$.

Theorem IX.8.11. $(\alpha)::\alpha \epsilon \text{OS}.: \supset :.(\text{E}\lambda):.\alpha = \bigcup\lambda:.(\beta):\beta \epsilon \lambda. \supset .(\text{E}x).\beta \epsilon H(x).$

Proof. Take A to be $\hat{\beta}((\text{E}x).\beta \epsilon H(x):\beta \subseteq \alpha)$. We easily get

(1) $$(\beta):\beta \epsilon A. \supset .(\text{E}x).\beta \epsilon H(x)$$

(2) $$(\beta):\beta \epsilon A. \supset .\beta \subseteq \alpha.$$

By (2) and Thm.IX.5.8, Part II,

(3) $$\bigcup A \subseteq \alpha.$$

Now assume $\alpha \epsilon$ OS, and $x \epsilon \alpha$. Then by rule C, $\beta \epsilon H(x).\beta \subseteq \alpha$. So $\beta \epsilon A$. As $x \epsilon \beta$ by Axiom 1b, we get $x \epsilon \bigcup A$. Hence

(4) $$\alpha \epsilon \text{OS}. \supset .\alpha \subseteq \bigcup A.$$

By (1), (3), and (4), we get

$$\alpha \epsilon \text{OS}.: \supset :.\alpha = \bigcup A:.(\beta):\beta \epsilon A. \supset .(\text{E}x).\beta \epsilon H(x).$$

Then our theorem follows by Thm.VIII.2.7.

We now prove some theorems using Axiom 4, beginning with the theorem that the derived set of a set is closed.

Theorem IX.8.12. $(\alpha).\alpha' \epsilon$ CS.

Proof. By Thm.IX.8.7, it suffices to prove $\alpha'' \subseteq \alpha'$, and this we do, using essentially the same proof given in Sec. 9 of Chapter VI, only now phrased in terms of neighborhoods instead of distances. So we assume

(1) $$x \epsilon \alpha'',$$

namely,

$$(\beta){:}x \in \beta . \beta \in \mathrm{OS}. \supset .(\mathrm{E}y).y \neq x.y \in \beta .y \in \alpha',$$

(2) $$x \in \beta,$$

(3) $$\beta \in \mathrm{OS}.$$

Then by Axiom scheme 6, we get $(\mathrm{E}y).y \neq x.y \in \beta .y \in \alpha'$, so that by rule C

(4) $$y \neq x,$$

(5) $$y \in \beta,$$

(6) $$y \in \alpha',$$

namely

$$(\gamma){:}y \in \gamma . \gamma \in \mathrm{OS}. \supset .(\mathrm{E}z).z \neq y.z \in \gamma .z \in \alpha.$$

By (3), (5), the definition of OS, and rule C, we get

(7) $$\phi \in H(y),$$

(8) $$\phi \subseteq \beta.$$

By (4), Axiom 4, and two uses of rule C, we get

(9) $$\theta \in H(x),$$

(10) $$\delta \in H(y),$$

(11) $$\theta \cap \delta = \Lambda.$$

As $x \in \theta$ by (9) and Axiom 1b, we have by (11),

(12) $$\sim x \in \delta.$$

By (7), (10), Axiom 2, and rule C,

(13) $$\gamma \in H(y),$$

(14) $$\gamma \subseteq \phi \cap \delta.$$

By (12) and (14),

(15) $$\sim x \in \gamma.$$

By (13), we get $y \in \gamma$ by Axiom 1b, and $\gamma \in \mathrm{OS}$ by Thm.IX.8.5, so that by (6) and rule C

(16) $$z \neq y,$$

(17) $$z \in \gamma,$$

(18) $$z \in \alpha.$$

By (15), (17), and Thm.VII.1.4,

(19) $$z \neq x,$$

and by (17), (14), and (8)

(20) $$z \in \beta.$$

Thus by (19), (20), and (18),

(21) $$(\mathrm{E}z).z \neq x.z \in \beta.z \in \alpha.$$

So

$$(1), (2), (3) \vdash (21).$$

Hence

$$(1) \vdash (\beta):x \in \beta.\beta \in \mathrm{OS}. \supset .(\mathrm{E}z).z \neq x.z \in \beta.z \in \alpha.$$

That is,

$$(1) \vdash x \in \alpha'.$$

Our theorem now follows.

Corollary. $(\alpha).\alpha'' \subseteq \alpha'$.

Note that the proof would still go through if we should replace Axiom 4 by the weaker

4′. $(x,y):x \neq y. \supset .(\mathrm{E}\beta).\beta \in H(y).\sim x \in \beta.$

Theorem IX.8.13. $(\alpha).\bar{\alpha}' = \alpha'$.

Proof. $\bar{\alpha} = \alpha \cup \alpha'$. So by Thm.IX.8.9, $\bar{\alpha}' = \alpha' \cup \alpha''$. So by Thm. IX.8.12, corollary, $\bar{\alpha}' = \alpha'$.

Corollary. $(\alpha).\bar{\alpha} \in \mathrm{CS}$.

Proof. Since $\bar{\alpha}' = \alpha'$, we have $\bar{\alpha}' \subseteq \bar{\alpha}$, and can use Thm.IX.8.7.

We now show that $\bar{\alpha}$ is the least closed set containing α.

Theorem IX.8.14. $(\alpha,\beta):\alpha \subseteq \beta.\beta \in \mathrm{CS}. \supset .\bar{\alpha} \subseteq \beta$.

Proof. Assume $\alpha \subseteq \beta$ and $\beta \in \mathrm{CS}$. Then by Thm.IX.8.8, corollary, $\bar{\alpha} \subseteq \bar{\beta}$ and by Thm.IX.8.7, Cor. 2, $\bar{\beta} = \beta$. So $\bar{\alpha} \subseteq \beta$.

We prove finally that $\bar{\alpha}$ is the product of all closed sets containing α.

Theorem IX.8.15. $(\alpha):\bar{\alpha} = \bigcap(\hat{\beta}(\alpha \subseteq \beta.\beta \in \mathrm{CS}))$.

Proof. By Thm.IX.8.14 and Thm.IX.5.8, Part I,

(1) $$\bar{\alpha} \subseteq \bigcap(\hat{\beta}(\alpha \subseteq \beta.\beta \in \mathrm{CS})).$$

Now clearly $\alpha \subseteq \bar{\alpha}$, so that by Thm.IX.8.13, corollary, $\bar{\alpha} \in \hat{\beta}(\alpha \subseteq \beta.\beta \in \mathrm{CS})$. So by Thm.IX.5.5, Part I,

$$\bigcap(\hat{\beta}(\alpha \subseteq \beta.\beta \in \mathrm{CS})) \subseteq \bar{\alpha}.$$

An alternative approach to Hausdorff spaces is not to take as an undefined idea the idea of sets of neighborhoods $H(x)$ associated with each x

but to take as undefined a general set of neighborhoods N. With this approach, only "three" axioms are needed, namely:

0b. $\Sigma \neq \Lambda$.
1. $\bigcup N = \Sigma$.
2. $(\alpha,\beta,x):\alpha,\beta \epsilon N.x \epsilon \alpha \cap \beta. \supset .(\mathrm{E}\gamma).\gamma \epsilon N.x \epsilon \gamma.\gamma \subseteq \alpha \cap \beta$.
3. $(x,y):x \neq y. \supset .(\mathrm{E}\alpha,\beta).\alpha,\beta \epsilon N.x \epsilon \alpha.y \epsilon \beta.\alpha \cap \beta = \Lambda$.

We can now define $H^*(x)$ to be $\hat{\alpha}(\alpha \epsilon N.x \epsilon \alpha)$. Then we easily derive the original set of axioms with $H^*(x)$ in place of $H(x)$ as follows. Axiom 0a of the old set follows immediately from the new Axiom 1. From the new Axiom 1, we can infer, since $(x)\ F(x)$ denotes $(u).u \epsilon \Sigma \supset F(u)$, $(x)(\mathrm{E}\alpha). \alpha \epsilon N.x \epsilon \alpha$, whence the old Axiom 1a comes immediately. The old Axiom 1b is immediate in view of the definition of $H^*(x)$. Clearly our new Axiom 2 is expressly designed to give the old Axiom 2. With our definition of $H^*(x)$, we can derive the old Axiom 3 by taking β to be α. Finally, the new Axiom 3 is expressly designed to give the old Axiom 4.

Conversely, given the old axioms with $H(x)$, we could define N^* to be $\hat{\alpha}(\mathrm{E}x).\alpha \epsilon H(x)$, and prove the new set of axioms with N^* in place of N. Hence we can prove exactly the same theorems about neighborhoods, open sets, etc., from either set of axioms.

EXERCISES

IX.8.1. With N^* defined as indicated above, prove the new set of axioms with N^* in place of N.

IX.8.2. With $H^*(x)$ defined as indicated above in terms of N and with OS defined by $\hat{\alpha}(x):x \epsilon \alpha. \supset .(\mathrm{E}\beta).\beta \epsilon H^*(x).\beta \subseteq \alpha$, show that an alternative form of the new Axiom 2 is

$$(\alpha,\beta):\alpha,\beta \epsilon N. \supset .\alpha \cap \beta \epsilon \mathrm{OS}.$$

IX.8.3. Prove

(a) $\Lambda,\Sigma \epsilon \mathrm{OS}$.
(b) $\Lambda,\Sigma \epsilon \mathrm{CS}$.

A space is said to be "connected" if Λ and Σ are the only sets which are both open and closed.

IX.8.4. Suppose we start with the "four" axioms for $H(x)$ and then define $H^*(x)$ to be $\hat{\alpha}(x \epsilon \alpha.\alpha \epsilon \mathrm{OS})$. Prove the "four" axioms with $H^*(x)$ in place of x, and also prove

$$(\alpha):.\alpha \epsilon \mathrm{OS}: \equiv :(x):x \epsilon \alpha. \supset .(\mathrm{E}\beta).\beta \epsilon H^*(x).\beta \subseteq \alpha.$$

IX.8.5. Two sets of neighborhoods, N_1 and N_2, are said to be equivalent if each satisfies the "three" axioms indicated above, and in addition each of the two following statements is valid:

(I) $(\alpha,x):\alpha \epsilon N_1.x \epsilon \alpha. \supset .(E\beta).\beta \epsilon N_2.\beta \subseteq \alpha.x \epsilon \beta.$

(II) $(\beta,x):\beta \epsilon N_2.x \epsilon \beta. \supset .(E\alpha).\alpha \epsilon N_1.\alpha \subseteq \beta.x \epsilon \alpha.$

Prove that, if N_1 and N_2 are equivalent sets of neighborhoods, then α would be classified as an open set in terms of N_1 if and only if it would be classified as an open set in terms of N_2.

IX.8.6. Let $N_1 = \text{USC}(\Sigma)$ and $N_2 = \text{SC}(\Sigma)$. Then prove that N_1 and N_2 are equivalent sets of neighborhoods in the sense of the preceding exercise, and that $(x).\{x\} \epsilon \text{OS}$.

IX.8.7. Prove:

(a) $(x).\{x\} \epsilon \text{CS}$.
(b) $(\alpha,\beta):\alpha,\beta \epsilon \text{OS}. \supset .\alpha \cup \beta \epsilon \text{OS}$.
(c) $(\alpha,\beta):\alpha,\beta \epsilon \text{CS}. \supset .\alpha \cap \beta \epsilon \text{CS}$.
(d) $(x).\bigcap H(x) = \{x\}$.

IX.8.8. Let N be a set of neighborhoods satisfying the "three" Hausdorff axioms, and let α be any nonnull subset of Σ. Writing Σ^* for α and

$$N^* = \hat{\beta}(E\gamma).\gamma \epsilon N.\beta = \alpha \cap \gamma,$$

prove that N^* satisfies the "three" Hausdorff axioms with respect to Σ^*.

CHAPTER X

RELATIONS AND FUNCTIONS

1. The Axiom of Infinity. Eventually in mathematical reasoning we shall need the axiom of infinity. One could put off its use for quite a while, but if it is introduced now, the theory of relations and functions will be much simplified. Actually, we introduce an alternative postulate which is equivalent to the axiom of infinity but which is more particularly suitable to our immediate needs than the more familiar forms of the axiom of infinity.

First we introduce the definitions

$A + B$ for $\{\alpha \cup \beta \mid \alpha \in A . \beta \in B . \alpha \cap \beta = \Lambda\}$

Nn for $\hat{x}((\beta)::0 \in \beta:(y).y \in \beta \supset y + 1 \in \beta.: \supset :.x \in \beta)$

where in the definition of $A + B$, α and β are distinct variables which do not occur at all in A or B.

$A + B$ is stratified if and only if $A = B$ is stratified. Stratification of $A + B$ requires that A and B have the same type, which will be the type of $A + B$ also. The occurrences of free variables in $A + B$ are exactly those in each of A and B. Nn is stratified. As it contains no free variables, it may be assigned any type. One may even assign different types to two occurrences of Nn in the same statement.

It will turn out that $A + B$ is the familiar notion of the numerical sum of two nonnegative integers A and B, and Nn is the class of nonnegative integers or nonnegative whole numbers.

Quine (see Quine, 1951) refers to Nn as the set of natural numbers, and thinks of the two "n's" in "Nn" as standing for "natural number." However, standard mathematical usage reserves the term "natural numbers" for the positive integers. Hence we shall have to think of the two "n's" in "Nn" as standing for "nonnegative."

****Theorem X.1.1.** $\vdash (m,n,\alpha):\alpha \in m + n. \equiv .(\mathrm{E}\beta,\gamma).\beta \in m.\gamma \in n.\beta \cap \gamma = \Lambda.\beta \cup \gamma = \alpha.$

Proof. Use Thms.IX.3.1 and IX.3.2, Cor. 3.

****Theorem X.1.2.** $\vdash (m).0 \neq m + 1.$

Proof. Assume $0 = m + 1$. Then by Thm.X.1.1 and $\vdash \Lambda \in 0$ and rule C, we get $\beta \in m$, $\gamma \in 1$, $\beta \cap \gamma = \Lambda$, and $\beta \cup \gamma = \Lambda$. From $\gamma \in 1$ by Thm. IX.6.10, Cor. 5, and rule C, we get $\gamma = \{y\}$. So $y \in \gamma$. So $y \in \beta \cup \gamma$. So $y \in \Lambda$. This is a contradiction.

Let us refer back to the definition of Clos(A,P). In this, take A to be $\{0\}$ and P to be $x + 1 = z$. Then $H(A,\beta,P)$ denotes

$$\{0\} \subseteq \beta{:}.(x,z){:}x \in \beta.x + 1 = z. \supset .z \in \beta.$$

We note that this is stratified, so that we have $\vdash \exists\hat{\beta}H(A,\beta,P)$.

Theorem X.1.3. $\vdash$ Clos$(\{0\}, x + 1 = z) =$ Nn.

Proof. Since we have $\vdash \exists\hat{\beta}H(\{0\},\beta,x + 1 = z)$ and $\vdash \exists$(Nn), it follows from Thm.IX.5.12 that we need merely prove

$$\vdash H(\{0\},\beta,x + 1 = z).{:} \equiv {:}.0 \in \beta{:}(y).y \in \beta \supset y + 1 \in \beta.$$

However, by Thm.IX.6.5,

$$\vdash 0 \in \beta. \equiv .\{0\} \subseteq \beta.$$

Also

$$\vdash (x,z){:}x \in \beta.x + 1 = z. \supset .z \in \beta{::} \equiv {::}(y,z){:}.y + 1 = z{:} \supset {:}y \in \beta. \supset .z \in \beta{::}$$
$$\equiv {::}(y){:}y \in \beta. \supset .y + 1 \in \beta.$$

****Theorem X.1.4.** $\vdash 0 \in$ Nn.

Proof. Use Thm.IX.5.13.

****Theorem X.1.5.** $\vdash (n){:}n \in$ Nn. $\supset .n + 1 \in$ Nn.

Proof. By Thm.IX.5.14, $\vdash (x,z){:}x \in$ Nn.$x + 1 = z. \supset .z \in$ Nn. From this, we get $\vdash (x){:}x \in$ Nn. $\supset .x + 1 \in$ Nn.

Theorem X.1.6. $\vdash (\beta){::}0 \in \beta{:}(y){:}y \in \beta.y \in$ Nn. $\supset .y + 1 \in \beta.{:} \supset {:}.$Nn $\subseteq \beta$.

Proof. By Thm.IX.5.15, $\vdash (\beta){::}\{0\} \subseteq \beta{:}(x,z){:}x \in \beta.x \in$ Nn.$x + 1 = z.$ $\supset .z \in \beta.{:} \supset {:}.$Nn $\subseteq \beta$.

***Theorem X.1.7.** $\vdash (n){:}.n \in$ Nn: $\equiv {:}n = 0.$**v**.(Em).$m \in$ Nn.$n = m + 1$.

Proof. By Thm.IX.5.16, $\vdash (z){:}.z \in$ Nn: $\equiv {:}z \in \{0\}.$**v**.(Ex).$x \in$ Nn. $x + 1 = z$.

We now have all the theorems dealing with + and Nn which we need for the present chapter. However, we might as well prove a few related theorems before passing on to other matters.

***Theorem X.1.8.** $\vdash (m).m = m + 0$.

Proof. Let $\alpha \in m$. Then $\alpha \in m.\Lambda \in 0.\alpha \cap \Lambda = \Lambda.\alpha \cup \Lambda = \alpha$. So (E$\beta,\gamma$). $\beta \in m.\gamma \in 0.\beta \cap \gamma = \Lambda.\beta \cup \gamma = \alpha$. So $\alpha \in m + 0$. Conversely, assume $\alpha \in m + 0$ and use rule C. Then $\beta \in m.\gamma \in 0.\beta \cap \gamma = \Lambda.\beta \cup \gamma = \alpha$. So $\gamma = \Lambda$. So $\beta \cup \Lambda = \alpha$. So $\beta = \alpha$. So $\alpha \in m$.

****Theorem X.1.9.** $\vdash (m,n).m + n = n + m$.

Proof. Obvious by Thm.X.1.1.

Theorem X.1.10. $\vdash (m,n,p,\alpha){:}\alpha \in (m + n) + p. \equiv .(\text{E}\beta,\gamma,\delta).\beta \in m.$ $\gamma \in n.\delta \in p.\beta \cap \gamma = \Lambda.\beta \cap \delta = \Lambda.\gamma \cap \delta = \Lambda.\beta \cup \gamma \cup \delta = \alpha$.

Proof. Assume $\alpha \in (m + n) + p$. Then by Thm.X.1.1 and rule C, $\theta \in m + n.\delta \in p.\theta \cap \delta = \Lambda.\theta \cup \delta = \alpha$. So by Thm.X.1.1 and rule C, $\beta \in m.$ $\gamma \in n.\beta \cap \gamma = \Lambda.\beta \cup \gamma = \theta.\delta \in p.\theta \cap \delta = \Lambda.\theta \cup \delta = \alpha$. Then $\theta \cap \delta =$

$(\beta \cap \delta) \cup (\gamma \cap \delta)$. Hence $\theta \cap \delta = \Lambda . \equiv .\beta \cap \delta = \Lambda.\gamma \cap \delta = \Lambda$. Hence $(E\beta,\gamma,\delta).\beta \in m.\gamma \in n.\delta \in p.\beta \cap \gamma = \Lambda.\beta \cap \delta = \Lambda.\gamma \cap \delta = \Lambda.\beta \cup \gamma \cup \delta = \alpha$. Conversely, if we assume $(E\beta,\gamma,\delta).\beta \in m.\gamma \in n.\delta \in p.\beta \cap \gamma = \Lambda.\beta \cap \delta = \Lambda.\gamma \cap \delta = \Lambda.\beta \cup \gamma \cup \delta = \alpha$, then by rule C, $\beta \in m.\gamma \in n.\beta \cap \gamma = \Lambda.\beta \cup \gamma = \beta \cup \gamma.\delta \in p.(\beta \cup \gamma) \cap \delta = \Lambda.(\beta \cup \gamma) \cup \delta = \alpha$. So $(\beta \cup \gamma) \in (m + n).\delta \in p.(\beta \cup \gamma) \cap \delta = \Lambda.(\beta \cup \gamma) \cup \delta = \alpha$. So $\alpha \in (m + n) + p$.

Theorem X.1.11. $\vdash (m,n,p,\alpha):\alpha \in m + (n + p). \equiv .(E\beta,\gamma,\delta).\beta \in m.\gamma \in n.\delta \in p.\beta \cap \gamma = \Lambda.\beta \cap \delta = \Lambda.\gamma \cap \delta = \Lambda.\beta \cup \gamma \cup \delta = \alpha$.

Proof. Similar to that of Thm.X.1.10.

****Corollary.** $\vdash (m,n,p).(m + n) + p = m + (n + p)$.

Henceforth we shall commonly write $m + n + p$ for $(m + n) + p$. By this corollary, $m + n + p$ can equally well denote $m + (n + p)$.

Theorem X.1.12. $\vdash 1 \in \text{Nn}$.

Proof. By Thms.X.1.4 and X.1.5, $\vdash 0 + 1 \in \text{Nn}$. So by Thm.X.1.9, $\vdash 1 + 0 \in \text{Nn}$. So by Thm.X.I.8, $\vdash 1 \in \text{Nn}$.

We now prove the principle of mathematical induction that, if $\vdash F(0)$ and $\vdash (n):F(n).n \in \text{Nn}. \supset .F(n + 1)$, then $\vdash (n):n \in \text{Nn}. \supset .F(n)$.

NOTE THAT THIS IS PROVED ONLY WHEN $F(x)$ IS STRATIFIED.

****Theorem X.1.13.** Let P be a stratified statement. Then {Sub in P: 0 for n}, $(n):n \in \text{Nn}.P. \supset .$ {Sub in P: $n + 1$ for n} $\vdash (n):n \in \text{Nn}. \supset .P$.

Proof. If P is stratified, then

(1) $$\vdash n \in \hat{n}P \equiv P,$$

(2) $$\vdash 0 \in \hat{n}P \equiv \{\text{Sub in } P\text{: 0 for } n\},$$

(3) $$\vdash n + 1 \in \hat{n}P \equiv \{\text{Sub in } P\text{: } n + 1 \text{ for } n\}.$$

However, by Thm.X.I.6, $0 \in \hat{n}P, (n):n \in \text{Nn}.n \in \hat{n}P. \supset .n + 1 \in \hat{n}P \vdash \text{Nn} \subseteq \hat{n}P$. From this our theorem follows by (1), (2), and (3).

Note that the presence or absence of additional free variables besides n in P is quite immaterial in the preceding theorem. Actually, P need not even contain free occurrences of n, but the theorem is quite trivial in this case.

In referring to Thm.X.1.13, we shall usually write $F(n)$ for P, $F(0)$ for {Sub in P: 0 for n}, and $F(n + 1)$ for {Sub in P: $n + 1$ for n}. Then Thm.X.1.13 says that, if $F(n)$ is stratified, then

$$F(0), (n):n \in \text{Nn}.F(n). \supset .F(n + 1) \vdash (n):n \in \text{Nn}. \supset .F(n).$$

One should carefully distinguish Thm.X.1.13 from the intuitive principle of mathematical induction which we have used on various occasions. In general form they are very similar. In each case one wishes to prove a statement about nonnegative integers. However, in the intuitive case, our statement was *about* the formal logic, and the integers involved are intuitive numbers, whereas in the result above the statement is *within* the formal logic, and the only thing that makes it even seem to be a statement about numbers is that the conclusion of our theorem has the additional hypothesis $n \epsilon \mathrm{Nn}$ prefixed to the statement $F(n)$. However, if we consider $n \epsilon \mathrm{Nn}$ to be the analogue within our formal logic of the statement "n is a nonnegative integer," then certainly Thm.X.1.13 is the analogue within our formal logic of the familiar principle of proof by mathematical induction.

Theorem X.1.14. $\vdash (m,n){:}m,n \epsilon \mathrm{Nn}. \supset .m + n \epsilon \mathrm{Nn}.$

Proof. In Thm.X.1.13, take $F(n)$ to be

$$(m){:}m \epsilon \mathrm{Nn}. \supset .m + n \epsilon \mathrm{Nn}.$$

Then $F(0)$ is

$$(m){:}m \epsilon \mathrm{Nn}. \supset .m + 0 \epsilon \mathrm{Nn},$$

and so we get

(1) $$\vdash F(0)$$

by Thm.X.1.8. By Thm.X.1.11, corollary, $\vdash (m + n) + 1 = m + (n + 1)$. Also by Thm.X.1.5, $\vdash m + n \epsilon \mathrm{Nn}. \supset .(m + n) + 1 \epsilon \mathrm{Nn}$. So $\vdash m + n \epsilon \mathrm{Nn}. \supset .m + (n + 1) \epsilon \mathrm{Nn}$. So

$$\vdash (m){:}m \epsilon \mathrm{Nn}. \supset .m + n \epsilon \mathrm{Nn}.{:} \supset {:}.(m){:}m \epsilon \mathrm{Nn}. \supset .m + (n + 1) \epsilon \mathrm{Nn}.$$

That is

(2) $$\vdash F(n) \supset F(n + 1).$$

Then by (1) and (2) and Thm.X.1.13,

$$\vdash (n){:}n \epsilon \mathrm{Nn}. \supset .F(n).$$

This readily gives our theorem.

Just in passing we make the natural definitions:

2	for	1 + 1,
3	for	2 + 1,
4	for	3 + 1,
5	for	4 + 1,
	etc.	

Theorem X.1.15. $\vdash 2 + 2 = 4.$

Proof. By definition $\vdash 3 + 1 = 4$. However, 3 is $2 + 1$, so that we have $\vdash (2 + 1) + 1 = 4$. Then by Thm.X.1.11, corollary, $\vdash 2 + (1 + 1) = 4$. By the definition of 2, this is $\vdash 2 + 2 = 4$.

In a similar manner, one could prove $\vdash 2 + 3 = 5$, $\vdash 2 + 4 = 6$, $\vdash 3 + 3 = 6$, etc.

We note that all members of 0, to wit Λ, contain zero members, and all classes which contain zero members, to wit Λ, are members of 0. Likewise all members of 1 contain one member (see Thm.IX.6.10, Cor. 5), and all classes which contain one member are unit classes and hence are members of 1. It will turn out that all members of 2 contain two members, and all classes which contain two members are members of 2. A similar state of affairs is true for 3, 4, 5, etc.

★Theorem X.1.16. $\vdash (m,\alpha){:}\alpha \in m + 1. \equiv .(E\beta,x).\beta \in m.\sim x \in \beta.\beta \cup \{x\} = \alpha.$

Proof. Use Thm.X.1.1, Thm.IX.6.10, Cor. 5, and Thm.IX.6.6, Cor. 1.

★Corollary 1. $\vdash (\alpha){:}\alpha \in 2. \equiv .(Ex,y).x \neq y.\{x,y\} = \alpha.$

Corollary 2. $\vdash (\alpha){:}\alpha \in 3. \equiv .(Ex,y,z).x \neq y.x \neq z.y \neq z.\{x,y,z\} = \alpha.$

etc.

Cor. 1 says that 2 consists of all classes with two members, Cor. 2 says that 3 consists of all classes with three members, etc.

We now adjoin an axiom which is equivalent to the axiom of infinity.

Axiom scheme 13. The following statement, and each statement got from it by prefixing some set of universal quantifiers, is an axiom:

$$(m,n){:}m,n \in \mathrm{Nn}.m + 1 = n + 1. \supset .m = n.$$

The five Peano axioms for the nonnegative integers (see Peano, 1891) are respectively expressed by:

Thm.X.1.4.
Thm.X.1.5.
Thm.X.1.2.
Axiom scheme 13.
Thm.X.1.13.

Actually, Peano stated his axioms for the positive integers, rather than for the nonnegative integers. However, his axioms are just what the above five statements become if we interpret Nn as the class of positive integers, and replace 0 by 1 throughout. Hence it seems appropriate to refer to the five results cited as the five Peano axioms for the nonnegative integers.

EXERCISES

X.1.1. Prove $\vdash (m,n){:}m + n = 0. \equiv .m = 0.n = 0.$

X.1.2. Prove $\vdash (m,n,p){:}m,n,p \in \mathrm{Nn}.m + p = n + p. \supset .m = n.$

X.1.3. Prove $\vdash (m){:}m \in \mathrm{Nn}. \supset .m \neq m + 1.$

X.1.4. Define:

$m \leq n$	as	$(Ep).p \in \mathrm{Nn}.n = m + p.$
$m < n$	as	$m \leq n.m \neq n.$
$m \geq n$	as	$n \leq m.$
$m > n$	as	$n < m.$

Prove:

(a) $\vdash (m).m \leq m.$
(b) $\vdash (m,n):m \leq n. \equiv .m < n.\mathbf{v}.m = n.$
(c) $\vdash (m):m \in \mathrm{Nn}. \supset .0 \leq m.$
(d) $\vdash (m):m \in \mathrm{Nn}. \supset .m = 0.\mathbf{v}.m \geq 1.$
(e) $\vdash (m,n):m,n \in \mathrm{Nn}.m \leq n.n \leq m. \supset .m = n.$
(f) $\vdash (m,n):m,n \in \mathrm{Nn}.m < n. \supset .\sim(n \leq m).$
(g) $\vdash (m,n):m < n. \supset .(\mathrm{E}p).p \in \mathrm{Nn}.n = m + p + 1.$
(h) $\vdash (m,n):.m,n \in \mathrm{Nn}: \supset :m < n. \equiv .(\mathrm{E}p).p \in \mathrm{Nn}.n = m + p + 1.$
(i) $\vdash (m,n,p):m \leq n.n \leq p. \supset .m \leq p.$
(j) $\vdash (m,n,p):.m,n,p \in \mathrm{Nn}: \supset :m < n.n \leq p. \supset .m < p.$
(k) $\vdash (m,n,p):.m,n,p \in \mathrm{Nn}: \supset :m \leq n.n < p. \supset .m < p.$
(l) $\vdash (m,n,p):m \leq n. \supset .m + p \leq n + p.$
(m) $\vdash (m,n,p):.m,n,p \in \mathrm{Nn}: \supset :m < n. \supset .m + p < n + p.$
(n) $\vdash (m_1,m_2,n_1,n_2):m_1 \leq n_1.m_2 \leq n_2: \supset :m_1 + m_2 \leq n_1 + n_2.$
(o) $\vdash (m,n,p):.m,n,p \in \mathrm{Nn}: \supset :m + p \leq n + p. \supset .m \leq n.$
(p) $\vdash (m,n,p):.m,n,p \in \mathrm{Nn}: \supset :m + p < n + p. \supset .m < n.$
(q) $\vdash (m,n):.m,n \in \mathrm{Nn}: \supset :m < n. \equiv .m + 1 \leq n.$
(r) $\vdash (m,n):.m,n \in \mathrm{Nn}: \supset :m < n + 1. \equiv .m \leq n.$
(s) $\vdash (m,n):m,n \in \mathrm{Nn}. \supset .m < n.\mathbf{v}.m = n.\mathbf{v}.m > n.$
(t) $\vdash (m,n):.m,n \in \mathrm{Nn}: \supset :m < n. \equiv .\sim(n \leq m).$
(u) $\vdash (m,n):.m,n \in \mathrm{Nn}: \supset :m \leq n. \equiv .\sim(n < m).$

X.1.5. Prove that $A + B$ is stratified if and only if $A = B$ is stratified, and that if it is stratified then A, B, and $A + B$ all have the same type.

X.1.6. Prove that Nn is stratified.

X.1.7. Prove:

(a) $\vdash 2 \in \mathrm{Nn}.$
(b) $\vdash 3 \in \mathrm{Nn}.$
etc.

2. Ordered Pairs and Triples. We shall now introduce the notion of the ordered pair $\langle x,y \rangle$ of two objects x and y. The notion is widely used in mathematics. In two-dimensional analytic geometry, points are designated by ordered pairs of the coordinates. Thus we speak of the point (2,3), or $(-7,5)$, or (x,y).

It would be a bit hard to say just what the ordered pair $\langle x,y \rangle$ of the two objects x and y consists of from an intuitive point of view. All that is really necessary is that it be uniquely determined by x and y, and that conversely it shall uniquely determine x and y and specify their order. Any object which does this can serve for us as the ordered pair $\langle x,y \rangle$.

We shall exhibit such an object and use it as the ordered pair $\langle x,y \rangle$. The definition which we give will seem extremely artificial and will certainly provoke the reaction that this is definitely not what one thinks of as the ordered pair $\langle x,y\rangle$. It is not our claim that what we shall use as the ordered pair $\langle x,y\rangle$ is what one would think of intuitively as an ordered pair. We merely claim that it does the things that an ordered pair should do. Hence we can and will do with it all the things that one could do with a more congenial kind of ordered pair. Moreover, we know no way to construct a less artificial ordered pair, and until someone shows how to construct a less artificial one, we shall use ours to do all the things that an ordered pair is expected to do.

We now introduce six definitions, of which the first three are temporary and apply only throughout the present section.

$\phi(A)$	for	$\hat{y}(\mathrm{E}x):x \in A:x \in \mathrm{Nn}.y = x + 1.\mathbf{v}.\sim x \in \mathrm{Nn}.y = x.$
$\theta_1(A)$	for	$\{\phi(x) \mid x \in A\}.$
$\theta_2(A)$	for	$\{\{0\} \cup \phi(x) \mid x \in A\}.$
$\langle A,B\rangle$	for	$\theta_1(A) \cup \theta_2(B).$
$Q_1(A)$	for	$\hat{x}(\phi(x) \in A).$
$Q_2(A)$	for	$\hat{x}(\{0\} \cup \phi(x) \in A).$

In all these, x and y are distinct variables which do not occur at all in A.

Clearly $\phi(A)$, $\theta_1(A)$, $\theta_2(A)$, $Q_1(A)$, and $Q_2(A)$ are stratified if and only if A is stratified, and if stratified are of the same type as A. $\langle A,B\rangle$ is stratified if and only if $A = B$ is stratified, and if it is stratified it must have the same type as A and B. The free occurrences of variables in $\phi(A)$, $\theta_1(A)$, $\theta_2(A)$, $\langle A,B\rangle$, $Q_1(A)$, and $Q_2(A)$ are just those in A and B.

Of the three permanent definitions, $\langle A,B\rangle$ is the ordered pair of A and B, and $Q_1(A)$ and $Q_2(A)$ are inverses of the ordered pair in the sense that

$$Q_1(\langle A,B\rangle) = A$$

and

$$Q_2(\langle A,B\rangle) = B.$$

To form $\phi(A)$, we replace each nonnegative integer member of A by the next larger integer and leave all other members of A unchanged. Thus $\phi(A)$ does not contain 0. Hence $\{0\} \cup \phi(A)$ is distinct from $\phi(B)$ for each A and B. To form $\theta_1(A)$ we take $\phi(x)$ for all x's in A, and to form $\theta_2(B)$ we take $\{0\} \cup \phi(x)$ for all x's in B. Clearly $\theta_1(A)$ and $\theta_2(B)$ have no members in common for each A and B. By combining the members of $\theta_1(A)$ and $\theta_2(B)$, we get $\langle A,B\rangle$. Those members of $\langle A,B\rangle$ which do not contain a 0 come from A, and those members of $\langle A,B\rangle$ which do contain a 0 come from B. Hence, given $\langle A,B\rangle$, we can reconstruct the A and B from which it is formed, and this is what Q_1 and Q_2 do.

Theorem X.2.1.

I. $\vdash (y,z)\mathbf{:.}y \in \phi(z)\mathbf{:} \equiv \mathbf{:}(\mathrm{E}x)\mathbf{:}x \in z\mathbf{:}x \in \mathrm{Nn}.y = x + 1.\mathbf{v}.\sim x \in \mathrm{Nn}.y = x.$

II. $\vdash (\alpha,x)\mathbf{:}x \in \theta_1(\alpha). \equiv .(\mathrm{E}y).y \in \alpha.x = \phi(y).$

III. $\vdash (\alpha,x)\mathbf{:}x \in \theta_2(\alpha). \equiv .(\mathrm{E}y).y \in \alpha.x = \{0\} \cup \phi(y).$

IV. $\vdash (x,y,z)\mathbf{:}z \in \langle x,y\rangle. \equiv .z \in \theta_1(x)\mathbf{v}z \in \theta_2(y).$

V. $\vdash (\alpha,x)\mathbf{:}x \in Q_1(\alpha). \equiv .\phi(x) \in \alpha.$

VI. $\vdash (\alpha,x)\mathbf{:}x \in Q_2(\alpha). \equiv .\{0\} \cup \phi(x) \in \alpha.$

Proof. Use Thm.IX.3.1 and Thm.IX.3.2, Cor. 1 and Cor. 3.

Theorem X.2.2. $\vdash (x,y)\mathbf{:}\phi(x) = \phi(y). \equiv .x = y.$

Proof. Clearly it suffices to prove $\vdash \phi(x) = \phi(y). \supset .x = y.$ Assume $\phi(x) = \phi(y)$ and $z \in x$.

Case 1. $z \in \mathrm{Nn}$. Then $z + 1 \in \phi(x)$. So $z + 1 \in \phi(y)$. By rule C, $w \in y$ and $w \in \mathrm{Nn}.z + 1 = w + 1.\mathbf{v}.\sim w \in \mathrm{Nn}.z + 1 = w$. As we have by $z \in \mathrm{Nn}$ and Thm.X.1.5 that $z + 1 \in \mathrm{Nn}$, we have

$$\sim(\sim w \in \mathrm{Nn}.z + 1 = w).$$

So $w \in \mathrm{Nn}.z + 1 = w + 1$. As $z \in \mathrm{Nn}$, we have by Axiom scheme 13, $z = w$. Hence $z \in y$.

Case 2. $\sim z \in \mathrm{Nn}$. Then $z \in \phi(x)$. So $z \in \phi(y)$. By rule C, $w \in y$ and $w \in \mathrm{Nn}.z = w + 1.\mathbf{v}.\sim w \in \mathrm{Nn}.z = w$. By Thm.X.1.5 and $\sim z \in \mathrm{Nn}$,

$$\sim(w \in \mathrm{Nn}.z = w + 1).$$

So $\sim w \in \mathrm{Nn}.z = w$. Hence $z \in y$.

Analogously, from $\phi(x) = \phi(y)$ and $z \in y$, we get $z \in x$.

Corollary. $\vdash (\alpha,x)\mathbf{:}\phi(x) \in \theta_1(\alpha). \equiv .x \in \alpha.$

Proof. Use Thm.IX.3.7.

Theorem X.2.3. $\vdash (x).\sim 0 \in \phi(x).$

Proof. Use Thm.X.2.1, Part I, together with Thm.X.1.4 and Thm. X.1.2.

Theorem X.2.4. $\vdash (x,y)\mathbf{:}\{0\} \cup \phi(x) = \{0\} \cup \phi(y). \equiv .x = y.$

Proof. Assume $\{0\} \cup \phi(x) = \{0\} \cup \phi(y)$. Let $z \in \phi(x)$. Then $z \neq 0$ and $z \in \{0\} \cup \phi(x)$. So $z \in \{0\} \cup \phi(y)$. As $z \neq 0$, $z \in \phi(y)$. Conversely, if $z \in \phi(y)$, then $z \in \phi(x)$. So $\phi(x) = \phi(y)$. So $x = y$.

Corollary. $\vdash (\alpha,x)\mathbf{:}\{0\} \cup \phi(x) \in \theta_2(\alpha). \equiv .x \in \alpha.$

Theorem X.2.5. $\vdash (\alpha,\beta)\mathbf{:}\theta_1(\alpha) = \theta_1(\beta). \equiv .\alpha = \beta.$

Proof. Assume $\theta_1(\alpha) = \theta_1(\beta)$ and $x \in \alpha$. Then $\phi(x) \in \theta_1(\alpha)$. So $\phi(x) \in \theta_1(\beta)$. So $x \in \beta$.

Theorem X.2.6. $\vdash (\alpha,\beta)\mathbf{:}\theta_2(\alpha) = \theta_2(\beta). \equiv .\alpha = \beta.$

Proof. Similar to that of Thm.X.2.5.

Theorem X.2.7. $\vdash (x,y).Q_1(\langle x,y\rangle) = x.$

Proof. Let $z \in Q_1(\langle x,y\rangle)$. Then $\phi(z) \in \langle x,y\rangle$. So $\phi(z) \in \theta_1(x).\mathbf{v}.\phi(z) \in \theta_2(y)$.

Case 1. $\phi(z) \in \theta_1(x)$. Then $z \in x$.

Case 2. $\phi(z) \in \theta_2(y)$. Then by rule C, $w \in y$ and $\phi(z) = \{0\} \cup \phi(w)$. So $0 \in \phi(z)$. By Thm.X.2.3, this is a contradiction. However, by truth values $\vdash P \sim P \supset Q$. So $\vdash 0 \in \phi(z). \sim 0 \in \phi(z). \supset .z \in x$. So $z \in x$.

Thus we conclude

$$\vdash Q_1(\langle x,y \rangle) \subseteq x.$$

Conversely, let $z \in x$. Then $\phi(z) \in \theta_1(x)$. So $\phi(z) \in \langle x,y \rangle$. So $z \in Q_1(\langle x,y \rangle)$.

Theorem X.2.8. $\vdash (x,y).Q_2(\langle x,y \rangle) = y$.

Proof. Similar to that of Thm.X.2.7.

****Theorem X.2.9.** $\vdash (x,y,u,v):\langle x,y \rangle = \langle u,v \rangle. \equiv .x = u.y = v$.

Proof. Assume $\langle x,y \rangle = \langle u,v \rangle$. Then $Q_1(\langle x,y \rangle) = Q_1(\langle u,v \rangle)$. So $x = u$. Similarly $y = v$.

As an ordered triple, $\langle A,B,C \rangle$, we can take $\langle\langle A,B \rangle, C \rangle$. Then we have:

Theorem X.2.10.

I. $\vdash (x,y,z).Q_1(\langle x,y,z \rangle) = \langle x,y \rangle$.
II. $\vdash (x,y,z).Q_1(Q_1(\langle x,y,z \rangle)) = x$.
III. $\vdash (x,y,z).Q_2(Q_1(\langle x,y,z \rangle)) = y$.
IV. $\vdash (x,y,z).Q_2(\langle x,y,z \rangle) = z$.

Theorem X.2.11. $\vdash (x,y,z,u,v,w):\langle x,y,z \rangle = \langle u,v,w \rangle. \equiv .x = u.y = v.z = w$.

We can define quadruples, quintuples, etc., as

$\langle A,B,C,D \rangle$	for	$\langle\langle A,B,C \rangle, D \rangle$
$\langle A,B,C,D,E \rangle$	for	$\langle\langle A,B,C,D \rangle, E \rangle$
etc.,		

and have similar theorems.

We define

$$A \times B \quad \text{for} \quad \{\langle x,y \rangle \mid x \in A.y \in B\}$$

where x and y are distinct variables not occurring at all in A or B.

$A \times B$ is stratified if and only if $A = B$ is stratified, and if stratified is of the same type as A and B. The free occurrences of variables in $A \times B$ are just those in A and B.

$A \times B$ is the class of all ordered pairs such that the first member is in A and the second member is in B. The class of all ordered pairs is then $V \times V$.

$A \times B$ is called the direct product of A and B or the Cartesian product of A and B.

***Theorem X.2.12.** $\vdash (\alpha,\beta,z):z \in \alpha \times \beta. \equiv .(Ex,y).x \in \alpha.y \in \beta.z = \langle x,y \rangle$.

Corollary 1. $\vdash (z):z \in V \times V. \equiv .(Ex,y).z = \langle x,y \rangle$.

Corollary 2. $\vdash V \times V \neq \Lambda$.

Corollary 3. $\vdash (\alpha).\Lambda \times \alpha = \alpha \times \Lambda = \Lambda$.

***Theorem X.2.13.** $\vdash (\alpha,\beta,x,y):\langle x,y \rangle \in \alpha \times \beta. \equiv .x \in \alpha.y \in \beta$.

Proof. Use Thm.IX.3.8.

We shall use **x**, **y**, and **z** with the understanding that they are restricted to the range $V \times V$. It will be recalled that, in dealing with variables of restricted range, it is necessary that the range not be Λ. This is stated for the range $V \times V$ by Thm.X.2.12, Cor. 2, above.

Since $V \times V$ is the class of all ordered pairs (see Thm.X.2.12, Cor. 1), $\mathbf{x}$, $\mathbf{y}$, and $\mathbf{z}$ serve as variables which denote ordered pairs. When they occur free, our conventions about the use of variables of restricted range would require explicit mention of the conditions $\mathbf{x} \in V \times V$, $\mathbf{y} \in V \times V$, and $\mathbf{z} \in V \times V$ which are implicit when $\mathbf{x}$, $\mathbf{y}$, and $\mathbf{z}$ occur bound. However, we shall often omit them in those cases where it is clear from the context how they should be supplied.

For classes of ordered pairs, we shall use **R**, **S**, and **T**. Accordingly, they are variables restricted to the range $SC(V \times V)$. We shall take similar liberties with free occurrences of **R**, **S**, and **T**.

The sort of ordered pair which we are using was invented by Quine (see Quine, 1945). The use of the letter Q in $Q_1(A)$ and $Q_2(A)$ is to signalize Quine's discovery of this means of dealing with ordered pairs.

EXERCISES

X.2.1. Show in detail that the definition of $\langle A,B\rangle$ does satisfy the stated stratification requirements.

X.2.2. Prove $\vdash (\alpha,\beta,x,y){:}\langle x,y\rangle \in \alpha \times \beta. \equiv .\langle y,x\rangle \in \beta \times \alpha.$

X.2.3. Prove $\vdash (\alpha,\beta,\gamma){:}(\alpha \cap \beta) \times \gamma = (\alpha \times \gamma) \cap (\beta \times \gamma).$

X.2.4. Prove $\vdash (\alpha,\beta,\gamma){:}\alpha \subseteq \beta. \supset .\alpha \times \gamma \subseteq \beta \times \gamma.$

X.2.5. Prove $\vdash (x,y){:}\{x\} \times \{y\} = \{\langle x,y\rangle\}.$

X.2.6. Prove:

(a) $\vdash (\alpha,\beta).(\alpha \times 0) \cap (\beta \times \{V\}) = \Lambda.$

(b) $\vdash (\alpha,x){:}\sim x \in \alpha. \equiv .\sim \langle x,\Lambda\rangle \in \alpha \times 0.$

X.2.7. Prove:

(a) $\vdash (\alpha,n){:}n \in \text{Nn}.\alpha \in n. \supset .\alpha \times 0 \in n.$

(b) $\vdash (\alpha,n){:}n \in \text{Nn}.\alpha \times 0 \in n. \supset .\alpha \in n.$

(*Hint.* Use Thm.X.1.13.)

3. The Calculus of Relations. In mathematics, a function is a class of ordered pairs $\langle x,y\rangle$, the x's being the arguments and the y's the values corresponding to the x's. Thus the function "square of" consists of all ordered pairs $\langle x,x^2\rangle$. This property of functions is the basis of analytic geometry, in which we define the graph of a function to consist of all points (x,y) such that $\langle x,y\rangle$ is one of the ordered pairs which comprise the function.

It is not an uncommon practice to reject "many-valued functions" and not to consider them as legitimate functions. We shall take this stand. Whenever we shall use the word "function" we shall mean "single-valued function" except for some explanatory remarks in the next few paragraphs. That is, we consider a function as a class of ordered pairs $\langle x,y \rangle$ with the special property that, if there is some x and y such that $\langle x,y \rangle$ is one of the ordered pairs comprising the function, then there is no z different from y such that $\langle x,z \rangle$ is also one of the ordered pairs comprising the function.

Although we reject "many-valued functions" as functions, nevertheless we must consider the type of object which is referred to as a "many-valued function." It is certainly true that a "many-valued function" is a class of ordered pairs. In analytic geometry, one graphs "many-valued functions" quite as legitimately as one graphs "single-valued functions." The graphs of

$$y^2 = x^2,$$
$$x^2 + y^2 = 25,$$
$$y = \arcsin x,$$

are perfectly well defined graphs, even though they are not graphs of functions. One can even "graph" still more general things, such as

$$x < y.$$

The "graph" would consist of all points above the line $x = y$. Thus we can think of $x < y$ as defining a kind of generalized "many-valued function" in which for any x the values of $f(x)$ are all y's greater than x. In this case, our "function" is still a class of ordered pairs, namely, the class of all ordered pairs $\langle x,y \rangle$ such that $x < y$, and its "graph" is drawn accordingly.

One usually thinks of "$x < y$" as expressing a relation between x and y rather than defining a "many-valued function" of x. The exact distinction between y being related to x (as when $x < y$) and y being a "many-valued function" of x (as when $y^2 = x^2$ or $x^2 + y^2 = 25$ or $y = \arcsin x$) is not very clear. Originally the distinction seems to have been that the graph of a "function" (whether single-valued or many-valued) should consist of various curves and isolated points, whereas the "graph" of a "relation" would comprise all points in some region. Thus

$$x^2 + y^2 = 25$$

expresses a function because its graph is the circumference of a circle, which is a perfectly good curve. On the other hand,

$$x^2 + y^2 < 25$$

expresses a relation, because its "graph" consists of all points in the interior of a circle.

This distinction may have been useful historically, but nowadays it is of little value; in fact the existence of space-filling curves makes it ambiguous.

We abandon it, and distinguish merely between relations and functions (by which we mean "single-valued functions").

A relation is defined to be any class of ordered pairs $\langle x,y \rangle$. A function is a relation such that there is exactly one y for each x.

We do not make the claim that the notion of "many-valued function" can never be of value. In the theory of functions of a complex variable, the condition of analyticity prevents the existence of space-filling curves and other such monstrosities and permits one to define the different branches of a function in an unambiguous sense. Hence in this theory one can talk intelligibly of "many-valued functions" as distinct from relations, and it is indeed very useful to do so. However, throughout the present text it is futile to try to preserve the distinction between relations and "many-valued functions," and we do not try.

We generalize the notions of relation and function to allow relations between arbitrary objects and functions of arbitrary objects instead of merely relations between numbers and functions of numbers.

We recall that **R**, **S**, and **T** are restricted to the range SC(V $\times$ V). That is, **R**, **S**, and **T** always denote subclasses of V $\times$ V. However V $\times$ V is the class of all ordered pairs. Thus **R**, **S**, and **T** always denote classes of ordered pairs, *i.e.*, relations. That is, SC(V $\times$ V) is the class of all relations. For this reason, the abbreviation Rel is often used to denote SC(V $\times$ V).

We say that x and y stand in the relation **R** if $\langle x,y \rangle \in \mathbf{R}$. This is commonly abbreviated to $x\mathbf{R}y$. This is analogous to the mathematical notations $x = y$ and $x < y$ where the signs for the relation, namely, "$=$" and "$<$" are placed between the objects which stand in the given relation to each other. One often reads "$x\mathbf{R}y$" as "x has the relation **R** to y."

Though we shall be interested in the notation xRy only in those cases where R is a relation, the notation xRy is permitted for any R whatever and will always mean $\langle x,y \rangle \in R$. When necessary to prevent ambiguity, we shall enclose x, R, y, or xRy in parentheses.

In considering the stratification of xRy it is usually the case that x and y are variables which do not occur in the term R. In such case xRy is stratified if and only if R is, and x and y must have the same type, which must be one less than the type of R.

We recollect that a stratified statement $F(x)$ which contains the free variable x determines a class $\hat{x}F(x)$, namely, the class such that x is in this class exactly whenever x makes $F(x)$ true. Thus, for stratified $F(x)$, we have

$$\vdash (x).x \in \hat{x}F(x) \equiv F(x).$$

Similarly, we expect a stratified statement $F(x,y)$ with the free variables x and y to determine a relation between x and y, namely, the relation such that x and y stand in that relation exactly whenever x and y make $F(x,y)$ true. By analogy with the notation for the class determined by $F(x)$, we denote the relation determined by $F(x,y)$ by $\hat{x}\hat{y}F(x,y)$. Then we expect to have

$$\vdash (x,y).x(\hat{x}\hat{y}F(x,y))y \equiv F(x,y).$$

We must say more here about the stratification requirements. It will not suffice merely for $F(x,y)$ to be stratified in order for it to determine a relation $\hat{x}\hat{y}F(x,y)$. Not only will $F(x,y)$ have to be stratified, it will have to be stratified in such a way that x and y have the same type. This is consistent with the requirement that for $x\mathbf{R}y$ to be stratified x and y must have the same type.

As a matter of fact, it is a good thing that in general $F(x,y)$ will not determine a relation $\hat{x}\hat{y}F(x,y)$ unless $F(x,y)$ is stratified with x and y having the same type. If $x = \{y\}$ should determine a relation

$$\hat{x}\hat{y}(x = \{y\}),$$

then we could derive the Russell, Cantor, and Burali-Forti paradoxes, which would be most unpleasant.

In those cases in which $F(x,y)$ is stratified but x and y do not have the same type, one can easily construct a substitute for the relation $\hat{x}\hat{y}F(x,y)$. For instance, suppose $F(x,y)$ is stratified, but the type of x is two higher than the type of y. Choose a z not occurring in $F(x,y)$. Then $(\mathrm{E}y).F(x,y).z = \{\{y\}\}$ is stratified with x and z of the same type. Hence it determines a relation

$$\hat{x}\hat{z}((\mathrm{E}y).F(x,y).z = \{\{y\}\}).$$

Then if we put

$$\mathbf{R} = \hat{x}\hat{z}((\mathrm{E}y).F(x,y).z = \{\{y\}\}),$$

we shall have

$$\vdash (x,y).x\mathbf{R}\{\{y\}\} \equiv F(x,y).$$

For most purposes, this $\mathbf{R}$ will serve as a relation determined by $F(x,y)$. Among the places where it would not so serve are in the derivations of the Russell, Cantor, and Burali-Forti paradoxes.

The case of any other difference in the types of x and y can be handled similarly.

We define $\hat{x}\hat{y}P$ as

$$\{\langle x,y\rangle \mid P.x = x.y = y\}.$$

Clearly, if P is stratified with x and y having the same type, then

$$\langle x,y\rangle = \langle x,y\rangle.P.x = x.y = y$$

is stratified, and so by Thm.IX.3.1, corollary, $\hat{x}\hat{y}P$ exists. Also, it will have type one higher than the common type of x and y. Thus the types are right so that

$$x(\hat{x}\hat{y}P)y \equiv P$$

will be stratified.

Theorem X.3.1. $\vdash (\mathbf{R})(z):.z \in \mathbf{R}: \equiv :(\mathrm{E}x,y).x\mathbf{R}y.z = \langle x,y\rangle$.

Proof. Assume

(1) $$\mathbf{R} \in \mathrm{Rel}.$$

Let $z \in \mathbf{R}$. Then by (1) and the definition of Rel, $z \in \mathrm{V} \times \mathrm{V}$. So by rule C and Thm.X.2.12, Cor. 1, $z = \langle x,y\rangle$. Hence $\langle x,y\rangle \in \mathbf{R}$. That is, $x\mathbf{R}y$. Hence

$$(\mathrm{E}x,y).x\mathbf{R}y.z = \langle x,y\rangle.$$

Conversely, assume this and use rule C. So $z = \langle x,y\rangle$ and $x\mathbf{R}y$. That is, $\langle x,y\rangle \in \mathbf{R}$. Hence $z \in \mathbf{R}$.

Theorem X.3.2. If z is a variable which does not occur in P, then $\vdash (\mathbf{R}):.(z):z \in \mathbf{R}. \equiv .(\mathrm{E}x,y).P.z = \langle x,y\rangle: \equiv :(x,y).x\mathbf{R}y \equiv P$.

Proof. Let us write $F(x,y)$ for P, $F(u,v)$ for $\{\text{Sub in } P\text{: } u \text{ for } x,\ v \text{ for } y\}$, etc. Assume

(1) $$\mathbf{R} \in \mathrm{Rel}.$$

Assume

(2) $$(z):z \in \mathbf{R}. \equiv .(\mathrm{E}x,y).F(x,y).z = \langle x,y\rangle.$$

Choose u and v distinct from any variables in the theorem. Let $u\mathbf{R}v$. That is, $\langle u,v\rangle \in \mathbf{R}$. So by (2) and rule C, $F(x,y).\langle u,v\rangle = \langle x,y\rangle$. Then $u = x$ and $v = y$. Hence $F(u,v)$. Conversely, assume $F(u,v)$. Then $(\mathrm{E}x,y).F(x,y).\langle u,v\rangle = \langle x,y\rangle$. So by (2), $\langle u,v\rangle \in \mathbf{R}$, which is $u\mathbf{R}v$. Thus we have deduced $(u,v).u\mathbf{R}v \equiv F(u,v)$. By a change of bound variables, $(x,y).x\mathbf{R}y \equiv F(x,y)$.

Conversely assume this. Then by Thm.VI.5.4,

$$(\mathrm{E}x,y).x\mathbf{R}y.z = \langle x,y\rangle. \equiv .(\mathrm{E}x,y).F(x,y).z = \langle x,y\rangle.$$

Now use Thm.X.3.1.

****Theorem X.3.3.** $\vdash (\mathbf{R},\mathbf{S}):\mathbf{R} = \mathbf{S}. \equiv .(x,y).x\mathbf{R}y \equiv x\mathbf{S}y$.

Proof. Take P to be $x\mathbf{S}y$ in Thm.X.3.2 and use Thm.X.3.1.

Theorem X.3.4. If $\mathbf{R}$ is a variable which does not occur in P, then $\vdash (\mathrm{E}\mathbf{R})(x,y).x\mathbf{R}y \equiv P: \supset :\exists\hat{x}\hat{y}P$.

Proof. Assume $(\mathrm{E}\mathbf{R})(x,y).x\mathbf{R}y \equiv P$. Then by Thm.X.3.2,

$$(\mathrm{E}\mathbf{R})(z):z \in \mathbf{R}. \equiv .(\mathrm{E}x,y).P.z = \langle x,y\rangle.$$

So

$$(\mathrm{E}\alpha)(z):z \in \alpha. \equiv .(\mathrm{E}x,y).P.z = \langle x,y\rangle.$$

Replacing P by $P.x = x.y = y$, we get $\exists\hat{x}\hat{y}P$.

****Theorem X.3.5.** If P is stratified with all free occurrences of x and y of the same type, then $\vdash \exists \hat{x}\hat{y}P$.

Proof. Use Thm.IX.3.1, corollary.

Theorem X.3.6. If z does not occur in P, then $\vdash \exists \hat{x}\hat{y}P.: \supset :.(z):z \in \hat{x}\hat{y}P. \equiv .(Ex,y).P.z = \langle x,y \rangle$.

Proof. Use Thm.IX.3.2, Cor. 3, and the fact that

$$\vdash P: \equiv :P.x = x.y = y.$$

****Corollary.** $\vdash \exists \hat{x}\hat{y}P. \supset .\hat{x}\hat{y}P \in \mathrm{Rel}$.

****Theorem X.3.7.** $\vdash \exists \hat{x}\hat{y}P: \supset :(x,y).x(\hat{x}\hat{y}P)y \equiv P$.

Proof. Use Thm.X.2.9 and Thm.IX.3.8.

Corollary 1. If $\mathbf{R}$ is a variable which does not occur in P, then $\vdash \exists \hat{x}\hat{y}P: \equiv :(E\mathbf{R})(x,y).x\mathbf{R}y \equiv P$.

Proof. To go from left to right, take $\mathbf{R}$ to be $\hat{x}\hat{y}P$. To go from right to left, use Thm.X.3.4.

Corollary 2. $\vdash (\mathbf{R}):(x,y).x\mathbf{R}y \equiv P. \supset .\mathbf{R} = \hat{x}\hat{y}P$.

Proof. From $(x,y).x\mathbf{R}y \equiv P$, we can get $(x,y).x\mathbf{R}y \equiv x(\hat{x}\hat{y}P)y$ by the theorem, and then we get $\mathbf{R} = \hat{x}\hat{y}P$ by Thm.X.3.3.

Corollary 3. $\vdash (\mathbf{R}).\mathbf{R} = \hat{x}\hat{y}(x\mathbf{R}y)$.

Theorem X.3.8. $\vdash (x,y).P \equiv Q: \supset :\hat{x}\hat{y}P = \hat{x}\hat{y}Q$.

Proof. Use Thm.IX.3.3, Cor. 1.

Theorem X.3.9. If $F(u,v)$ is the result of replacing all free occurrences of x and y, respectively, in $F(x,y)$ by occurrences of u and v, and $F(x,y)$ is the result of replacing all free occurrences of u and v, respectively, in $F(u,v)$ by occurrences of x and y, then $\vdash \hat{x}\hat{y}F(x,y) = \hat{u}\hat{v}F(u,v)$.

Proof. Use Thm.IX.3.5.

Theorem X.3.10. If $\mathbf{z}$ is a variable which does not occur in $F(x,y)$, then $\vdash \exists \hat{x}\hat{y}F(x,y). \supset .\hat{x}\hat{y}F(x,y) = \hat{\mathbf{z}}F(Q_1(\mathbf{z}),Q_2(\mathbf{z}))$.

Proof. By Thm.IX.7.6, it suffices to prove $\vdash (Ex,y).F(x,y).z = \langle x,y \rangle. \equiv .z \in V \times V.F(Q_1(z),Q_2(z))$. Assume the left side and use rule C. Then $F(x,y).z = \langle x,y \rangle$. So $Q_1(z) = x$ and $Q_2(z) = y$. So $F(Q_1(z),Q_2(z))$. Also, since $z = \langle x,y \rangle$, $z \in V \times V$. Conversely, assume the right side and use rule C on $z \in V \times V$. Then $z = \langle x,y \rangle$ and $F(Q_1(z),Q_2(z))$. Then $Q_1(z) = x$ and $Q_2(z) = y$. Hence $F(x,y)$.

Corollary. $\vdash (\alpha,\beta).\alpha \times \beta = \hat{\mathbf{z}}(Q_1(\mathbf{z}) \in \alpha.Q_2(\mathbf{z}) \in \beta)$.

The observation that $\alpha \times \beta$ is $\hat{x}\hat{y}(x \in \alpha.y \in \beta)$ enables us to prove the existence of unstratified relations. If one takes α and β to be of different types, as, for instance, if we take α to be $\hat{y}(\beta \in y)$, then $\alpha \times \beta$ will be unstratified but will nevertheless exist by Thm.X.2.12. It does not appear that one can get into any difficulties by this device.

Since relations are classes, $\mathbf{R} \cap \mathbf{S}$ and $\mathbf{R} \cup \mathbf{S}$ have a perfectly explicit meaning. So does $-\mathbf{R}$, except that we ask the reader to recall that, because of the restriction on the range of $\mathbf{R}$, $-\mathbf{R}$ denotes $(V \times V) - \mathbf{R}$, the "$V \times V$" usually being suppressed for typographical convenience. In the case of $-(\hat{x}\hat{y}P)$, no such convention exists, and we make none. Thus $-(\hat{x}\hat{y}P)$ denotes all objects not in $\hat{x}\hat{y}P$, and to denote the class of all ordered pairs not in $\hat{x}\hat{y}P$ we should have to write $(V \times V) - \hat{x}\hat{y}P$.

Because of our convention, $-\mathbf{R}$ always denotes the class of all ordered pairs not in $\mathbf{R}$. That is, $-\mathbf{R}$ is the complementary *relation* to $\mathbf{R}$. To denote the complementary *class* to $\mathbf{R}$, that is, the class of all objects not in $\mathbf{R}$, we would have to resort to some such expression as $\hat{x}(\sim x \in \mathbf{R})$. However, the need for this almost never arises.

We note a few elementary applications of $\cup$, $\cap$, and $-$ as applied to relations. If $\mathbf{R}$ is "father of" and $\mathbf{S}$ is "mother of," then $\mathbf{R} \cup \mathbf{S}$ is "parent of." Also if $\mathbf{R}$ and $\mathbf{S}$ are $<$ and $=$, respectively, then $\mathbf{R} \cup \mathbf{S}$ is $\leq$. The notation of $\cap$ is less commonly used for relations, but as an example, if $\mathbf{R}$ and $\mathbf{S}$ are $\leq$ and $\geq$, then $\mathbf{R} \cap \mathbf{S}$ is $=$. This is the basis of many proofs of equality, where $x = y$ is proved by proving both $x \leq y$ and $x \geq y$. Clearly if $\mathbf{R}$ is $=$, then $-\mathbf{R}$ is $\neq$. Also, if we are restricting attention to the range of real numbers and $\mathbf{R}$ is $<$, then $-\mathbf{R}$ is $\geq$.

Such terms as $\mathbf{R} \cup \mathbf{S}$, $\mathbf{R} \cap \mathbf{S}$, and $-\mathbf{R}$ are not extensively used but are convenient on occasion. Moreover, such theorems as Thm.IX.4.4, Thm. IX.4.5, etc., hold for relations as well as classes if we put $V \times V$ for V throughout. Indeed, the fact that they hold for relations is merely a special case of the fact that they hold generally for variables over a restricted range. By writing $x\mathbf{R}y$ for $\langle x,y\rangle \in \mathbf{R}$, some of them take novel forms. For example, Thms.IX.4.10 through IX.4.12 take such forms as

$\vdash (x,y).x(V \times V)y.$
$\vdash (x,y).\sim(x\Lambda y).$
$\vdash (x,y)\ P: \supset :(x,y).x(V \times V)y \equiv P.$
$\vdash (x,y)\ \sim P: \supset :(x,y).x\Lambda y \equiv P.$
$\vdash (x,y)\ P. \supset .\exists\hat{x}\hat{y}P.$
$\vdash (x,y)\ \sim P. \supset .\exists\hat{x}\hat{y}P.$
$\vdash (x,y)\ P. \supset .V \times V = \hat{x}\hat{y}P.$
$\vdash (x,y)\ \sim P. \supset .\Lambda = \hat{x}\hat{y}P.$
$\vdash (\mathbf{R}):.(x,y).x\mathbf{R}y: \equiv :\mathbf{R} = V \times V.$
$\vdash (\mathbf{R}):.(x,y).\sim(x\mathbf{R}y): \equiv :\mathbf{R} = \Lambda.$
$\vdash (\mathbf{R}):.(\mathrm{E}x,y).\sim(x\mathbf{R}y): \equiv :\mathbf{R} \neq V \times V.$
$\vdash (\mathbf{R}):.(\mathrm{E}x,y).x\mathbf{R}y: \equiv :\mathbf{R} \neq \Lambda.$

The analogues of all theorems of Sec. 4 of Chapter IX are easily proved for relations, provided that one puts $V \times V$ for V. They are then available for the proofs of theorems peculiar to the theory of relations, such as the two following theorems.

Theorem X.3.11.

I. $\vdash (\alpha,\beta,\gamma).(\alpha \cap \beta) \times \gamma = (\alpha \times \gamma) \cap (\beta \times \gamma)$.

II. $\vdash (\alpha,\beta,\gamma).\gamma \times (\alpha \cap \beta) = (\gamma \times \alpha) \cap (\gamma \times \beta)$.

III. $\vdash (\alpha,\beta,\gamma).(\alpha \cup \beta) \times \gamma = (\alpha \times \gamma) \cup (\beta \times \gamma)$.

IV. $\vdash (\alpha,\beta,\gamma).\gamma \times (\alpha \cup \beta) = (\gamma \times \alpha) \cup (\gamma \times \beta)$.

Proof of Part I.

$$\begin{aligned} \vdash x((\alpha \cap \beta) \times \gamma)y{:}\\ &\equiv {:}x \in (\alpha \cap \beta).y \in \gamma{:}\\ &\equiv {:}x \in \alpha.x \in \beta.y \in \gamma{:}\\ &\equiv {:}x \in \alpha.y \in \gamma.x \in \beta.y \in \gamma{:}\\ &\equiv {:}x(\alpha \times \gamma)y.x(\beta \times \gamma)y{:}\\ &\equiv {:}x((\alpha \times \gamma) \cap (\beta \times \gamma))y. \end{aligned}$$

Then $\vdash (\alpha \cap \beta) \times \gamma = (\alpha \times \gamma) \cap (\beta \times \gamma)$ follows by Thm.X.3.3.

Proof of Parts II, III, *and* IV. Similar.

Theorem X.3.12.

I. $\vdash (\alpha,\beta,\gamma){:}\alpha \subseteq \beta. \supset .\alpha \times \gamma \subseteq \beta \times \gamma$.

II. $\vdash (\alpha,\beta,\gamma){:}\alpha \subseteq \beta. \supset .\gamma \times \alpha \subseteq \gamma \times \beta$.

Proof of Part I. Let $\alpha \subseteq \beta$. Then $\alpha = \alpha \cap \beta$. So $\alpha \times \gamma = (\alpha \cap \beta) \times \gamma = (\alpha \times \gamma) \cap (\beta \times \gamma)$ by Thm.X.3.11. So $\alpha \times \gamma \subseteq \beta \times \gamma$.

Proof of Part II. Similar.

Corollary. $\vdash (\alpha,\beta,\gamma,\delta){:}\alpha \subseteq \beta.\gamma \subseteq \delta. \supset .\alpha \times \gamma \subseteq \beta \times \delta$.

The following useful theorem for relations is an analogue of the definition of $\subseteq$ for classes.

***Theorem X.3.13.** $\vdash (\mathbf{R},\mathbf{S}){:}.(x,y).x\mathbf{R}y \supset x\mathbf{S}y{:} \equiv {:}\mathbf{R} \subseteq \mathbf{S}$.

Proof. The implication from right to left goes easily. Conversely, assume $(x,y).x\mathbf{R}y \supset x\mathbf{S}y$. Then $(x,y){:}x\mathbf{R}y.z = \langle x,y\rangle. \supset .x\mathbf{S}y.z = \langle x,y\rangle$. So by Thm.VI.7.6, $(\mathrm{E}x,y).x\mathbf{R}y.z = \langle x,y\rangle. \supset .(\mathrm{E}x,y).x\mathbf{S}y.z = \langle x,y\rangle$. Then by Thm.X.3.1, $\mathbf{R} \subseteq \mathbf{S}$.

Generalizations of the theorems of Secs. 5 and 6 of Chapter IX are of little use in the theory of relations. However, a generalized form of the set of unit subclasses is quite useful. The members of USC($\mathbf{R}$) are the unit classes of the ordered pairs $\langle x,y\rangle$ which are members of $\mathbf{R}$. Hence USC($\mathbf{R}$) would not in general be a relation, and even if it were a relation, it would have little connection, as a relation, with $\mathbf{R}$. To generate a relation corresponding to $\mathbf{R}$, but one type higher, we take the class of ordered pairs of the unit classes, $\{x\}$ and $\{y\}$, of the constituents, x and y, of the ordered pairs $\langle x,y\rangle$ which are members of $\mathbf{R}$. This will be denoted by RUSC($\mathbf{R}$). So we define

$$\mathrm{RUSC}(A) \qquad \text{for} \qquad \{\langle\{x\},\{y\}\rangle \mid xAy\}$$

where x and y are distinct variables which do not occur in A. We also define

$$\begin{array}{lll} \mathrm{RUSC}^2(A) & \text{for} & \mathrm{RUSC}(\mathrm{RUSC}(A)), \\ \mathrm{RUSC}^3(A) & \text{for} & \mathrm{RUSC}(\mathrm{RUSC}^2(A)), \\ \text{etc.} & & \end{array}$$

RUSC(A) is stratified if and only if A is, and if it is stratified, is one type higher than A. The free occurrences of variables in RUSC(A) are just those in A.

Theorem X.3.14. $\vdash (R).\mathrm{RUSC}(R) \in \mathrm{Rel}$.

Proof. Simple.

★**Theorem X.3.15.** $\vdash (R,x,y):x(\mathrm{RUSC}(R))y. \equiv .(\mathrm{E}u,v).uRv.x = \{u\}. y = \{v\}$.

Proof. Use Thms.IX.3.1 and IX.3.2, Cor. 3.

Corollary. $\vdash (R).\mathrm{RUSC}(R) = \hat{x}\hat{y}(\mathrm{E}u,v).uRv.x = \{u\}.y = \{v\}$.

★**Theorem X.3.16.** $\vdash (R,x,y):\{x\}(\mathrm{RUSC}(R))\{y\}. \equiv .xRy$.

Proof. Use Thm.IX.3.8.

Corollary. $\vdash (R,x,y):\{\{x\}\}(\mathrm{RUSC}^2(R))\{\{y\}\}. \equiv .xRy$.

Theorem X.3.17. $\vdash (\mathbf{R},\mathbf{S}):\mathrm{RUSC}(\mathbf{R}) = \mathrm{RUSC}(\mathbf{S}). \equiv .\mathbf{R} = \mathbf{S}$.

Proof. Assume $\mathrm{RUSC}(\mathbf{R}) = \mathrm{RUSC}(\mathbf{S})$. Let $x\mathbf{R}y$. Then $\{x\}(\mathrm{RUSC}(\mathbf{R}))\{y\}$. So $\{x\}(\mathrm{RUSC}(\mathbf{S}))\{y\}$. So $x\mathbf{S}y$. Hence by Thm.X.3.13, $\mathbf{R} \subseteq \mathbf{S}$. Similarly $\mathbf{S} \subseteq \mathbf{R}$.

Theorem X.3.18.

I. $\vdash (R,S).\mathrm{RUSC}(R \cap S) = \mathrm{RUSC}(R) \cap \mathrm{RUSC}(S)$.
II. $\vdash (R,S).\mathrm{RUSC}(R \cup S) = \mathrm{RUSC}(R) \cup \mathrm{RUSC}(S)$.
III. $\vdash (R,S).\mathrm{RUSC}(R - S) = \mathrm{RUSC}(R) - \mathrm{RUSC}(S)$.
IV. $\vdash \mathrm{RUSC}(\Lambda) = \Lambda$.
V. $\vdash (\mathbf{R},\mathbf{S}):\mathbf{R} \subseteq \mathbf{S}. \equiv .\mathrm{RUSC}(\mathbf{R}) \subseteq \mathrm{RUSC}(\mathbf{S})$.
VI. $\vdash (\mathbf{R},\mathbf{S}):\mathbf{R} \subset \mathbf{S}. \equiv .\mathrm{RUSC}(\mathbf{R}) \subset \mathrm{RUSC}(\mathbf{S})$.

Proof of Part I. Assume $x(\mathrm{RUSC}(R \cap S))y$. Then by rule C, $u(R \cap S)v. x = \{u\}.y = \{v\}$. So $\langle u,v\rangle \in R \cap S$. So $\langle u,v\rangle \in R$ and $\langle u,v\rangle \in S$. Hence uRv and uSv. So $x(\mathrm{RUSC}(R))y$ and $x(\mathrm{RUSC}(S))y$. That is, $\langle x,y\rangle \in \mathrm{RUSC}(R)$ and $\langle x,y\rangle \in \mathrm{RUSC}(S)$. Hence $\langle x,y\rangle \in \mathrm{RUSC}(R) \cap \mathrm{RUSC}(S)$. Thus $x(\mathrm{RUSC}(R) \cap \mathrm{RUSC}(S))y$. Then by Thm.X.3.13,

(1) $$\vdash \mathrm{RUSC}(R \cap S) \subseteq \mathrm{RUSC}(R) \cap \mathrm{RUSC}(S).$$

Conversely, let $x(\mathrm{RUSC}(R) \cap \mathrm{RUSC}(S))y$. Then $x(\mathrm{RUSC}(R))y$ and $x(\mathrm{RUSC}(S))y$. By rule C,

$$uRv.x = \{u\}.y = \{v\},$$
$$u'Sv'.x = \{u'\}.y = \{v'\}.$$

Hence $u = u'$ and $v = v'$. So uSv. So $u(R \cap S)v$. So $x(\mathrm{RUSC}(R \cap S))y$. Hence

(2) $\vdash \mathrm{RUSC}(R) \cap \mathrm{RUSC}(S) \subseteq \mathrm{RUSC}(R \cap S).$

Proof of Part II.

$$\begin{aligned}&\vdash x(\mathrm{RUSC}(R \cup S))y\\ &\quad : \equiv :(\mathrm{E}u,v).u(R \cup S)v.x = \{u\}.y = \{v\}\\ &\quad : \equiv :(\mathrm{E}u,v):uRv.x = \{u\}.y = \{v\}.\mathbf{v}.uSv.x = \{u\}.y = \{v\}\\ &\quad : \equiv :(\mathrm{E}u,v).uRv.x = \{u\}.y = \{v\}.\mathbf{v}.(\mathrm{E}u,v).uSv.x = \{u\}.y = \{v\}\\ &\quad : \equiv :x(\mathrm{RUSC}(R))y.\mathbf{v}.x(\mathrm{RUSC}(S))y\\ &\quad : \equiv :x(\mathrm{RUSC}(R) \cup \mathrm{RUSC}(S))y.\end{aligned}$$

So by Thm.X.3.3, we infer Part II.

Proof of Part IV. It suffices to prove $\vdash (x,y) \sim (x(\mathrm{RUSC}(\Lambda))y)$. That is, $\vdash (x,y,u,v). \sim (u\Lambda v.x = \{u\}.y = \{v\})$. This is easily proved.

The proofs of Parts III, V, and VI are similar to the proofs of Parts III, V, and VI of Thm.IX.6.12.

Theorem X.3.19. $\vdash (\alpha,\beta).\mathrm{RUSC}(\alpha \times \beta) = \mathrm{USC}(\alpha) \times \mathrm{USC}(\beta).$

Proof. By Thm.X.2.13,

$$\begin{aligned}&\vdash x(\mathrm{RUSC}(\alpha \times \beta))y\\ &\quad : \equiv :(\mathrm{E}u,v).u(\alpha \times \beta)v.x = \{u\}.y = \{v\}\\ &\quad : \equiv :(\mathrm{E}u,v).u \in \alpha.v \in \beta.x = \{u\}.y = \{v\}\\ &\quad : \equiv :(\mathrm{E}u).u \in \alpha.x = \{u\}:(\mathrm{E}v).v \in \beta.y = \{v\}\\ &\quad : \equiv :x \in \mathrm{USC}(\alpha).y \in \mathrm{USC}(\beta)\\ &\quad : \equiv :x(\mathrm{USC}(\alpha) \times \mathrm{USC}(\beta))y.\end{aligned}$$

Corollary 1. $\vdash \mathrm{RUSC}(\mathrm{V} \times \mathrm{V}) = 1 \times 1.$

Corollary 2. $\vdash (x,y).\{x\}(1 \times 1)\{y\}.$

Proof. Put $R = \mathrm{V} \times \mathrm{V}$ in Thm.X.3.16.

Theorem X.3.20.

I. $\vdash (R,x,y):x(\hat{x}\hat{y}(\{x\}R\{y\}))y. \equiv .\{x\}R\{y\}.$

II. $\vdash (R,S):R \subseteq \mathrm{RUSC}(S). \supset .\hat{x}\hat{y}(\{x\}R\{y\}) \subseteq S.R = \mathrm{RUSC}(\hat{x}\hat{y}(\{x\}R\{y\})).$

Proof. Similar to the proof of Thm.IX.6.14.

Corollary 1. $\vdash (R):R \subseteq 1 \times 1. \supset .R = \mathrm{RUSC}(\hat{x}\hat{y}(\{x\}R\{y\})).$

Corollary 2. $\vdash (R,\mathbf{R}):R \subseteq \mathrm{RUSC}(\mathbf{R}). \equiv .(\mathrm{E}\mathbf{S}).\mathbf{S} \subseteq \mathbf{R}.R = \mathrm{RUSC}(\mathbf{S}).$

EXERCISES

X.3.1. Prove $\vdash (R,x,y):x(\hat{x}\hat{y}(xRy))y. \equiv .xRy.$

X.3.2. Prove:

(a) $\vdash (R,S):.(x,y).xRy \equiv xSy: \equiv :\hat{x}\hat{y}(xRy) = \hat{x}\hat{y}(xSy).$

(b) $\vdash (R,S):.(x,y).\{x\}(\mathrm{RUSC}(R))\{y\} \equiv \{x\}(\mathrm{RUSC}(S))\{y\}: \equiv :$ $\mathrm{RUSC}(R) = \mathrm{RUSC}(S).$

(c) $\vdash (R).\mathrm{RUSC}(R) = \mathrm{RUSC}(\hat{x}\hat{y}(xRy)).$

(d) $\vdash (R,x,y):x(\mathrm{RUSC}^2(R))y. \equiv .(\mathrm{E}u,v).uRv.x = \{\{u\}\}.y = \{\{v\}\}.$

X.3.3. Prove:

(a) $\vdash (R).R \cap (V \times V) = \hat{x}\hat{y}(xRy)$.
(b) $\vdash (R,S):.(x,y).xRy \equiv xSy: \equiv :R \cap (V \times V) = S \cap (V \times V)$.
(c) $\vdash (R).R \cap (V \times V) \in \mathrm{Rel}$.
(d) $\vdash (R,\mathbf{R}).R \cap \mathbf{R} \in \mathrm{Rel}$.
(e) $\vdash (R,S):R,S \in \mathrm{Rel}. \supset .R \cup S \in \mathrm{Rel}$.

4. Special Properties of Relations. If $\mathbf{R}$ is a function and $x\mathbf{R}y$, then x is called the argument and y the corresponding value. It is customary to write $y = f(x)$ in such a case. We generalize these terms, and in general if $x\mathbf{R}y$ then we say that x is an argument and y is a corresponding value. The set of all x's such that $x\mathbf{R}y$ for some y is the set of arguments of $\mathbf{R}$, and is denoted by Arg($\mathbf{R}$). Likewise, the set of all y's such that $x\mathbf{R}y$ for some x is the set of all values of $\mathbf{R}$, and is denoted by Val($\mathbf{R}$). So we put

$\mathrm{Arg}(A)$	for	$\hat{x}(\mathrm{E}y).xAy$,
$\mathrm{Val}(A)$	for	$\hat{y}(\mathrm{E}x).xAy$,
$\mathrm{AV}(A)$	for	$\mathrm{Arg}(A) \cup \mathrm{Val}(A)$,

where x and y are distinct variables not occurring in A. Arg(A) and Val(A) are stratified if and only if A is, and if stratified have the same type as A. Hence the same applies to AV(A). Free occurrences of variables are exactly those in A.

Some logicians refer to Arg(A) and Val(A) as the domain and converse domain of A. We see no reason for deviating from the standard mathematical terms "argument" and "value." The sum AV(A) of the arguments and values of A is called the field of A.

When A is a function, mathematicians often refer to Arg(A) as the range of A.

If one is dealing with real variables, then if $\mathbf{R}$ is the relation determined by $x^2 + y^2 = 25$, $\mathrm{Arg}(\mathbf{R}) = \mathrm{Val}(\mathbf{R}) = \mathrm{AV}(\mathbf{R}) = \hat{x}(-5 \leq x \leq 5)$; if $\mathbf{R}$ is the relation determined by $y = \sin x$, $\mathrm{Val}(\mathbf{R}) = \hat{y}(-1 \leq y \leq 1)$; if $\mathbf{R}$ is the relation determined by $y^2 = x$, $\mathrm{Arg}(\mathbf{R}) = \hat{x}(0 \leq x)$.

Theorem X.4.1.

**I. $\vdash (R,x):x \in \mathrm{Arg}(R). \equiv .(\mathrm{E}y)\ xRy$.
**II. $\vdash (R,y):y \in \mathrm{Val}(R). \equiv .(\mathrm{E}x)\ xRy$.
*III. $\vdash (R,x):x \in \mathrm{AV}(R). \equiv .(\mathrm{E}y).xRy \vee yRx$.

Theorem X.4.2.

I. $\vdash (R,S):R \subseteq S. \supset .\mathrm{Arg}(R) \subseteq \mathrm{Arg}(S)$.
II. $\vdash (R,S):R \subseteq S. \supset .\mathrm{Val}(R) \subseteq \mathrm{Val}(S)$.
III. $\vdash (R,S):R \subseteq S. \supset .\mathrm{AV}(R) \subseteq \mathrm{AV}(S)$.

Proof of Part I. Assume $R \subseteq S$ and let $x \in \mathrm{Arg}(R)$. Then by rule C, xRy. That is, $\langle x,y\rangle \in R$. So $\langle x,y\rangle \in S$. That is, xSy. So $x \in \mathrm{Arg}(S)$.

Proof of Part II. Similar.

Proof of Part III. Use Thm.IX.4.16, Cor. 2.

Theorem X.4.3.

★I. $\vdash (\mathbf{R}):\mathrm{Arg}(\mathbf{R}) = \Lambda. \equiv .\mathbf{R} = \Lambda.$

II. $\vdash (\mathbf{R}):\mathrm{Val}(\mathbf{R}) = \Lambda. \equiv .\mathbf{R} = \Lambda.$

III. $\vdash (\mathbf{R}):\mathrm{AV}(\mathbf{R}) = \Lambda. \equiv .\mathbf{R} = \Lambda.$

Theorem X.4.4.

I. $\vdash (\alpha,\beta):\beta \neq \Lambda. \supset .\mathrm{Arg}(\alpha \times \beta) = \alpha.$

II. $\vdash (\alpha,\beta):\alpha \neq \Lambda. \supset .\mathrm{Val}(\alpha \times \beta) = \beta.$

Corollary.

I. $\vdash (\alpha,\beta,\gamma):\gamma \neq \Lambda.\alpha \times \gamma = \beta \times \gamma. \supset .\alpha = \beta.$

II. $\vdash (\alpha,\beta,\gamma):\gamma \neq \Lambda.\gamma \times \alpha = \gamma \times \beta. \supset .\alpha = \beta.$

III. $\vdash (\alpha,\beta,\gamma):\gamma \neq \Lambda.\alpha \times \gamma \subseteq \beta \times \gamma. \supset .\alpha \subseteq \beta.$

IV. $\vdash (\alpha,\beta,\gamma):\gamma \neq \Lambda.\gamma \times \alpha \subseteq \gamma \times \beta. \supset .\alpha \subseteq \beta.$

To prove Parts III and IV, use Thm.X.4.2.

We now define relations with restricted arguments and restricted values. We agree that $\alpha\urcorner\mathbf{R}$ shall denote $\mathbf{R}$ with its arguments restricted to lie in α, $\mathbf{R}\upharpoonright\beta$ shall denote $\mathbf{R}$ with its values restricted to lie in β, and $\alpha\urcorner\mathbf{R}\upharpoonright\beta$ shall denote $\mathbf{R}$ with its arguments restricted to α and its values restricted to β. We define

$A\urcorner C$	for	$(A \times \mathrm{V}) \cap C$
$C\upharpoonright B$	for	$(\mathrm{V} \times B) \cap C$
$A\urcorner C\upharpoonright B$	for	$(A \times B) \cap C.$

$A\urcorner C$ is stratified if and only if $A = C$ is stratified. If $A\urcorner C$ is stratified, it has the same type as A and C. The free occurrences of variables in $A\urcorner C$ are just those in A and C. Similarly for $C\upharpoonright B$ and $A\urcorner C\upharpoonright B$.

If $\mathbf{R}$ is the relation determined by $x = \sin y$, then $\mathbf{R}\upharpoonright(\hat{y}(-\pi/2 \leq y \leq \pi/2))$ is the function determined by $y = \arcsin x$, using only the principal value of the arcsin. If $\mathbf{R}$ is the relation determined by $y^2 = x$, then $\mathbf{R}\upharpoonright(\hat{y}(0 \leq y))$ is the function determined by $y = +\sqrt{x}$.

Theorem X.4.5.

★I. $\vdash (\alpha,R,x,y):x(\alpha\urcorner R)y. \equiv .x \in \alpha.xRy.$

II. $\vdash (\beta,R,x,y):x(R\upharpoonright\beta)y. \equiv .xRy.y \in \beta.$

★III. $\vdash (\alpha,\beta,R,x,y):x(\alpha\urcorner R\upharpoonright\beta)y. \equiv .x \in \alpha.xRy.y \in \beta.$

Proof of Part I.

$$\begin{aligned}\vdash x(\alpha\urcorner R)y. &\equiv .x(\alpha \times \mathrm{V})y.xRy \\ . &\equiv .x \in \alpha.y \in \mathrm{V}.xRy \\ . &\equiv .x \in \alpha.xRy.\end{aligned}$$

Proof of Parts II *and* III. Similar.

Theorem X.4.6.

I. $\vdash (\alpha,R).\alpha\rceil R \subseteq R.$

II. $\vdash (\beta,R).R\lceil\beta \subseteq R.$

III. $\vdash (\alpha,\beta,R).\alpha\rceil R\lceil\beta \subseteq R.$

Proof. Use Thm.IX.4.13, Cor. 6, with the definitions of $\alpha\rceil R$, $R\lceil\beta$, and $\alpha\rceil R\lceil\beta$.

Theorem X.4.7.

I. $\vdash (\alpha,R).\alpha\rceil R \in \text{Rel}.$

II. $\vdash (\beta,R).R\lceil\beta \in \text{Rel}.$

III. $\vdash (\alpha,\beta,R).\alpha\rceil R\lceil\beta \in \text{Rel}.$

Proof. Use Ex. X.3.3, part (d).

Theorem X.4.8.

I. $\vdash (\alpha,\beta,R).(\alpha\rceil R)\lceil\beta = \alpha\rceil R\lceil\beta.$

II. $\vdash (\alpha,\beta,R).\alpha\rceil(R\lceil\beta) = \alpha\rceil R\lceil\beta.$

Proof of Part I. By Thm.X.4.5,

$$\begin{aligned}\vdash x((\alpha\rceil R)\lceil\beta)y. &\equiv .x(\alpha\rceil R)y.y \in \beta\\ &.\equiv .x \in \alpha.xRy.y \in \beta.\end{aligned}$$

Proof of Part II. Similar.

Theorem X.4.9.

★I. $\vdash (\alpha,R).\text{Arg}(\alpha\rceil R) = \alpha \cap \text{Arg}(R).$

II. $\vdash (\beta,R).\text{Val}(R\lceil\beta) = \beta \cap \text{Val}(R).$

Proof of Part I. Let $x \in \text{Arg}(\alpha\rceil R)$. Then $x(\alpha\rceil R)y$. So $x \in \alpha.xRy$. So $x \in \alpha.x \in \text{Arg}(R)$. The converse proceeds readily.

Proof of Part II. Similar.

Theorem X.4.10.

I. $\vdash (\alpha,\mathbf{R}):\text{Arg}(\mathbf{R}) \subseteq \alpha. \equiv .\mathbf{R} = \alpha\rceil\mathbf{R}.$

II. $\vdash (\beta,\mathbf{R}):\text{Val}(\mathbf{R}) \subseteq \beta. \equiv .\mathbf{R} = \mathbf{R}\lceil\beta.$

Proof of Part I. If $\mathbf{R} = \alpha\rceil\mathbf{R}$, then by Thm.X.4.9, $\text{Arg}(\mathbf{R}) = \alpha \cap \text{Arg}(\mathbf{R})$, so that $\text{Arg}(\mathbf{R}) \subseteq \alpha$. Conversely, let $\text{Arg}(\mathbf{R}) \subseteq \alpha$, and let $x\mathbf{R}y$. Then $x \in \text{Arg}(\mathbf{R})$. So $x \in \alpha$. So $x(\alpha\rceil\mathbf{R})y$. So $\mathbf{R} \subseteq \alpha\rceil\mathbf{R}$. However, $\alpha\rceil\mathbf{R} \subseteq \mathbf{R}$.

Proof of Part II. Similar.

Corollary.

I. $\vdash (\mathbf{R}).\mathbf{R} = \text{Arg}(\mathbf{R})\rceil\mathbf{R}.$

II. $\vdash (\mathbf{R}).\mathbf{R} = \mathbf{R}\lceil\text{Val}(\mathbf{R}).$

III. $\vdash (\mathbf{R}).\mathbf{R} = \text{Arg}(\mathbf{R})\rceil\mathbf{R}\lceil\text{Val}(\mathbf{R}).$

Theorem X.4.11.

I. $\vdash (\alpha,\beta,R).(\alpha \cap \beta)\rceil R = (\alpha\rceil R) \cap (\beta\rceil R).$

II. $\vdash (\alpha,\beta,R).R\lceil(\alpha \cap \beta) = (R\lceil\alpha) \cap (R\lceil\beta).$

III. $\vdash (\alpha,\beta,R).(\alpha \cup \beta)\rceil R = (\alpha\rceil R) \cup (\beta\rceil R).$

IV. $\vdash (\alpha,\beta,R).R\lceil(\alpha \cup \beta) = (R\lceil\alpha) \cup (R\lceil\beta).$

V. $\vdash (\alpha,\beta,R).(\alpha \cap \beta)\upharpoonleft R = \alpha\upharpoonleft(\beta\upharpoonleft R)$.
VI. $\vdash (\alpha,\beta,R).R\restriction(\alpha \cap \beta) = (R\restriction\alpha)\restriction\beta$.

Proof. Use the definitions of $\alpha\upharpoonleft R$ and $R\restriction\beta$ with Thm.X.3.11.

Theorem X.4.12.

I. $\vdash (\alpha,R,S):R \subseteq S. \supset .\alpha\upharpoonleft R \subseteq \alpha\upharpoonleft S$.
II. $\vdash (\beta,R,S):R \subseteq S. \supset .R\restriction\beta \subseteq S\restriction\beta$.
III. $\vdash (\alpha,\beta,R,S):R \subseteq S. \supset .\alpha\upharpoonleft R\restriction\beta \subseteq \alpha\upharpoonleft S\restriction\beta$.
IV. $\vdash (\alpha,\beta,R):\alpha \subseteq \beta. \supset .\alpha\upharpoonleft R \subseteq \beta\upharpoonleft R$.
V. $\vdash (\alpha,\beta,R):\alpha \subseteq \beta. \supset .R\restriction\alpha \subseteq R\restriction\beta$.

Proof. Use Thm.IX.4.16, Part I, and for Parts IV and V, use Thm. X.3.12 in addition.

We define the converse of a relation **R** as the relation which holds between x and y when $y\mathbf{R}x$. Thus $>$ is the converse of $<$, arcsine is the converse of sine, square root is the converse of square, the logarithm is the converse of the exponential, and in general the converse of a function is just the inverse function. We use two different notations for the converse of **R**, namely, Cnv(**R**) or $\breve{\mathbf{R}}$. So we define

$$\text{Cnv}(A) \quad \text{for} \quad \hat{x}\hat{y}(yAx),$$
$$\breve{A} \quad \text{for} \quad \hat{x}\hat{y}(yAx),$$

where x and y are distinct variables not occurring in A. Cnv(A) is stratified if and only if A is, and if stratified has the same type as A. Free occurrences of variables are exactly those in A.

Theorem X.4.13.

*I. $\vdash (R,x,y):x\breve{R}y. \equiv .yRx$.
II. $\vdash (R).\breve{R} \in \text{Rel}$.

Corollary 1. $\vdash (R,x,y):x(\text{Cnv}(\breve{R}))y. \equiv .xRy$.
Corollary 2. $\vdash (\mathbf{R}).\text{Cnv}(\breve{\mathbf{R}}) = \mathbf{R}$.
Corollary 3. $\vdash (\mathbf{R},\mathbf{S}):\breve{\mathbf{R}} = \breve{\mathbf{S}}. \equiv .\mathbf{R} = \mathbf{S}$.
Corollary 4. $\vdash (\alpha,\beta).\text{Cnv}(\alpha \times \beta) = \beta \times \alpha$.
Corollary 5. $\vdash (\mathbf{R},\mathbf{S}):\mathbf{R} \subseteq \mathbf{S}. \equiv .\breve{\mathbf{R}} \subseteq \breve{\mathbf{S}}$.

Theorem X.4.14. $\vdash (R,S).\text{Cnv}(R \cap S) = \text{Cnv}(R) \cap \text{Cnv}(S)$.

Proof.

$$\begin{aligned} \vdash x(\text{Cnv}(R \cap S))y. &\equiv .y(R \cap S)x \\ . &\equiv .yRx.ySx \\ . &\equiv .x\breve{R}y.x\breve{S}y \\ . &\equiv .x(\breve{R} \cap \breve{S})y. \end{aligned}$$

Corollary 1. $\vdash (\alpha,R).\text{Cnv}(\alpha\upharpoonleft R) = \breve{R}\restriction\alpha$.
Corollary 2. $\vdash (\beta,R).\text{Cnv}(R\restriction\beta) = \beta\upharpoonleft\breve{R}$.
Corollary 3. $\vdash (\alpha,\beta,R).\text{Cnv}(\alpha\upharpoonleft R\restriction\beta) = \beta\upharpoonleft\breve{R}\restriction\alpha$.

Theorem X.4.15. $\vdash (R,S).\text{Cnv}(R \cup S) = \text{Cnv}(R) \cup \text{Cnv}(S)$.

Proof. Similar to that of Thm.X.4.14.

Theorem X.4.16.

★I. $\vdash (R).\mathrm{Arg}(\breve{R}) = \mathrm{Val}(R)$.

★II. $\vdash (R).\mathrm{Val}(\breve{R}) = \mathrm{Arg}(R)$.

Proof of Part I. Let $x \in \mathrm{Arg}(\breve{R})$. Then $x\breve{R}y$. So yRx. So $x \in \mathrm{Val}(R)$. Conversely, if $x \in \mathrm{Val}(R)$, then $x \in \mathrm{Arg}(\breve{R})$.

Proof of Part II. Similar.

We define the relative product $R|S$ of R and S as the relation which holds between x and z when there is a y such that $xRy.ySz$. That is, we define

$$A|B \quad \text{for} \quad \hat{x}\hat{z}(\mathrm{E}y).xAy.yBz,$$

where x, y, and z are distinct variables not occurring in either A or B. $A|B$ is stratified if and only if $A = B$ is stratified, and if stratified has the same type as A and B. The free occurrences of variables are just those in A and B.

In mathematics, if we have two functions f and g, then the relation $z = f(g(x))$ defines the function $g|f$. As a transformation is just a function, we see that if **R** and **S** are two transformations, then **R**|**S** is the product **RS** of **R** and **S** in the usual sense of the product of two transformations, since to form the product **RS**, we first apply **R** and then apply **S**. Thus the associative law of multiplication for transformations is a special use of Thm.X.4.18 below.

Incidentally, if **R** is a transformation with an inverse, then $\breve{\mathbf{R}}$ is that inverse. Hence the corollary to Thm.X.4.17 below gives as a special case the familiar result,

$$(\mathbf{RS})^{-1} = (\mathbf{S}^{-1})(\mathbf{R}^{-1}),$$

that the inverse of a product is the product of the inverses in reverse order.

If $x = f(t)$ and $y = g(t)$ are the parametric equations of a curve, then the relation between x and y which has this same curve for a graph is $\breve{f}|g$. That is, the single equation $y = (\breve{f}|g)(x)$ is equivalent to the two parametric equations $x = f(t)$ and $y = g(t)$.

There is a striking similarity between the notation $\{A \mid P\}$ for the class of all A's such that P and the notation $\{R|S\}$ for the unit class of the relative product $R|S$. Theoretically, confusion between the two is impossible, since in the first case P must be a statement and in the second case S must be a term. Also in the first case we customarily leave a space on each side of the | and in the second case we do not. Also the second case is not used anywhere that we know of. However, to render confusion impossible, we shall agree that in the second case we shall always enclose $R|S$ in parentheses before enclosing it in braces, so that the second case will always be written $\{(R|S)\}$. As the first case could not conceivably be written $\{(A|P)\}$, we now have a unique determination of the notation.

Theorem X.4.17.

★I. $\vdash (R,S,x,z):x(R|S)z. \equiv .(Ey).xRy.ySz.$

II. $\vdash (R,S).R|S \in \text{Rel}.$

★★**Corollary.** $\vdash (R,S).\text{Cnv}(R|S) = \breve{S}|\breve{R}.$

★★**Theorem X.4.18.** $\vdash (R,S,T).R|(S|T) = (R|S)|T.$

Proof.

$$\begin{aligned} \vdash x(R|(S|T))y. &\equiv .(Eu).xRu.u(S|T)y \\ .&\equiv .(Eu,v).xRu.uSv.vTy \\ .&\equiv .(Ev,u).xRu.uSv.vTy \\ .&\equiv .(Ev).x(R|S)v.vTy \\ .&\equiv .x((R|S)|T)y. \end{aligned}$$

Let $R|S|T$ denote either of $(R|S)|T$ or $R|(S|T)$.

Theorem X.4.19.

I. $\vdash (R,S).\text{Arg}(R|S) = \text{Arg}(R\upharpoonright\text{Arg}(S)).$

II. $\vdash (R,S).\text{Val}(R|S) = \text{Val}(\text{Val}(R)\upharpoonleft S).$

Proof of Part I.

$$\begin{aligned} &\vdash x \in \text{Arg}(R|S) \\ &\quad .\equiv .(Ez).x(R|S)z \\ &\quad .\equiv .(Ez,y).xRy.ySz \\ &\quad .\equiv .(Ey).xRy.(Ez).ySz \\ &\quad .\equiv .(Ey).xRy.y \in \text{Arg}(S) \\ &\quad .\equiv .(Ey).x(R\upharpoonright\text{Arg}(S))y \\ &\quad .\equiv .x \in \text{Arg}(R\upharpoonright\text{Arg}(S)). \end{aligned}$$

Proof of Part II. Similar.

Corollary.

I. $\vdash (R,S).\text{Arg}(R|S) \subseteq \text{Arg}(R).$

★II. $\vdash (R,S).\text{Val}(R|S) \subseteq \text{Val}(S).$

★III. $\vdash (R,S):\text{Val}(R) \subseteq \text{Arg}(S). \supset .\text{Arg}(R|S) = \text{Arg}(R).$

IV. $\vdash (R,S):\text{Arg}(S) \subseteq \text{Val}(R). \supset .\text{Val}(R|S) = \text{Val}(S).$

In Parts I and II use Thm.X.4.6 and Thm.X.4.2, and in Parts III and IV use Thm.X.4.10.

Theorem X.4.20.

I. $\vdash (\alpha,R,S).(\alpha\upharpoonleft R)|S = \alpha\upharpoonleft(R|S).$

II. $\vdash (\beta,R,S).R|(S\upharpoonright\beta) = (R|S)\upharpoonright\beta.$

Proof of Part I.

$$\begin{aligned} &\vdash x((\alpha\upharpoonleft R)|S)z \\ &\quad .\equiv .(Ey).x(\alpha\upharpoonleft R)y.ySz \\ &\quad .\equiv .(Ey).x \in \alpha.xRy.ySz \\ &\quad .\equiv .x \in \alpha.(Ey).xRy.ySz \\ &\quad .\equiv .x \in \alpha.x(R|S)z \\ &\quad .\equiv .x(\alpha\upharpoonleft(R|S))z. \end{aligned}$$

Proof of Part II. Similar.

Corollary. $\vdash (\alpha,\beta,R,S).(\alpha\rceil R)|(S\restriction\beta) = \alpha\rceil(R|S)\restriction\beta.$

Theorem X.4.21. $\vdash (\alpha,R,S).(R\restriction\alpha)|S = R|(\alpha\rceil S).$

Proof. Similar to that of Thm.X.4.20.

The notion $\mathrm{Val}(\alpha\rceil R)$ is very important. In terms of the "graph" of R, it may be thought of as the projection on the y-axis of those points whose x-coordinate is in α. Although we have already available one notation for this notion, there is another notation in common use, namely,

$$A``B \qquad \text{for} \qquad \mathrm{Val}(B\rceil A).$$

The stratification conditions for $A``B$ are the same as those for $\mathrm{Val}(B\rceil A)$, namely, that $A = B$ must be stratified, and if stratified $A``B$ has the same type as A and B. The free occurrences of variables are just those in A and B.

Whenever $R``\alpha$ occurs as part of a formula we shall give the smallest possible scope to ``. Thus

$R``\alpha \cup \beta$	means	$(R``\alpha) \cup \beta$	rather than	$R``(\alpha \cup \beta)$,
$\alpha \cup R``\beta$	means	$\alpha \cup (R``\beta)$	rather than	$(\alpha \cup R)``\beta$,
etc.				

In the case of $S``R``\alpha$, the convention about the scope of `` is ambiguous. We agree that $S``R``\alpha$ stands for $S``(R``\alpha)$, rather than for $(S``R)``\alpha$.

If R is a transformation, then $R``\alpha$ is the region that $\alpha$ is mapped into by $R$. Hence the notion $R``\alpha$ is important in transformation theory. If we start with a region α and apply successively the transformations R and S, we transform α into $S``(R``\alpha)$.

We refer to $R``\alpha$ as the map of α or projection of α by R.

Logicians usually define $R``\alpha$ as $\mathrm{Arg}(R\restriction\alpha)$. In our notation, this would be $\breve{R}``\alpha$. Thus our theorems about $R``\alpha$ will differ from the usual ones by having R replaced by $\breve{R}$.

The reason for our variance from the usual convention is that, in the formula $\langle x,y\rangle \in R$, we think of x as the argument and y as the value, in accordance with the usual analytical geometry convention, whereas most logicians think of y as the argument and x as the value in xRy.

***Theorem X.4.22.** $\vdash (\alpha,R,y){:}y \in R``\alpha. \equiv .(\mathrm{E}x).xRy.x \in \alpha.$

***Corollary.** $\vdash (R,x,y){:}y \in R``\{x\}. \equiv .xRy.$

Theorem X.4.23. $\vdash (\beta,R).\breve{R}``\beta = \mathrm{Arg}(R\restriction\beta).$

Proof.

$$\begin{aligned} \vdash \breve{R}``\beta &= \mathrm{Val}(\beta\rceil\breve{R}) \\ &= \mathrm{Val}(\mathrm{Cnv}(R\restriction\beta)) \\ &= \mathrm{Arg}(R\restriction\beta). \end{aligned}$$

Corollary. $\vdash (\beta,R,x){:}x \in \breve{R}``\beta. \equiv .(\mathrm{E}y).xRy.y \in \beta.$

Theorem X.4.24.

I. $\vdash (\alpha,R).R``\alpha \subseteq \text{Val}(R)$.

II. $\vdash (\beta,R).\breve{R}``\beta \subseteq \text{Arg}(R)$.

Proof of Part I. By Thm.X.4.6, $\alpha\rceil R \subseteq R$. So by Thm.X.4.2, $\text{Val}(\alpha\rceil R) \subseteq \text{Val}(R)$.

Proof of Part II. Similar.

Theorem X.4.25. $\vdash (\alpha,\beta,R):\alpha \subseteq \beta. \supset .R``\alpha \subseteq R``\beta$.

Proof. Use Thm.X.4.12, Part IV, and Thm.X.4.2.

Theorem X.4.26.

I. $\vdash (R).\text{Val}(R) = R``\text{Arg}(R)$.

II. $\vdash (R).\text{Arg}(R) = \breve{R}``\text{Val}(R)$.

Proof of Part I. Let $y \in \text{Val}(R)$. Then xRy. So $xRy.x \in \text{Arg}(R)$. So $y \in R``\text{Arg}(R)$. The converse goes easily.

Proof of Part II. Similar.

Theorem X.4.27.

I. $\vdash (\alpha,R).R``\alpha = R``(\alpha \cap \text{Arg}(R))$.

II. $\vdash (\beta,R).\breve{R}``\beta = \breve{R}``(\beta \cap \text{Val}(R))$.

Proof of Part I. By Thm.X.4.9, Part I, $\vdash \text{Arg}(\alpha\rceil R) \subseteq \text{Arg}(R)$. So by Thm.X.4.10, Part I, $\vdash \alpha\rceil R = \text{Arg}(R)\rceil(\alpha\rceil R)$. So by Thm.X.4.11, Part V, $\vdash \alpha\rceil R = (\alpha \cap \text{Arg}(R))\rceil R$. So $\vdash \text{Val}(\alpha\rceil R) = \text{Val}((\alpha \cap \text{Arg}(R))\rceil R)$.

Proof of Part II. Similar.

Corollary.

I. $\vdash (R).R``\text{V} = \text{Val}(R)$.

II. $\vdash (R).\breve{R}``\text{V} = \text{Arg}(R)$.

Theorem X.4.28. $\vdash (\alpha,R,S).(R|S)``\alpha = S``R``\alpha$.

Proof. By Thm.X.4.20, Part I, $\vdash \alpha\rceil(R|S) = (\alpha\rceil R)|S$. So $\vdash (R|S)``\alpha = \text{Val}((\alpha\rceil R)|S)$. But by Thm.X.4.19, Part II, $\vdash \text{Val}((\alpha\rceil R)|S) = S``\text{Val}(\alpha\rceil R) = S``R``\alpha$.

This theorem has an interesting interpretation in terms of transformation theory. As we noted earlier, $R|S$ is the product of the transformations R and S (in the sense of applying first R, then S). This theorem says that we get the same map whether we apply R and S successively, getting $S``R``\alpha$, or whether we apply the product transformation directly, getting $(R|S)``\alpha$.

Usually in mathematics, transformations are functions, so that we would usually be interested in the special cases of Thm.X.4.17, corollary, Thm. X.4.18, Thm.X.4.19, Thm.X.4.20, and Thm.X.4.28 which result when we take R and S to be functions. However, in algebraic geometry, use is made of many-valued mappings called correspondences, and there the full strength of these theorems is useful. Note that the product of two correspondences **R** and **S** is exactly **R**|**S** (see Coolidge, 1931, page 125).

Theorem X.4.29.

I. $\vdash (R).\text{Arg}(\text{RUSC}(R)) = \text{USC}(\text{Arg}(R))$.

II. $\vdash (R).\mathrm{Val}(\mathrm{RUSC}(R)) = \mathrm{USC}(\mathrm{Val}(R))$.
III. $\vdash (R).\mathrm{AV}(\mathrm{RUSC}(R)) = \mathrm{USC}(\mathrm{AV}(R))$.

Proof of Part I. Let $x \in \mathrm{Arg}(\mathrm{RUSC}(R))$. Then by rule C, $x(\mathrm{RUSC}(R))y$. Then by Thm.X.3.15 and rule C, $uRv.x = \{u\}.y = \{v\}$. So $u \in \mathrm{Arg}(R).x = \{u\}$. So by Thm.IX.6.10, Part III, $x \in \mathrm{USC}(\mathrm{Arg}(R))$. Conversely, let $x \in \mathrm{USC}(\mathrm{Arg}(R))$. Then $u \in \mathrm{Arg}(R).x = \{u\}$. So $uRv.x = \{u\}$. Hence $uRv.x = \{u\}.\{v\} = \{v\}$. So $x(\mathrm{RUSC}(R))\{v\}$. So $x \in \mathrm{Arg}(\mathrm{RUSC}(R))$.

Proof of Part II. Similar.

Theorem X.4.30.

I. $\vdash (\alpha,R).\mathrm{RUSC}(\alpha \upharpoonleft R) = \mathrm{USC}(\alpha)\upharpoonleft\mathrm{RUSC}(R)$.
II. $\vdash (\beta,R).\mathrm{RUSC}(R\restriction\beta) = \mathrm{RUSC}(R)\restriction\mathrm{USC}(\beta)$.

Proof of Part I.

$$\begin{aligned}\vdash x(&\mathrm{RUSC}(\alpha\upharpoonleft R))y\\ &: \equiv :(\mathrm{E}u,v).u(\alpha\upharpoonleft R)v.x = \{u\}.y = \{v\}\\ &: \equiv :(\mathrm{E}u,v).u \in \alpha.uRv.x = \{u\}.y = \{v\}\\ &: \equiv :(\mathrm{E}u,v).\{u\} \in \mathrm{USC}(\alpha).uRv.x = \{u\}.y = \{v\}\\ &: \equiv :(\mathrm{E}u,v).x \in \mathrm{USC}(\alpha).uRv.x = \{u\}.y = \{v\}\\ &: \equiv :x \in \mathrm{USC}(\alpha):(\mathrm{E}u,v).uRv.x = \{u\}.y = \{v\}\\ &: \equiv :x \in \mathrm{USC}(\alpha).x(\mathrm{RUSC}(R))y\\ &: \equiv :x(\mathrm{USC}(\alpha)\upharpoonleft\mathrm{RUSC}(R))y.\end{aligned}$$

Proof of Part II. Similar.

Corollary. $\vdash (\beta,R).(\mathrm{RUSC}(R))``\mathrm{USC}(\beta) = \mathrm{USC}(R``\beta)$.

Theorem X.4.31. $\vdash (R).\mathrm{RUSC}(\breve{R}) = \mathrm{Cnv}(\mathrm{RUSC}(R))$.

Proof.

$$\begin{aligned}\vdash x(&\mathrm{RUSC}(\breve{R}))y\\ &. \equiv .(\mathrm{E}u,v).u\breve{R}v.x = \{u\}.y = \{v\}\\ &. \equiv .(\mathrm{E}u,v).vRu.y = \{v\}.x = \{u\}\\ &. \equiv .y(\mathrm{RUSC}(R))x\\ &. \equiv .x(\mathrm{Cnv}(\mathrm{RUSC}(R)))y.\end{aligned}$$

Theorem X.4.32. $\vdash (R,S).\mathrm{RUSC}(R|S) = \mathrm{RUSC}(R)|\mathrm{RUSC}(S)$.

Proof. Assume $x(\mathrm{RUSC}(R|S))z$. Then by rule C, $u(R|S)w.x = \{u\}.z = \{w\}$. Then by rule C, $uRv.vSw.x = \{u\}.z = \{w\}$. So $x(\mathrm{RUSC}(R))\{v\}.\{v\}(\mathrm{RUSC}(R))z$. So $x(\mathrm{RUSC}(R)|\mathrm{RUSC}(S))z$.

Conversely, assume $x(\mathrm{RUSC}(R)|\mathrm{RUSC}(S))z$. Then by rule C, $x(\mathrm{RUSC}(R))y.y(\mathrm{RUSC}(S))z$. So by rule C, $uRv.x = \{u\}.y = \{v\}.wSt.y = \{w\}.z = \{t\}$. So $w = v$. So $uRv.vSt.x = \{u\}.z = \{t\}$. So $u(R|S)t.x = \{u\}.z = \{t\}$. So $x(\mathrm{RUSC}(R|S))z$.

An important notion is the closure of a class α with respect to a function f. Intuitively, we get this as follows. We start with the members of α. For each x which is a member of α, we form $f(x)$. We enlarge α by adding each of these $f(x)$'s to it as a new member. We now repeat this process with the enlarged α, getting a further enlarged α. We reiterate this process (an infinite number of times if necessary) until we arrive at a class β that cannot be further enlarged by this process. Such a class β is said to be "closed with respect to f" and is called the closure of α with respect to f.

More generally, we can form the closure of a class α with respect to a relation R. If we think of R as a many-valued function, the procedure is quite analogous. Instead of adding $f(x)$ to α, we add all members of $R``\{x\}$. As soon as we get to a β which cannot be enlarged by this procedure, we stop. We say that β is closed with respect to R and is the closure of α with respect to R.

Another way to imagine forming β is to add to α its map $R``\alpha$ by R, then to add the map of this, etc. In other words, the closure of α with respect to R is

$$\alpha \cup (R``\alpha) \cup (R``R``\alpha) \cup (R``R``R``\alpha) \cup \cdots$$

As a matter of fact, the notion of the closure of α with respect to R in the sense just described is merely a special case of the notion of closure discussed in Sec. 5 of Chapter IX. In the notation proposed there, the closure of α with respect to R would be denoted by $\mathrm{Clos}(\alpha,xRz)$, which would denote

$$\bigcap\hat{\beta}(\alpha \subseteq \beta{:}.(x,z){:}x \in \beta.xRz. \supset .z \in \beta).$$

Now

$$\vdash (\beta,R){::}(x,z){:}x \in \beta.xRz. \supset .z \in \beta.{:} \equiv {:}.R``\beta \subseteq \beta.$$

So

$$\vdash (\alpha,R){:}\mathrm{Clos}(\alpha,xRz). = .\bigcap\hat{\beta}(\alpha \subseteq \beta.R``\beta \subseteq \beta).$$

Then Thms.IX.5.12 to IX.5.16 reduce to:

Theorem X.4.33. $\vdash (\alpha,R,y){:}.y \in \mathrm{Clos}(\alpha,xRz){:} \equiv {:}(\beta){:}\alpha \subseteq \beta.\ R``\beta \subseteq \beta. \supset .y \in \beta.$

Theorem X.4.34. $\vdash (\alpha,R).\alpha \subseteq \mathrm{Clos}(\alpha,xRz).$

Theorem X.4.35. $\vdash (\alpha,R).R``\mathrm{Clos}(\alpha,xRz) \subseteq \mathrm{Clos}(\alpha,xRz).$

Theorem X.4.36. $\vdash (\alpha,\beta,R){:}\alpha \subseteq \beta.R``(\beta \cap \mathrm{Clos}(\alpha,xRz)) \subseteq \beta. \supset . \mathrm{Clos}(\alpha,xRz) \subseteq \beta.$

Theorem X.4.37. $\vdash (\alpha,R).\mathrm{Clos}(\alpha,xRz) = \alpha \cup R``\mathrm{Clos}(\alpha,xRz).$

EXERCISES

X.4.1. Prove:

I. $\vdash (\alpha,\beta,\gamma){:}\gamma \neq \Lambda. \supset .\alpha \subset \beta \equiv \alpha \times \gamma \subset \beta \times \gamma.$
II. $\vdash (\alpha,\beta,\gamma){:}\gamma \neq \Lambda. \supset .\alpha \subset \beta \equiv \gamma \times \alpha \subset \gamma \times \beta.$

X.4.2. Prove:

I. $\vdash (\alpha,\beta).\alpha \times \beta = (\alpha \times \mathrm{V})|(\mathrm{V} \times \beta).$
II. $\vdash (\alpha,\beta).\alpha \times \beta = (\alpha \times \mathrm{V}) \cap (\mathrm{V} \times \beta).$
III. $\vdash (\alpha,\beta).\alpha \times \beta = \alpha\upharpoonleft(\mathrm{V} \times \mathrm{V})\upharpoonright\beta.$
IV. $\vdash (\alpha,\beta).\alpha \times \beta = \alpha\upharpoonleft\mathrm{V}\upharpoonright\beta.$

X.4.3. Under what circumstances would one have $\vdash R = V\upharpoonleft R$?

X.4.4. Prove $\vdash (\alpha,\beta,\gamma,\delta).(\alpha \times \beta) \cap (\gamma \times \delta) = (\alpha \cap \gamma) \times (\beta \cap \delta)$.

X.4.5. Prove:

(a) $\vdash (R,S,T):R \subseteq S. \supset .R|T \subseteq S|T.$

(b) $\vdash (R,S,T):R \subseteq S. \supset .T|R \subseteq T|S.$

(c) $\vdash (\alpha,R,S):R \subseteq S. \supset .R\text{``}\alpha \subseteq S\text{``}\alpha.$

(d) $\vdash (R).\Lambda\upharpoonleft R = \Lambda.$

(e) $\vdash (R).R\upharpoonright\Lambda = \Lambda.$

(f) $\vdash (R).R\text{``}\Lambda = \Lambda.$

(g) $\vdash (\alpha).\alpha\upharpoonleft\Lambda = \Lambda.$

(h) $\vdash (\beta).\Lambda\upharpoonright\beta = \Lambda.$

(i) $\vdash (\alpha).\Lambda\text{``}\alpha = \Lambda.$

(j) $\vdash \mathrm{Cnv}(\Lambda) = \Lambda.$

X.4.6. Prove:

(a) $\vdash (R,S).\mathrm{Arg}(R \cup S) = \mathrm{Arg}(R) \cup \mathrm{Arg}(S).$

(b) $\vdash (R,S).\mathrm{Val}(R \cup S) = \mathrm{Val}(R) \cup \mathrm{Val}(S).$

(c) $\vdash (R,S).\mathrm{AV}(R \cup S) = \mathrm{AV}(R) \cup \mathrm{AV}(S).$

(d) $\vdash (\alpha,\beta,R).R\text{``}(\alpha \cup \beta) = (R\text{``}\alpha) \cup (R\text{``}\beta).$

(e) $\vdash (R,S).\mathrm{Arg}(R \cap S) \subseteq \mathrm{Arg}(R) \cap \mathrm{Arg}(S).$

(f) $\vdash (R,S).\mathrm{Val}(R \cap S) \subseteq \mathrm{Val}(R) \cap \mathrm{Val}(S).$

(g) $\vdash (R,S).\mathrm{AV}(R \cap S) \subseteq \mathrm{AV}(R) \cap \mathrm{AV}(S).$

(h) $\vdash (\alpha,\beta,R).R\text{``}(\alpha \cap \beta) \subseteq (R\text{``}\alpha) \cap (R\text{``}\beta).$

(i) $\vdash (\alpha,R,S).(R \cup S)\text{``}\alpha = (R\text{``}\alpha) \cup (S\text{``}\alpha).$

(j) $\vdash (\alpha,R,S).(\alpha\upharpoonleft R) \cap (\alpha\upharpoonleft S) = \alpha\upharpoonleft(R \cap S).$

(k) $\vdash (\beta,R,S).(R\upharpoonright\beta) \cap (S\upharpoonright\beta) = (R \cap S)\upharpoonright\beta.$

(l) $\vdash (\alpha,R,S).(\alpha\upharpoonleft R) \cup (\alpha\upharpoonleft S) = \alpha\upharpoonleft(R \cup S).$

(m) $\vdash (\beta,R,S).(R\upharpoonright\beta) \cup (S\upharpoonright\beta) = (R \cup S)\upharpoonright\beta.$

X.4.7. Find illustrations to show the falsity of each of:

(a) $(R,S).\mathrm{Arg}(R) \cap \mathrm{Arg}(S) \subseteq \mathrm{Arg}(R \cap S).$

(b) $(R,S).\mathrm{Val}(R) \cap \mathrm{Val}(S) \subseteq \mathrm{Val}(R \cap S).$

(c) $(R,S).\mathrm{AV}(R) \cap \mathrm{AV}(S) \subseteq \mathrm{AV}(R \cap S).$

(d) $(\alpha,\beta,R).(R\text{``}\alpha) \cap (R\text{``}\beta) \subseteq R\text{``}(\alpha \cap \beta).$

X.4.8. Prove:

(a) $\vdash (R,S,T):R|(S \cap T) \subseteq (R|S) \cap (R|T).$

(b) $\vdash (R):R|\Lambda = \Lambda|R = \Lambda.$

(c) $\vdash (R,S,T):R|(S \cup T) = (R|S) \cup (R|T).$

(d) $\vdash (R,x):xRx. \supset .x(R|R)x.$

(e) $\vdash (R,S):R \subseteq S. \supset .(R|R) \subseteq (S|S).$

(f) $\vdash (\alpha,\beta,R,S):(\alpha\upharpoonleft R) \cap (\beta\upharpoonleft S) = (\alpha \cap \beta)\upharpoonleft(R \cap S).$

(g) $\vdash (\alpha,\beta,\gamma):\beta \neq \Lambda. \supset .(\alpha \times \beta)|(\beta \times \gamma) = \alpha \times \gamma.$
(h) $\vdash (R,S).\mathrm{Val}(R|S) = S``\mathrm{Val}(R).$
(i) $\vdash (R,S).\mathrm{Arg}(R|S) = \breve{R}``\mathrm{Arg}(S).$

X.4.9. Prove:

(a) $\vdash (\beta,R)::(x,z):x \in \beta.xRz. \supset .z \in \beta.: \equiv :.R``\beta \subseteq \beta.$
(b) $\vdash (\alpha,\beta,R).R``(\beta \cap \mathrm{Clos}(\alpha,xRz)) \subseteq \mathrm{Clos}(\alpha,xRz).$

X.4.10. Whitehead and Russell denote the ancestral relation of R by R_*, which they define as

$$\hat{u}\hat{v}(u \in \mathrm{AV}(R).v \in \mathrm{Clos}(\{u\},xRz))$$

where u and v do not occur in xRz. Prove:

(a) $\vdash (R,x,y)::xR_*y.: \equiv :.x \in \mathrm{AV}(R):.(\beta):x \in \beta.R``\beta \subseteq \beta. \supset .y \in \beta.$
(b) $\vdash (R,x):x \in \mathrm{AV}(R). \equiv .xR_*x.$
(c) $\vdash (R,x,y,z):xR_*y.yRz. \supset .xR_*z.$
(d) $\vdash (R).(R_*|R) \subseteq R_*.$
(e) $\vdash (R,u):u \in \mathrm{AV}(R). \supset .R_*``\{u\} = \mathrm{Clos}(\{u\},xRz).$
(f) $\vdash (R,u):.\sim u \in \mathrm{AV}(R): \supset :R_*``\{u\} = \Lambda.\mathrm{Clos}(\{u\},xRz) = \{u\}.$
(g) $\vdash (\beta,R,x,y):R``(\beta \cap R``\{x\}) \subseteq \beta.x \in \beta \cap \mathrm{AV}(R).xR_*y. \supset .y \in \beta.$
(h) $\vdash (R,x):.x \in \mathrm{AV}(R): \supset :(y).xR_*y. \equiv .x = y.\mathbf{v}.x(R_*|R)y.$
(i) $\vdash (R).(R|(R_*)) \subseteq R_*.$
(j) $\vdash (\mathbf{R}).\mathbf{R} \subseteq (\mathbf{R}_*|\mathbf{R}).$
(k) $\vdash (\mathbf{R}).\mathbf{R} \subseteq (\mathbf{R}|(\mathbf{R}_*)).$
(l) $\vdash (\mathbf{R}).\mathbf{R} \subseteq \mathbf{R}_*.$
(m) $\vdash (R).\mathrm{Arg}(R_*) = \mathrm{Val}(R_*) = \mathrm{AV}(R).$
(n) $\vdash (R).(R_*)|(R_*) = R_*.$
(o) $\vdash (R).(R_*)_* = R_*.$
(p) $\vdash (R).\mathrm{Cnv}(R_*) = (\mathrm{Cnv}(R))_*.$
(q) $\vdash (R).(R_*)|R = R|(R_*).$

5. Functions. As we said earlier, we are restricting the term "function" to mean "single-valued function." So a relation **R** is a function if and only if

$$(x,y,z):x\mathbf{R}y.x\mathbf{R}z. \supset .y = z.$$

Accordingly we define

$$\mathrm{Funct} \quad \text{for} \quad \hat{\mathbf{R}}(x,y,z):x\mathbf{R}y.x\mathbf{R}z. \supset .y = z.$$

Thus Funct is the class of all functions. To state that R is a function, we write $R \in \mathrm{Funct}$. Because we used in the definition of Funct the variable **R** which is restricted to the range Rel, every function is a relation (see Thm.IX.7.9).

Funct is stratified and may be assigned any arbitrary type since it has no free variables.

Functions are sometimes referred to as many-one relations.

If **R** is a function and $x \epsilon \mathrm{Arg}(\mathbf{R})$, then there is a unique y such that $x\mathbf{R}y$. In the standard mathematical notation, this y is denoted by $\mathbf{R}(x)$, or sometimes by just $\mathbf{R}x$ (as when **R** is cos, log, etc.). We shall uniformly use $\mathbf{R}(x)$ to denote the unique y such that $x\mathbf{R}y$. Thus we put

$$A(B) \qquad \text{for} \qquad \iota y\ (BAy),$$

where y does not occur in A or B. $A(B)$ is stratified if and only if $B \epsilon A$ is stratified, and if stratified has the same type as B, which would be one less than the type of A. The free occurrences of variables are just those in A and B, respectively.

Most mathematicians will agree that x^2 is a function of x. We have said that a function is a class of ordered pairs. Is then x^2 a class of ordered pairs? We think not. If x is a "real variable," then x^2 is a variable, nonnegative, real number got by multiplying x by itself and can scarcely be a class of ordered pairs.

Although x^2 is not itself a class of ordered pairs, it determines such a class. If we graph $y = x^2$, the points of the graph are a class of ordered pairs. To be precise, the graph consists of the class of ordered pairs $\{\langle x,y\rangle \mid y = x^2\}$, and when one speaks of x^2 as a function, it is precisely this class of ordered pairs which one has in mind. However, x^2 itself is certainly not this class of ordered pairs.

If we denote temporarily $\{\langle x,y\rangle \mid y = x^2\}$ by f, then by our definition of $f(x)$ given above we have

$$\vdash (x).f(x) = x^2.$$

Thus with $\{\langle x,y\rangle \mid y = x^2\}$ for f, $f(x)$ is x^2. That is, the relationship between x^2 and $\{\langle x,y\rangle \mid y = x^2\}$ is the same as the relationship between $f(x)$ and f. That is, x^2 is the *result* of applying the operation of squaring to the variable x, whereas $\{\langle x,y\rangle \mid y = x^2\}$ denotes the actual operation of squaring.

It would appear that we are trying to discredit the common belief that x^2 is a function of x. This is not the case at all. We are merely trying to emphasize rather strongly that the word "function" is used in two quite different senses. It is common to refer to x^2 as a function, and it is also common to speak of $\{\langle x,y\rangle \mid y = x^2\}$ as a function (indeed, as the *same* function!!!). Nevertheless, x^2 and $\{\langle x,y\rangle \mid y = x^2\}$ are quite different objects. Lest there be any lingering doubts on this point, let us note that unquestionably x^2 is a variable and unquestionably $\{\langle x,y\rangle \mid y = x^2\}$ is a constant.

To put the matter in terms of more familiar notation, it is common to speak of $f(x)$ as a function and also common to speak of f as a function, and yet certainly $f(x)$ and f are not the same. It is unfortunate that there is this double usage of the word "function." It is perhaps worth while to give a little thought to the historical development of the notion of function, so as to see how the present state of affairs came about.

We go back to Euler, who was perhaps one of the first mathematicians to give a fairly precise specification of his notion of a function. In modern terms, Euler's notion of a function of x is what we would speak of as a formula involving x, such as x^2, $\sin x$, etc. It is perhaps not known whether Euler would have regarded

$$\int_0^x e^{-y^2}\,dy$$

as a function or not, but certainly he would not have considered as a function the modern function whose value is unity at all rational points and zero at all irrational points.

Euler's notion of function was soon found to be far too restrictive, and it was generalized to somewhat the following:

"If a variable y is so related to a variable x that for each value of x in a range R there is determined a unique value of y, then y is a function of the variable x, defined over R, and we write $y = f(x)$."

This definition, or some approximation thereto, is to be found in the usual modern calculus textbook. Nevertheless, this definition is quite unclear. When y is an explicit formula containing x, it is clear how there can be a relation between x and y. However, the definition given above certainly intends something more general. Unfortunately, if y is to be thought of as an abstract variable, it is hard to see how it can keep its values sorted out and properly related to the values of x, or indeed how it goes about having values at all. That this point is far from clear is evident if one looks over a large number of calculus textbooks and observes the very confused descriptions of the notion of function which appear in the poorer ones.

In order to clear up this point, there evolved the modern notion of a function as a rule for determining values for y from values for x in the range R, or (which amounts to the same thing) as a class of ordered pairs $\langle x,y\rangle$. This is a very precise idea and is very satisfactory for the development of function theory, but it is quite a different idea from that which is intended in the definition quoted earlier. In the definition quoted earlier, one is thinking of $f(x)$ as the function, whereas in the modern definition of a function as a rule (or class of ordered pairs), one is thinking of f as the function.

Actually, f and $f(x)$, the rule and the result of applying the rule, are very different, and it is confusing to use the word "function" to apply to both. One should definitely decide to call one by the name "function" and then devise a new name for the other. The present trend in higher mathematics is to reserve the name "function" for f, but even those who advocate this are usually inconsistent in their use of the word "function." Moreover, they have given no name to "$f(x)$." Probably this trend is due to the difficulty of making precise the definition of a function which conceives of $f(x)$ as a function.

Let us return to this definition and consider more carefully the difficulties which it raises. We are to conceive of the variable y as being so related to a variable x that values of x in R determine values of y. Again we ask, what manner of object is y? For instance, it is clearly intended in this definition that the relation between x and y could be such that y has the value 3 for each value of x in R. But then y is not a variable. Worse still, if the range R of x consists of a single point, then neither x nor y is variable. Clearly, what is intended is some generalization of Euler's idea that y is a formula containing x. This would permit y to be constant, *e.g.*, $y = (3 + x) - x$, or even permit the range of x to be a single point, *e.g.*, $y = \sqrt{-x^2}$, where in real variables x could only be zero. The trouble is that classical mathematics has no precise way of prescribing such a generalization.

If we use the resources of symbolic logic, such a generalization is quite easy. We merely conceive of y as a term, A, containing free occurrences of x. This will include all the familiar "formulas" of mathematics. It also includes definitions by cases, as we saw in detail in Chapter VIII. Thus we can write a term A, with free occurrences of x, such that

$$\vdash (x){:}x \text{ is rational.} \supset .A = 1.$$
$$\vdash (x){:}x \text{ is irrational.} \supset .A = 0.$$

It will turn out that we can write terms A which will serve as $f(x)$ even in the most difficult cases, such as when $f(x)$ is defined by transfinite induction. In fact, if we achieve our aim of constructing a symbolic logic in which we can state all theorems of mathematics and prove those which are generally accepted as true, then we can certainly write a term A to represent any given function $f(x)$, for one merely translates the specification of $f(x)$ into symbolic logic, and the resulting formula of the logic is A.

Hence we propose to make the familiar definition precise by replacing "variable y" by "term A." Then the definition would read:

"If A is a term containing no free occurrences of any variable other than x, then A is a function of the variable x."

If we define $f = \{\langle x,y\rangle \mid y = A\}$, then we have as a theorem

$$\vdash (x).f(x) = A$$

if A contains free occurrences of x.

We thus have available precise definitions of both uses of the word function, namely, to denote f or to denote $f(x)$. Thus we can call R a function and then $R(x) = \iota y\ (xRy)$ is the corresponding value, or we can call A a function and then $\{\langle x,y\rangle \mid y = A\}$ is the rule f which determines a value of A for each value of x (in the sense that $\vdash (x).f(x) = A$). Either procedure is equally precise in terms of symbolic logic. That is, in symbolic logic we have adequate machinery for dealing with either f or $f(x)$ with complete precision, and so are at liberty to designate either as a "function." But we must then use a different name for the other!

Actually, a perfectly good name for the notion f is available, namely, "transformation." In algebraic geometry, a careful distinction is usually made between a "transformation" f and a "general value" $f(x)$ of the transformation. Thus, one way out of our impasse would be always to refer to f as a transformation and to reserve the term "function" to refer to $f(x)$. This would be quite satisfactory if it were generally adopted.

Another possible way would be to agree to refer to f as a "function" but to $f(x)$ as a "function of x." This sounds rather attractive at first but would probably not work. In the first place, it requires that we treat the phrase "function of x" as an indissoluble unit, which is contrary to the rules of English grammar. Also, it is quite certain that "function of x" would usually be abbreviated to "function," and we would be back to the double usage of "function" which now prevails.

There is a third solution which is the one which we shall adopt. It is not highly satisfactory, but it does seem most nearly in accord with the present trend of mathematical thought. We shall refer to f as a "function" and to $f(x)$ as a "function value," or more fully as a "function value of x," or still more fully as a "function value corresponding to x." If A is a term, such as x^2, containing no free variables other than x, we shall refer to A also as a "function value," or "function value of x," or "function value corresponding to x" because in such case we can always define a function f to be $\{\langle x,y\rangle \mid y = A\}$, and then we have $\vdash (x).A = f(x)$.

We note that there is a general correspondence between functions and function values, which we shall illustrate by a few examples.

Given two function values, $f(x)$ and $g(x)$, we can construct the function value which is their sum, namely, $f(x) + g(x)$.

Correspondingly, given two functions, f and g, we can construct the function which is their sum, namely,

$$f + g = \{\langle x,y\rangle \mid y = f(x) + g(x)\}.$$

Clearly the sum of the function values is related to the sum of the functions by the relation

$$\vdash (x).(f + g)(x) = f(x) + g(x),$$

which is usually taken as the definition of the sum of two functions in a function space, or as the sum of two transformations.

There are two notions of product of functions. One corresponds to the notion of product of function values, and one does not. Suppose we define

$$f \cdot g \qquad \text{as} \qquad \{\langle x,y\rangle \mid y = f(x)\cdot g(x)\},$$

then this corresponds to the product of function values, since

$$\vdash (x).(f\cdot g)(x) = f(x)\cdot g(x).$$

On the other hand, if we define

$$f \times g \qquad \text{as} \qquad \{\langle x,y\rangle \mid y = g(f(x))\},$$

then

$$\vdash (x).(f \times g)(x) = g(f(x)).$$

The latter is the type of product which is used when we speak of the product of two transformations. We shall see that it is identical with the notion $f|g$ which we introduced for the product of two relations.

The notion of derivative is another instance of the correspondence between functions and function values. Given a function value, $f(x)$, we can construct the function value which is the derivative with respect to x of the original function value, namely,

$$\frac{d}{dx} f(x) = D_x(f(x)) = \lim_{h\to 0} \frac{f(x+h) - f(x)}{h}.$$

Correspondingly, given a function, f, we can construct the function which is the derivative of the original function, namely,

$$Df = f' = \{\langle x,y\rangle \mid y = \lim_{h\to 0} \frac{f(x+h) - f(x)}{h}\}.$$

Then one has

$$\vdash (x).(Df)(x) = f'(x) = \frac{d}{dx} f(x) = D_x(f(x)).$$

We note one point here, namely, that in speaking of the derivative of a function value, one must specify what variable one is going to differentiate with respect to, whereas in speaking of the derivative of a function, the specification of the variable of differentiation is automatic.

Thus we cannot speak simply of the derivative of x^2, since we may differentiate with respect to x, getting

$$\frac{d}{dx} x^2 = D_x x^2 = 2x,$$

or we may differentiate with respect to $2x$, getting

$$\frac{d}{d(2x)}\, x^2 = D_{2x}x^2 = x,$$

or we may differentiate with respect to x^2, getting

$$\frac{d}{d(x^2)}\, x^2 = D_{x^2}x^2 = 1.$$

The point is that one may think of a given function value as being a function value for each of many different functions. Thus, if we put

$$\begin{aligned} f_1 &= \{\langle x,y\rangle \mid y = x^2\}, \\ f_2 &= \{\langle x,y\rangle \mid y = \tfrac{1}{4}x^2\}, \\ f_3 &= \{\langle x,y\rangle \mid y = x\}, \end{aligned}$$

then

$$\begin{aligned} f_1(x) &= x^2, \\ f_2(2x) &= x^2, \\ f_3(x^2) &= x^2. \end{aligned}$$

Thus x^2 is a function value of each of f_1, f_2, and f_3, and indeed of many other functions. The derivatives of the functions f_1, f_2, f_3 are given by

$$\begin{aligned} Df_1 &= f_1' = \{\langle x,y\rangle \mid y = 2x\}, \\ Df_2 &= f_2' = \{\langle x,y\rangle \mid y = \tfrac{1}{2}x\}, \\ Df_3 &= f_3' = \{\langle x,y\rangle \mid y = 1.x = x\}. \end{aligned}$$

So

$$\begin{aligned} (Df_1)(x) &= 2x, \\ (Df_2)(x) &= \tfrac{1}{2}x, \\ (Df_3)(x) &= 1. \end{aligned}$$

These accord with the general relation

$$(Df)(x) = D_x(f(x)).$$

However,

$$\begin{aligned} (Df_2)(2x) &= x \neq D_x(f_2(2x)) = 2x, \\ (Df_3)(x^2) &= 1 \neq D_x(f_3(x^2)) = 2x. \end{aligned}$$

The error of writing $(Df)(g(x))$ for $D_x(f(g(x)))$ is a common one with beginning students in calculus. Thus, if f is "sin," then $Df = f' =$ "cos." So

$$(D \sin)(x) = D_x(\sin x) = \cos x,$$

but

$$(D \sin)(x^2) = \cos x^2 \neq D_x(\sin x^2) = 2x \cos x^2.$$

The process of finding $D_x(f(g(x)))$ is accomplished by means of the so-called "chain rule." We may express this either in terms of function values as

$$\frac{dy}{dx} = \frac{dy}{du} \cdot \frac{du}{dx},$$

or in terms of functions as

$$D(g \times f) = (g \times Df) \cdot Dg,$$

or (as is sometimes done) partly in terms of function values and partly in terms of functions as

$$\frac{d}{dx} f(g(x)) = f'(g(x)) \cdot \frac{d}{dx} g(x).$$

The trouble with the form

$$(1) \qquad \frac{dy}{dx} = \frac{dy}{du} \cdot \frac{du}{dx}$$

is that it does not seem to convey to the beginning calculus student the information that

$$(2) \qquad \frac{d}{dx} \sin x^2 = 2x \cos x^2.$$

For the average beginning student, (1) and (2) are separate and unrelated formulas.

We are not intending to suggest that the other forms of the chain rule would be more useful to the beginning calculus student, but merely to indicate the difficulties which can arise because of the fact that a given function value can be a function value for each of many different functions. These difficulties are greatly increased when we come to functions of several variables and try to deal with partial derivatives (we shall give below an illustration of a problem involving partial derivatives which is particularly baffling to the average student). This situation is particularly aggravated in some subject such as thermodynamics, where it is usually the functions, rather than the function values, which are significant, but in which it is always the function values which appear in the formulas.

Another subject in which there is a delicate interplay between the use of functions and function values is the subject of differential equations. This interplay is completely concealed by the notation, which is traditionally in terms exclusively of function values. For example, the average student in a course in differential equations will find it extremely difficult (if not impossible) to prove the following true statement:

"If y is a solution of $y'' - 2xy' + ny = 0$, and z is got from y by replacing n by $-n - 2$ and x by ix, then

$$z\, e^{x^2}$$

is also a solution."

In passing, we might say a word about differentials. The standard definition is

$$df(x) = f'(x)\, dx.$$

The expression on the right is a function value of *three* independent quantities, namely, f, x, and dx. In the earliest tradition of calculus, before a clear notion of limit, derivative, etc., evolved, it was considered that dy is a function value of y only. It is quite clear that $f'(x)\, dx$ is not a function value of y alone, but numerous attempts have been made to interpret it so, and controversies have raged between proponents of differing interpretations. The truth simply is that $f'(x)\, dx$ is a function value of three independent quantities f, x, and dx, which behaves sufficiently like the traditional symbol dy that one can preserve the traditional formulas of calculus. Perhaps the time is overdue for a break with a few more of the traditional formulas of calculus.

Clearly, an important fact about function values is that, unless the independent variable is carefully specified, one cannot claim that the function value determines a definite function. This fact is widely known but often carelessly ignored. This may explain part of the reason for concentrating on the function rather than the function value in modern mathematics. This point is relevant in connection with such notions as continuity, integrability, etc. When applied to functions, no specification of the independent variable is necessary, but when applied to function values, the independent variable must be carefully specified.

Failure to make such specification leads to such confusing remarks as the classic remark which appears in a certain text on the theory of functions of a real variable, and which says that, although every continuous function of a continuous function is a continuous function, it is not true that every integrable function of an integrable function is an integrable function.

Upon looking at the proof given for this remarkable statement, one is able to see that its author was using the word "function" in the sense of "function value" and that the meaning of the statement is:

"If $f(x)$ and $g(x)$ are continuous function values of x with respect to x, then $g(f(x))$ is a continuous function value of x with respect to x, but it is not true that if $f(x)$ and $g(x)$ are integrable function values of x with respect to x, then $g(f(x))$ is an integrable function value of x with respect to x."

Using the fact that $g(f(x)) = (f|g)(x)$, the above statement can be put much more simply in terms of functions as follows:

"If f and g are continuous functions, then $f|g$ is a continuous function, but it is not true that if f and g are integrable functions, then $f|g$ is an integrable function."

In most calculus texts $f(x)$ is called a "function" rather than a "function value." As we said earlier, this is perfectly acceptable provided that one does not use the word "function" to refer to f. This leaves the writer of the calculus text with no terminology for the "function" f. One could quite properly call f a transformation, but there is a prejudice against this, particularly at the calculus level. As a result, the writer of the calculus text will usually prefer to express formulas in terms of function values rather than in terms of functions. A notable exception is the formula for Taylor's series, which is usually written by means of the function notation as

$$f(a+h) = f(a) + \frac{h}{1!}f'(a) + \frac{h^2}{2!}f''(a) + \cdots,$$

instead of being written in the more cumbersome function-value notation as

$$[y]_{x=a+h} = [y]_{x=a} + \frac{h}{1!}\left[\frac{dy}{dx}\right]_{x=a} + \frac{h^2}{2!}\left[\frac{d^2y}{dx^2}\right]_{x=a} + \cdots.$$

This usually confuses the students, since the earlier explanation of $f'(x)$ as $\frac{d}{dx}f(x)$ is likely to lead the student to think of $\frac{d}{dx}f(a)$ rather than

$$\left[\frac{d}{dx}f(x)\right]_{x=a}$$

as the interpretation of $f'(a)$. This is why there is nearly always some student in a class (usually one of the better students) who inquires why $f'(a)$, $f''(a)$, . . . are not all zero.

In elementary calculus, this preoccupation with function values, to the almost total exclusion of functions, is not particularly disadvantageous, except in connection with partial derivatives. There the need for accurate specification of what the arguments of the function values are and what the variable of differentiation is, and what the variable is which is "held constant," make it much more suitable to deal with functions rather than function values, except for the lack of any suitable terminology for doing so at the calculus level. As a result of the lack of care in the usual function-value presentation of partial derivatives, the average student is completely unprepared to deal with such problems as the transformation from coordinates (x,y) to coordinates (r,θ), with subsequent manipulation of such quantities as

$$\frac{\partial x}{\partial y} \qquad (\theta \text{ constant}),$$

$$\frac{\partial}{\partial r} f(x,\theta),$$

etc.

We are not suggesting that one should go to the other extreme and try to dispense with function values in favor of functions at all points. Rather, we favor having a terminology for both functions and function values, so that one can use whichever is most suitable to the occasion at hand.

Such terminology is gradually coming into use. In the meantime, there is the question how one should teach functions in a calculus course. There is one calculus book on the market (Randolph and Kac) which tries consistently to refer to f rather than $f(x)$ as a function. However, they lack a name for $f(x)$, and this involves them in many difficulties. All other calculus texts that we know of refer to $f(x)$ as a function and have no name for f. In teaching from such a text, it will probably be best to go along with the text in calling $f(x)$ a function. One can explain to the students that f stands for the rule which determines for any value of x the value to be assigned to $f(x)$. One could consistently refer to f as the "function rule" of the "function" $f(x)$. One should of course emphasize most strongly the necessity for specifying the argument variable when referring to a "function" or to differentiation, continuity, etc., of a "function." One should probably not expect any but the best students to comprehend the distinction between the derivative of a "function rule" f and the derivative with respect to x of a "function" $f(x)$. A careful treatment of such subtleties, like a careful treatment of limits and real numbers, must probably be postponed to the course in analysis, at which time one can change terminology and begin referring to f as the function, using some suitable (and different) terminology for $f(x)$.

Such a program is very unsound, in that it requires the student to learn two contradictory uses of the word "function." It is to be hoped that a suitable calculus text which refers to f as a function and has a suitable terminology for $f(x)$ will soon be available, or else that the present trend in higher mathematics toward calling f a function will be reversed. As we have repeatedly said, one could call $f(x)$ a function and f a transformation. However, the present trend is not in this direction.

In higher mathematics beyond the calculus, it becomes much more necessary to have facility in the use of both functions and function values. However, even in higher mathematics, confusion of functions with function values is the rule at the present time. Even writers who are very careful about other matters allow the bad habits acquired in some early calculus course to prevail when speaking of functions. The most common practice is to perpetuate the calculus custom of calling $f(x)$ a function and having no terminology for f. When one wishes to deal with function spaces, such as the space L^2, such a treatment of functions is very awkward. Alternatively, other writers set out to use "function" to mean f and then have no terminology for $f(x)$. For instance, we could cite one excellent and (in the main) carefully written text which introduces functions with the statement:

"The notion of function is identical with the notion of transformation of one space with another."

This is an unequivocal statement that the author proposes to use the word "function" in our sense, as denoting f rather than $f(x)$. However, his old habits are too strong for him, and only eight pages later, we find him using and defining the statement "the function $f(x)$ tends to b as x tends to a."

It would be very awkward to make this statement in terms of functions rather than function values, and we approve of using function values rather than functions in the statement. However, after the author has reserved the word "function" to denote f, he should not use it to denote $f(x)$. If the statement were written "the function value $f(x)$ tends to b as x tends to a," it would be quite unobjectionable.

Here, as usually, the source of the difficulty is in failing to provide separate terminologies for f and $f(x)$.

If one has a function f and an argument x, there is the standard notation for the corresponding function value, to wit, $f(x)$. The problem is, given a function value, x^2, to write a formula for the corresponding function. We have been using $\{\langle x,y\rangle \mid y = x^2\}$, which is adequate, but space-consuming. Following a suggestion of Church, we define

$$\lambda x(A) \qquad \text{for} \qquad \{\langle x,y\rangle \mid y = A.x = x\}$$

where y is a variable not appearing in A. Then

$$\vdash (\lambda x(A))(x) = A.$$

The additional "$x = x$" which we have inserted on the right side plays no role except to ensure that both x and y have free occurrences on the right (even when A contains no free occurrences of x) so that our conventions as to the meaning of $\{\langle x,y\rangle \mid y = A.x = x\}$ will make it denote the class of all ordered pairs $\langle x,y\rangle$ such that $y = A$. Thus, we have the notation $\lambda x(x^2)$ for the function determined by the function value x^2 considered as a function value of the independent variable x, and

$$\vdash (x).(\lambda x(x^2))(x) = x^2,$$

and in general

$$\vdash (\lambda x(x^2))(B) = B^2,$$

where B is any term.

The decision to reserve the word "function" to denote f and use some other term, such as "function value" to denote $f(x)$ will require various changes in our familiar treatment of mathematical entities if one is to be consistent. Thus it is standard procedure to consider a sequence as a function of positive integers. That is, we identify a_n with $a(n)$. Then a_n would be a function value rather than a function. The sequence, being the corresponding function would be denoted by $\lambda n(a_n)$. It is significant that some writers feel the distinction between the sequence, $\lambda n(a_n)$, and an arbitrary term of the sequence, a_n, sufficiently to write $\{a_n\}$ to denote the sequence, and to distinguish carefully between $\{a_n\}$ and a_n.

Although inconsistency in the use of the word "function" is common, inconsistency in the use of the symbols f and $f(x)$ is rare. An exception is in the treatment of group characters. A group character is a function whose argument range is the set of members of the group. Nevertheless, it is current practice to denote a group character by some such symbol as $\chi(s)$, where s denotes a variable which takes the members of the group as values. Thus, $\chi(s)$, which is a symbol for a function value, is used to denote a function. This is quite confusing. Clearly $\chi(s)$ depends on s, since by giving different values to s, we get different values for $\chi(s)$. However, the group character depends only on the group and the particular representation of the group which is involved; in fact, we have the theorem that (under appropriate hypotheses as to the nature of the group), "two representations are identical when and only when their characters are the same." Thus a notation such as $\chi(s)$, which certainly depends upon s, is clearly unsuitable for referring to a group character. The obvious solution is to speak of χ as the group character and use $\chi(s)$ only when one wishes to speak of the value of χ for the argument s (this happens occasionally).

Another case in which one uses $f(x)$ where f should be used is in Laplace transforms. A standard notation is to write $F(s) = \mathfrak{L}(f(t))$ to denote

$$F(s) = \int_0^\infty e^{-st} f(t)\, dt.$$

Clearly a more suitable notation would be $F = \mathfrak{L}(f)$, since it is really the functions rather than the function values which are transformed by the Laplace operator. This becomes clear if one tries to ascribe any connection between the variables s and t in $F(s) = \mathfrak{L}(f(t))$. In any genuine relation between function values, such as $(d/dx)x^2 = 2x$, the x's on one side of the equation must have some connection with the x's on the other side. There can be no such connection between the s and t in $F(s) = \mathfrak{L}(f(t))$, and so this might better be written $F = \mathfrak{L}(f)$.

If we differentiate the formula which this represents, we get

$$F'(s) = \int_0^\infty e^{-st}(-t\, f(t))\, dt.$$

This is commonly written

$$F'(s) = \mathcal{L}(-t\,f(t)).$$

In fact, books on Laplace transforms commonly state as a theorem:

If $F(s) = \mathcal{L}(f(t))$, then $F'(s) = \mathcal{L}(-t\,f(t))$.

Without a notation for the function associated with a function value, it would be difficult to write this theorem properly. However, using the notation which we suggested, we can write it as:

If $F = \mathcal{L}(f)$, then $DF = \mathcal{L}(\lambda t(-t\,f(t)))$.

Indeed, one can write it more simply still as:

$$D\mathcal{L}(f) = \mathcal{L}(\lambda t(-t\,f(t))).$$

A few careful writers write $\{F(s)\} = \mathcal{L}\{f(t)\}$, the $\{\quad\}$ indicating that one is dealing with the function rather than the function value. In fact, one may conjecture that for such writers the following definition is tacitly in effect:

If A is a term containing free occurrences of one and only one variable, x, then $\{A\}$ shall denote $\lambda x(A)$.

We could not use such a notation ourselves, since it would collide with another interpretation for $\{A\}$ which we have already adopted. Also, it is much less flexible than the notation $\lambda x(A)$, which permits that A not contain free occurrences of x at all (so that one can get a constant function) or that A contain additional free variables (so that the function $\lambda x(A)$ can depend on various parameters). Also there is apparently a reluctance to use $\{F(x)\}$ interchangeably with F, $\{F'(x)\}$ interchangeably with DF, etc. This latter is a minor point but results in a considerable loss of flexibility. There is also the difficulty that in $\{F(x)\}$ it must be clear that x is a variable and F is not.

When one deals with functions as well as function values, it is very easily seen that D is a function whose function values are derivatives of functions. Thus we can define

$$D = \{\langle f,g\rangle \mid g = f'\} = \lambda f(f'),$$

and then have

$$\vdash (f).D(f) = Df = f'.$$

Because the arguments and values of D are functions, D is often referred to as an "operator" rather than as a "function." This is probably due in part to the confusion in the use of the word "function." Similarly, the $\mathcal{L}$ of the Laplace transform is called an operator rather than a function. In our sense of the word "function," an operator is a perfectly good function but rather specialized.

In case f and x are both variables, then $f(x)$ contains free variables other than x, namely, f, and is not strictly a function value of x, any more than

$x + y$ is. Rather $f(x)$ is a function value of the two argument variables f and x, just as $x + y$ is a function value of the two argument variables x and y. However, in the combination $f(x)$, it is usual to think of f as standing for some particular function, and not a variable, and x as standing for (or being) a variable. In such case, it is proper to refer to $f(x)$ as a function value of x. This is analogous to $x + a$, where a is thought of as a constant but x as a variable. Then $x + a$ is a function value of the argument variable x; however, as long as a remains unspecified, we do not know just what function $x + a$ is a value of, any more than we know what function $f(x)$ is a function value of as long as f remains unspecified.

We can write $\lambda x(x + y)$, and then we have a function depending on the parameter y. In such a case, mathematical tradition would require that we use $\lambda x(x + a)$ instead, but clearly the difference is one of notation only. The function $\lambda x(x + y)$ is the function of "adding y."

The fact that we allow in the symbolic logic terms with no meaning leads to minor discrepancies between our terminology and that current in mathematics. This comes about as follows.

By Thm.VII.2.2,

$$\vdash (f,x)(\mathrm{E}_1 z).z = f(x).$$

This would seem to say that $f(x)$ is defined and unique for every f and x. Such is not the case at all.

We recall that $f(x)$ is $\iota y\ (xfy)$. In Chapter VIII, we pointed out that, for any $F(y)$, we could form the combination $\iota y\ F(y)$ and prove various insignificant properties of $\iota y\ F(y)$ by means of Axiom schemes 8, 9, and 10. However, to prove any really significant properties of $\iota y\ F(y)$, we must have $(\mathrm{E}_1 y)\ F(y)$, so that we can use Axiom scheme 11 to infer $F(\iota y\ F(y))$.

So it is with $f(x)$. In case we have $(\mathrm{E}_1 y)\ xfy$, then we can use Axiom scheme 11 to infer that $xf(f(x))$. In such case $f(x)$ exists in the usual mathematical sense of the existence of a function value. Alternatively one says that $f(x)$ is defined at x.

The fact that Axiom schemes 8, 9, and 10 give $f(x)$ a sort of spurious existence for any x or f is a trifle confusing. What it means is that "existence of $f(x)$" in the mathematical sense is not actually a statement about $f(x)$, despite its misleading grammatical form, but rather a statement about f and x separately. Thus the statement "$f(x)$ is defined at x" would be rendered symbolically as $(\mathrm{E}_1 y)\ xfy$, and in this form does not contain the combination $f(x)$ at all.

Thus if we are dealing with real variables and put

$$f = \{\langle x,y\rangle \mid y \geq 0.y^2 = x\},$$

then

$$\vdash (x)(\mathrm{E}_1 z).z = f(x).$$

However, only for $x \geq 0$ do we have $(E_1 y)\ xfy$, and so only for $x \geq 0$ do we have $xf(f(x))$. That is, we have

$$\vdash (x){:}x \geq 0. \supset .f(x) \geq 0.(f(x))^2 = x,$$

but not

$$\vdash (x).f(x) \geq 0.(f(x))^2 = x,$$

although we do have

$$\vdash (x)(E_1 z).z = f(x)$$

as well as

$$\vdash (x){:}x \geq 0. \supset .(E_1 z).z = f(x).$$

So "$f(x)$ is defined" only for $x \geq 0$. For this f, the values of x for which "$f(x)$ is defined" are just Arg(f), which in the case of a function is called the range.

If we wish to restrict the range of "existence" of $f(x)$ to some class α, we have only to replace f by $\alpha \rceil f$.

There is one unfortunate aspect of the notation $y = \mathbf{R}(x)$, and this is that it reverses the accustomed order of x and $\mathbf{R}$ in $x\mathbf{R}y$. Thus for a function $\mathbf{R}$ we have (for x in Arg($\mathbf{R}$), where "$\mathbf{R}(\mathbf{R})$ is defined")

$$y = \mathbf{R}(x). \equiv .x\mathbf{R}y,$$

in which x, $\mathbf{R}$, and y run in reverse order on the two sides of the equivalence. One could have avoided this, as Whitehead and Russell did, by always writing $x\mathbf{R}y$ in the reverse order $y\mathbf{R}x$. However, this would require

$$\langle x,y \rangle \in \mathbf{R}. \equiv .y\mathbf{R}x,$$

and the reversal of order here seems even worse. As a matter of fact, mathematicians habitually derive points (x,y) from equations $y = f(x)$, and are accustomed to the reversal, and so we have followed the current mathematical practice. If $\mathbf{R}$ and $\mathbf{S}$ are functions, then the reversal appears again in the fact that $(\mathbf{R}|\mathbf{S})(x) = \mathbf{S}(\mathbf{R}(x))$. This same reversal appears in mathematics, in that if one has transformations f and g and forms the product transformation fg (which is just $f|g$), then fg transforms the point x into $g(f(x))$.

We turn now to formal properties of functions.

****Theorem X.5.1.** $\vdash (R){::}R \in \text{Funct.}{:} \equiv {:}.R \in \text{Rel}{:}(x,y,z){:}xRy.xRz. \supset .\ y = z.$

Corollary 1. $\vdash \text{Funct} \subseteq \text{Rel}.$

Corollary 2. $\vdash (\mathbf{R}){:}.\mathbf{R} \in \text{Funct}{:} \equiv {:}(x,y,z){:}x\mathbf{R}y.x\mathbf{R}z. \supset .y = z.$

Corollary 3. $\vdash (\mathbf{R}){:}.\breve{\mathbf{R}} \in \text{Funct}{:} \equiv {:}(x,y,z){:}x\mathbf{R}z.y\mathbf{R}z. \supset .x = y.$

Theorem X.5.2. $\vdash (\mathbf{R}){:}.\mathbf{R} \in \text{Funct}{:} \equiv {:}(x){:}x \in \text{Arg}(\mathbf{R}). \equiv .(E_1 y).x\mathbf{R}y.$

Proof. Assume $\mathbf{R} \in$ Funct. Then $(y,z){:}x\mathbf{R}y.x\mathbf{R}z. \supset .y = z$. So

$$(Ey).x\mathbf{R}y{::} \equiv {::}(Ey)\ x\mathbf{R}y{:}.(y,z){:}x\mathbf{R}y.x\mathbf{R}z. \supset .y = z.$$

So by Thm.X.4.1, Part I, and Thm.VII.2.1,

$$x \in \text{Arg}(\mathbf{R}). \equiv .(\text{E}_1 y).x\mathbf{R}y.$$

Conversely, assume the latter and let $x\mathbf{R}y.x\mathbf{R}z$. Then $x \in \text{Arg}(\mathbf{R})$. So $(\text{E}_1 y)\ x\mathbf{R}y$. That is, $(\text{E}w)(y):w = y. \equiv .x\mathbf{R}y$. So by rule C, $(y):w = y. \equiv .x\mathbf{R}y$. Hence $w = y$ and $w = z$, and so $y = z$.

Corollary. $\vdash (\mathbf{R}):.\breve{\mathbf{R}} \in \text{Funct}: \equiv :(y):y \in \text{Val}(\mathbf{R}). \equiv .(\text{E}_1 x).x\mathbf{R}y.$

This theorem says that for a function f the range of arguments is just the set of values of x for which "$f(x)$ is defined."

****Theorem X.5.3.** $\vdash (R,x):.R \in \text{Funct}.x \in \text{Arg}(R): \supset :(y):y = R(x). \equiv .xRy.$

Proof. Use Thm.X.5.1, Cor. 1, Thm.X.5.2, and Axiom scheme 11.

Corollary 1. $\vdash (R,x):R \in \text{Funct}.x \in \text{Arg}(R). \supset .xR(R(x)).$

Corollary 2. $\vdash (R,y):.\breve{R} \in \text{Funct}.y \in \text{Val}(R): \supset :(x): x = \breve{R}(y). \equiv .xRy.$

Corollary 3. $\vdash (R,y):\breve{R} \in \text{Funct}.y \in \text{Val}(R). \supset .(\breve{R}(y))Ry.$

***Corollary 4.** $\vdash (R,x):R \in \text{Funct}.x \in \text{Arg}(R). \supset .R(x) \in \text{Val}(R).$

***Corollary 5.** $\vdash (R,x):\breve{R} \in \text{Funct}.y \in \text{Val}(R). \supset .\breve{R}(y) \in \text{Arg}(R).$

Theorem X.5.4. $\vdash (R,y).y \in \text{Val}(R). \supset .y(\breve{R}|R)y.$

Proof. Assume $y \in \text{Val}(R)$. Then $(\text{E}x).xRy$. So $(\text{E}x).y\breve{R}x.xRy$. That is, $y(\breve{R}|R)y$.

Corollary. $\vdash (R).\text{Arg}(\breve{R}|R) = \text{Val}(\breve{R}|R) = \text{Val}(R).$

Theorem X.5.5. $\vdash (R,y,z):R \in \text{Funct}.y(\breve{R}|R)z. \supset .y = z.$

Proof. Assume $R \in \text{Funct}$ and $y(\breve{R}|R)z$. Then by rule C, $y\breve{R}x.xRz$. So xRy and xRz. So $y = z$.

Corollary 1. $\vdash (R):.R \in \text{Funct}: \supset :(y,z):y(\breve{R}|R)z. \equiv .y = z.y \in \text{Val}(R).$

Corollary 2. $\vdash (R):R \in \text{Funct}. \supset .\breve{R}|R \in \text{Funct}.$

Corollary 3. $\vdash (R,y):R \in \text{Funct}.y \in \text{Val}(R). \supset .y = (\breve{R}|R)(y).$

This tells us that sin (arcsin x) $= x$ regardless of the determination of arcsin x. Also, if f is a continuous function and we define $\int f(x)\,dx$ as an antiderivative, then

$$\frac{d}{dx}\int f(x)\,dx = f(x)$$

regardless of the constant of integration used in

$$\int f(x)\,dx.$$

Theorem X.5.6. $\vdash (R,\alpha,\beta):R \in \text{Funct}.\beta \subseteq R``\alpha. \supset .\beta = R``((\breve{R}``\beta) \cap \alpha).$

Proof. Assume $R \in \text{Funct}$ and $\beta \subseteq R``\alpha$. Let $y \in \beta$. Then $y \in R``\alpha$. So by Thm.X.4.22 and rule C, $xRy.x \in \alpha$. So $xRy.x \in \alpha.xRy.y \in \beta$. So by Thm.X.4.23, corollary, $xRy.x \in \alpha.x \in \breve{R}``\beta$. So $xRy.x \in (\breve{R}``\beta) \cap \alpha$. So $y \in R``((\breve{R}``\beta) \cap \alpha)$. Conversely, assume $y \in R``((\breve{R}``\beta) \cap \alpha)$. Then by rule C, $xRy.x \in (\breve{R}``\beta) \cap \alpha$. So by rule C, $xRy.x \in \alpha.xRz.z \in \beta$. So $y = z$, $z \in \beta$. So $y \in \beta$.

Corollary. $\vdash (R)::R \epsilon \text{Funct}.: \supset :.(\alpha,\beta).\beta \subseteq R``\alpha: \equiv :(\text{E}\gamma).\gamma \subseteq \alpha.\beta = R``\gamma$.

Proof. To go from left to right, take γ to be $(\breve{R}``\beta) \cap \alpha$. To go from right to left, use Thm.X.4.25.

From the point of view of transformation theory, $R``\alpha$ is the map of the class $\alpha$ by the transformation $R$. Our corollary states that, if $\beta$ is included in the map of $\alpha$, then $\beta$ is the map of some $\gamma$ which is included in $\alpha$. Moreover, the theorem names such a $\gamma$, to wit, $(\breve{R}``\beta) \cap \alpha$. In general, such a γ need not be unique, though if R is univalent (meaning that $R,\breve{R} \epsilon$ Funct), then the γ will be unique.

Theorem X.5.7. $\vdash (R,S):R \epsilon \text{Funct}.S \subseteq R. \supset .S \epsilon \text{Funct}$.

Proof. Assume $R \epsilon$ Funct and $S \subseteq R$. Then $R \epsilon$ Rel and so $S \epsilon$ Rel. Now let $xSy.xSz$. Then, by $S \subseteq R$, $xRy.xRz$. So by $R \epsilon$ Funct, $y = z$.

***Corollary.** $\vdash (R,\alpha,\beta):R \epsilon \text{Funct}. \supset .\alpha\rceil R, R\lceil\beta, \alpha\rceil R\lceil\beta \epsilon \text{Funct}$.

Theorem X.5.8. $\vdash (R,S):R \epsilon \text{Funct}.S \subseteq R. \supset .S = \text{Arg}(S)\rceil R$.

Proof. Assume $R \epsilon$ Funct and $S \subseteq R$. Let xSy. Then $x \epsilon \text{Arg}(S)$ and xRy. So $x(\text{Arg}(S)\rceil R)y$. Conversely, let $x(\text{Arg}(S)\rceil R)y$. Then by rule C, xSz and xRy. So xRz. Hence $y = z$. Hence xSy.

This tells us that a relation S is included in a function R if and only if S is a function got by restricting the range of definition of the function R.

****Theorem X.5.9.** $\vdash (R,S):R,S \epsilon \text{Funct}. \supset .R|S \epsilon \text{Funct}$.

Proof. Assume $R,S \epsilon$ Funct. By Thm.X.4.17, Part II, $R|S \epsilon$ Rel. Now let $x(R|S)y$ and $x(R|S)z$. By rule C, $xRu.uSy$ and $xRv.vSz$. So, since $R \epsilon$ Funct, $u = v$. So uSy and uSz. So, since $S \epsilon$ Funct, $y = z$.

This tells us that the product of two transformations is a transformation, since $R|S$ is just the product of the transformations R and S. With Thm.X.4.18 telling us that the multiplication of transformations is associative, and with $\hat{x}\hat{y}(x = y)$ serving as the identity transformation, we see that the set of all transformations of a set into itself forms a semigroup.

We define the identity transformation, I, taking

$$I \quad \text{for} \quad \hat{x}\hat{y}(x = y).$$

I is stratified and may be assigned any desired type, since it has no free variables.

Theorem X.5.10.

I. $\vdash (x,y):xIy. \equiv .x = y$.

II. $\vdash I \epsilon \text{Funct}$.

III. $\vdash I = \breve{I}$.

IV. $\vdash \text{Arg}(I) = \text{Val}(I) = \text{V}$.

V. $\vdash (x).I(x) = x$.

****Theorem X.5.11.** $\vdash (\mathbf{R}).\mathbf{R} = \mathbf{R}|I = I|\mathbf{R}$.

Proof of $\vdash \mathbf{R} = \mathbf{R}|I$.

$$\vdash x\mathbf{R}z. \equiv .(Ey).x\mathbf{R}y.y = z$$
$$. \equiv .(Ey).x\mathbf{R}y.yIz$$
$$. \equiv .x(\mathbf{R}|I)z.$$

The proof of $\vdash \mathbf{R} = I|\mathbf{R}$ is similar.

This theorem tells us that multiplication by the identity transformation leaves any transformation unchanged.

Theorem X.5.12. $\vdash (\alpha).\alpha\rceil I = I\lceil\alpha = \alpha\rceil I\lceil\alpha.$

Proof.

$$\vdash x \epsilon \alpha.x = y. \equiv .x = y.y \epsilon \alpha.$$
$$\equiv .x \epsilon \alpha.x = y.y \epsilon \alpha.$$

Corollary. $\vdash (R):R \epsilon \text{Funct}. \supset .\breve{R}|R = \text{Val}(R)\rceil I = I\lceil\text{Val}(R) = \text{Val}(R)\rceil I\lceil\text{Val}(R).$

Use Thm.X.5.5, Cor. 1.

Theorem X.5.13. $\vdash (R)::R \epsilon \text{Funct}.: \supset :.(S,x,y):x(R|S)y. \equiv .x \epsilon \text{Arg}(R).(R(x))Sy.$

Proof. Assume $R \epsilon$ Funct. Now let $x(R|S)y$. Then by rule C, xRz and zSy. So $x \epsilon \text{Arg}(R)$. Then by Thm.X.5.3, $z = R(x)$. So $(R(x))Sy$. Conversely, let $x \epsilon \text{Arg}(R)$ and $(R(x))Sy$. Then by Thm.X.5.3, Cor. 1, $xR(R(x))$. So $x(R|S)y$.

Corollary. $\vdash (R,x):.R \epsilon \text{Funct}.x \epsilon \text{Arg}(R): \supset :(S,y):x(R|S)y. \equiv .(R(x))Sy.$

Theorem X.5.14. $\vdash (R,x):.R \epsilon \text{Funct}.x \epsilon \text{Arg}(R): \supset :(S).(R|S)(x) = S(R(x)).$

Proof. Assume $R \epsilon$ Funct and $x \epsilon \text{Arg}(R)$. So by Thm.X.5.13, corollary, $(y).x(R|S)y \equiv (R(x))Sy$. So by Axiom scheme 9, $\iota y\ (x(R|S)y) = \iota y\ ((R(x))Sy)$. That is, $(R|S)(x) = S(R(x))$.

This theorem merely verifies what we have said several times already, that the product fg of two transformations f and g is a transformation h such that

$$h(x) = g(f(x)).$$

The fact that we do not require that g be a transformation is a convenient peculiarity due to our method of treating ι. For fg to be a transformation, it will usually be necessary for both f and g to be transformations.

Theorem X.5.15. $\vdash (\alpha,R,x):R \epsilon \text{Funct}.x \epsilon \alpha \cap \text{Arg}(R). \supset .R(x) \epsilon R``\alpha.$

Proof. Assume $R \epsilon$ Funct and $x \epsilon \alpha \cap \text{Arg}(R)$. Then by Thm.X.5.3, Cor. 1, $xR(R(x)).x \epsilon \alpha$. So by Thm.X.4.22, $R(x) \epsilon R``\alpha$.

****Theorem X.5.16.** $\vdash (R,S)::R,S \epsilon \text{Funct}.\text{Arg}(R) = \text{Arg}(S):.(x):x \epsilon \text{Arg}(R). \supset .R(x) = S(x).: \supset :.R = S.$

Proof. Assume the hypothesis, and let xRy. Then $x \epsilon \text{Arg}(R)$. Then $R(x) = S(x)$ by hypothesis, and $y = R(x)$ by Thm.X.5.3, so that $y = S(x)$. Now from $x \epsilon \text{Arg}(R)$, we get $x \epsilon \text{Arg}(S)$ by hypothesis, thence $xS(S(x))$ by

Thm.X.5.3, Cor. 1. Combining with $y = S(x)$ gives xSy. As $R,S \in$ Funct, we have $R,S \in$ Rel, and so $R \subseteq S$. One proves $S \subseteq R$ similarly.

In words, this theorem states that, if two functions are defined for the same set of arguments, and always take equal values, then the functions are the same. This provides the most commonly used means of proving two functions equal.

Theorem X.5.17. $\vdash (\mathbf{R}){:}\mathbf{R} \in \text{Funct}. \equiv .\text{RUSC}(\mathbf{R}) \in \text{Funct}.$

Proof. Assume $\mathbf{R} \in$ Funct and let $x(\text{RUSC}(\mathbf{R}))y$ and $x(\text{RUSC}(\mathbf{R}))z$. By rule C, $u\mathbf{R}v.x = \{u\}.y = \{v\}$ and $u'\mathbf{R}v'.x = \{u'\}.z = \{v'\}$. Then $\{u\} = \{u'\}$. So $u' = u$. So $u\mathbf{R}v'$. So $v = v'$. So $y = z$. Conversely let RUSC($\mathbf{R}$) $\in$ Funct, and let $x\mathbf{R}y$ and $x\mathbf{R}z$. Then $\{x\}(\text{RUSC}(\mathbf{R}))\{y\}$ and $\{x\}(\text{RUSC}(\mathbf{R}))\{z\}$. So $\{y\} = \{z\}$. So $y = z$.

Theorem X.5.18. $\vdash (R,x){:}R \in \text{Funct}.x \in \text{Arg}(R). \supset .(\text{RUSC}(R))(\{x\}) = \{R(x)\}.$

Proof. Assume $R \in$ Funct and $x \in \text{Arg}(R)$. Then $\{x\} \in \text{USC}(\text{Arg}(R))$. So by Thm.X.4.29, Part I, $\{x\} \in \text{Arg}(\text{RUSC}(R))$. Also, by Thm.X.5.17, RUSC(R) $\in$ Funct. So by Thm.X.5.3

$$(1) \qquad (y).\{x\}(\text{RUSC}(R))y \equiv y = (\text{RUSC}(R))(\{x\}).$$

By the hypothesis and Thm.X.5.3, $xR(R(x))$. So $\{x\}(\text{RUSC}(R))\{R(x)\}$. So by (1), $\{R(x)\} = (\text{RUSC}(R))(\{x\})$.

Of considerable importance are univalent transformations or 1-1 relations, that is, relations R such that $R,\breve{R} \in$ Funct. So we define

$$\text{1-1} \quad \text{for} \quad \hat{R}(R,\breve{R} \in \text{Funct}).$$

Clearly 1-1 is stratified, and may be assigned any type, since it contains no free variables.

Theorem X.5.19. $\vdash (R){:}R \in \text{1-1}. \equiv .R,\breve{R} \in \text{Funct}.$

Corollary 1. $\vdash \text{1-1} \subseteq \text{Funct}.$

Corollary 2. $\vdash (R){:}R \in \text{Funct}. \supset .\breve{R}|R \in \text{1-1}.$

Proof. Use Thm.X.5.5, Cor. 2, to get $\breve{R}|R \in$ Funct. But $\vdash \text{Cnv}(\breve{R}|R) = \breve{R}|\text{Cnv}(\breve{R}) = \breve{R}|R$, so that also $\text{Cnv}(\breve{R}|R) \in$ Funct.

Corollary 3. $\vdash (R){:}R \in \text{1-1}. \supset .\breve{R}|R,\ R|\breve{R} \in \text{1-1}.$

Corollary 4. $\vdash (R,S){:}R \in \text{1-1}.S \subseteq R. \supset .S \in \text{1-1}.$

Corollary 5. $\vdash (\alpha,\beta,R){:}R \in \text{1-1}. \supset .\alpha\rceil R, R\lceil\beta,\ \alpha\rceil R\lceil\beta \in \text{1-1}.$

Corollary 6. $\vdash (R,S){:}R,S \in \text{1-1}. \supset .R|S \in \text{1-1}.$

Corollary 7. $\vdash (\mathbf{R}){:}\mathbf{R} \in \text{1-1}. \equiv .\breve{\mathbf{R}} \in \text{1-1}.$

Corollary 8. $\vdash I \in \text{1-1}.$

Corollary 9. $\vdash (\mathbf{R}){:}\mathbf{R} \in \text{1-1}. \equiv .\text{RUSC}(\mathbf{R}) \in \text{1-1}.$

Theorem X.5.20.

I. $\vdash (R,x){:}R \in \text{1-1}.x \in \text{Arg}(R). \supset .\breve{R}(R(x)) = x.$

*II. $\vdash (R,y){:}R \in \text{1-1}.y \in \text{Val}(R). \supset .R(\breve{R}(y)) = y.$

Proof of Part I. Assume $R \epsilon$ 1-1 and $x \epsilon \mathrm{Arg}(R)$. Then by Thm.X.5.14,

$$\breve{R}(R(x)) = (R|\breve{R})(x).$$

However $\breve{R} \epsilon$ Funct, so that by Thm.X.5.5, Cor. 3, $x \epsilon \mathrm{Val}(\breve{R}). \supset . x = (R|\breve{R})(x)$. As $\mathrm{Val}(\breve{R}) = \mathrm{Arg}(R)$, we get $x = (R|\breve{R})(x)$.

Proof of Part II. Similar.

Theorem X.5.21. $\vdash (R,S){:}R,S \epsilon \mathrm{Funct}.\mathrm{Arg}(R) \cap \mathrm{Arg}(S) = \Lambda. \supset . R \cup S \epsilon \mathrm{Funct}.$

Proof. Assume the hypothesis. Let $x(R \cup S)y.x(R \cup S)z$. Then $xRy.xRz.\mathbf{v}.xRy.xSz.\mathbf{v}.xSy.xRz.\mathbf{v}.xSy.xSz.$

Case 1. $xRy.xRz$. Then $y = z$.

Case 2. $xRy.xSz$. Then $x \epsilon \mathrm{Arg}(R).x \epsilon \mathrm{Arg}(S)$. This contradicts $\mathrm{Arg}(R) \cap \mathrm{Arg}(S) = \Lambda$, and so by reductio ad absurdum, $y = z$.

Case 3. Like Case 2.

Case 4. $xSy.xSz$. Then $y = z$.

So in any case $y = z$.

Corollary 1. $\vdash (R,S){:}\breve{R},\breve{S} \epsilon \mathrm{Funct}.\mathrm{Val}(R) \cap \mathrm{Val}(S) = \Lambda. \supset .\mathrm{Cnv}(R \cup S) \epsilon \mathrm{Funct}.$

Corollary 2. $\vdash (R,S){:}R,S \epsilon 1\text{-}1.\mathrm{Arg}(R) \cap \mathrm{Arg}(S) = \Lambda.\mathrm{Val}(R) \cap \mathrm{Val}(S) = \Lambda. \supset .R \cup S \epsilon 1\text{-}1.$

Theorem X.5.22. $\vdash (\alpha,R){:}R \epsilon \mathrm{Funct}. \supset .(\breve{R}|R)``\alpha = \alpha \cap \mathrm{Val}(R).$

Proof. Assume $R \epsilon$ Funct. Then by Thm.X.5.5, Cor. 1,

$$\begin{aligned} y \epsilon (\breve{R}|R)``\alpha. &\equiv .(\mathrm{E}x).x(\breve{R}|R)y.x \epsilon \alpha \\ .&\equiv .(\mathrm{E}x).x = y.x \epsilon \mathrm{Val}(R).x \epsilon \alpha \\ .&\equiv .y \epsilon \mathrm{Val}(R).y \epsilon \alpha. \end{aligned}$$

Corollary 1. $\vdash (\alpha,R){:}R \epsilon \mathrm{Funct}. \supset .R``(\breve{R}``\alpha) = \alpha \cap \mathrm{Val}(R).$

Corollary 2. $\vdash (\alpha,\beta,R){:}R \epsilon \mathrm{Funct}.\breve{R}``\alpha = \breve{R}``\beta. \supset .\alpha \cap \mathrm{Val}(R) = \beta \cap \mathrm{Val}(R).$

Corollary 3. $\vdash (\alpha,\beta,R){:}R \epsilon 1\text{-}1.R``\alpha = R``\beta. \supset .\alpha \cap \mathrm{Arg}(R) = \beta \cap \mathrm{Arg}(R).$

Suppose A is a term containing no free variables other than x. Then A is a function value of x. The corresponding function is $\hat{x}\hat{y}(y = A)$, where y is a variable not occurring in A. Because of the importance of this function, we introduce a shorter notation for it, namely,

$$\lambda x(A) \qquad \text{for} \qquad \hat{x}\hat{y}(y = A)$$

where y is a variable not occurring in A. Other than our specification on y, we make no specification about occurrences of variables in A. Thus, though the common usage of $\lambda x(A)$ is for A which contains free occurrences of x and of x only, we are permitted to use the notation for A with no free variables, so as to get a constant function, or for A with additional free variables, in which case we get a function involving parameters, namely, the free variables other than x which have occurrences in A. For stratification, it is necessary and sufficient that $x = A$ be stratified, and if $\lambda x(A)$ is stratified, it has type one higher than x (or A). All occurrences of x are bound in $\lambda x(A)$, but any other free occurrences of variables in A are free occurrences in $\lambda x(A)$ and constitute all the free occurrences in $\lambda x(A)$.

Clearly $\lambda x(x^2)$ is the function "square of," $\lambda x(4x)$ is the function "four times," etc. Consequently,

$$D(\lambda x(x^2)) = \lambda x(2x),$$

$$D(\lambda x(e^x)) = \lambda x(e^x),$$

etc.

Theorem X.5.23. If $x = A$ is stratified, then:

*I. $\vdash (x,y){:}x(\lambda x(A))y. \equiv .y = A.$

*II. $\vdash \lambda x(A) \epsilon$ Funct.

III. $\vdash (x).x(\lambda x(A))A.$

*IV. $\vdash \text{Arg}(\lambda x(A)) = \text{V}.$

V. $\vdash (x).(\lambda x(A))(x) = A.$

VI. $\vdash (w).(\lambda x(A))(w) = \{\text{Sub in } A{:}\ w \text{ for } x\}$, provided that the substitution indicated by $\{\text{Sub in } A{:}\ w \text{ for } x\}$ causes no confusion.

Proof. Part I follows by Thm.X.3.7. Then Part II follows by Thm. X.5.1. From Part I, we get Part III by replacing y by A. Then by Part III, we get $\vdash (x).x \,\epsilon\, \text{Arg}(\lambda x(A))$, so that Part IV follows. Now Part V follows by Thm.X.5.3 from Parts II, IV, and III. If we replace x by w in Part V, then we get Part VI.

Notice that, in this theorem, it is permitted that A contain other free variables besides x. Thus by Part VI we would have

$$\vdash (\lambda x(x + y))(w) = w + y,$$

$$\vdash (\lambda x(x + y))(y) = y + y,$$

etc.

However, $\lambda x(x + y)$ is not a function. It is a function value of y. If one gives y a particular value, such as 3, then one gets a function, namely, $\lambda x(x + 3)$, the function "plus 3." Nevertheless,

$$\vdash (\lambda x(x + y))(x) = x + y,$$

so that $\lambda x(x + y)$ has the behavior characteristic of a function (of x). The classical mathematical phrase for this situation is to say that $\lambda x(x + y)$ is a function dependent on the parameter y.

Theorem X.5.24. If the variable x occurs free in A and the variable α does not occur in A, and $x = A$ is stratified, then

$$\vdash (\alpha)\mathbf{:}(\lambda x(A))``\alpha = \{A \mid x \in \alpha\}.$$

Proof.

$$\begin{aligned}\vdash y \in (\lambda x(A))``\alpha\mathbf{:} &\equiv \mathbf{:}(\mathrm{E}x).x(\lambda x(A))y.x \in \alpha\mathbf{:}\\ &\equiv \mathbf{:}(\mathrm{E}x).y = A.x \in \alpha\mathbf{:}\\ &\equiv \mathbf{:}y \in \{A \mid x \in \alpha\}.\end{aligned}$$

Theorem X.5.25. $\vdash (R)\mathbf{:}R \in \mathrm{Funct.} \supset .\mathrm{Arg}(R)\rceil(\lambda x(R(x))) = R.$

Proof. Assume $R \in$ Funct. Let $x(\mathrm{Arg}(R)\rceil(\lambda x(R(x))))y$. Then $x \in \mathrm{Arg}(R).x(\lambda x(R(x)))y$. So $xR(R(x))$ and $y = R(x)$. So xRy. Conversely, assume xRy. Then $x \in \mathrm{Arg}(R)$. So $y = R(x)$. So $x(\lambda x(R(x)))y$. So $x(\mathrm{Arg}(R)\rceil(\lambda x(R(x))))y$.

Theorem X.5.26. $\vdash (\alpha,\beta,R)\mathbf{:.}\beta = \mathrm{Clos}(\alpha,xRz).R \in \mathrm{Funct}\mathbf{:} \supset \mathbf{:}(x)\mathbf{:} x \in \beta \cap \mathrm{Arg}(R). \supset .R(x) \in \beta.$

Proof. Assume $\beta = \mathrm{Clos}(\alpha,xRz)$, $R \in$ Funct, $x \in \beta$, $x \in \mathrm{Arg}(R)$. Then $x \in \beta.xR(R(x))$. So $R(x) \in R``\beta$. So by Thm.X.4.35, $R(x) \in \beta$.

Theorem X.5.27. If $x = A$ is stratified, and z has no free occurrences in A, then $\vdash (\alpha,\beta)\mathbf{:.}\beta = \mathrm{Clos}(\alpha,x(\lambda x(A))z)\mathbf{:} \supset \mathbf{:}(x).x \in \beta. \supset .A \in \beta.$

A function of two variables has to be a class of ordered triples. We recall that the ordered triple $\langle x,y,z\rangle$ is $\langle\langle x,y\rangle,z\rangle$. Then, since $\langle x,y\rangle Rz$ means $\langle\langle x,y\rangle,z\rangle \in R$, we have

$$\vdash \langle x,y,z\rangle \in R. \equiv .\langle x,y\rangle Rz.$$

We say that R is a function of the two variables x and y if

$$(x,y,u,v)\mathbf{:}\langle x,y\rangle Ru.\langle x,y\rangle Rv. \supset .u = v.$$

We write

$$R(x,y) \qquad \text{for} \qquad \iota z\ (\langle x,y\rangle Rz).$$

This makes $R(x,y)$ identical with $R(\langle x,y\rangle)$. Also, given a term A, we write

$$\lambda xy(A) \qquad \text{for} \qquad \{\langle x,y,z\rangle \mid z = A.x = x.y = y\}.$$

Then we have:

Theorem X.5.28. If $x = y = A$ is stratified, then:

$\star$I. $\vdash (x,y,z)\mathbf{:}\langle x,y\rangle(\lambda xy(A))z. \equiv .z = A.$

II. $\vdash (x,y,u,v)\mathbf{:}\langle x,y\rangle(\lambda xy(A))u.\langle x,y\rangle(\lambda xy(A))v. \supset .u = v.$

III. $\vdash \lambda xy(A) \in$ Funct.

IV. $\vdash (x,y).\langle x,y\rangle(\lambda xy(A))A.$

V. $\vdash \mathrm{Arg}(\lambda xy(A)) = \mathrm{V} \times \mathrm{V}.$

VI. $\vdash (x,y).(\lambda xy(A))(x,y) = A.$

VII. $\vdash (u,v).(\lambda xy(A))(u,v) = \{\text{Sub in } A : u \text{ for } x, v \text{ for } y\}$, provided that the substitutions indicated by $\{\text{Sub in } A : u \text{ for } x, v \text{ for } y\}$ cause no confusion.

We can proceed quite analogously to functions of n variables.

Let us now consider the question of how we handle relations and functions when dealing with variables of restricted range. If x,y,z are restricted to Σ, then $\mathbf{x},\mathbf{y},\mathbf{z}$ would be restricted to $\Sigma \times \Sigma$, and the corresponding $\mathbf{R},\mathbf{S},\mathbf{T}$ would be restricted to $\mathrm{SC}(\Sigma \times \Sigma)$. Thus Rel would be interpreted as $\mathrm{SC}(\Sigma \times \Sigma)$. These reinterpretations would not affect those theorems of the present chapter which are stratified. Theorems dealing with $\mathrm{USC}(\alpha)$ would not hold in general.

Of rather more interest is the case where x is restricted to Σ_1 and y to Σ_2. Then the corresponding relation $\hat{x}\hat{y}P$ would be restricted to $\Sigma_1 \times \Sigma_2$, and its converse to $\Sigma_2 \times \Sigma_1$. It does not seem profitable to try to record precisely the changes that must be made in the theorems of this chapter to accord with such restrictions on x and y, since these are usually applied only in special cases, in which one can just as easily replace relations R by $\Sigma_1 \upharpoonleft R \upharpoonright \Sigma_2$ and their converses by $\Sigma_2 \upharpoonleft \breve{R} \upharpoonright \Sigma_1$. In other words, complicated cases can best be handled by going to relations of the form $\alpha \upharpoonleft R \upharpoonright \beta$. The most common situation of this sort is that in which we are considering transformations from Σ_1 to Σ_2 and vice versa. It appears that the device of using restricted variables in such case is of little value, since Σ_1 and Σ_2 do not stay fixed long enough, and the best procedure is to use unrestricted variables and state the necessary restrictions explicitly. Detailed treatments of two special cases of this will occur in Sec. 1 of Chapter XI and Sec. 1 of Chapter XII.

EXERCISES

A relation R is called a transformation of α into β if $R \,\epsilon\, \mathrm{Funct}$, $\mathrm{Arg}(R) = \alpha$, and $\mathrm{Val}(R) \subseteq \beta$.

A relation R is called a transformation of α onto β if $R \,\epsilon\, \mathrm{Funct}$, $\mathrm{Arg}(R) = \alpha$, and $\mathrm{Val}(R) = \beta$.

A subset β of α is said to be invariant under a transformation R if $R``\beta = \beta$.

A set of objects γ is called a semigroup with respect to an operator $\circ$ if:

1. $(x,y):x,y \,\epsilon\, \gamma. \supset .x \circ y \,\epsilon\, \gamma.$
2. $(x,y,z):x,y,z \,\epsilon\, \gamma. \supset .x \circ (y \circ z) = (x \circ y) \circ z.$
3. $(\mathrm{E}e):.e \,\epsilon\, \gamma:(x):x \,\epsilon\, \gamma. \supset .e \circ x = x \circ e = x.$

We say that γ is a group if in addition:

4. $(e)::e \,\epsilon\, \gamma:(x):x \,\epsilon\, \gamma. \supset .e \circ x = x \circ e = x.: \supset :.(y):.y \,\epsilon\, \gamma: \supset :(\mathrm{E}z).z \,\epsilon\, \gamma. y \circ z = z \circ y = e.$

X.5.1. If α is a given set, and γ is the set of all transformations of α into α, prove that γ is a semigroup with respect to the operator $|$. (*Hint.* Take e to be $\alpha \upharpoonleft I$.)

X.5.2. If α is a given set, and β is a given subset of α, and γ is the set of all transformations of α into α under which β is invariant, prove that γ is a semigroup with respect to the operator $|$.

X.5.3. If α is a given set, and β is a given subset of α, and γ is the set of all transformations of α onto α under which β is invariant, prove that γ is a semigroup with respect to the operator $|$. Discuss the cases $\beta = \Lambda$ and $\beta = \alpha$.

X.5.4. If γ is a semigroup with respect to the operator $\circ$, prove that

$$(\mathrm{E}_1 e){:}e \in \gamma{:}(x){:}x \in \gamma. \supset .e \circ x = x \circ e = x.$$

X.5.5. If α is a given set, and β is a given subset of α, and γ is the set of all relations R such that both R and $\breve{R}$ are transformations of α onto α and β is invariant under both R and $\breve{R}$, then prove that γ is a group with respect to the operator $|$. (*Hint.* Take $\breve{R}$ to be the inverse of R.)

X.5.6. Prove that, if $x = A$ is stratified, then $\vdash (\alpha,\beta){:}(\lambda x(A))``\alpha \subseteq \beta. \equiv .(x).\ x \in \alpha \supset A \in \beta.$

X.5.7. Prove $\vdash I = \lambda x(x)$.

X.5.8. Prove $\vdash (R,S){:}R,S \in \mathrm{Funct.} \supset .R \cap S \in \mathrm{Funct.}$

X.5.9. Bohr (see Bohr, 1947, page 39) defines the mean value of a "function" $f(x)$ as

$$\lim_{T\to\infty} \frac{1}{T} \int_0^T f(x)\,dx$$

and denotes this by $M\{f(x)\}$. Explain why $M(f)$ would be a better notation. On page 48, Bohr writes $a(k)$ for $M\{f(x)e^{-ikx}\}$. Explain why $a(f,k)$ would be a better notation than $a(k)$ and show how to write the definition of $a(f,k)$ in terms of $M(\quad)$ if one is writing $M(f)$ for the mean value of f.

X.5.10. Explain why one cannot prove $\vdash (f).(\lambda f(f(0)))(f) = f(0)$.

X.5.11. Explain why one cannot prove $\vdash (x,y){:}((\lambda x(\lambda y(x + y)))(x))(y) = x + y$.

X.5.12. Prove:

(a) $\vdash \Lambda \in \mathrm{Funct.}$
(b) $\vdash \Lambda \in 1\text{-}1.$

X.5.13. If R_* is defined as in Ex.X.4.10, prove:

(a) $\vdash (R).\breve{R}|R \subseteq R_*.$
(b) $\vdash (R).(\breve{R}|R) \cup (R|R_*) = R_*.$

X.5.14. If $\leq$ is defined as in Ex.X.1.4. and R_* is defined as in Ex.X.4.10, prove $\vdash \mathrm{Nn}\upharpoonleft(\hat{x}\hat{y}(x \leq y))\restriction\mathrm{Nn} = (\mathrm{Nn}\upharpoonleft(\lambda x(x + 1))\restriction\mathrm{Nn})_*.$

X.5.15. Prove $\vdash (\alpha).I``\alpha = \alpha.$

X.5.16. Prove $\vdash (\beta,x).(\beta \times \{x\}) \in \mathrm{Funct.}$

X.5.17. Prove $\vdash (R,S,T){::}R,S \in 1\text{-}1{:}T = S|R|\mathrm{Cnv}(\mathrm{RUSC}(S)){:}.(x,y){:} xRy. \supset .y = \{x\}.{:} \supset {:}.T \in 1\text{-}1{:}(x,y){:}xTy. \supset .y = \{x\}.$

6. Ordered Sets. Let us have a set α. It is ordered if there is an ordering relation R such that, for various distinct members x and y of α, xRy holds but yRx does not hold. Then, by means of the relation R, we could decide for the x and y in question to put them in the order x,y rather than the order y,x because xRy holds but yRx does not hold.

It is not generally required that for each x and y at least one of xRy or yRx must hold. This property is usually present only for special ordering relations which induce what is called a simple ordering of the set α.

For a set of real numbers, $<$, $\leq$, $>$, etc., would be ordering relations. For a set of integers, the relation of "being a factor of" would be an ordering relation. For a set of classes, the relation $\subseteq$ would be an ordering relation.

Whitehead and Russell consider $<$ between real numbers as the typical ordering relation. The current mathematical practice is to take $\leq$ between real numbers as the typical ordering relation. Thus if R is an ordering relation for the class α, we should have

$$(x):x \in \alpha. \supset .xRx.$$

That is, $\alpha 1 I \subseteq R$ should hold. If it does not, we can easily arrange for it to hold by replacing R by $R \cup (\alpha 1 I)$. Such a replacement does not alter any ordering of the members of α which was imposed by R. For example, if R is $<$ between real numbers and α is the class of real numbers, then $\alpha 1 I \subseteq R$ fails to hold. However, we can replace R by $R \cup (\alpha 1 I)$ and have the same ordering, since $R \cup (\alpha 1 I)$ is merely $\leq$ between real numbers.

A somewhat similar situation holds with regard to the property

$$(x,y):xRy. \supset .x,y \in \alpha.$$

This need not hold in general. For instance, R might be the relation of $\leq$ between real numbers and α might be the class of rational numbers. Then $\sqrt{2} \leq \pi$, but $\sim\sqrt{2} \in \alpha$ and $\sim \pi \in \alpha$. However, we can readily make the property

$$(x,y):xRy. \supset .x,y \in \alpha$$

hold by replacing R by $\alpha 1 R \upharpoonright \alpha$ (see Thm.X.4.5, Part III). As far as members of α are concerned, R and $\alpha 1 R \upharpoonright \alpha$ would induce the same ordering. For instance, if R is $\leq$ between real numbers and α is the class of rational numbers, then $\alpha 1 R \upharpoonright \alpha$ is just $\leq$ between rational numbers.

Thus it is feasible as well as convenient to make the convention that, if R is to be considered an ordering relation for α, then

$$(x):x \in \alpha. \supset .xRx$$

$$(x,y):xRy. \supset .x,y \in \alpha$$

should both hold.

If R is an ordering relation for α, then from the two conditions just given, we have

$$\alpha = \text{Arg}(R) = \text{Val}(R) = \text{AV}(R).$$

Thus an ordering relation R for α will determine α uniquely. Hence, instead of dealing with an ordered set, which consists of a set α with an associated ordering relation R, we can deal exclusively with the ordering relation R, since R determines α by the relation $\alpha = \text{AV}(R)$. That is, all statements about ordered sets are equivalent to statements about their ordering relations, and vice versa.

Thus we do not introduce the notion of an ordered set at all, but only the notion of an ordering relation. The set ordered by an ordering relation R is just $\text{AV}(R)$.

If one wished to introduce the notion of an ordered set, one would have to devise a formalism for the notion of a set α with an associated ordering relation R. One could use the ordered pair $\langle\alpha,R\rangle$ for this purpose and write

$$\text{Ord Set} \qquad \text{for} \qquad \hat{\alpha}\hat{R}((x){:}x \in \alpha. \supset .xRx{:}.(x,y){:}xRy. \supset .x,y \in \alpha).$$

Then we would have

$$\vdash \langle\alpha,R\rangle \in \text{Ord Set}.{:} \equiv {:}.(x){:}x \in \alpha. \supset .xRx{:}.(x,y){:}xRy. \supset .x,y \in \alpha,$$

so that Ord Set would be the class of all ordered sets. However, it will be more economical to deal merely with the ordering relations.

We define a reflexive relation R as one such that xRx for all x in $\text{AV}(R)$. Thus we define

$$\text{Ref} \qquad \text{for} \qquad \hat{\mathbf{R}}(x){:}x \in \text{AV}(\mathbf{R}). \supset .x\mathbf{R}x.$$

Ref is stratified and has no free occurrences of a variable and so may be assigned any type.

Theorem X.6.1.

★I. $\vdash (R){:}.R \in \text{Ref}{:} \equiv {:}R \in \text{Rel}{:}(x){:}x \in \text{AV}(R). \supset .xRx.$

II. $\vdash \text{Ref} \subseteq \text{Rel}.$

III. $\vdash (\mathbf{R}){:}.\mathbf{R} \in \text{Ref}{:} \equiv {:}(x){:}x \in \text{AV}(\mathbf{R}). \supset .x\mathbf{R}x.$

IV. $\vdash (R){:}R \in \text{Ref}. \supset .\text{Arg}(R) = \text{Val}(R) = \text{AV}(R).$

V. $\vdash (\beta,R){:}R \in \text{Ref}. \supset .\beta{\upharpoonleft}R{\upharpoonright}\beta \in \text{Ref}.$

VI. $\vdash (R){:}R \in \text{Ref}. \supset .\breve{R} \in \text{Ref}.$

VII. $\vdash (\beta,R){:}R \in \text{Ref}. \supset .\text{Arg}(\beta{\upharpoonleft}R{\upharpoonright}\beta) = \text{Val}(\beta{\upharpoonleft}R{\upharpoonright}\beta) = \text{AV}(\beta{\upharpoonleft}R{\upharpoonright}\beta) = \beta \cap \text{AV}(R).$

We define a transitive relation R as one such that $xRy.yRz. \supset .xRz.$ Thus we define

$$\text{Trans} \qquad \text{for} \qquad \hat{\mathbf{R}}(x,y,z){:}x\mathbf{R}y.y\mathbf{R}z. \supset .x\mathbf{R}z.$$

Trans is stratified and has no free occurrences of a variable and so may be assigned any type.

Theorem X.6.2.

$\star$I. $\vdash (R):.R \epsilon \text{Trans}: \equiv :R \epsilon \text{Rel}:(x,y,z):xRy.yRz. \supset .xRz.$

II. $\vdash \text{Trans} \subseteq \text{Rel}.$

III. $\vdash (\mathbf{R}):\mathbf{R} \epsilon \text{Trans}. \equiv .\mathbf{R}|\mathbf{R} \subseteq \mathbf{R}.$

IV. $\vdash (\alpha,\beta,R):R \epsilon \text{Trans}. \supset .\alpha \upharpoonleft R \upharpoonright \beta \epsilon \text{Trans}.$

V. $\vdash (R):R \epsilon \text{Trans}. \supset .\breve{R} \epsilon \text{Trans}.$

An ordered set is said to be quasi-ordered if its ordering relation is reflexive and transitive. Accordingly we shall say that a relation is a quasi-ordering relation if it is reflexive and transitive. So we define

$$\text{Qord} \quad \text{for} \quad \text{Ref} \cap \text{Trans}.$$

Theorem X.6.3.

I. $\vdash (R):R \epsilon \text{Qord}. \equiv .R \epsilon \text{Ref}.R \epsilon \text{Trans}.$

II. $\vdash \text{Qord} \subseteq \text{Rel}.$

III. $\vdash (\beta,R):R \epsilon \text{Qord}. \supset .\beta \upharpoonleft R \upharpoonright \beta \epsilon \text{Qord}.$

IV. $\vdash (R):R \epsilon \text{Qord}. \supset .\breve{R} \epsilon \text{Qord}.$

As an example of a quasi-ordering relation, consider the relation R which holds between two complex numbers z and w when and only when the real part of z is less than or equal to the real part of w.

Suppose R is an ordering relation of α and β is any subset of α. Then $\beta \upharpoonleft R \upharpoonright \beta$ is an ordering relation of β which imposes the same ordering on the elements of β which is imposed by R. This is expressed in words as:

"Any subset of an ordered set is itself an ordered set relative to the same ordering relation."

Part III of Thm.X.6.3 gives a special case of this, namely, that if α is a quasi-ordered set, then any subset of α is a quasi-ordered set relative to the same ordering relation.

Part IV of Thm.X.6.3 says that a quasi-ordered set is still quasi-ordered if one reverses the order.

We define an antisymmetric relation R as one such that $xRy.yRx. \supset . x = y$. Thus we define

$$\text{Antisym} \quad \text{for} \quad \hat{\mathbf{R}}(x,y):x\mathbf{R}y.y\mathbf{R}x. \supset .x = y.$$

Antisym is stratified and has no free occurrences of a variable and so may be assigned any type.

Theorem X.6.4.

I. $\vdash (R):.R \epsilon \text{Antisym}: \equiv :R \epsilon \text{Rel}:(x,y):xRy.yRx. \supset .x = y.$

II. $\vdash \text{Antisym} \subseteq \text{Rel}.$

III. $\vdash (\alpha,\beta,R):R \epsilon \text{Antisym}. \supset .\alpha \upharpoonleft R \upharpoonright \beta \epsilon \text{Antisym}.$

IV. $\vdash (R):R \epsilon \text{Antisym}. \supset .\breve{R} \epsilon \text{Antisym}.$

★V. $\vdash (R,x,y):R \epsilon \text{Antisym}.x(R - I)y. \supset .\sim(yRx).$

VI. $\vdash (R,x,y,z):R \epsilon \text{Antisym}.xRy.y(R - I)z. \supset .x \neq z.$

VII. $\vdash (R,x,y,z):R \epsilon \text{Antisym}.x(R - I)y.yRz. \supset .x \neq z.$

Proof of Part V. Assume $R \epsilon$ Antisym. Then by Part I, $xRy.yRx. \supset . x = y.$ So $xRy.x \neq y. \supset .\sim(yRx).$

Proof of Part VI. Assume $R \epsilon$ Antisym. Then by Part I, $xRy.yRz. x = z. \supset .y = z.$ So $xRy.yRz.y \neq z. \supset .x \neq z.$

When R is a relation like $\leq$, then $R - I$ corresponds to $<$. Then Part V above is just the familiar statement

$$x < y. \supset .\sim(y \leq x).$$

An ordered set is said to be partially ordered if its ordering relation is reflexive, transitive, and antisymmetric. Accordingly, we shall say that a relation is a partial ordering relation if it is reflexive, transitive, and antisymmetric. So we define

$$\text{Pord} = \text{Ref} \cap \text{Trans} \cap \text{Antisym}.$$

Theorem X.6.5.

I. $\vdash (R):R \epsilon \text{Pord}: \equiv :R \epsilon \text{Ref}.R \epsilon \text{Trans}.R \epsilon \text{Antisym}.$

II. $\vdash \text{Pord} = \text{Qord} \cap \text{Antisym}.$

III. $\vdash \text{Pord} \subseteq \text{Rel}.$

IV. $\vdash (\beta,R):R \epsilon \text{Pord}. \supset .\beta \rceil R \lceil \beta \epsilon \text{Pord}.$

V. $\vdash (R):R \epsilon \text{Pord}. \supset .\breve{R} \epsilon \text{Pord}.$

VI. $\vdash (R,x,y,z):R \epsilon \text{Pord}.xRy.y(R - I)z. \supset .x(R - I)z.$

VII. $\vdash (R,x,y,z):R \epsilon \text{Pord}.x(R - I)y.yRz. \supset .x(R - I)z.$

VIII. $\vdash (R,x,y,z):R \epsilon \text{Pord}.x(R - I)y.y(R - I)z. \supset .x(R - I)z.$

We may interpret Part IV as saying that any subset of a partially ordered set is partially ordered relative to the same ordering relation.

We may interpret Part V as saying that any partially ordered set is still partially ordered if we reverse the order.

If R is $\leq$, then we may interpret Parts VI, VII, and VIII as saying

$$x \leq y.y < z. \supset .x < z$$

$$x < y.y \leq z. \supset .x < z$$

$$x < y.y < z. \supset .x < z$$

respectively.

Examples of partial ordering relations are the relation of "being a factor of" among positive integers (we recall that any positive integer is a factor of itself), or the relation $\subseteq$ among subsets of any given set Σ, or the relation R which holds between any two complex numbers z and w when and only when the real part of z is less than or equal to the real part of w and the imaginary parts of z and w are equal.

A "least" member of β relative to R (if there is one) is an x such that $x \in \beta \cap \mathrm{AV}(R)$, and $(y):y \in \beta \cap \mathrm{AV}(R). \supset .xRy$. A "minimal" member of β relative to R (if there is one) is an x such that $x \in \beta \cap \mathrm{AV}(R)$, and $(y):y \in \beta \cap \mathrm{AV}(R). \supset .\sim(y(R - I)x)$.

Accordingly we define

$x \text{ least}_R\ \beta$	for	$x \in \beta \cap \mathrm{AV}(R):(y):y \in \beta \cap \mathrm{AV}(R). \supset .xRy,$
$x \min_R \beta$	for	$x \in \beta \cap \mathrm{AV}(R):(y):y \in \beta \cap \mathrm{AV}(R). \supset . \sim(y(R - I)x),$
$x \text{ greatest}_R\ \beta$	for	$x \text{ least}_{\mathrm{Cnv}(R)}\ \beta,$
$x \max_R \beta$	for	$x \min_{\mathrm{Cnv}(R)} \beta,$

where y is a variable not occurring at all in x, R, or β.

For stratification of $x \text{ least}_R\ \beta$, $x \min_R \beta$, $x \text{ greatest}_R\ \beta$, and $x \max_R \beta$, the types of R and β should be one higher than the type of x. The free occurrences of variables are those in x, R, or β.

Theorem X.6.6.

I. $\vdash (\beta,R,x):R \in \mathrm{Antisym}.x \text{ least}_R\ \beta. \supset .x \min_R \beta.$

II. $\vdash (\beta,R,x):R \in \mathrm{Antisym}.x \text{ greatest}_R\ \beta. \supset .x \max_R \beta.$

Theorem X.6.7.

I. $\vdash (\beta,R,x,y):R \in \mathrm{Antisym}.x \text{ least}_R\ \beta.y \text{ least}_R\ \beta. \supset .x = y.$

II. $\vdash (\beta,R,x,y):R \in \mathrm{Antisym}.x \text{ greatest}_R\ \beta.y \text{ greatest}_R\ \beta. \supset .x = y.$

Thus, for an antisymmetric relation a "least" member of a set is unique, so that one should speak of "the least" member of a set. On the other hand, a minimal member may well fail to be unique, so that one must speak of "a minimal" member rather than "the minimal" member.

Theorem X.6.8. $\vdash (\beta,\gamma,R,S,x):.R \in \mathrm{Ref}.S = \gamma\rceil R\lceil\gamma: \supset :x \text{ least}_R\ (\beta \cap \gamma). \equiv .x \text{ least}_S\ \beta.$

Proof. Assume $R \in \mathrm{Ref}$ and $S = \gamma\rceil R\lceil\gamma$. Then by Thm.X.6.1, Part VII, $\mathrm{AV}(S) = \gamma \cap \mathrm{AV}(R)$. So

$$(1) \qquad \beta \cap \mathrm{AV}(S) = (\beta \cap \gamma) \cap \mathrm{AV}(R).$$

Now

$$\vdash x \in (\beta \cap \gamma) \cap \mathrm{AV}(R):(y):y \in (\beta \cap \gamma) \cap \mathrm{AV}(R). \supset .xRy:.$$
$$\equiv :.x \in (\beta \cap \gamma) \cap \mathrm{AV}(R):(y):y \in (\beta \cap \gamma) \cap \mathrm{AV}(R). \supset .x \in \gamma.xRy.y \in \gamma:.$$
$$\equiv :.x \in (\beta \cap \gamma) \cap \mathrm{AV}(R):(y):y \in (\beta \cap \gamma) \cap \mathrm{AV}(R). \supset .xSy.$$

So by (1),

$$x \text{ least}_R\ (\beta \cap \gamma). \equiv .x \text{ least}_S\ \beta.$$

We define a connected relation R as one such that if $x, y \in \mathrm{AV}(R)$, then either xRy or yRx. So we define

Connex for $\hat{\mathbf{R}}(x,y){:}x,y \in \mathrm{AV}(\mathbf{R}).\supset .x\mathbf{R}y \vee y\mathbf{R}x.$

Connex is stratified and has no free occurrences of a variable and so may be assigned any type.

Theorem X.6.9.

I. $\vdash (R){:}.R \in \mathrm{Connex}{:} \equiv {:}R \in \mathrm{Rel}{:}(x,y){:}x,y \in \mathrm{AV}(R).\supset .xRy \vee yRx.$

II. $\vdash \mathrm{Connex} \subseteq \mathrm{Rel}.$

III. $\vdash (\beta,R){:}R \in \mathrm{Connex}.\supset .\beta\rceil R\lceil\beta \in \mathrm{Connex}.$

IV. $\vdash (R){:}R \in \mathrm{Connex}.\supset .\breve{R} \in \mathrm{Connex}.$

V. $\vdash \mathrm{Connex} \subseteq \mathrm{Ref}.$

Proof of Part V. Suppose $R \in \mathrm{Connex}$. Then let $x \in \mathrm{AV}(R)$. Then by Part I, $xRx \vee xRx$.

Note that many familiar ordering relations such as $\subseteq$ are not connected.

Theorem X.6.10.

I. $\vdash (\beta,R,x){:}.R \in \mathrm{Antisym} \cap \mathrm{Connex}{:} \supset {:}x \text{ least}_R\, \beta. \equiv .x \min_R \beta.$

II. $\vdash (\beta,R,x){:}.R \in \mathrm{Antisym} \cap \mathrm{Connex}{:} \supset {:}x \text{ greatest}_R\, \beta. \equiv .x \max_R \beta.$

Proof of Part I. Let $R \in \mathrm{Antisym} \cap \mathrm{Connex}$. Then by Thm.X.6.6, Part I,

(1) $$x \text{ least}_R\, \beta. \supset .x \min_R \beta.$$

Now let $x \min_R \beta$. Then $x \in \beta \cap \mathrm{AV}(R)$. So xRx by Thm.X.6.9, Part V, and Thm.X.6.1, Part I. Now assume $y \in \beta \cap \mathrm{AV}(R)$. Then $xRy \vee yRx$ by Thm.X.6.9, Part I. That is

(2) $$\sim(yRx) \supset xRy.$$

Case 1. $y = x$. Then xRy follows from xRx.

Case 2. $y \neq x$. Then $\sim(yRx)$ follows from the definition of $x \min_R \beta$. Then xRy follows from (2).

Proof of Part II. Similar.

An ordered set is said to be simply ordered if its ordering relation is reflexive, transitive, antisymmetric, and connected. A simply ordered set is sometimes called a chain. Accordingly, we shall say that a relation is a simple ordering relation or a chain relation if it is reflexive, transitive, antisymmetric, and connected. So we define

Sord for $\mathrm{Ref} \cap \mathrm{Trans} \cap \mathrm{Antisym} \cap \mathrm{Connex}.$

Theorem X.6.11.

I. $\vdash (R){:}R \in \mathrm{Sord}{:} \equiv {:}R \in \mathrm{Ref}.R \in \mathrm{Trans}.R \in \mathrm{Antisym}.R \in \mathrm{Connex}.$

II. $\vdash \mathrm{Sord} = \mathrm{Pord} \cap \mathrm{Connex}.$

III. $\vdash \mathrm{Sord} \subseteq \mathrm{Rel}.$

IV. $\vdash (\beta,R){:}R \in \mathrm{Sord}.\supset .\beta\rceil R\lceil\beta \in \mathrm{Sord}.$

V. $\vdash (R){:}R \in \mathrm{Sord}.\supset .\breve{R} \in \mathrm{Sord}.$

Thus any subset of a simply ordered set is itself a simply ordered set relative to the same ordering relation. Likewise, reversing the order leaves the set simply ordered. Moreover, by Thm.X.6.10, in a simply ordered set, the notions of least and minimal coincide, and the notions of greatest and maximal coincide.

The notions of $\leq$ between real numbers, or between rational numbers, or between positive integers, etc., are all especially typical examples of simple ordering relations. A less familiar example would be the relation R which holds between two complex numbers z and w when either the imaginary part of z is less than the imaginary part of w or else the imaginary parts of z and w are equal and the real part of z is less than or equal to the real part of w.

Given any simply ordered set α and any element x of α, we define the segment of α determined by x to be the set of all elements which "precede" x, that is, the set of all elements y such that $y(R - I)x$. Since this segment is a subset of α, it is also a simply ordered set. If R is the ordering relation of α, we denote by $\text{seg}_x R$ the ordering relation of the segment of α determined by x. So we define

$$\text{seg}_x R \quad \text{for} \quad (\hat{y}(y(R - I)x))1R\upharpoonright(\hat{y}(y(R - I)x)),$$

where y is a variable not occurring in R or x.

For stratification of $\text{seg}_x R$, R and $\text{seg}_x R$ have to be one type higher than x. Any free occurrences of variables in $\text{seg}_x R$ will be those in x or R.

By Thm.X.6.1, Part V, Thm.X.6.2, Part IV, Thm.X.6.4, Part III, and Thm.X.6.9, Part III, we see that $\text{seg}_x R$ will have any of the properties Ref, Trans, Antisym, and Connex that R has.

Theorem X.6.12.

I. $\vdash (R,x,y,z){:}y(\text{seg}_x R)z. \equiv .y(R - I)x.yRz.z(R - I)x.$

II. $\vdash (R,x,y,z){:}.R \in \text{Trans}.R \in \text{Antisym}{:} \supset {:}y(\text{seg}_x R)z. \equiv .yRz.z(R - I)x.$

★III. $\vdash (R,x){:}R \in \text{Ref}. \supset .\text{AV}(\text{seg}_x R) = \hat{y}(y(R - I)x).$

Proof of Part II. Use Thm.X.6.2, Part I, and Thm.X.6.4, Part VI.

Proof of Part III. One easily gets $\vdash \text{AV}(\text{seg}_x R) \subseteq \hat{y}(y(R - I)x)$. Now let $R \in \text{Ref}$ and $y(R - I)x$. Then $y(R - I)x.yRy.y(R - I)x$. So by Part I, $y(\text{seg}_x R)y$. So $y \in \text{AV}(\text{seg}_x R)$.

Theorem X.6.13. $\vdash (R,x,y){:}R \in \text{Trans}.R \in \text{Antisym}.y(R - I)x. \supset . \text{seg}_y(\text{seg}_x R) = \text{seg}_y R.$

Proof. Assume the hypothesis. Temporarily put

$$\begin{aligned} A &= \hat{y}(y(R - I)x), \\ S &= \text{seg}_x R = A1R\upharpoonright A, \\ B &= \hat{z}(z(S - I)y), \\ C &= \hat{z}(z(R - I)y). \end{aligned}$$

Then

$$\begin{aligned}\mathrm{seg}_y(\mathrm{seg}_x R) &= \mathrm{seg}_y S = B{\upharpoonleft}S{\upharpoonright}B \\ &= B{\upharpoonleft}(A{\upharpoonleft}R{\upharpoonright}A){\upharpoonright}B \\ &= (A \cap B){\upharpoonleft}R{\upharpoonright}(A \cap B),\end{aligned}$$

and

$$\mathrm{seg}_y R = C{\upharpoonleft}R{\upharpoonright}C.$$

Thus it suffices to prove $A \cap B = C$.

First let $z \in A \cap B$. So $z \in B$. So $zSy.z \neq y$. So $zRy.z \neq y$. So $z \in C$.

Conversely, let $z \in C$. So $zRy.z \neq y$. However, by hypothesis, $yRx.$ $y \neq x$. So since $R \in \mathrm{Trans}$, zRx. Also since $R \in \mathrm{Antisym}$, $z \neq x$. So $z \in A$. Also $y \in A$. Thus $z \in A.zRy.y \in A$. That is, $z(A{\upharpoonleft}R{\upharpoonright}A)y$. That is, zSy. So $z \in B$.

★**Corollary.** $\vdash (R,S,x,y){:}R \in \mathrm{Pord}.S = \mathrm{seg}_x R.y \in \mathrm{Arg}(S). \supset .\mathrm{seg}_y S = \mathrm{seg}_y R$.

This theorem says in effect that, if y is in the segment of α determined by x, then the segment of that segment determined by y is the same as the segment of α determined by y.

We say that an ordered set α satisfies the "ascending chain condition" (descending chain condition) if and only if each nonempty subset of α has a maximal (minimal) element. We shall be interested only in the special case where we have a simply ordered set satisfying a descending chain condition. Such a set is called "well ordered." As always, we shall deal only with the ordering relation of the set, which shall be called a well-ordering relation. So we define

$$\mathrm{Word} \quad \text{for} \quad \hat{R}(R \in \mathrm{Sord}{:}(\beta){:}\beta \cap \mathrm{AV}(R) \neq \Lambda. \supset .(\mathrm{E}y).y \ \mathrm{min}_R\ \beta).$$

Word is stratified and has no free occurrences of a variable and so may be assigned any type.

Theorem X.6.14.

I. $\vdash (R){:}.R \in \mathrm{Word}{:} \equiv {:}R \in \mathrm{Sord}{:}(\beta){:}\beta \cap \mathrm{AV}(R) \neq \Lambda. \supset .(\mathrm{E}y).y \ \mathrm{min}_R\ \beta$.

★II. $\vdash (R){:}.R \in \mathrm{Word}{:} \equiv {:}R \in \mathrm{Sord}{:}(\beta){:}\beta \cap \mathrm{AV}(R) \neq \Lambda. \supset .(\mathrm{E}y).y \ \mathrm{least}_R\ \beta$.

III. $\vdash (R){:}.R \in \mathrm{Word}{:} \equiv {:}R \in \mathrm{Sord}{:}(\beta){:}\beta \cap \mathrm{AV}(R) \neq \Lambda. \supset .(\mathrm{E}_1 y).y \ \mathrm{least}_R\ \beta$.

IV. $\vdash (\gamma,R){:}R \in \mathrm{Word}. \supset .\gamma{\upharpoonleft}R{\upharpoonright}\gamma \in \mathrm{Word}$.

V. $\vdash (R,x){:}R \in \mathrm{Word}. \supset .\mathrm{seg}_x R \in \mathrm{Word}$.

Proof of Part II. Use Thm.X.6.10.

Proof of Part III. Use Thm.X.6.7.

Proof of Part IV. Assume $R \in \mathrm{Word}$ and put temporarily $S = \gamma{\upharpoonleft}R{\upharpoonright}\gamma$. Then $S \in \mathrm{Sord}$. Also by Thm.X.6.1, Part VII, $\mathrm{AV}(S) = \gamma \cap \mathrm{AV}(R)$. So

$$(1) \qquad \beta \cap \mathrm{AV}(S) = (\beta \cap \gamma) \cap \mathrm{AV}(R).$$

Also by Thm.X.6.8,

(2) $$y \text{ least}_S\ \beta. \equiv .y \text{ least}_R\ (\beta \cap \gamma).$$

Now by Part II,

$$(\beta \cap \gamma) \cap \mathrm{AV}(R) \neq \Lambda. \supset .(\mathrm{E}y).y \text{ least}_R\ (\beta \cap \gamma).$$

So by (1) and (2),

$$\beta \cap \mathrm{AV}(S) \neq \Lambda. \supset .(\mathrm{E}y).y \text{ least}_S\ \beta.$$

We say that x is an upper bound of y and z with respect to R if $yRx.zRx$. We say that x is a least upper bound of y and z if x is an upper bound and if xRw for every upper bound w. In symbols

$$x \text{ lub}_R\ y,z \qquad \text{for} \qquad yRx.zRx:(w):yRw.zRw. \supset .xRw.$$

We say that x is a greatest lower bound (glb) of y and z with respect to R if it is a lub with respect to $\breve{R}$.

If R is the relation of "being a factor of" among positive integers, then the lub of y and z with respect to R is their least common multiple, and the glb of y and z with respect to R is their greatest common factor.

If R is the relation $\subseteq$ among subsets of a given set Σ, then by Thm. IX.4.18, $\alpha \cup \beta$ is the lub of α and β and $\alpha \cap \beta$ is the glb of α and β.

A lattice is a partially ordered set such that each pair of elements y and z of the set has a lub and a glb.

In symbols we write

Lattice

for

$$\hat{R}(R \in \mathrm{Pord}::(y,z)::y,z \in \mathrm{AV}(R).: \supset :.(\mathrm{E}x):yRx.zRx:(w):yRw.zRw. \supset .xRw:. (\mathrm{E}x):xRy.xRz:(w).wRy.wRz. \supset .wRx).$$

As elsewhere in this section, we are dealing with the ordering relation instead of with the class which it ordered. So our definition of "Lattice" makes it contain all ordering relations of lattices. As examples of such relations, we cite the relation of "being a factor of" among positive integers and the relation of $\subseteq$ among subsets of a given set Σ.

One may find an extensive treatment of lattices in Birkhoff, 1948, from which most of the material of this section was taken.

Theorem X.6.15.

I. $\vdash (\mathbf{R}):\mathbf{R} \in \mathrm{Ref}. \equiv .\mathrm{RUSC}(\mathbf{R}) \in \mathrm{Ref}.$

II. $\vdash (\mathbf{R}):\mathbf{R} \in \mathrm{Trans}. \equiv .\mathrm{RUSC}(\mathbf{R}) \in \mathrm{Trans}.$

III. $\vdash (\mathbf{R}):\mathbf{R} \in \mathrm{Antisym}. \equiv .\mathrm{RUSC}(\mathbf{R}) \in \mathrm{Antisym}.$

IV. $\vdash (\mathbf{R}):\mathbf{R} \in \mathrm{Connex}. \equiv .\mathrm{RUSC}(\mathbf{R}) \in \mathrm{Connex}.$

V. $\vdash (\mathbf{R}):\mathbf{R} \in \mathrm{Word}. \equiv .\mathrm{RUSC}(\mathbf{R}) \in \mathrm{Word}.$

VI. $\vdash (\beta,R,x):x \text{ least}_R\ \beta. \equiv .\{x\}\text{least}_{\mathrm{RUSC}(R)}\ \mathrm{USC}(\beta).$

VII. $\vdash (R,x).\mathrm{RUSC}(\mathrm{seg}_x R) = \mathrm{seg}_{\{x\}}\ \mathrm{RUSC}(R).$

EXERCISES

X.6.1. Prove:

(a) $\vdash (\mathbf{R}){:}\mathbf{R} \in \text{Antisym.} \equiv .\mathbf{R} \cap \breve{\mathbf{R}} \subseteq I.$
(b) $\vdash (\alpha,\beta,R).\beta\rceil(\alpha\rceil R\lceil\alpha)\lceil\beta = (\alpha \cap \beta)\rceil R\lceil(\alpha \cap \beta).$

X.6.2. Let A be a fixed point and let R be the relation which holds between two points x and y of three-dimensional space when the distance from x to A is less than or equal to the distance from y to A. Which of the properties Ref, Trans, Antisym, and Connex does R have?

X.6.3. Prove:

$$\vdash (R,S){:}.S \in \text{Qord}.R = \hat{x}\hat{y}(xSy.ySx){:} \supset {:}R \in \text{Qord}{:}(x,y){:}xRy. \supset .yRx.$$

X.6.4. Prove $\vdash \Lambda \in \text{Word}$.

X.6.5. If we define

$$\subseteq \quad \text{for} \quad \hat{\alpha}\hat{\beta}(\alpha \subseteq \beta),$$

then prove:

$$\vdash (\Sigma).\Sigma\rceil\subseteq\lceil\Sigma \in \text{Lattice}.$$

X.6.6. Prove:

(a) $\vdash (R,x,y){:}.R \in \text{Ref}.x,y \in AV(R){:} \supset {:}xRy. \equiv .x(R - I)y.\mathbf{v}.x = y.$
(b) $\vdash (R,x,y){:}R \in \text{Ref}.R \in \text{Connex}.x,y \in AV(R). \supset .x(R - I)y.\mathbf{v}.x = y.\mathbf{v}.$ $y(R - I)x.$
(c) $\vdash (R,x,y){:}R \in \text{Ref}.R \in \text{Antisym}.R \in \text{Connex}.x,y \in AV(R). \supset .$ $x(R - I)y \equiv \sim(yRx).$
(d) $\vdash (R,x,y){:}R \in \text{Ref}.R \in \text{Antisym}.R \in \text{Connex}.x,y \in AV(R). \supset .$ $xRy \equiv \sim(y(R - I)x).$

X.6.7. Prove $\vdash (x){:}\{\langle x,x\rangle\} \in \text{Word}$.

7. Equivalence Relations. We have defined reflexive and transitive relations. We say that a relation R is symmetric if $xRy \supset yRx$. So we define

$$\text{Sym} \quad \text{for} \quad \hat{\mathbf{R}}(x,y){:}x\mathbf{R}y. \supset .y\mathbf{R}x.$$

Sym is stratified and has no free occurrences of a variable and so may be assigned any type.

Theorem X.7.1.

I. $\vdash (R){:}.R \in \text{Sym}{:} \equiv {:}R \in \text{Rel}{:}(x,y){:}xRy. \supset .yRx.$
II. $\vdash \text{Sym} \subseteq \text{Rel}.$
III. $\vdash (\beta,R){:}R \in \text{Sym}. \supset .\beta\rceil R\lceil\beta \in \text{Sym}.$
IV. $\vdash (R){:}R \in \text{Sym}. \supset .\breve{R} \in \text{Sym}.$

Notice that the identity relation I is reflexive, symmetric, and transitive. In general, any kind of relation of equivalence or congruence will be reflexive, symmetric, and transitive. Hence we refer to any relation which is reflexive, symmetric, and transitive as an equivalence relation. We define

$$\text{Equiv} \quad \text{for} \quad \text{Ref} \cap \text{Sym} \cap \text{Trans}.$$

Theorem X.7.2.

I. $\vdash (R){:}R \in \text{Equiv}. \equiv .R \in \text{Ref}.R \in \text{Sym}.R \in \text{Trans}.$

II. $\vdash (\beta,R){:}R \in \text{Equiv}. \supset .\beta \mathord{\upharpoonleft} R \mathord{\upharpoonright} \beta \in \text{Equiv}.$

III. $\vdash (R){:}R \in \text{Equiv}. \supset .\breve{R} \in \text{Equiv}.$

IV. $\vdash (R,x,y){:}.R \in \text{Equiv}.xRy{:} \supset {:}(z).xRz \equiv yRz.$

Proof of IV. From xRy and xRz, we get yRx by $R \in \text{Sym}$ and then yRz by $R \in \text{Trans}$. Similarly, from xRy and yRz, we get xRz.

If R is an equivalence relation, and we have xRy, we say that x and y are equivalent with respect to R. Because R is transitive, things equivalent to the same thing will be equivalent to each other.

The examples of equivalence relations are many and important, and we cite a few.

1. The relation of congruence of integers modulo an integer k, for a fixed k:

$$R = \hat{x}\hat{y}(\text{E}n).x = y + kn.$$

2. The relation, between two elements x and y of a group G, which holds when there is an element h from a fixed subgroup H such that $y = xh$:

$$R = \hat{x}\hat{y}(\text{E}h).h \in H.y = xh.$$

3. When $S \in \text{Qord}$, the relation:

$$R = \hat{x}\hat{y}(xSy.ySx).$$

4. The relation of similarity between geometrical figures.

5. The relation that holds between two ordered pairs of positive integers $\langle x,y\rangle$ and $\langle u,v\rangle$ when $xv = yu$:

$$R = \hat{\alpha}\hat{\beta}(\text{E}x,y,u,v).\alpha = \langle x,y\rangle.\beta = \langle u,v\rangle.xv = yu.$$

6. The relation, between two sequences $\lambda n(a_n)$ and $\lambda n(b_n)$ of rational numbers, which holds when $(\varepsilon){:}.\varepsilon > 0{:} \supset {:}(\text{E}M,N)(m,n){:}m > M.n > N. \supset .|a_m - b_n| < \varepsilon.$

7. The relation, between classes, of having an equal number of members.

Given an element x in $\text{AV}(R)$, we can form the class of all elements equivalent to x, namely, $R``\{x\}$. If we form such classes for every x in $\text{AV}(R)$, the resulting set of classes is called the set of equivalence classes of R. Two elements are equivalent if and only if they belong to the same equivalence class. Two equivalence classes either have no member in common, or else they are identical. Thus we define

$$\text{EqC}(R) \quad \text{for} \quad \hat{\alpha}(\text{E}x).x \in \text{AV}(R).\alpha = R``\{x\}$$

where α and x are variables not occurring in R.

EqC(R) is stratified if and only if R is stratified, and if stratified is of type one higher than R. All free occurrences of variables in EqC(R) are those in R.

Theorem X.7.3. $\vdash (\alpha,R):\alpha \in \text{EqC}(R). \equiv .(\text{E}x).x \in \text{AV}(R).\alpha = R``\{x\}$.

Theorem X.7.4. $\vdash (R):.R \in \text{Equiv}: \supset :(x,y):xRy. \equiv .x,y \in \text{AV}(R). R``\{x\} = R``\{y\}$.

Proof. Let $R \in$ Equiv. If xRy, then $x,y \in \text{AV}(R)$. Also by Thm.X.7.2, Part IV, $(z).xRz \equiv yRz$. Then by Thm.X.4.22, corollary, $(z):z \in R``\{x\}. \equiv .z \in R``\{y\}$. That is, $R``\{x\} = R``\{y\}$.

Conversely, let $x,y \in \text{AV}(R)$ and $R``\{x\} = R``\{y\}$. Since $R \in$ Ref, xRx. So by Thm.X.4.22, corollary, $x \in R``\{x\}$. So $x \in R``\{y\}$. So yRx. So xRy, since $R \in$ Sym.

Theorem X.7.5. $\vdash (\alpha,R):.R \in \text{Equiv}.\alpha \in \text{EqC}(R): \supset :(x):x \in \alpha. \equiv . \alpha = R``\{x\}$.

Proof. Assume $R \in$ Equiv and $\alpha \in$ EqC(R). Then by rule C

(1) $$y \in \text{AV}(R).\alpha = R``\{y\}.$$

Now let $x \in \alpha$. Then $x \in R``\{y\}$. So $yRx$. So by Thm.X.7.4, $R``\{y\} = R``\{x\}$. So $\alpha = R``\{x\}$.

Conversely, let $\alpha = R``\{x\}$. Then by (1),

(2) $$R``\{x\} = R``\{y\}.$$

Since $y \in \text{AV}(R)$ and $R \in$ Ref, yRy. So by Thm.X.4.22, corollary,

(3) $$y \in R``\{y\}.$$

Hence by (2), $y \in R``\{x\}$. Hence by Thm.X.4.22, corollary, $xRy$. Since $R \in$ Sym, $yRx$. Hence by Thm.X.4.22, corollary, $x \in R``\{y\}$. So by (1), $x \in \alpha$.

Theorem X.7.6. $\vdash (\alpha,\beta,R):R \in \text{Equiv}.\alpha,\beta \in \text{EqC}(R).\alpha \cap \beta \neq \Lambda. \supset .\alpha = \beta$.

Proof. Assume the hypothesis. From $\alpha \cap \beta \neq \Lambda$ by rule C, we get $x \in \alpha \cap \beta$. So by Thm.X.7.5, $\alpha = R``\{x\}$ and $\beta = R``\{x\}$. So $\alpha = \beta$.

Theorem X.7.7. $\vdash (R,x):R \in \text{Equiv}.x \in \text{AV}(R). \supset .(\text{E}_1\alpha).x \in \alpha.\alpha \in \text{EqC}(R)$.

Proof. Assume $R \in$ Equiv and $x \in \text{AV}(R)$. Then by Thm.X.7.3, $R``\{x\} \in \text{EqC}(R)$. Also $xRx$, since $R \in$ Ref, and so $x \in R``\{x\}$ by Thm. X.4.22, corollary. So

(1) $$(\text{E}\alpha).x \in \alpha.\alpha \in \text{EqC}(R).$$

Now assume $x \in \alpha.\alpha \in \text{EqC}(R).x \in \beta.\beta \in \text{EqC}(R)$. Then by Thm.X.7.6, $\alpha = \beta$. So by (1) and Thm.VII.2.1, we get $(\text{E}_1\alpha).x \in \alpha.\alpha \in \text{EqC}(R)$.

Theorem X.7.8. $\vdash (\alpha,R):R \in \text{Equiv}.\alpha \in \text{EqC}(R). \supset .\alpha \neq \Lambda$.

Proof. Assume $R \epsilon$ Equiv and $\alpha \epsilon$ EqC(R). Then by rule C, $x \epsilon$ AV(R). $\alpha = R``\{x\}$. Then $xRx$, since $R \epsilon$ Ref. So $x \epsilon R``\{x\}$ by Thm.X.4.22, corollary. So $x \epsilon \alpha$, and $\alpha \neq \Lambda$.

If we take R to be the first of our seven listed instances of equivalence relations, namely, congruence modulo k, then EqC(R) is just the set of residue classes modulo k, and $R``\{x\}$ is the residue class of x modulo k.

If we take the second R listed, then EqC(R) is the set of left cosets of H in G (see Birkhoff and MacLane, page 146) and $R``\{x\}$ is the left coset corresponding to a given x.

By dealing with the equivalence classes of R rather than with the elements of AV(R), we have the effect of identifying any two equivalent elements. For this reason, various structural features of AV(R) will appear in EqC(R) also, but simplified by the elimination of any distinction between equivalent elements.

Thus with our first listed R, EqC(R) is a ring, and if k is prime it is even a field. With our second listed R, EqC(R) is a group if H is a normal subgroup (Birkhoff and MacLane, page 158). With our third listed R, EqC(R) is partially ordered. We find this idea of using equivalence classes to produce the effect of identification of elements mentioned on page 3 of Lefschetz, 1942. It is a standard device in many parts of mathematics, particularly higher algebra.

Besides their many important uses in mathematics, equivalence classes are useful in formalizing mathematical notions. For instance, suppose we wish a term denoting the shape of a geometrical figure. Similarity of geometrical figures is defined without reference to shape, but nevertheless two figures have the same shape if and only if they are similar. Hence the equivalence class of a given geometrical figure is the class of all figures with the same shape, wherever situated. One can then define this equivalence class to be the shape of the figure. Intuitively, this might not be considered a good definition, but as a formal definition of shape, it serves very nicely. In a certain sense, one is thus thinking of a given equivalence class as being the abstraction of the common property of all its members.

To see another application of this idea, consider our fifth listed equivalence relation. We have $xv = yu$ if and only if the ratios x/y and u/v are equal. Thus our relation defines equality of two ratios without making use of the notion of a ratio. Thus we can use the corresponding equivalence classes to define the notion of ratio.

As this is a very important point, let us be more explicit. Suppose we have constructed the positive integers and wish to construct the rational numbers. We can use the ratios between integers to serve as rational numbers in case we can define the ratios between integers. Now with our fifth listed R, we have $\langle x,y\rangle R\langle u,v\rangle$ if and only if the ratio x/y equals the ratio u/v. So the equivalence class $R``\{\langle x,y\rangle\}$ of $\langle x,y\rangle$ will be the class of all ordered pairs $\langle u,v\rangle$ with the ratio u/v equal to the ratio x/y. Hence we can take this equivalence class to be the definition of the ratio x/y. That is, we define

$$\frac{x}{y} = R``\{\langle x,y\rangle\}.$$

We shall have

$$R``\{\langle 3,4\rangle\} = R``\{\langle 9,12\rangle\}$$

(see Thm.X.7.4). So we have

$$\frac{3}{4} = \frac{9}{12}.$$

In similar fashion, we derive other familiar properties of ratios.

Incidentally, the foregoing discussion illuminates the distinction between a certain ratio, $R``\{\langle 3,4\rangle\}$ and various names of it, such as 3/4, 9/12, etc.

Thus, by defining the notion of having equal ratios without referring to ratios, and then abstracting from this notion by means of equivalence classes, we are able to define ratios, and thus introduce rational numbers.

How can we proceed from rational numbers to reals? The reals can be thought of as limits of sequences of rationals. If we can define the notion of two sequences having the same limit without referring to limits, then we can abstract from this notion by means of equivalence classes, and thus define the common limit of the sequences. Our sixth listed relation is just the notion of two sequences having the same limit. Thus $R``\{\lambda n(a_n)\}$ is the class of all sequences $\lambda n(b_n)$ with the same limit as $\lambda n(a_n)$. So we can take the equivalence class $R``\{\lambda n(a_n)\}$ of a sequence $\lambda n(a_n)$ as constituting the real number which is the limit of the sequence. The totality of such limits will comprise the set of real numbers.

If we can define our seventh listed relation without reference to number, we can abstract from it by means of equivalence classes and get a definition of number. This will constitute the developments of the next chapter.

EXERCISES

X.7.1. Prove:

(a) $\vdash (R):R \in \text{Funct.} \supset .R|\breve{R} \in \text{Equiv.}$

(b) $\vdash (\mathbf{R}):\mathbf{R} \in \text{Equiv.} \equiv .\text{RUSC}(\mathbf{R}) \in \text{Equiv.}$

(c) $\vdash (R,S):S \in \text{Equiv.}R = \{\langle\{x\},\alpha\rangle \mid x \in \text{AV}(S).\alpha \in \text{EqC}(S).x \in \alpha\}. \supset .$ $R \in \text{Funct.RUSC}(S) = R|\breve{R}.$

(d) $\vdash (\mathbf{S}):\mathbf{S} \in \text{Equiv.} \equiv .(\text{E}R).R \in \text{Funct.RUSC}(\mathbf{S}) = R|\breve{R}.$

X.7.2. Prove $\vdash \text{Sym} \cap \text{Trans} \subseteq \text{Ref}$.

X.7.3. What conditions should one impose on λ so that $R = \hat{x}\hat{y}(\text{E}\alpha)$.

$\alpha \in \lambda . x,y \in \alpha$ should be an equivalence relation? If R (as defined) is an equivalence relation, what are AV(R) and EqC(R)?

X.7.4. Prove $\vdash (R,S){:}S \in \text{Qord}.R = \hat{x}\hat{y}(xSy.ySx). \supset .\hat{\alpha}\hat{\beta}(\alpha,\beta \in \text{EqC}(R){:} (\text{E}x,y).xSy.x \in \alpha.y \in \beta) \in \text{Pord}.$

X.7.5. Prove that the relation of being equidistant from a fixed point of three-dimensional space is an equivalence relation. What are the corresponding equivalence classes?

X.7.6. Prove that congruence (modulo Σ) as defined in Sec. 7 of Chapter IX is an equivalence relation.

X.7.7. Prove:

(a) $\vdash \Lambda \in \text{Equiv}$.
(b) $\vdash I \in \text{Equiv}$.

X.7.8. What are EqC(Λ) and EqC(I)?

X.7.9. Prove $\vdash (R){:}R \in \text{Funct}. \supset .\hat{x}\hat{y}(x,y \in \text{Arg}(R).R(x) = R(y)) \in \text{Equiv}.$

8. Applications. We have now got sufficiently close to mathematics that the applications begin to be quite direct, and we have noted these applications as we progressed. Thus, in Sec. 4, we noted many applications of $R|S$, $R``\alpha$, etc., as we proved the theorems involved. The material on functions, in Sec. 5, is of constant application. Several of the exercises at the end of Sec. 5 are considered to be purely mathematical theorems. The material of Sec. 6 is taken almost entirely from Birkhoff, 1948, and is of constant use in the theory of ordered sets. The theory of equivalence classes presented in Sec. 7 is of frequent use as a means of "identifying" sets of objects in some structure to get a new structure with special properties. Also, many useful abstract ideas can be defined as equivalence classes of properly chosen equivalence relations. We mentioned the definition of rationals as equivalence classes of ordered pairs of integers, and the definition of reals as equivalence classes of sequences of rationals. In later chapters we shall define cardinal and ordinal numbers as equivalence classes with respect to properly chosen equivalence relations.

CHAPTER XI

CARDINAL NUMBERS

1. Cardinal Similarity. As noted at the end of the preceding chapter, if we can define the notion of two classes having the same number of members, without referring to number, then we can define number by abstraction from this notion. Clearly two classes have the same number of members if and only if we can pair each member of the first class with exactly one member of the second class in such a way that each member of the second class is paired with a member of the first class. The collection of pairs which comprise such a pairing would constitute a 1–1 relation having the members of the first class for its arguments and the members of the second class for its values. Conversely, given such a 1–1 relation, the ordered pairs constituting the relation would comprise a pairing of all members of the first class with all members of the second class.

So two classes have the same number of members if and only if there exists a 1–1 relation which has the first class for its arguments and the second class for its values.

We say that α and β are similar (or equinumerous) with respect to R if $R \in 1\text{–}1$ and $\alpha = \text{Arg}(R)$ and $\beta = \text{Val}(R)$. That is, we define

$$\alpha \text{ sm}_R\, \beta \qquad \text{for} \qquad R \in 1\text{–}1 . \alpha = \text{Arg}(R) . \beta = \text{Val}(R).$$

α and β are said to be similar (or equinumerous) if there is a relation R with respect to which they are similar. So we define

$$\text{sm} \qquad \text{for} \qquad \hat{\alpha}\hat{\beta}(\text{E}R) . \alpha \text{ sm}_R\, \beta.$$

Thus sm is the relation of having the same number of members. In the next section we shall define the notion of cardinal number by abstraction from sm. However, first we prove various properties of sm, beginning with a proof that it is an equivalence relation.

If α, β, and R are variables, then the indicated occurrences of α, β, and R are the only free occurrences of variables in $\alpha \text{ sm}_R\, \beta$, and $\alpha \text{ sm}_R\, \beta$ is stratified if and only if α, β, and R all have the same type. The term sm is stratified and has no free variables and may be assigned any type.

Theorem XI.1.1.

I. $\vdash \exists(\text{sm})$.

II. $\vdash \text{sm} \in \text{Rel}$.

III. $\vdash (\alpha,\beta) : \alpha \text{ sm } \beta . \equiv . (\text{E}R) . \alpha \text{ sm}_R\, \beta$.

*IV. $\vdash (\alpha,\beta) :. \alpha \text{ sm } \beta : \equiv : (\text{E}R) : R \in 1\text{–}1 . \alpha = \text{Arg}(R) . \beta = \text{Val}(R)$.

Proof. Use Thm.X.3.5, Thm.X.3.6, corollary, and Thm.X.3.7.

Theorem XI.1.2. $\vdash (\alpha,\beta){:}\alpha \text{ sm } \beta . \equiv .(ER).R \,\epsilon\, 1\text{–}1.\alpha \subseteq \text{Arg}(R).\beta = R``\alpha.$

Proof. Assume α sm β. Then by rule C and the definition of $\alpha \text{ sm}_R\, \beta$, we get $R \,\epsilon\, 1\text{–}1.\alpha = \text{Arg}(R).\beta = \text{Val}(R)$. Then by Thm.X.4.26, we get $R \,\epsilon\, 1\text{–}1.\alpha \subseteq \text{Arg}(R).\beta = R``\alpha$. Conversely, assume $(ER).R \,\epsilon\, 1\text{–}1.\alpha \subseteq \text{Arg}(R).\beta = R``\alpha$. Use rule C and let S denote $\alpha \upharpoonright R$. Then by Thm.X.5.19, Cor. 5, $S \,\epsilon\, 1\text{–}1$, and by Thm.X.4.9, Part I, $\alpha = \text{Arg}(S)$. Also, by the definition of $R``\alpha$, we get $\beta = \text{Val}(S)$. So $\alpha \text{ sm}_S\, \beta$. So α sm β.

⋆**Theorem XI.1.3.** $\vdash (\alpha).\alpha \text{ sm } \alpha.$

Proof. We have $\vdash I \,\epsilon\, 1\text{–}1$ and $\vdash \alpha \subseteq \text{Arg}(I)$. Also by Ex.X.5.15, $\vdash \alpha = I``\alpha$. Accordingly, by Thm.XI.1.2, $\vdash \alpha \text{ sm } \alpha$.

Corollary 1. $\vdash \text{Arg(sm)} = \text{Val(sm)} = \text{AV(sm)} = \text{V}.$

Corollary 2. $\vdash \text{sm} \,\epsilon\, \text{Ref}.$

Theorem XI.1.4. $\vdash (\alpha,\beta,R,S){:}S = \breve{R}.\alpha \text{ sm}_R\, \beta . \supset .\beta \text{ sm}_S\, \alpha.$

Proof. Use Thm.X.5.19, Cor. 7, and Thm.X.4.16.

⋆**Corollary 1.** $\vdash (\alpha,\beta){:}\alpha \text{ sm } \beta . \supset .\beta \text{ sm } \alpha.$

Corollary 2. $\vdash \text{sm} \,\epsilon\, \text{Sym}.$

Theorem XI.1.5. $\vdash (\alpha,\beta,\gamma,R,S,T){:}T = R|S.\alpha \text{ sm}_R\, \beta.\beta \text{ sm}_S\, \gamma . \supset .\alpha \text{ sm}_T\, \gamma.$

Proof. Assume the hypothesis. Then by Thm.X.5.19, Cor. 6, $T \,\epsilon\, 1\text{–}1$. Also by Parts III and IV of the corollary to Thm.X.4.19, $\text{Arg}(T) = \text{Arg}(R) = \alpha$ and $\text{Val}(T) = \text{Val}(S) = \gamma$.

⋆**Corollary 1.** $\vdash (\alpha,\beta,\gamma){:}\alpha \text{ sm } \beta.\beta \text{ sm } \gamma . \supset .\alpha \text{ sm } \gamma.$

Corollary 2. $\vdash \text{sm} \,\epsilon\, \text{Trans}.$

Corollary 3. $\vdash \text{sm} \,\epsilon\, \text{Equiv}.$

There is in intuitive mathematics a theorem, known as Cantor's theorem, to the effect that no class is similar to the class of all its subclasses. That is, $(\alpha).\sim(\alpha \text{ sm SC}(\alpha))$. The standard proof is as follows: Assume that α sm SC(α), so that there is a 1–1 correspondence between members of α and subclasses of α. Consider those members of α which are not members of the subclasses with which they are paired. Let A be the set of all such. Then A is a subclass of α, and so is paired with some x which is a member of α. If $x \,\epsilon\, A$, then x must fail to be a member of the subclass with which it is paired (because A was defined to contain just such x's). But the subclass with which x is paired is A, and so $\sim x \,\epsilon\, A$. Thus the supposition $x \,\epsilon\, A$ led to a contradiction, and so we conclude $\sim x \,\epsilon\, A$. Recalling that A is paired with x, we infer that x is not a member of the subclass with which it is paired. However, A contains all such members of α, so that $x \,\epsilon\, A$. Thus we again get a contradiction, and so refute our original assumption that α sm SC(α).

This theorem is very useful in the classical theory of cardinal numbers. Unfortunately it seems to be false. For $\vdash \text{V} = \text{SC(V)}$, so that by Thm. XI.1.3, $\vdash \text{V sm SC(V)}$; this result contradicts the theorem.

The resulting contradiction is the Cantor paradox, and it is difficult to see how to avoid it in classical mathematics. However, in our symbolic logic, it is easily avoided. The condition by which we defined the class A, in the proof given above, is unstratified. Thus we have no way to prove that there is such a class A, and the proof breaks down.

Actually, if we modify the theorem slightly, then the proof will go through. This we do in the following theorem.

Theorem XI.1.6. $\vdash (\alpha).\sim(\text{USC}(\alpha) \text{ sm } \text{SC}(\alpha))$.

Proof. Assume $\text{USC}(\alpha)$ sm $\text{SC}(\alpha)$. Then by rule C, $R \in 1\text{–}1$, $\text{USC}(\alpha) = \text{Arg}(R)$, $\text{SC}(\alpha) = \text{Val}(R)$. Put

$$A = \hat{x}(x \in \alpha.\sim(x \in R(\{x\}))).$$

A is stratified, and so

(1) $$(x){:}x \in A. \equiv .x \in \alpha.\sim(x \in R(\{x\})).$$

So by (1), $A \subseteq \alpha$. Hence $A \in \text{SC}(\alpha)$. So $A \in \text{Val}(R)$. Then by rule C, uRA. As $R \in$ 1-1, we infer

(2) $$A = R(u).$$

As uRA, we get $u \in \text{Arg}(R)$. So $u \in \text{USC}(\alpha)$. Then by rule C, $u = \{x\}$. $x \in \alpha$. Then by (2), $A = R(\{x\})$. So by (1),

$$x \in A. \equiv .x \in \alpha.\sim(x \in A).$$

By truth values

$$\vdash P. \equiv .Q\sim P{:} \supset {:}\sim Q.$$

Taking P to be $x \in A$ and Q to be $x \in \alpha$ gives $\sim(x \in \alpha)$. This is a contradiction.

Intuitively, one would expect that α sm $\text{USC}(\alpha)$, the 1–1 relation being that which pairs x with $\{x\}$ for each x in α. However, this relation would be unstratified, and we have no way in general of proving that it exists. Actually this is fortunate, for if we could infer $(\alpha).\alpha$ sm $\text{USC}(\alpha)$, then by Thm.XI.1.6 we could infer $(\alpha).\sim(\alpha \text{ sm } \text{SC}(\alpha))$, and then the Cantor paradox would be forthcoming.

Nevertheless, for most of the classes α of mathematics, we do have α sm $\text{USC}(\alpha)$. In such case, we say that α is Cantorian, and write

$$\text{Can}(\alpha) \qquad \text{for} \qquad \alpha \text{ sm } \text{USC}(\alpha).$$

Note. $\text{Can}(\alpha)$ is not stratified.

Theorem XI.1.7. $\vdash (\alpha){:}\text{Can}(\alpha). \supset .\sim(\alpha \text{ sm } \text{SC}(\alpha))$.

Proof. Assume $\text{Can}(\alpha)$ and α sm $\text{SC}(\alpha)$. Then we get $\text{USC}(\alpha)$ sm α and α sm $\text{SC}(\alpha)$, whence we get $\text{USC}(\alpha)$ sm $\text{SC}(\alpha)$. By Thm.XI.1.6, this is a contradiction.

This is close enough to Cantor's theorem that we shall refer to it by that name. Actually, as the theorem was stated by Cantor, the hypothesis $\mathrm{Can}(\alpha)$ was missing. This is because it was "obvious" to Cantor that α sm $\mathrm{USC}(\alpha)$. The concept of stratification had not then been invented. It is our stratification restriction which apparently prevents us from proving $\mathrm{Can}(\alpha)$ for general α, even though we can prove it for many α's. In other words, because of our stratification requirements, we apparently cannot prove Cantor's theorem without the additional hypothesis $\mathrm{Can}(\alpha)$, and thus are saved from the Cantor paradox.

Theorem XI.1.8. $\vdash \sim\mathrm{Can}(\mathrm{V})$.

Proof. Put V for α in Thm.XI.1.7. Then we get $\vdash (\mathrm{V} \text{ sm } \mathrm{SC}(\mathrm{V})). \supset . \sim\mathrm{Can}(\mathrm{V})$. However, by Thm.IX.6.19, Part II, $\vdash \mathrm{V} = \mathrm{SC}(\mathrm{V})$. So by Thm.XI.1.3, $\vdash \mathrm{V} \text{ sm } \mathrm{SC}(\mathrm{V})$.

This theorem states $\vdash \sim(\mathrm{V} \text{ sm } \mathrm{USC}(\mathrm{V}))$, which seems intuitively wrong, since we have the feeling that for any class α we should be able to prove α sm $\mathrm{USC}(\alpha)$ by letting x correspond to $\{x\}$ for each x of α. Actually, our stratification restrictions apparently prevent this, fortunately.

We have here the first case in which our formal system deviates in any important particular from our intuitive ideas. Actually, we shall prove $\mathrm{Can}(\alpha)$ for the more common classes of mathematics (such as the class of integers, the class of real numbers, etc.), so that for most purposes of mathematics our formal logic is still following the intuitive logic fairly well. In fact, the classes α for which we apparently cannot prove $\mathrm{Can}(\alpha)$ are the classes with a very large number of members such as V, or the class of all ordinal numbers, or classes of this sort, which, from an intuitive point of view, are not at all sharply defined. For such large, vague classes on the frontier of our comprehension, it is not really surprising that some properties, such as $\mathrm{Can}(\alpha)$, which we have extrapolated from finite classes, should fail to hold.

We now prove some results which will be needed when we study addition of cardinal numbers.

Theorem XI.1.9. $\vdash (\alpha):\alpha \text{ sm } \Lambda. \equiv .\alpha = \Lambda$.

Proof. By Thm.XI.1.3, $\vdash \alpha = \Lambda. \supset .\alpha \text{ sm } \Lambda$. Now assume α sm Λ. Then by rule C,

$$R \in 1\text{–}1.\alpha = \mathrm{Arg}(R).\Lambda = \mathrm{Val}(R).$$

Then by Thm.X.4.3, $R = \Lambda$ and $\alpha = \Lambda$.

Corollary. $\vdash (\alpha):\alpha \text{ sm } \Lambda. \equiv .\alpha \in 0$.

Theorem XI.1.10. $\vdash (x,y).\{x\} \text{ sm } \{y\}$.

Proof. Take R to be $\{\langle x,y\rangle\}$. Then $\vdash (u,v):uRv. \equiv .u = x.v = y$ and $\vdash R \in \mathrm{Rel}$. So $\vdash R \in 1\text{–}1.\{x\} = \mathrm{Arg}(R).\{y\} = \mathrm{Val}(R)$.

Theorem XI.1.11. $\vdash (\alpha,x):\alpha \text{ sm } \{x\}. \equiv .\alpha \in 1$.

Proof. Let α sm $\{x\}$. Then by rule C, $R \epsilon 1\text{–}1.\alpha = \text{Arg}(R).\{x\} = \text{Val}(R)$. So $x \epsilon \text{Val}(R)$, and by rule C, yRx. So $y \epsilon \text{Arg}(R)$, whence $y \epsilon \alpha$, whence

(1) $$\{y\} \subseteq \alpha.$$

To show that also $\alpha \subseteq \{y\}$, let $z \epsilon \alpha$. Then $z \epsilon \text{Arg}(R)$ and by rule C, zRw. So $w \epsilon \text{Val}(R)$, $w \epsilon \{x\}$, $x = w$, and finally zRx. Since yRx and $R \epsilon 1\text{–}1$, we get $z = y$ and $z \epsilon \{y\}$. Then by (1) $\alpha = \{y\}$, and thus $\alpha \epsilon 1$.

Conversely, let $\alpha \epsilon 1$. Then by rule C, $\alpha = \{y\}$. Then by Thm.XI.1.10, α sm $\{x\}$.

Theorem XI.1.12. $\vdash (\alpha,\beta,\gamma,\delta,R,S,T){:}T = R \cup S.\alpha \text{ sm}_R\ \gamma.\beta \text{ sm}_S\ \delta.\ \alpha \cap \beta = \Lambda.\gamma \cap \delta = \Lambda. \supset .(\alpha \cup \beta) \text{ sm}_T\ (\gamma \cup \delta)$.

Proof. Assume the hypothesis. Then by Thm.X.5.21, Cor. 2, $T \epsilon 1\text{–}1$. Also by Ex.X.4.6, Parts (a) and (b), $\alpha \cup \beta = \text{Arg}(T)$ and $\gamma \cup \delta = \text{Val}(T)$.

Corollary. $\vdash (\alpha,\beta,\gamma,\delta){:}\alpha \cap \beta = \Lambda.\gamma \cap \delta = \Lambda.\alpha \text{ sm } \gamma.\beta \text{ sm } \delta. \supset .\ (\alpha \cup \beta) \text{ sm } (\gamma \cup \delta)$.

Theorem XI.1.13. $\vdash (\alpha,\beta,x,y){:}\alpha \cup \{x\} = \beta \cup \{y\}.\sim x \epsilon \alpha.\sim y \epsilon \beta. \supset .\alpha \text{ sm } \beta$.

Proof. Assume

(1) $$\alpha \cup \{x\} = \beta \cup \{y\},$$

(2) $$\sim x \epsilon \alpha,$$

(3) $$\sim y \epsilon \beta.$$

Then by Thm.IX.6.6, Cor. 1,

(4) $$\alpha \cap \{x\} = \Lambda.$$

(5) $$\beta \cap \{y\} = \Lambda.$$

Case 1. $x = y$. Then $\{x\} = \{y\}$. Then by (1), (4), and (5) and Thm.IX.4.9, Cor. 3, we get $\alpha = \beta$. So α sm β.

Case 2. $x \neq y$. By (1), $x \epsilon \beta \cup \{y\}$. However, $\sim x \epsilon \{y\}$. So

(6) $$x \epsilon \beta.$$

Similarly

(7) $$y \epsilon \alpha.$$

Put

(8) $$\gamma = \alpha - \{y\}.$$

Then by (7) and Thm.IX.6.5, Cor. 3,

(9) $$\alpha = \gamma \cup \{y\}.$$

Also

(10) $$\Lambda = \gamma \cap \{y\}.$$

By (2) and (8), $\sim x \in \gamma$. So by Thm.IX.6.6, Cor. 1,

(11) $$\Lambda = \gamma \cap \{x\}.$$

Now let $z \in \beta$. Then by (3),

(12) $$z \neq y$$

and by (1)

(13) $$z \in \alpha \cup \{x\}.$$

If $z = x$, then $z \in \gamma \cup \{x\}$. If $z \neq x$, then by (13), $z \in \alpha$, and so by (12) and (8), $z \in \gamma$, and hence $z \in \gamma \cup \{x\}$. So

(14) $$\beta \subseteq \gamma \cup \{x\}.$$

Conversely, let $z \in \gamma \cup \{x\}$. If $z \in \gamma$, then by (8), $z \in \alpha$ and $z \neq y$. So by (1), $z \in \beta$. If $z \in \{x\}$, then $z = x$ and by (6), $z \in \beta$. So by (14),

(15) $$\beta = \gamma \cup \{x\}.$$

Now $\vdash \gamma$ sm γ by Thm.XI.1.3 and $\vdash \{x\}$ sm $\{y\}$ by Thm.XI.1.10. So by (10), (11), (9), and (15), we get α sm β by Thm.XI.1.12, corollary.

We now prove some results which will be needed when we study inequalities between cardinal numbers.

Theorem XI.1.14. $\vdash (\beta,R){:}R \in 1\text{–}1.\beta \subseteq \text{Arg}(R).\text{Val}(R) \subseteq \beta. \supset .$ β sm $(\text{Val}(R))$.

Proof. Assume

(1) $$R \in 1\text{–}1,$$

(2) $$\beta \subseteq \text{Arg}(R),$$

(3) $$\text{Val}(R) \subseteq \beta.$$

Define

(4) $$\gamma = \text{Clos}(\beta - \text{Val}(R),xRz),$$

(5) $$A = \beta \cap \gamma,$$

(6) $$B = \beta \cap \bar{\gamma},$$

(7) $$C = \text{Val}(R) \cap \gamma,$$

(8) $$D = \text{Val}(R) \cap \bar{\gamma}.$$

We have immediately

(9) $$\vdash A \cap B = \Lambda,$$

(10) $$\vdash C \cap D = \Lambda,$$

(11) $$\vdash A \cup B = \beta,$$

(12) $$\vdash C \cup D = \text{Val}(R).$$

So by Thm.XI.1.12, corollary, it suffices to prove A sm C and B sm D. Clearly by (2) and (5)

(13) $$A \subseteq \text{Arg}(R).$$

By (4) and Thm.X.4.37,

(14) $$\vdash \gamma = (\beta - \text{Val}(R)) \cup R``\gamma.$$

Clearly $\vdash (\beta - \text{Val}(R)) \subseteq \beta$, and by (3) and Thm.X.4.24, Part I, $R``\gamma \subseteq \beta$. So by (14) and Thm.IX.4.18, Part II, $\gamma \subseteq \beta$, so that by (5),

(15) $$A = \gamma.$$

By (14) and (15), $R``A \subseteq \gamma$. Also by Thm.X.4.24, Part I, $R``A \subseteq \text{Val}(R)$. So by Thm.X.4.18, Part I, and (7)

(16) $$R``A \subseteq C.$$

By (7) and (14),

$$\begin{aligned} \vdash C &= \text{Val}(R) \cap ((\beta - \text{Val}(R)) \cup R``\gamma) \\ &= (\text{Val}(R) \cap (\beta - \text{Val}(R))) \cup (\text{Val}(R) \cap R``\gamma) \\ &= \Lambda \cup (\text{Val}(R) \cap R``\gamma) \\ &= \text{Val}(R) \cap R``\gamma. \end{aligned}$$

So $\vdash C \subseteq R``\gamma$, and so by (15), $C \subseteq R``A$. With (16), this gives

(17) $$C = R``A.$$

Then by (1), (13), (17), and Thm.XI.1.2,

(18) $$A \text{ sm } C.$$

By (3), (6), (8), and Thm.IX.4.16, Part I,

(19) $$D \subseteq B.$$

By (4) and Thm.X.4.34, $\vdash \beta - \text{Val}(R) \subseteq \gamma$. So by Thm.IX.4.17, $\vdash \bar{\gamma} \subseteq \bar{\beta} \cup \text{Val}(R)$. So by (6) and Thm.IX.4.16, Part I, $\vdash B \subseteq \beta \cap (\bar{\beta} \cup \text{Val}(R))$. So by Thm.IX.4.4, Part XVIII, $\vdash B \subseteq \beta \cap \text{Val}(R)$. Then by (3), $B \subseteq \text{Val}(R)$. Also, by (6), $B \subseteq \bar{\gamma}$. So by (8) and Thm.IX.4.18, Part I, $B \subseteq D$. So by (19), $B = D$ and hence

(20) $$B \text{ sm } D.$$

Our theorem now follows by Thm.XI.1.12, corollary.

Let us consider a geometrical illustration of this theorem. Let α consist of the points interior to a square and let β consist of the points interior to the circle inscribed in the square. Let R be a one-to-one transformation which shrinks the square in the ratio $1/\sqrt{2}$. Then $\text{Arg}(R)$ is α and $\text{Val}(R)$ consists of the points interior to the square which we have shown inscribed in the circle in Fig. XI.1.1. We have $\beta \subseteq \text{Arg}(R)$ and $\text{Val}(R) \subseteq \beta$.

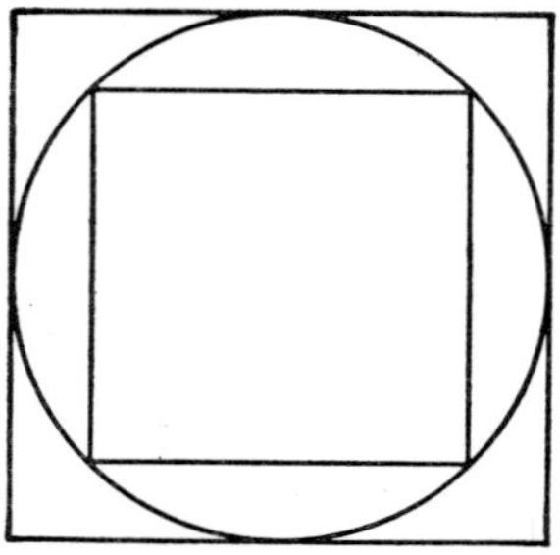

FIG. XI.1.1.

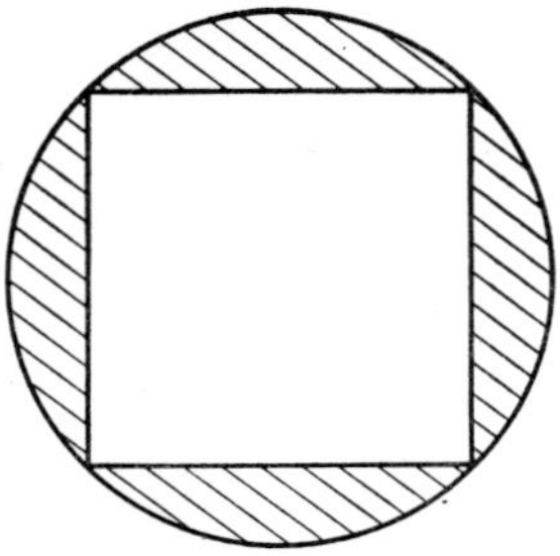

FIG. XI.1.2.

Then by the theorem just proved, $\beta \text{ sm } \text{Val}(R)$. That is, there is a one-to-one correspondence between the interior points of the circle and the interior points of the square inscribed in the circle.

One could set up directly such a one-to-one correspondence as follows. We note that $\beta - \text{Val}(R)$ is a region shaped like the shaded portion of Fig. XI.1.2. Since R shrinks figures in the ratio $1/\sqrt{2}$, $R``(\beta - \text{Val}(R))$ is a smaller region of similar shape lying just inside the given region, $R``R``(\beta - \text{Val}(R))$ is a similar still smaller region, etc. Now we make the points of $\beta$ correspond to those of $\text{Val}(R)$ by the following scheme. The points of $\beta - \text{Val}(R)$ in $\beta$ are to be paired with the points of $R``(\beta - \text{Val}(R))$ in $\text{Val}(R)$. The points of $R``(\beta - \text{Val}(R))$ in $\beta$ are to be paired with the points of $R``R``(\beta - \text{Val}(R))$ in $\text{Val}(R)$. We continue in this way, pairing regions $\delta$ in $\beta$ with $R``\delta$ in $\text{Val}(R)$. By this process we pair the points of

$$(\beta - \text{Val}(R)) \cup R``(\beta - \text{Val}(R)) \cup R``R``(\beta - \text{Val}(R)) \cup \cdots$$

in β with the points of

$$R``(\beta - \text{Val}(R)) \cup R``R``(\beta - \text{Val}(R)) \cup \cdots$$

in $\text{Val}(R)$. The remaining set of unpaired points of β lies in $\text{Val}(R)$, and coincides exactly with the set of unpaired points of $\text{Val}(R)$. All these points are then paired with themselves.

In point of fact, the above scheme for setting β and $\text{Val}(R)$ into one-to-one correspondence is just that used in our proof of Thm.IX.1.14. Thus, by taking γ to be $\text{Clos}(\beta - \text{Val}(R), xRz)$, we arrange that γ is

$$(\beta - \text{Val}(R)) \cup R``(\beta - \text{Val}(R)) \cup R``R``(\beta - \text{Val}(R)) \cup \cdots.$$

Our definitions of A, B, C, and D are such that A is just γ and C is just $R``A$, so that C is

$$R``(\beta - \text{Val}(R)) \cup R``R``(\beta - \text{Val}(R)) \cup \cdots.$$

Then the points of A and C are paired by R. It also turns out that $B = D$, and so the points of B and D are paired with themselves.

Our Theorem XI.1.14 is a lemma for the Schröder-Bernstein theorem to the effect that, if α is similar to a subset of β and β is similar to a subset of α, then α is similar to β.

Theorem XI.1.15. $\vdash (\alpha,\beta,\gamma,\delta):\alpha \text{ sm } \gamma.\gamma \subseteq \beta.\beta \text{ sm } \delta.\delta \subseteq \alpha. \supset .\alpha \text{ sm } \beta.$

Proof. Assume α sm γ, $\gamma \subseteq \beta$, β sm δ, $\delta \subseteq \alpha$. Then by rule C,

$$R \in 1\text{–}1.\alpha = \text{Arg}(R).\gamma = \text{Val}(R),$$

$$S \in 1\text{–}1.\beta = \text{Arg}(S).\delta = \text{Val}(S).$$

We have $\text{Val}(R) \subseteq \text{Arg}(S)$. So by Thm.X.4.10, Part II, $R = R{\restriction}\text{Arg}(S)$. So by Thm.X.4.19, Part I,

(1) $$\text{Arg}(R|S) = \text{Arg}(R) = \alpha.$$

Also by Thm.X.4.19, corollary, Part II, $\text{Val}(R|S) \subseteq \text{Val}(S)$. So

(2) $$\text{Val}(R|S) \subseteq \delta.$$

By (1),

(3) $$\delta \subseteq \text{Arg}(R|S).$$

Also by Thm.X.5.19, Cor. 6,

(4) $$R|S \in 1\text{–}1.$$

Hence by (2), (3), (4), and Thm.XI.1.14,

(5) $$\delta \text{ sm } \text{Val}(R|S).$$

However, by definition of sm_T, if $T \in 1\text{–}1$, then $\text{Arg}(T) \text{ sm}_T \text{ Val}(T)$. Taking T to be $R|S$ gives $\text{Arg}(R|S)$ sm $\text{Val}(R|S)$. So by (1) and (5), α sm δ. However, β sm δ. So α sm β.

We now prove some results which will be needed when we study multiplication of cardinal numbers.

Let α and β be finite classes, with m members in α and n members in β. How many members does $\alpha \times \beta$ have? To get a member of $\alpha \times \beta$ we must choose a member x from α and a member y from β and form the ordered pair $\langle x,y\rangle$. For each given x of α, we can choose y from β in n ways and form n ordered pairs $\langle x,y\rangle$. Doing this for each of the m members x of α, we get m groups of n ordered pairs. Clearly these ordered pairs are all distinct, so that we have a total of $m \times n$ ordered pairs. That is, $\alpha \times \beta$ has $m \times n$ members. We generalize to the case in which either α or β is an infinite class, and define the product $m \times n$ as the number of members of $\alpha \times \beta$.

The next theorem and its mate, Thm.XI.1.18, state that the number of members of $\alpha \times \beta$ depends only on the numbers of members of α and β, respectively, and not on any other properties of α and β. This is as it should be.

Theorem XI.1.16. $\vdash (\alpha,\beta,\gamma){:}\alpha \text{ sm } \beta. \supset .(\alpha \times \gamma) \text{ sm } (\beta \times \gamma)$.

Proof. Let α sm β. Then by rule C, $R \in 1\text{–}1.\alpha = \text{Arg}(R).\beta = \text{Val}(R)$. Put

$$S = \hat{u}\hat{v}(\text{E}x,y,z).u = \langle x,z\rangle.v = \langle y,z\rangle.xRy.$$

Clearly S is stratified and so

$$(1) \qquad S \in \text{Rel}.$$

Now let uSv_1 and uSv_2. Then by rule C,

$$u = \langle x_1,z_1\rangle.v_1 = \langle y_1,z_1\rangle.x_1Ry_1$$

and

$$u = \langle x_2,z_2\rangle.v_2 = \langle y_2,z_2\rangle.x_2Ry_2.$$

So $x_1 = x_2$ and $z_1 = z_2$. Then from x_1Ry_1, x_2Ry_2, and $R \in 1\text{–}1$, we get $y_1 = y_2$. So $v_1 = v_2$. Similarly, from u_1Sv and u_2Sv, we get $u_1 = u_2$. Hence

$$(2) \qquad S \in 1\text{–}1.$$

Now let $u \in \alpha \times \gamma$. Then by Thm.X.2.12 and rule C, $u = \langle x,z\rangle.x \in \alpha.z \in \gamma$. Then $x \in \text{Arg}(R)$ so that xRy. So $uS(\langle y,z\rangle)$. So $u \in \text{Arg}(S)$. Thus

$$(3) \qquad \alpha \times \gamma \subseteq \text{Arg}(S).$$

Now let $v \in \beta \times \gamma$. Then similarly $v = \langle y,z\rangle.y \in \beta.z \in \gamma$ and xRy, and $(\langle x,z\rangle)Sv$. Accordingly $x \in \text{Arg}(R)$ so that $x \in \alpha$. Then $\langle x,z\rangle \in \alpha \times \gamma$. So $v \in S``(\alpha \times \gamma)$. Thus

$$(4) \qquad \beta \times \gamma \subseteq S``(\alpha \times \gamma).$$

Now let $v \in S``(\alpha \times \gamma)$. Then $u \in \alpha \times \gamma.uSv$. So by rule C with Thm.X.2.12, $u = \langle x_1,z_1\rangle.x_1 \in \alpha.z_1 \in \gamma$ and $u = \langle x,z\rangle.v = \langle y,z\rangle.xRy$. So $z = z_1$ and $z \in \gamma$. Also, from xRy, we get $y \in \text{Val}(R)$ and so $y \in \beta$. So $v = \langle y,z\rangle.y \in \beta.z \in \gamma$. Thence $v \in \beta \times \gamma$. Thus $S``(\alpha \times \gamma) \subseteq \beta \times \gamma$. So by (4),

$$(5) \qquad \beta \times \gamma = S``(\alpha \times \gamma).$$

Then by (2), (3), (5), and Thm.XI.1.2, our theorem follows.

We could prove

$$\vdash (\alpha,\beta,\gamma):\alpha \text{ sm } \beta. \supset .(\gamma \times \alpha) \text{ sm } (\gamma \times \beta)$$

by the same methods. However, we shall give an alternative proof later.

We now prove that $\alpha \times \beta$ and $\beta \times \alpha$ have the same number of elements. In other words, multiplication of cardinal numbers is commutative. In case α and β are classes of real numbers, one can give an intuitive proof as follows. Mark the members of α as points on the x-axis and the members of β as points on the y-axis. Then the members $\langle x,y\rangle$ of $\alpha \times \beta$ are just the points (x,y) in the x-y plane which are simultaneously on a vertical line through a point of α and on a horizontal line through a point of β. If now we reflect the entire figure in the 45-degree line $y = x$, the points of $\alpha \times \beta$ go into the points of $\beta \times \alpha$.

This is the basic idea of the proof which we now give.

Theorem XI.1.17. $\vdash (\alpha,\beta).(\alpha \times \beta) \text{ sm } (\beta \times \alpha)$.

Proof. Put

$$R = \hat{x}\hat{y}(\text{E}u,v).x = \langle u,v\rangle.y = \langle v,u\rangle.$$

One proves easily

$$(1) \qquad \vdash R \in 1\text{–}1$$

and $\vdash \text{Arg}(R) = \text{V} \times \text{V}$. So

$$(2) \qquad \alpha \times \beta \subseteq \text{Arg}(R).$$

Now let $y \in \beta \times \alpha$. So by rule C and Thm.X.2.12, $y = \langle v,u\rangle.v \in \beta.u \in \alpha$. So $\langle u,v\rangle \in \alpha \times \beta$ and $\langle u,v\rangle Ry$. Hence $y \in R``(\alpha \times \beta)$.

Conversely, let $y \in R``(\alpha \times \beta)$. So by rule C, xRy and $x \in \alpha \times \beta$. Then by rule C with xRy, we get

$$x = \langle u,v\rangle.y = \langle v,u\rangle,$$

and by rule C with Thm.X.2.12,

$$x = \langle z,w\rangle.z \in \alpha.w \in \beta.$$

Then $z = u$ and $v = w$. So $y = \langle v,u\rangle.v \in \beta.u \in \alpha$. That is, $y \in \beta \times \alpha$. So

$$(3) \qquad \vdash \beta \times \alpha = R``(\alpha \times \beta).$$

From (1), (2), and (3), our theorem follows by Thm.XI.1.2.

Theorem XI.1.18.

I. $\vdash (\alpha,\beta,\gamma):\alpha \text{ sm } \beta. \supset .(\gamma \times \alpha) \text{ sm } (\gamma \times \beta)$.

II. $\vdash (\alpha,\beta,\gamma,\delta):\alpha \text{ sm } \gamma.\beta \text{ sm } \delta. \supset .(\alpha \times \beta) \text{ sm } (\gamma \times \delta)$.

Proof of I. By Thm.XI.1.17, $\vdash (\gamma \times \alpha) \text{ sm } (\alpha \times \gamma)$ and $\vdash (\beta \times \gamma) \text{ sm } (\gamma \times \beta)$. Also, if $\alpha \text{ sm } \beta$, then $(\alpha \times \gamma) \text{ sm } (\beta \times \gamma)$ by Thm.XI.1.16.

Proof of II. From $\alpha \text{ sm } \gamma$ we get $(\alpha \times \beta) \text{ sm } (\gamma \times \beta)$ and from $\beta \text{ sm } \delta$ we get $(\gamma \times \beta) \text{ sm } (\gamma \times \delta)$.

We now give proofs for theorems which will lead to the two results that cardinal multiplication is associative and that if a cardinal number is multiplied by unity the product is the number.

Theorem XI.1.19. $\vdash (\alpha,\beta,\gamma).((\alpha \times \beta) \times \gamma) \text{ sm } (\alpha \times (\beta \times \gamma))$.

Proof. Put

$$R = \hat{x}\hat{y}(\mathrm{E}u,v,w).x = \langle\langle u,v\rangle,w\rangle.y = \langle u,\langle v,w\rangle\rangle,$$

and proceed as in the proof of Thm.XI.1.17 to prove

(1) $$\vdash R \in 1\text{–}1,$$

(2) $$\vdash (\alpha \times \beta) \times \gamma \subseteq \mathrm{Arg}(R),$$

(3) $$\vdash \alpha \times (\beta \times \gamma) = R``((\alpha \times \beta) \times \gamma).$$

Theorem XI.1.20. $\vdash (\alpha,x).\alpha \text{ sm } (\alpha \times \{x\})$.

Proof. Put

$$R = \hat{z}\hat{y}(y = \langle z,x\rangle),$$

and proceed as in the proof of Thm.XI.1.17 to prove

(1) $$\vdash R \in 1\text{–}1,$$

(2) $$\vdash \alpha \subseteq \mathrm{Arg}(R),$$

(3) $$\vdash \alpha \times \{x\} = R``\alpha.$$

We now prove some results which will be needed when we study exponentiation of cardinal numbers. We first introduce the definition

$$\alpha \wedge \beta \quad \text{for} \quad \hat{R}(R \in \mathrm{Funct}.\mathrm{Arg}(R) = \alpha.\mathrm{Val}(R) \subseteq \beta).$$

If α and β are variables, the explicitly indicated occurrences of α and β are free and are the only free occurrences of any variables in $\alpha \wedge \beta$. Also $\alpha \wedge \beta$ is stratified if and only if α and β have the same type, and the type of $\alpha \wedge \beta$ will be one greater than the type of α and β.

The motivation for the definition of $\alpha \wedge \beta$ comes about as follows. Let α and β be finite classes, with m members in α and n members in β. How many members does $\alpha \wedge \beta$ have? To get a member of $\alpha \wedge \beta$, we must form a function R whose argument range is α and whose values all lie in β. To form such a function R, we have to designate a member of β to go with each member of α. To the first member of α, we can assign any of the n members of β, so that we have n possible choices. Quite independently, we can assign a member of β to the second member of α in n distinct ways.

Indeed, quite independently, we can assign members of β to each given member of α in n distinct ways. Thus the total number of possible ways to assign a member of β to each member of α is $n \times n \times \cdots \times n$ ways, where the product is taken over m factors. That is, n^m distinct functions can be defined such that they assign a member of β to each member of α. Thus $\alpha \curlywedge \beta$ has n^m members.

Accordingly, we can define exponentiation for finite cardinals in terms of $\alpha \curlywedge \beta$. Indeed, we can and will define exponentiation for any cardinal numbers, finite or infinite, in terms of $\alpha \curlywedge \beta$.

The use of $\curlywedge$, which is just an upside-down $\curlyvee$, as a symbol for use in exponentiation has occurred elsewhere (see Quine, 1940, for instance).

We now proceed to prove a series of theorems about $\alpha \curlywedge \beta$ from which the familiar laws of exponents will be forthcoming.

It is difficult to motivate the proofs of these theorems. The theorems themselves are devised by considering the laws of exponents and noting what theorems about similarity are needed to prove them. In some cases it was fairly clear how to choose the 1–1 relation which would prove the desired similarity. However, since $\alpha \curlywedge \beta$ is a type higher than α and β, the issue is somewhat confused by the necessity for preserving stratification. Thus, in Thm.XI.1.30, we shall find USC(δ) at a place where intuitively we should expect to find δ. From an intuitive point of view, Can(δ) is obvious, so that it would not matter whether we have δ or USC(δ). However, in the symbolic logic, we know how to prove Can(δ) for only special δ's and so must take care to distinguish between USC(δ) and δ in general.

In the next section, in which we prove the laws of exponents, it will be seen which law of exponents is derived from each of the various theorems which we now prove.

Theorem XI.1.21.

I. $\vdash (\alpha,\beta).\exists(\alpha \curlywedge \beta)$.

$\star$II. $\vdash (\alpha,\beta,R){:}R \in (\alpha \curlywedge \beta). \equiv .R \in \text{Funct}.\text{Arg}(R) = \alpha.\text{Val}(R) \subseteq \beta$.

Theorem XI.1.22. $\vdash (\alpha,\beta,\gamma){:}\alpha \text{ sm } \beta. \supset .(\alpha \curlywedge \gamma) \text{ sm } (\beta \curlywedge \gamma)$.

Proof. Let α sm β. Then

$$R \in 1\text{–}1.\text{Arg}(R) = \alpha.\text{Val}(R) = \beta. \tag{1}$$

Let

$$W = (\alpha \curlywedge \gamma)\upharpoonleft(\lambda S(\breve{R}|S)). \tag{2}$$

By Thm.X.5.23, Part II, and Thm.X.5.7, corollary,

$$W \in \text{Funct}, \tag{3}$$

and by Thm.X.5.23, Part IV, and Thm.X.4.9, Part I,

$$\text{Arg}(W) = (\alpha \curlywedge \gamma). \tag{4}$$

Let SWT. Then by (2), $S \in \text{Rel}$, $\text{Arg}(S) = \alpha$, and $T = \breve{R}|S$. So $R|T = (R|\breve{R})|S$. However, by Thm.X.5.12, corollary, and (1), $R|\breve{R} = \text{Val}(\breve{R})\upharpoonleft I = \text{Arg}(R)\upharpoonleft I = \alpha\upharpoonleft I$. So by Thm.X.4.20, Part I, $R|T = (\alpha\upharpoonleft I)|S = \alpha\upharpoonleft(I|S) = \alpha\upharpoonleft S$ by Thm.X.5.11. So by $\text{Arg}(S) = \alpha$ and Thm.X.4.10, Part I, $R|T = S$. So $SWT. \supset .S = R|T$. Hence $\breve{W} \in \text{Funct}$, and so by (3),

$$(5) \qquad W \in 1\text{–}1.$$

Now let $T \in \text{Val}(W)$. Then $S \in \text{Funct}$, $\text{Arg}(S) = \alpha$, $\text{Val}(S) \subseteq \gamma$, $T = \breve{R}|S$. Then by Thm.X.4.19, corollary, Part III, $\text{Arg}(T) = \text{Arg}(\breve{R}|S) = \text{Arg}(\breve{R}) = \text{Val}(R) = \beta$. Also by Thm.X.4.19, corollary, Part II, $\text{Val}(T) \subseteq \gamma$. Also by Thm.X.5.9, $\breve{R}|S \in \text{Funct}$, so that $T \in \text{Funct}$. Then $T \in (\beta \wedge \gamma)$. So

$$(6) \qquad \text{Val}(W) \subseteq (\beta \wedge \gamma).$$

Conversely, let $T \in (\beta \wedge \gamma)$. So $T \in \text{Funct}$, $\text{Arg}(T) = \beta$, $\text{Val}(T) \subseteq \gamma$. Then $R|T \in \text{Funct}$, $\text{Arg}(R|T) = \alpha$, $\text{Val}(R|T) \subseteq \gamma$. Also $\breve{R}|(R|T) = (\breve{R}|R)|T = (\beta\upharpoonleft I)|T = \beta\upharpoonleft(I|T) = \beta\upharpoonleft T = T$. So by (2), $(R|T)WT$. Hence $T \in \text{Val}(W)$. So by (6),

$$(7) \qquad \text{Val}(W) = (\beta \wedge \gamma).$$

Then by (5), (4), and (7), $(\alpha \wedge \gamma) \text{ sm } (\beta \wedge \gamma)$.

Theorem XI.1.23. $\vdash (\alpha,\beta,\gamma):\alpha \text{ sm } \beta. \supset .(\gamma \wedge \alpha) \text{ sm } (\gamma \wedge \beta)$.

Proof. Let α sm β. Then $R \in 1\text{–}1.\text{Arg}(R) = \alpha.\text{Val}(R) = \beta$. So let

$$W = (\gamma \wedge \alpha)\upharpoonleft(\lambda S(S|R))$$

and proceed as in the proof of Thm.XI.1.22.

Corollary. $\vdash (\alpha,\beta,\gamma,\delta):\alpha \text{ sm } \gamma.\beta \text{ sm } \delta. \supset .(\alpha \wedge \beta) \text{ sm } (\gamma \wedge \delta)$.

Theorem XI.1.24. $\vdash (\beta).(\Lambda \wedge \beta) = 0$.

Proof. Let $R \in (\Lambda \wedge \beta)$. Then $\text{Arg}(R) = \Lambda$. So by Thm.X.4.3, Part I, $R = \Lambda$. So $R \in 0$. Conversely, let $R \in 0$. Then $R = \Lambda$. So $R \in \text{Funct}$. $\text{Arg}(R) = \Lambda.\text{Val}(R) \subseteq \beta$. So $R \in (\Lambda \wedge \beta)$.

Theorem XI.1.25. $\vdash (\alpha):\alpha \neq \Lambda. \supset .(\alpha \wedge \Lambda) = \Lambda$.

Proof. Let $R \in (\alpha \wedge \Lambda)$. Then $\text{Arg}(R) = \alpha$, $\text{Val}(R) \subseteq \Lambda$. So by Thm.IX.4.13, Cor. 2, $\text{Val}(R) = \Lambda$, $R = \Lambda$, $\text{Arg}(R) = \Lambda$, $\alpha = \Lambda$. Thus

$$\vdash R \in (\alpha \wedge \Lambda). \supset .\alpha = \Lambda.$$

So

$$\vdash \alpha \neq \Lambda. \supset .\sim R \in (\alpha \wedge \Lambda).$$

So by Thm.IX.4.12, Part II,

$$\vdash \alpha \neq \Lambda. \supset .(\alpha \wedge \Lambda) = \Lambda.$$

Theorem XI.1.26. $\vdash (\alpha,x):(\{x\} \wedge \alpha) = \text{USC}(\{x\} \times \alpha)$.

Proof. Let $R \in (\{x\} \wedge \alpha)$. Then $R \in \text{Funct}.\text{Arg}(R) = \{x\}.\text{Val}(R) \subseteq \alpha$.

Then $x \in \mathrm{Arg}(R)$, so that by Thm.X.5.3, Cor. 4, $R(x) \in \mathrm{Val}(R)$, so that $R(x) \in \alpha$ and

(1) $$\langle x,R(x)\rangle \in \{x\} \times \alpha.$$

Also $\langle x,R(x)\rangle \in R$, so that

(2) $$\{\langle x,R(x)\rangle\} \subseteq R.$$

In addition to our assumption $R \in (\{x\} \wedge \alpha)$, let us further assume $z \in R$. Then by Thm.X.3.1 and rule C, $z = \langle u,v\rangle$ and uRv, so that $u \in \mathrm{Arg}(R)$. Hence $u \in \{x\}$, $u = x$, so that xRv. By Thm.X.5.3, $v = R(x)$, so that $z = \langle x,R(x)\rangle$. So $z \in \{\langle x,R(x)\rangle\}$. Thus by (2),

(3) $$\{\langle x,R(x)\rangle\} = R.$$

Then by (1), (3), and Thm.IX.6.10, Part III, $R \in \mathrm{USC}(\{x\} \times \alpha)$. So finally

(4) $$\vdash (\{x\} \wedge \alpha) \subseteq \mathrm{USC}(\{x\} \times \alpha).$$

Conversely, let $R \in \mathrm{USC}(\{x\} \times \alpha)$. Then by rule C, $R = \{z\}$ and $z \in \{x\} \times \alpha$. So $R \subseteq \{x\} \times \alpha$, so that

(5) $$R \in \mathrm{Rel}.$$

Also $z \in R$, and by Thm.X.2.12 and rule C, $z = \langle u,v\rangle$, $u \in \{x\}$, $v \in \alpha$. So uRv and $u = x$. Thus xRv, giving

(6) $$\{x\} \subseteq \mathrm{Arg}(R),$$

(7) $$\{v\} \subseteq \mathrm{Val}(R).$$

In addition to our assumption $R \in \mathrm{USC}(\{x\} \times \alpha)$, let us further assume wRy. Then $\langle w,y\rangle \in R$. So $\langle w,y\rangle = z = \langle u,v\rangle$, giving $w = u$, $y = v$, and hence $w = x$. Thus

$$wRy. \supset .w = x.y = v.$$

From this follows

(8) $$R \in \mathrm{Funct},$$

and $\mathrm{Arg}(R) \subseteq \{x\}$, $\mathrm{Val}(R) \subseteq \{v\}$. Then by (6) and (7),

(9) $$\mathrm{Arg}(R) = \{x\}$$

and $\mathrm{Val}(R) = \{v\}$. However, we had $v \in \alpha$, so that

(10) $$\mathrm{Val}(R) \subseteq \alpha.$$

Thus $R \in (\{x\} \wedge \alpha)$, and

(11) $$\vdash \mathrm{USC}(\{x\} \times \alpha) \subseteq (\{x\} \wedge \alpha).$$

Theorem XI.1.27. $\vdash (\alpha,x).(\alpha \wedge \{x\}) = \{\alpha \upharpoonright \lambda y(x)\}$.

Proof. Let $R \in (\alpha \wedge \{x\})$. Then $R \in \text{Funct}.\text{Arg}(R) = \alpha.\text{Val}(R) \subseteq \{x\}$. If in addition uRv, then we get $u \in \alpha$, $v = x$, so that by Thm.X.5.23, Part I, $u(\alpha \upharpoonright \lambda y(x))v$. Conversely, if $u(\alpha \upharpoonright \lambda y(x))v$, then $u \in \alpha$, $v = x$, so that $u \in \text{Arg}(R)$. Hence uRw, $w \in \text{Val}(R)$, $w = x$, $w = v$, and finally uRv. Accordingly, we have shown $R = \alpha \upharpoonright \lambda y(x)$. Hence

(1) $$\vdash (\alpha \wedge \{x\}) \subseteq \{\alpha \upharpoonright \lambda y(x)\}.$$

Conversely, let $R \in \{\alpha \upharpoonright \lambda y(x)\}$. Then $R = \alpha \upharpoonright \lambda y(x)$. So $R \in \text{Funct}$ and $\text{Arg}(R) = \alpha$. Let in addition $v \in \text{Val}(R)$. Then uRv. So $u \in \alpha.u(\lambda y(x))v$. So by Thm.X.5.23, Part I, $v = x$. So $v \in \{x\}$. Hence $\text{Val}(R) \subseteq \{x\}$. So $R \in (\alpha \wedge \{x\})$. Thus

(2) $$\vdash \{\alpha \upharpoonright \lambda y(x)\} \subseteq (\alpha \wedge \{x\}).$$

The proof of the next theorem is based on the idea of characteristic functions. If α is a set of real numbers, then we say that f is the corresponding characteristic function provided that for every real x

$$f(x) = \begin{cases} 1 & \text{if} \quad x \in \alpha \\ 0 & \text{if} \quad \sim x \in \alpha. \end{cases}$$

Clearly, each α determines a unique characteristic function, and conversely each characteristic function determines a unique α.

More generally, if α is a subclass of a class β, we say that f is a characteristic function corresponding to α if for every x in β

$$f(x) = \begin{cases} 1 & \text{if} \quad x \in \alpha \\ 0 & \text{if} \quad \sim x \in \alpha. \end{cases}$$

Then there is exactly one characteristic function for each subclass of β, and vice versa. So the class of characteristic functions over β is equinumerous with $\text{SC}(\beta)$. However, if A is $\{1,0\}$, then the class of characteristic functions over β is exactly $\beta \wedge A$. So $(\beta \wedge A)$ sm $\text{SC}(\beta)$.

Clearly there is nothing magical in the choice of 1 and 0 as the values for our characteristic functions over β. When β is the class of real numbers, there is a certain analytical convenience in the choice of 1 and 0. However, in general we may use any two distinct objects. So, in general, if $A \in 2$, then $(\beta \wedge A)$ sm $\text{SC}(\beta)$.

This is our next theorem, and its proof is essentially that just indicated.

Theorem XI.1.28. $\vdash (\alpha):\alpha \in 2. \supset .(\beta).(\beta \wedge \alpha)$ sm $\text{SC}(\beta)$.

Proof. Let $\alpha \in 2$. Then by Thm.X.1.16, Cor. 1, and rule C,

(1) $$x \neq y,$$

(2) $$\alpha = \{x,y\}.$$

Put

(3) $$W = (\beta \wedge \alpha)\upharpoonleft(\lambda R(\breve{R}``\{x\})).$$

Then

(4) $$W \in \text{Funct},$$

(5) $$\text{Arg}(W) = (\beta \wedge \alpha).$$

As an additional assumption, let $RW\phi$ and $SW\phi$. Then

(6) $$R,S \in \text{Funct},$$

(7) $$\text{Arg}(R) = \beta = \text{Arg}(S),$$

(8) $$\text{Val}(R) \subseteq \alpha,$$

(9) $$\text{Val}(S) \subseteq \alpha,$$

(10) $$\breve{R}``\{x\} = \phi = \breve{S}``\{x\}.$$

We now wish to prove $R = S$ by use of Thm.X.5.16, to which end we make the further assumption $z \in \text{Arg}(R)$. Then by (7) and Thm.X.5.3, Cor. 1,

(11) $$zR(R(z)),$$

(12) $$zS(S(z)).$$

So $R(z) \in \text{Val}(R)$ and $S(z) \in \text{Val}(S)$, so that by (8) and (9), $R(z)$, $S(z) \in \alpha$. Then by (2) and Thm.IX.6.2, Part II,

(13) $$R(z) = x \vee R(z) = y,$$

(14) $$S(z) = x \vee S(z) = y.$$

Case 1. $R(z) = x$. Then by (11), zRx, $x\breve{R}z$, and so by (10), $z \in \phi$, and $x\breve{S}z$, and zSx. Then by (12) and Thm.X.5.3, $x = S(z)$. So $R(z) = S(z)$.

Case 2. $S(z) = x$. Then by similar reasoning, $R(z) = S(z)$.

Case 3. $R(z) \neq x.S(z) \neq x$. Then by (13) and (14), $R(z) = y$ and $S(z) = y$, and hence $R(z) = S(z)$.

So in all cases $R(z) = S(z)$. So from the assumptions $\alpha \in 2$, and $RW\phi.SW\phi$, we can infer by Thm.X.5.16 that $R = S$. So from the single assumption $\alpha \in 2$, we get $\breve{W} \in \text{Funct}$, and so by (4)

(15) $$W \in 1\text{–}1.$$

Now make the additional assumption $\phi \in \text{Val}(W)$. Then $RW\phi$, and so $\text{Arg}(R) = \beta$ and $\phi = \breve{R}``\{x\}$. Then by Thm.X.4.23, $\phi = \text{Arg}(R\upharpoonleft\{x\})$, whence $\phi \subseteq \beta$ by Thm.X.4.6, Part II, and Thm.X.4.2, Part I. So $\phi \in \text{SC}(\beta)$. Thus

(16) $$\text{Val}(W) \subseteq \text{SC}(\beta).$$

Conversely, make the additional assumption $\phi \in \mathrm{SC}(\beta)$, whence $\phi \subseteq \beta$. Put

$$R = \beta\upharpoonright(\hat{u}\hat{v}(u \in \phi . v = x . \mathbf{v} . \sim u \in \phi . v = y)).$$

Clearly

(17) $$R \in \mathrm{Rel},$$

(18) $$\mathrm{Arg}(R) = \beta,$$

(19) $$\mathrm{Val}(R) \subseteq \alpha.$$

Also $u \in \phi . uRv . \supset . v = x$ and $\sim u \in \phi . uRv . \supset . v = y$, so that we can prove by cases that $uRv . uRw . \supset . v = w$. Hence $R \in \mathrm{Funct}$, and so by (18) and (19)

(20) $$R \in (\beta \wedge \alpha).$$

Now since $\phi \subseteq \beta$, we can infer successively $z \in \phi . \supset . z \in \beta . z \in \phi$, $z \in \phi . \supset . zRx$, $z \in \phi . \supset . x\breve{R}z$, $z \in \phi . \supset . z \in \breve{R}``\{x\}$. Thus

(21) $$\phi \subseteq \breve{R}``\{x\}.$$

Likewise, from $\sim z \in \phi . zRx . \supset . x = y$, we get $x \neq y : \supset : zRx . \supset . z \in \phi$. Then by (1), $zRx . \supset . z \in \phi$, $z \in \breve{R}``\{x\} . \supset . z \in \phi$. Then by (21), $\phi = \breve{R}``\{x\}$, and so by (20) and (3), $RW\phi$. Then $\phi \in \mathrm{Val}(W)$, and we have shown $\mathrm{SC}(\beta) \subseteq \mathrm{Val}(W)$. Then by (16), we have $\mathrm{SC}(\beta) = \mathrm{Val}(W)$, and so by (15) and (5), $(\beta \wedge \alpha)$ sm $\mathrm{SC}(\beta)$.

Theorem XI.1.29. $\vdash (\alpha,\beta,\gamma) : \alpha \cap \beta = \Lambda . \supset . ((\alpha \cup \beta) \wedge \gamma)$ sm $((\alpha \wedge \gamma) \times (\beta \wedge \gamma))$.

Proof. Let

(1) $$W = (\mathrm{Rel} \cap \hat{R}(\mathrm{Arg}(R) = \alpha \cup \beta))\upharpoonright \lambda R(\langle \alpha\upharpoonright R, \beta\upharpoonright R\rangle).$$

Then

(2) $$\vdash W \in \mathrm{Funct},$$

and $\vdash \mathrm{Arg}(W) = \mathrm{Rel} \cap \hat{R}(\mathrm{Arg}(R) = \alpha \cup \beta)$. So

(3) $$\vdash ((\alpha \cup \beta) \wedge \gamma) \subseteq \mathrm{Arg}(W).$$

Let RWT and SWT. Then $R, S \in \mathrm{Rel}$ and $\mathrm{Arg}(R) = \mathrm{Arg}(S) = \alpha \cup \beta$ and $\langle \alpha\upharpoonright R, \beta\upharpoonright R\rangle = T = \langle \alpha\upharpoonright S, \beta\upharpoonright S\rangle$. Then $\alpha\upharpoonright R = \alpha\upharpoonright S$ and $\beta\upharpoonright R = \beta\upharpoonright S$. Then by Thm.X.4.11, Part III, $(\alpha \cup \beta)\upharpoonright R = (\alpha\upharpoonright R) \cup (\beta\upharpoonright R) = (\alpha\upharpoonright S) \cup (\beta\upharpoonright S) = (\alpha \cup \beta)\upharpoonright S$. So by Thm.X.4.10, corollary, Part I, $R = (\alpha \cup \beta)\upharpoonright R = (\alpha \cup \beta)\upharpoonright S = S$. We infer $\vdash \breve{W} \in \mathrm{Funct}$, and so by (2)

(4) $$\vdash W \in 1\text{–}1.$$

Assume $\alpha \cap \beta = \Lambda$ and $S \in ((\alpha \wedge \gamma) \times (\beta \wedge \gamma))$. Then by rule C, we get $S = \langle T,U \rangle$, $T \epsilon (\alpha \wedge \gamma)$, and $U \epsilon (\beta \wedge \gamma)$. Then T, $U \epsilon$ Funct, $\text{Arg}(T) = \alpha$, $\text{Arg}(U) = \beta$, $\text{Val}(T) \subseteq \gamma$, $\text{Val}(U) \subseteq \gamma$. Put $R = T \cup U$. Then by Thm.X.5.21,

(5) $$R \epsilon \text{Funct}$$

and by Ex.X.4.6, Parts (a) and (b), with Thm.IX.4.18, Part II,

(6) $$\text{Arg}(R) = \alpha \cup \beta,$$
$$\text{Val}(R) \subseteq \gamma.$$

By these and (5),

(7) $$R \epsilon ((\alpha \cup \beta) \wedge \gamma).$$

By the definition of $\alpha \upharpoonright R$, we have $\alpha \upharpoonright R = (\alpha \times \text{V}) \cap R = (\alpha \times \text{V}) \cap (T \cup U) = ((\alpha \times \text{V}) \cap T) \cup ((\alpha \times \text{V}) \cap U) = (\alpha \upharpoonright T) \cup (\alpha \upharpoonright U)$. However, $\text{Arg}(\alpha \upharpoonright U) = \alpha \cap \text{Arg}(U) = \alpha \cap \beta = \Lambda$. So $\alpha \upharpoonright U = \Lambda$. Also, by Thm. X.4.10, corollary, Part I, $\alpha \upharpoonright T = T$. So

(8) $$\alpha \upharpoonright R = T.$$

In a similar manner,

(9) $$\beta \upharpoonright R = U.$$

So by (8) and (9), $S = \langle \alpha \upharpoonright R, \beta \upharpoonright R \rangle$. Then by (5) and (6), RWS. From this and (7), $S \epsilon W``((\alpha \cup \beta) \wedge \gamma)$. So

(10) $$\vdash \alpha \cap \beta = \Lambda . \supset .((\alpha \wedge \gamma) \times (\beta \wedge \gamma)) \subseteq W``((\alpha \cap \beta) \wedge \gamma).$$

Conversely, let $S \epsilon W``((\alpha \cup \beta) \wedge \gamma)$. Then RWS, $R \epsilon ((\alpha \cup \beta) \wedge \gamma)$. So $\text{Arg}(R) = \alpha \cup \beta$, $S = \langle \alpha \upharpoonright R, \beta \upharpoonright R \rangle$, $R \epsilon$ Funct, $\text{Val}(R) \subseteq \gamma$. Then by Thm.X.5.7, corollary, $\alpha \upharpoonright R \epsilon$ Funct and $\beta \upharpoonright R \epsilon$ Funct. Also by Thm.X.4.9, Part I, and Thm.IX.4.13, Cor. 7, $\text{Arg}(\alpha \upharpoonright R) = \alpha$ and $\text{Arg}(\beta \upharpoonright R) = \beta$. Also, by Thm.X.4.6, Part I, and Thm.X.4.2, Part II, $\text{Val}(\alpha \upharpoonright R) \subseteq \gamma$ and $\text{Val}(\beta \upharpoonright R) \subseteq \gamma$. So $\alpha \upharpoonright R \epsilon (\alpha \wedge \gamma)$, $\beta \upharpoonright R \epsilon (\beta \wedge \gamma)$. Then $S \epsilon ((\alpha \wedge \gamma) \times (\beta \wedge \gamma))$. So

(11) $$\vdash W``((\alpha \cup \beta) \wedge \gamma) \subseteq ((\alpha \wedge \gamma) \times (\beta \wedge \gamma)).$$

By (4), (3), (10), (11), and Thm.XI.1.2, our theorem follows.

Theorem XI.1.30. $\vdash (\alpha,\beta,\gamma,\delta){:}(\beta \wedge \alpha) \text{ sm } \text{USC}(\delta) . \supset .(\gamma \wedge \delta) \text{ sm } ((\gamma \times \beta) \wedge \alpha)$.

Proof. Let

(1) $$R \epsilon 1\text{–}1 . \text{Arg}(R) = (\beta \wedge \alpha) . \text{Val}(R) = \text{USC}(\delta).$$

Define

(2) $$W = (\gamma \wedge \delta) \upharpoonright (\lambda S((\gamma \times \beta) \upharpoonright (\lambda xy((\breve{R}(\{S(x)\}))(y))))).$$

Then

(3) $$W \in \text{Funct},$$

(4) $$\text{Arg}(W) = (\gamma \wedge \delta).$$

Lemma 1. If U_1 and U_2 are two terms which contain free occurrences of x but no free occurrences of y, and if U_1 and U_2 are stratified so that their types are exactly one higher than the type of x, then

$$\vdash (x):x \in \gamma.(\gamma \times \beta)\upharpoonright(\lambda xy(U_1(y))) = (\gamma \times \beta)\upharpoonright(\lambda xy(U_2(y))).U_1 \in (\beta \wedge \alpha). U_2 \in (\beta \wedge \alpha). \supset .U_1 = U_2.$$

Proof. Assume

(i) $$x \in \gamma,$$

(ii) $$(\gamma \times \beta)\upharpoonright(\lambda xy(U_1(y))) = (\gamma \times \beta)\upharpoonright(\lambda xy(U_2(y))),$$

(iii) $$U_1 \in (\beta \wedge \alpha),$$

(iv) $$U_2 \in (\beta \wedge \alpha).$$

Then by (iii) and (iv), $U_1 \in$ Funct, $U_2 \in$ Funct, $\text{Arg}(U_1) = \beta$, and $\text{Arg}(U_2) = \beta$. Hence we use Thm.X.5.16 to prove our lemma, to which end we assume $y \in \beta$. Then by (i), $\langle x,y\rangle \in (\gamma \times \beta)$, and so by Thm.X.5.28, Part I,

$$\langle x,y\rangle((\gamma \times \beta)\upharpoonright(\lambda xy(U_1(y))))(U_1(y)).$$

So by (ii),

$$\langle x,y\rangle((\gamma \times \beta)\upharpoonright(\lambda xy(U_2(y))))(U_1(y)).$$

So by Thm.X.5.28, Part I, $U_1(y) = U_2(y)$. Then our lemma follows by Thm.X.5.16.

Now, to prove $\breve{W} \in$ Funct, we assume S_1WT and S_2WT. Then $S_1 \in$ Funct, $S_2 \in$ Funct, $\text{Arg}(S_1) = \gamma = \text{Arg}(S_2)$, $\text{Val}(S_1) \subseteq \delta$, $\text{Val}(S_2) \subseteq \delta$, and

$$(\gamma \times \beta)\upharpoonright(\lambda xy((\breve{R}(\{S_1(x)\}))(y))) = (\gamma \times \beta)\upharpoonright(\lambda xy((\breve{R}(\{S_2(x)\}))(y))) = T.$$

We now wish to prove $S_1 = S_2$ by Thm.X.5.16, and so assume further $x \in \gamma$. Then by Thm.X.5.3, Cor. 4, $S_1(x) \in \text{Val}(S_1)$ and $S_2(x) \in \text{Val}(S_2)$, and hence $S_1(x) \in \delta$ and $S_2(x) \in \delta$. Then by Thm.IX.6.10, Part II, $\{S_1(x)\} \in \text{USC}(\delta)$ and $\{S_2(x)\} \in \text{USC}(\delta)$. Then by (1), $\{S_1(x)\} \in \text{Val}(R)$ and $\{S_2(x)\} \in \text{Val}(R)$. So by Thm.X.5.3, Cor. 5, $\breve{R}(\{S_1(x)\}) \in \text{Arg}(R)$ and $\breve{R}(\{S_2(x)\}) \in \text{Arg}(R)$. Then by (1), $\breve{R}(\{S_1(x)\}) \in (\beta \wedge \alpha)$ and $\breve{R}(\{S_2(x)\}) \in (\beta \wedge \alpha)$. Then by Lemma 1, $\breve{R}(\{S_1(x)\}) = \breve{R}(\{S_2(x)\})$. So, as $(\breve{R}(\{S_1(x)\}))R\{S_1(x)\}$ and $(\breve{R}(\{S_2(x)\}))R\{S_2(x)\}$ by Thm.X.5.3, Cor. 3, we get $\{S_1(x)\} = \{S_2(x)\}$, whence $S_1(x) = S_2(x)$. So by Thm.X.5.16, we conclude $S_1 = S_2$ from the assumptions S_1WT and S_2WT. So $\breve{W} \in$ Funct, and by (3) we get

(5) $$W \in 1\text{–}1.$$

Assume

(6) $$T \epsilon ((\gamma \times \beta) \wedge \alpha)$$

and define

(7) $$S = \hat{x}\hat{u}(x \epsilon \gamma . \{u\} = R(\hat{y}\hat{z}(\langle x,y,z\rangle \epsilon T))).$$

Lemma 2. $(U,x):x \epsilon \gamma . U = \hat{y}\hat{z}(\langle x,y,z\rangle \epsilon T) . \supset . U \epsilon (\beta \wedge \alpha)$.
Proof. Assume

(i) $$x \epsilon \gamma,$$

(ii) $$U = \hat{y}\hat{z}(\langle x,y,z\rangle \epsilon T).$$

Then by (6),

(iii) $$T \epsilon \text{Funct},$$

(iv) $$\text{Arg}(T) = \gamma \times \beta,$$

(v) $$\text{Val}(T) \subseteq \alpha.$$

If we assume yUz, then $\langle x,y,z\rangle \epsilon T$, so that by (iii) and Thm.X.5.3, $z = T(\langle x,y\rangle)$. So

(vi) $$U \epsilon \text{Funct}.$$

If we assume yUz, then $(\langle x,y\rangle)Tz$, so that $z \epsilon \alpha$ by (v). Hence

(vii) $$\text{Val}(U) \subseteq \alpha.$$

If we assume yUz, then $(\langle x,y\rangle)Tz$, so that $\langle x,y\rangle \epsilon \gamma \times \beta$ by (iv), so that $y \epsilon \beta$. Hence

(viii) $$\text{Arg}(U) \subseteq \beta.$$

If we assume $y \epsilon \beta$, then $\langle x,y\rangle \epsilon \gamma \times \beta$ by (i), so that by (iv) and rule C, $(\langle x,y\rangle)Tz$, and so yUz. Hence

(ix) $$\beta \subseteq \text{Arg}(U).$$

Our lemma follows by (vi), (vii), (viii), and (ix).
Lemma 3. $S \epsilon (\gamma \wedge \delta)$.
Proof. Let xSu and xSv. Then

$$\{u\} = R(\hat{y}\hat{z}(\langle x,y,z\rangle \epsilon T)) = \{v\}.$$

So $u = v$. Hence

(i) $$S \epsilon \text{Funct}.$$

Let $x \epsilon \gamma$. Then define

$$U = \hat{y}\hat{z}(\langle x,y,z\rangle \epsilon T).$$

Then by Lemma 2, $U \epsilon (\beta \wedge \alpha)$. Then by (1) and Thm.X.5.3, Cor. 4, $R(U) \epsilon \mathrm{USC}(\delta)$. So by rule C and Thm.IX.6.10, Part III, $\{u\} = R(U)$ and $u \epsilon \delta$. So by (7), xSu. So $x \epsilon \mathrm{Arg}(S)$. Hence

(ii) $$\gamma \subseteq \mathrm{Arg}(S).$$

Clearly, $xSu. \supset .x \epsilon \gamma$, so that

(iii) $$\mathrm{Arg}(S) \subseteq \gamma.$$

If $u \epsilon \mathrm{Val}(S)$, then by rule C, xSu, so that $x \epsilon \gamma$ and $\{u\} = R(\hat{y}\hat{z}(\langle x,y,z\rangle \epsilon T))$. Define

$$U = \hat{y}\hat{z}(\langle x,y,z\rangle \epsilon T).$$

Then $\{u\} = R(U)$. By Lemma 2, $U \epsilon (\beta \wedge \alpha)$, so that by (1) and Thm. X.5.3, Cor. 4, $R(U) \epsilon \mathrm{USC}(\delta)$. Hence $\{u\} \epsilon \mathrm{USC}(\delta)$, so that by Thm. X.6.10, Part II, $u \epsilon \delta$. Hence

(iv) $$\mathrm{Val}(S) \subseteq \delta.$$

Then our lemma follows by (i), (ii), (iii), and (iv).

Lemma 4. $(U,x):x \epsilon \gamma.U = \hat{y}\hat{z}(\langle x,y,z\rangle \epsilon T). \supset .U = \breve{R}(\{S(x)\})$.

Proof. Assume

(i) $$x \epsilon \gamma,$$

(ii) $$U = \hat{y}\hat{z}(\langle x,y,z\rangle \epsilon T).$$

Then by Lemma 2, $U \epsilon (\beta \wedge \alpha)$, so that by (1), $R(U) \epsilon \mathrm{USC}(\delta)$. Then by rule C and Thm.IX.6.10, Part III, $v \epsilon \delta$ and $\{v\} = R(U)$. Then by (i) and (7), xSv. So since $S \epsilon \mathrm{Funct}$ by Lemma 3, we get $v = S(x)$ by Thm.X.5.3. So

(iii) $$R(U) = \{S(x)\}.$$

Since $U \epsilon (\beta \wedge \alpha)$, we have by (1), (iii), and Thm.X.5.3,

$$UR\{S(x)\}.$$

Then by Thm.X.5.3, Cor. 2, we get

$$U = \breve{R}(\{S(x)\}).$$

Lemma 5. $T = (\gamma \times \beta)\upharpoonright(\lambda xy((\breve{R}(\{S(x)\}))(y)))$.

Proof. First assume uTz. Then, since $\mathrm{Arg}(T) = \gamma \times \beta$ by (6), we get $u \epsilon \gamma \times \beta$. So by rule C, $u = \langle x,y\rangle$, $x \epsilon \gamma$, $y \epsilon \beta$. Define

$$U = \hat{y}\hat{z}(\langle x,y,z\rangle \epsilon T).$$

Then yUz, and so since $U \epsilon \mathrm{Funct}$ by Lemma 2, we get $z = U(y)$ by Thm. X.5.3. So by Lemma 4, $z = (\breve{R}(\{S(x)\}))(y)$. Then by Thm.X.5.28, Part I, $\langle x,y\rangle(\lambda xy((\breve{R}(\{S(x)\}))(y)))z$. As $u = \langle x,y\rangle$ and $u \epsilon \gamma \times \beta$, we have

$$u((\gamma \times \beta)\upharpoonright(\lambda xy((\breve{R}(\{S(x)\}))(y))))z.$$

So

(i) $$T \subseteq (\gamma \times \beta)\upharpoonright(\lambda xy((\breve{R}(\{S(x)\}))(y))).$$

Conversely, assume

$$u((\gamma \times \beta)\upharpoonright(\lambda xy((\breve{R}(\{S(x)\}))(y))))z.$$

Then $u \in \gamma \times \beta$ and $u(\lambda xy((\breve{R}(\{S(x)\}))(y)))z$. So by rule C, $u = \langle x,y \rangle$, $x \in \gamma$, $y \in \beta$. So by Thm.X.5.28, Part I, $z = (\breve{R}(\{S(x)\}))(y)$. If we define

$$U = \hat{y}\hat{z}(\langle x,y,z \rangle \in T),$$

then by Lemma 4, $z = U(y)$. However, by Lemma 2, $\mathrm{Arg}(U) = \beta$, so that $y \in \mathrm{Arg}(U)$. Hence by Thm.X.5.3, yUz. So $\langle x,y,z \rangle \in T$. That is, uTz. So

(ii) $$(\gamma \times \beta)\upharpoonright(\lambda xy((\breve{R}(\{S(x)\}))(y))) \subseteq T.$$

Our lemma now follows by (i) and (ii).

By Lemma 3,

$$S \in (\gamma \wedge \delta),$$

and by Lemma 5,

$$T = (\gamma \times \beta)\upharpoonright(\lambda xy((\breve{R}(\{S(x)\}))(y))).$$

Then by (2), SWT, so that $T \in \mathrm{Val}(W)$. Hence

(8) $$((\gamma \times \beta) \wedge \alpha) \subseteq \mathrm{Val}(W).$$

Conversely, assume $T \in \mathrm{Val}(W)$. Then SWT. So

(9) $$S \in (\gamma \wedge \delta),$$

(10) $$T = (\gamma \times \beta)\upharpoonright(\lambda xy((\breve{R}(\{S(x)\}))(y))).$$

Then by Thm.X.5.28, Part III,

(11) $$T \in \mathrm{Funct}.$$

Also by Thm.X.5.28, Part V,

(12) $$\mathrm{Arg}(T) = \gamma \times \beta.$$

Further assume $z \in \mathrm{Val}(T)$. Then by rule C, uTz, and so $u \in \gamma \times \beta$ and $u(\lambda xy((\breve{R}(\{S(x)\}))(y)))z$. So by rule C, $u = \langle x,y \rangle$, $x \in \gamma$, $y \in \beta$. So $z = (\breve{R}(\{S(x)\}))(y)$. By $x \in \gamma$ and (9), we have $x \in \mathrm{Arg}(S)$. So by (9) and Thm.X.5.3, Cor. 4, $S(x) \in \mathrm{Val}(S)$. So by (9), $S(x) \in \delta$. So $\{S(x)\} \in \mathrm{USC}(\delta)$. Then by (1) and Thm.X.5.3, Cor. 5, $\breve{R}(\{S(x)\}) \in \mathrm{Arg}(R)$, and by (1), $\breve{R}(\{S(x)\}) \in (\beta \wedge \alpha)$. Then, since $y \in \beta$, we have $y \in \mathrm{Arg}(\breve{R}(\{S(x)\}))$. Then $(\breve{R}(\{S(x)\}))(y) \in \mathrm{Val}(\breve{R}(\{S(x)\}))$. So $(\breve{R}(\{S(x)\}))(y) \in \alpha$. So $z \in \alpha$. Then

(13) $$\mathrm{Val}(T) \subseteq \alpha.$$

So by (11), (12), and (13), $T \in ((\gamma \times \beta) \wedge \alpha)$. Hence

(14) $$\mathrm{Val}(W) \subseteq ((\gamma \times \beta) \wedge \alpha).$$

Our theorem now follows by (5), (4), (8), and (14).

Theorem XI.1.31. $\vdash (\alpha,\beta,\gamma):\alpha \subseteq \beta. \supset .(\gamma \wedge \alpha) \subseteq (\gamma \wedge \beta).$

Proof. Let $\alpha \subseteq \beta$ and let $R \in (\gamma \wedge \alpha)$. Then $R \in \mathrm{Funct}$, $\mathrm{Arg}(R) = \gamma$, $\mathrm{Val}(R) \subseteq \alpha$. Then $\mathrm{Val}(R) \subseteq \beta$.

Theorem XI.1.32. $\vdash (\alpha,\beta):\alpha \neq \Lambda. \supset .(\beta \wedge \alpha) \neq \Lambda.$

Proof. Assume $\alpha \neq \Lambda$. Then $x \in \alpha$, so that $\{x\} \subseteq \alpha$. Now clearly $u(\beta \times \{x\})v. \supset .v = x$, so that

(1) $$\beta \times \{x\} \in \mathrm{Funct}.$$

Also, $\{x\} \neq \Lambda$, so that by Thm.X.4.4, Part I,

(2) $$\mathrm{Arg}(\beta \times \{x\}) = \beta.$$

If $\beta = \Lambda$, then by Thm.X.2.12, Cor. 3, $\beta \times \{x\} = \Lambda$, so that by Thm. X.4.3, Part II, $\mathrm{Val}(\beta \times \{x\}) = \Lambda$, so that by Thm.IX.4.13, Cor. 5, $\mathrm{Val}(\beta \times \{x\}) \subseteq \alpha$. If $\beta \neq \Lambda$, then by Thm.X.4.4, Part II, $\mathrm{Val}(\beta \times \{x\}) = \{x\}$, so that in this case also $\mathrm{Val}(\beta \times \{x\}) \subseteq \alpha$. So

(3) $$\mathrm{Val}(\beta \times \{x\}) \subseteq \alpha.$$

Then $\beta \times \{x\} \in (\beta \wedge \alpha)$.

We now close the section with some miscellaneous results.

***Theorem XI.1.33.** $\vdash (\alpha,\beta):\alpha \mathrm{\ sm\ } \beta. \equiv .\mathrm{USC}(\alpha) \mathrm{\ sm\ } \mathrm{USC}(\beta).$

Proof. By Thm.X.5.19, Cor. 9, and Thm.X.4.29, we readily verify that

$$\vdash (\alpha,\beta,R,S):\alpha \mathrm{\ sm}_R\ \beta.S = \mathrm{RUSC}(R). \supset .\mathrm{USC}(\alpha) \mathrm{\ sm}_S\ \mathrm{USC}(\beta).$$

So

(1) $$\vdash (\alpha,\beta):\alpha \mathrm{\ sm\ } \beta. \supset .\mathrm{USC}(\alpha) \mathrm{\ sm\ } \mathrm{USC}(\beta).$$

Conversely, assume $\mathrm{USC}(\alpha) \mathrm{\ sm\ } \mathrm{USC}(\beta)$. Then by rule C, $S \in 1\text{–}1$, $\mathrm{USC}(\alpha) = \mathrm{Arg}(S)$, $\mathrm{USC}(\beta) = \mathrm{Val}(S)$. Put $R = \hat{x}\hat{y}(\{x\}S\{y\})$. Then one can prove $\alpha \mathrm{\ sm}_R\ \beta$ without difficulty.

Corollary. $\vdash (\alpha):\mathrm{Can}(\alpha) \equiv \mathrm{Can}(\mathrm{USC}(\alpha)).$

Proof. Put $\mathrm{USC}(\alpha)$ for β in the theorem.

Theorem XI.1.34. $\vdash (\alpha,\beta):\mathrm{Can}(\alpha).\alpha \mathrm{\ sm\ } \beta. \supset .\mathrm{Can}(\beta).$

Proof. Assume $\mathrm{Can}(\alpha)$ and $\alpha \mathrm{\ sm\ } \beta$. Then $\alpha \mathrm{\ sm\ } \mathrm{USC}(\alpha)$ and $\mathrm{USC}(\alpha) \mathrm{\ sm\ } \mathrm{USC}(\beta)$. So $\beta \mathrm{\ sm\ } \alpha$, $\alpha \mathrm{\ sm\ } \mathrm{USC}(\alpha)$, $\mathrm{USC}(\alpha) \mathrm{\ sm\ } \mathrm{USC}(\beta)$, and hence $\beta \mathrm{\ sm\ } \mathrm{USC}(\beta)$.

Theorem XI.1.35. $\vdash (\alpha).\mathrm{USC}(\mathrm{SC}(\alpha)) \mathrm{\ sm\ } \mathrm{SC}(\mathrm{USC}(\alpha)).$

Proof. Take

$$W = \hat{x}\hat{y}(\mathrm{E}z).x = \{z\}.y = \mathrm{USC}(z).$$

One proves easily

(1) $$\vdash W \in 1\text{–}1,$$

(2) $$\vdash \mathrm{USC}(\mathrm{SC}(\alpha)) \subseteq \mathrm{Arg}(W).$$

Let $y \in \mathrm{SC}(\mathrm{USC}(\alpha))$. Then $y \subseteq \mathrm{USC}(\alpha)$. So by Thm.IX.6.14, Cor. 2, and rule C, $z \subseteq \alpha . y = \mathrm{USC}(z)$. Hence $z \in \mathrm{SC}(\alpha)$, $\{z\}Wy$. Hence $\{z\} \in \mathrm{USC}(\mathrm{SC}(\alpha)).\{z\}Wy$. Thus $y \in W``\mathrm{USC}(\mathrm{SC}(\alpha))$. So we have shown

(3) $$\vdash \mathrm{SC}(\mathrm{USC}(\alpha)) \subseteq W``\mathrm{USC}(\mathrm{SC}(\alpha)).$$

Conversely, let $y \in W``\mathrm{USC}(\mathrm{SC}(\alpha))$. Then by rule C, xWy. $x \in \mathrm{USC}(\mathrm{SC}(\alpha))$. So by rule C, $x = \{z\}$, $y = \mathrm{USC}(z)$, and $x = \{w\}$, $w \in \mathrm{SC}(\alpha)$. So $z = w$, and $y = \mathrm{USC}(z).z \subseteq \alpha$. Hence by Thm.IX.6.12, Part V, $y \subseteq \mathrm{USC}(\alpha)$. So $y \in \mathrm{SC}(\mathrm{USC}(\alpha))$. So

$$\vdash W``\mathrm{USC}(\mathrm{SC}(\alpha)) \subseteq \mathrm{SC}(\mathrm{USC}(\alpha)).$$

Then by (1), (2), and (3), our theorem follows by Thm.XI.1.2.

Theorem XI.1.36. $\vdash (\alpha,\beta){:}\alpha \text{ sm } \beta. \supset .\mathrm{SC}(\alpha) \text{ sm } \mathrm{SC}(\beta)$.

Proof. Let $A = \{\Lambda,\mathrm{V}\}$. Then by Thm.IX.4.6, corollary, and Thm. X.1.16, Cor. 1, $\vdash A \in 2$. Then by Thm.XI.1.28, $\vdash \mathrm{SC}(\alpha) \text{ sm } (\alpha \wedge A)$, $\vdash \mathrm{SC}(\beta) \text{ sm } (\beta \wedge A)$. However, by Thm.XI.1.22, $\vdash \alpha \text{ sm } \beta. \supset .(\alpha \wedge A) \text{ sm } (\beta \wedge A)$.

Theorem XI.1.37. $\vdash (\alpha){:}\mathrm{Can}(\alpha). \supset .\mathrm{Can}(\mathrm{SC}(\alpha))$.

Proof. Assume $\mathrm{Can}(\alpha)$. That is, $\alpha \text{ sm } \mathrm{USC}(\alpha)$. Then by Thm.XI.1.36, $\mathrm{SC}(\alpha) \text{ sm } \mathrm{SC}(\mathrm{USC}(\alpha))$. Then by Thm.XI.1.35, $\mathrm{SC}(\alpha) \text{ sm } \mathrm{USC}(\mathrm{SC}(\alpha))$. That is, $\mathrm{Can}(\mathrm{SC}(\alpha))$.

Theorem XI.1.38. $\vdash (\alpha,x){:}(\{x\} \wedge \alpha) \text{ sm } \mathrm{USC}(\alpha)$.

Proof. By Thm.XI.1.17 and Thm.XI.1.20, $\vdash (\{x\} \times \alpha) \text{ sm } \alpha$. So by Thm.XI.1.33, $\vdash \mathrm{USC}(\{x\} \times \alpha) \text{ sm } \mathrm{USC}(\alpha)$. Then our theorem follows by Thm.XI.1.26.

Theorem XI.1.39. $\vdash (\alpha,\beta){:}\mathrm{Can}(\alpha).\mathrm{Can}(\beta).\alpha \cap \beta = \Lambda. \supset .\mathrm{Can}(\alpha \cup \beta)$.

Proof. Assume $\mathrm{Can}(\alpha)$, $\mathrm{Can}(\beta)$, $\alpha \cap \beta = \Lambda$. Then by Thm.IX.6.12, Part I, $\mathrm{USC}(\alpha) \cap \mathrm{USC}(\beta) = \mathrm{USC}(\Lambda)$. Then by Thm.IX.6.12, Part IV, $\mathrm{USC}(\alpha) \cap \mathrm{USC}(\beta) = \Lambda$. Also we have $\alpha \text{ sm } \mathrm{USC}(\alpha)$ and $\beta \text{ sm } \mathrm{USC}(\beta)$. So by Thm.XI.1.12, corollary, $(\alpha \cup \beta) \text{ sm } (\mathrm{USC}(\alpha) \cup \mathrm{USC}(\beta))$. Then by Thm.IX.6.12, Part II, $(\alpha \cup \beta) \text{ sm } \mathrm{USC}(\alpha \cup \beta)$. That is, $\mathrm{Can}(\alpha \cup \beta)$.

Theorem XI.1.40. $\vdash (R){:}R \in \mathrm{Rel}. \supset .\mathrm{RUSC}(R) \text{ sm } \mathrm{USC}(R)$.

Proof. Define

$$W = \hat{u}\hat{v}(\mathrm{E}x,y).u = \langle\{x\},\{y\}\rangle.v = \{\langle x,y\rangle\}.$$

Clearly

(1) $$\vdash W \in 1\text{–}1.$$

Let $R \in \mathrm{Rel}$ and $u \in \mathrm{RUSC}(R)$. By Thm.X.3.14, $\mathrm{RUSC}(R) \in \mathrm{Rel}$, and so by Thm.X.3.1, $u = \langle w,z \rangle$, $w(\mathrm{RUSC}(R))z$. Then $w = \{x\}$, $z = \{y\}$, xRy. So $u = \langle \{x\},\{y\} \rangle$. So $uW\{\langle x,y \rangle\}$. So $u \in \mathrm{Arg}(W)$. Hence

(2) $$\vdash R \in \mathrm{Rel}. \supset .\mathrm{RUSC}(R) \subseteq \mathrm{Arg}(W).$$

Let $R \in \mathrm{Rel}$ and $v \in \mathrm{USC}(R)$. Then $z \in R$ and $v = \{z\}$. Then $z = \langle x,y \rangle$, xRy. So $v = \{\langle x,y \rangle\}$ and $\{x\}(\mathrm{RUSC}(R))\{y\}$. Then $\langle \{x\},\{y\} \rangle \in \mathrm{RUSC}(R)$ and $\langle \{x\},\{y\} \rangle Wv$. Thus $v \in W``\mathrm{RUSC}(R)$. So

(3) $$\vdash R \in \mathrm{Rel}. \supset .\mathrm{USC}(R) \subseteq W``\mathrm{RUSC}(R).$$

Let $v \in W``\mathrm{RUSC}(R)$. Then uWv and $u \in \mathrm{RUSC}(R)$. So $u = \langle \{x\},\{y\} \rangle$ and $v = \{\langle x,y \rangle\}$. So $\{x\}(\mathrm{RUSC}(R))\{y\}$. Then xRy, and so $\langle x,y \rangle \in R$ and so $\{\langle x,y \rangle\} \in \mathrm{USC}(R)$. Thus $v \in \mathrm{USC}(R)$. So

(4) $$\vdash W``\mathrm{RUSC}(R) \subseteq \mathrm{USC}(R).$$

Theorem XI.1.41. $\vdash (\alpha,\beta).\mathrm{USC}(\alpha \times \beta)\ \mathrm{sm}\ (\mathrm{USC}(\alpha) \times \mathrm{USC}(\beta))$.

Proof. Use Thm.X.3.19 and Thm.XI.1.40.

Theorem XI.1.42. $\vdash (\alpha,\beta){:}\mathrm{Can}(\alpha).\mathrm{Can}(\beta). \supset .\mathrm{Can}(\alpha \times \beta)$.

Proof. Let $\mathrm{Can}(\alpha)$ and $\mathrm{Can}(\beta)$. Then α sm $\mathrm{USC}(\alpha)$ and β sm $\mathrm{USC}(\beta)$. So by Thm.XI.1.18, Part II, $(\alpha \times \beta)$ sm $(\mathrm{USC}(\alpha) \times \mathrm{USC}(\beta))$. Then by Thm.XI.1.41, $(\alpha \times \beta)$ sm $(\mathrm{USC}(\alpha \times \beta))$. That is, $\mathrm{Can}(\alpha \times \beta)$.

Theorem XI.1.43. $\vdash (\alpha,\beta,\mathbf{R}){:}\mathbf{R} \in (\alpha \wedge \beta). \equiv .\mathrm{RUSC}(\mathbf{R}) \in (\mathrm{USC}(\alpha) \wedge \mathrm{USC}(\beta))$.

Proof. Let $R \in \mathrm{Rel}$. If now $R \in (\alpha \wedge \beta)$, then $R \in \mathrm{Funct}$, $\mathrm{Arg}(R) = \alpha$, and $\mathrm{Val}(R) \subseteq \beta$. By Thm.X.5.17, $\mathrm{RUSC}(R) \in \mathrm{Funct}$. By Thm.X.4.29, Part I, $\mathrm{Arg}(\mathrm{RUSC}(R)) = \mathrm{USC}(\alpha)$. By Thm.X.4.29, Part II, and Thm. IX.6.12, Part V, $\mathrm{Val}(\mathrm{RUSC}(R)) \subseteq \mathrm{USC}(\beta)$. So $\mathrm{RUSC}(R) \in (\mathrm{USC}(\alpha) \wedge \mathrm{USC}(\beta))$. Conversely, if $\mathrm{RUSC}(R) \in (\mathrm{USC}(\alpha) \wedge \mathrm{USC}(\beta))$, then by the same theorems, $R \in (\alpha \wedge \beta)$.

Theorem XI.1.44. $\vdash (\alpha,\beta).\mathrm{USC}(\alpha \wedge \beta)\ \mathrm{sm}\ (\mathrm{USC}(\alpha) \wedge \mathrm{USC}(\beta))$.

Proof. Define

$$W = \hat{u}\hat{v}(ER).R \in \mathrm{Rel}.u = \{R\}.v = \mathrm{RUSC}(R).$$

By Thm.IX.6.3 and Thm.X.3.17,

(1) $$\vdash W \in 1\text{–}1.$$

Let $u \in \mathrm{USC}(\alpha \wedge \beta)$. Then $u = \{R\}$ and $R \in (\alpha \wedge \beta)$. So $uW(\mathrm{RUSC}(R))$. Hence $u \in \mathrm{Arg}(W)$. So

(2) $$\vdash \mathrm{USC}(\alpha \wedge \beta) \subseteq \mathrm{Arg}(W).$$

Let $S \in (\mathrm{USC}(\alpha) \wedge \mathrm{USC}(\beta))$. So $S \in \mathrm{Funct}.\mathrm{Arg}(S) = \mathrm{USC}(\alpha).\mathrm{Val}(S) \subseteq \mathrm{USC}(\beta)$. Define

$$R = \hat{x}\hat{y}(\{x\}S\{y\}).$$

Then

(3) $$(\mathrm{E}u,v).uRv.x = \{u\}.y = \{v\}: \supset :xSy.$$

If xSy, then $x \in \mathrm{Arg}(S)$, $y \in \mathrm{Val}(S)$. So $x \in \mathrm{USC}(\alpha)$, $y \in \mathrm{USC}(\beta)$. So $x = \{u\}$, $u \in \alpha$, and $y = \{v\}$, $v \in \beta$. So $\{u\}S\{v\}$. Then uRv. So

(4) $$xSy: \supset :(\mathrm{E}u,v).uRv.x = \{u\}.y = \{v\}.$$

Then by (3), (4), and Thm.X.3.15, $(x,y):xSy. \equiv .x(\mathrm{RUSC}(R))y$. So $S = \mathrm{RUSC}(R)$. Thus $\mathrm{RUSC}(R) \in (\mathrm{USC}(\alpha) \wedge \mathrm{USC}(\beta))$. Then by Thm. XI.1.43, $R \in (\alpha \wedge \beta)$. So $\{R\} \in \mathrm{USC}(\alpha \wedge \beta)$. Also, since $S = \mathrm{RUSC}(R)$, we have $\{R\}WS$. So $S \in W``\mathrm{USC}(\alpha \wedge \beta)$. Thus

(5) $$\vdash (\mathrm{USC}(\alpha) \wedge \mathrm{USC}(\beta)) \subseteq W``\mathrm{USC}(\alpha \wedge \beta).$$

Conversely, let $S \in W``\mathrm{USC}(\alpha \wedge \beta)$. Then uWS and $u \in \mathrm{USC}(\alpha \wedge \beta)$. So $R \in \mathrm{Rel}$, $u = \{R\}$, $S = \mathrm{RUSC}(R)$. Then $\{R\} \in \mathrm{USC}(\alpha \wedge \beta)$. So $R \in (\alpha \wedge \beta)$, and by Thm.XI.1.43, $\mathrm{RUSC}(R) \in (\mathrm{USC}(\alpha) \wedge \mathrm{USC}(\beta))$. That is, $S \in (\mathrm{USC}(\alpha) \wedge \mathrm{USC}(\beta))$. Hence

(6) $$\vdash W``\mathrm{USC}(\alpha \wedge \beta) \subseteq (\mathrm{USC}(\alpha) \wedge \mathrm{USC}(\beta)).$$

Our theorem now follows by (1), (2), (5), and (6).

Theorem XI.1.45. $\vdash (\alpha,\beta):\mathrm{Can}(\alpha).\mathrm{Can}(\beta). \supset .\mathrm{Can}(\alpha \wedge \beta)$.

Proof. Assume $\mathrm{Can}(\alpha)$ and $\mathrm{Can}(\beta)$. Then $\alpha \mathrm{\ sm\ } \mathrm{USC}(\alpha)$, $\beta \mathrm{\ sm\ } \mathrm{USC}(\beta)$. So by Thm.XI.1.23, corollary, $(\alpha \wedge \beta) \mathrm{\ sm\ } (\mathrm{USC}(\alpha) \wedge \mathrm{USC}(\beta))$. Then by Thm.XI.1.44, $(\alpha \wedge \beta) \mathrm{\ sm\ } \mathrm{USC}(\alpha \wedge \beta)$. That is, $\mathrm{Can}(\alpha \wedge \beta)$.

EXERCISES

XI.1.1. Prove $\vdash (\alpha,\beta):\alpha,\beta \in 2. \supset .\alpha \mathrm{\ sm\ } \beta$.

XI.1.2. Prove $\vdash (\alpha,\beta,R,S):\alpha \mathrm{\ sm}_R\ \beta.S = \mathrm{SC}(\alpha)\upharpoonright(\lambda x(R``x)). \supset .\mathrm{SC}(\alpha) \mathrm{\ sm}_S\ \mathrm{SC}(\beta)$.

XI.1.3. Prove $\vdash (\alpha,\beta):\alpha \cap \beta = \Lambda. \supset .\mathrm{SC}(\alpha \cup \beta) \mathrm{\ sm\ } (\mathrm{SC}(\alpha) \times \mathrm{SC}(\beta))$. (*Hint.* Take γ to be $\{\Lambda,\mathrm{V}\}$ in Thm.XI.1.29 and use Thm.XI.1.28.)

XI.1.4. Prove $\vdash (\alpha,\beta,R):\alpha \cap \beta = \Lambda.R = \mathrm{SC}(\alpha \cup \beta)\upharpoonright\lambda x(\langle\alpha \cap x,\beta \cap x\rangle). \supset .\mathrm{SC}(\alpha \cup \beta) \mathrm{\ sm}_R\ (\mathrm{SC}(\alpha) \times \mathrm{SC}(\beta))$.

XI.1.5. Prove $\vdash \sim\mathrm{Can}(1)$.

XI.1.6. Give the details of the proof of Thm.XI.1.23.

2. Elementary Properties of Cardinal Numbers. Since $\alpha \mathrm{\ sm\ } \beta$ expresses the fact that α and β have the same number of members, we can define the number of members of α by abstraction with respect to the equivalence relation sm. Accordingly, we now define the cardinal number $\mathrm{Nc}(\alpha)$ of a class α by abstraction with respect to sm, namely,

$$\mathrm{Nc}(\alpha) \quad \text{for} \quad \mathrm{sm}``\{\alpha\}.$$

Thus $\mathrm{Nc}(\alpha)$ is the equivalence class of α relative to sm. We define the set of cardinal numbers as the set of equivalence classes with respect to sm, namely,

$$\mathrm{NC} \quad \text{for} \quad \mathrm{EqC}(\mathrm{sm}).$$

If α is a variable, then the indicated occurrence of α is the only free occurrence of a variable in $\mathrm{Nc}(\alpha)$. Also $\mathrm{Nc}(A)$ is stratified if and only if A is stratified, and if stratified is one type higher than A. The term NC is stratified and has no free variables, and so may be assigned any type.

By Thm.X.4.22, corollary, we infer the following theorem.

***Theorem XI.2.1.** $\vdash (\alpha,\beta){:}\beta \in \mathrm{Nc}(\alpha). \equiv .\alpha \text{ sm } \beta.$

***Corollary 1.** $\vdash (\alpha).\alpha \in \mathrm{Nc}(\alpha).$

Corollary 2. $\vdash (\alpha,\beta){:}\alpha \in \mathrm{Nc}(\beta). \equiv .\beta \in \mathrm{Nc}(\alpha).$

Corollary 3. $\vdash (\alpha,\beta,\gamma){:}\alpha,\beta \in \mathrm{Nc}(\gamma). \supset .\alpha \text{ sm } \beta.$

Corollary 4. $\vdash (\alpha,\beta,\gamma){:}\alpha \in \mathrm{Nc}(\gamma).\alpha \text{ sm } \beta. \supset .\beta \in \mathrm{Nc}(\gamma).$

By combining Thm.XI.1.3, Cor. 1, and Thm.XI.1.5, Cor. 3, with the theorems of Sec. 7 of Chapter X, we infer the following theorem.

Theorem XI.2.2.

I. $\vdash (n){:}n \in \mathrm{NC}. \equiv .(\mathrm{E}\alpha).n = \mathrm{Nc}(\alpha).$

II. $\vdash (\alpha,\beta){:}\alpha \text{ sm } \beta. \equiv .\mathrm{Nc}(\alpha) = \mathrm{Nc}(\beta).$

III. $\vdash (n){:}.n \in \mathrm{NC}{:} \supset {:}(\alpha){:}\alpha \in n. \equiv .n = \mathrm{Nc}(\alpha).$

IV. $\vdash (m,n){:}m,n \in \mathrm{NC}.m \cap n \neq \Lambda. \supset .m = n.$

V. $\vdash (\alpha)(\mathrm{E}_1 n).\alpha \in n.n \in \mathrm{NC}.$

VI. $\vdash (n){:}n \in \mathrm{NC}. \supset .n \neq \Lambda.$

Corollary 1. $\vdash (\alpha).\mathrm{Nc}(\alpha) \in \mathrm{NC}.$

Corollary 2. $\vdash (\alpha).\mathrm{Nc}(\alpha) \neq \Lambda.$

Corollary 3. $\vdash (\alpha,\beta){:}\mathrm{Nc}(\alpha) \cap \mathrm{Nc}(\beta) \neq \Lambda. \equiv .\mathrm{Nc}(\alpha) = \mathrm{Nc}(\beta).$

Corollary 4. $\vdash (\alpha,\beta){:}\mathrm{Nc}(\alpha) \cap \mathrm{Nc}(\beta) \neq \Lambda. \equiv .\alpha \text{ sm } \beta.$

Theorem XI.2.3.

*I. $\vdash (\alpha,\beta,n){:}n \in \mathrm{NC}.\alpha,\beta \in n. \supset .\alpha \text{ sm } \beta.$

*II. $\vdash (\alpha,\beta,n){:}n \in \mathrm{NC}.\alpha \in n.\alpha \text{ sm } \beta. \supset .\beta \in n.$

Proof of I. Assume $n \in \mathrm{NC}$ and $\alpha,\beta \in n$. Then by Thm.XI.2.2, Part I, and rule C, $n = \mathrm{Nc}(\gamma)$. Then our result follows by Thm.XI.2.1, Cor. 3.

Proof of II. Similar.

Theorem XI.2.4. $\vdash (\alpha).\mathrm{Nc}(\mathrm{USC}(\alpha)) \neq \mathrm{Nc}(\mathrm{SC}(\alpha)).$

Proof. Use Thm.XI.1.6 and Thm.XI.2.2, Part II.

Theorem XI.2.5. $\vdash (\alpha){:}\mathrm{Can}(\alpha). \equiv .\mathrm{Nc}(\alpha) = \mathrm{Nc}(\mathrm{USC}(\alpha)).$

Proof. Use the definition of $\mathrm{Can}(\alpha)$ with Thm.XI.2.2, Part II.

Theorem XI.2.6. $\vdash (\alpha){:}\mathrm{Can}(\alpha). \supset .\mathrm{Nc}(\alpha) \neq \mathrm{Nc}(\mathrm{SC}(\alpha)).$

Proof. Use Thm.XI.1.7.

Theorem XI.2.7. $\vdash 0 = \mathrm{Nc}(\Lambda).$

Proof. By Thm.XI.2.1, $\vdash \beta \in \mathrm{Nc}(\Lambda). \equiv .\beta \text{ sm } \Lambda.$ So by Thm.XI.1.9, corollary, $\vdash \beta \in \mathrm{Nc}(\Lambda). \equiv .\beta \in 0.$

Corollary 1. $\vdash 0 \in \mathrm{NC}$.
Corollary 2. $\vdash (\alpha){:}\mathrm{Nc}(\alpha) = 0. \equiv .\alpha = \Lambda$.
Corollary 3. $\vdash (\alpha){:}\Lambda \in \mathrm{Nc}(\alpha). \equiv .\alpha = \Lambda$.
Corollary 4. $\vdash (n){:}.n \in \mathrm{NC}{:} \supset {:}\Lambda \in n. \equiv .n = 0$.
Note. In Cors. 2 and 3, we use Thm.XI.1.9.
Theorem XI.2.8. $\vdash (x).1 = \mathrm{Nc}(\{x\})$.
Proof. Use Thm.XI.2.1 and Thm.XI.1.11.
Corollary 1. $\vdash 1 = \mathrm{Nc}(0)$.
Corollary 2. $\vdash 1 \in \mathrm{NC}$.
Corollary 3. $\vdash (\alpha,x){:}\{x\} \in \mathrm{Nc}(\alpha). \equiv .\alpha \in 1$.
Corollary 4. $\vdash (n,x){:}.n \in \mathrm{NC}{:} \supset {:}\{x\} \in n. \equiv .n = 1$.
Theorem XI.2.9. $\vdash (\alpha,\beta){:}\alpha \cap \beta = \Lambda. \supset .\mathrm{Nc}(\alpha) + \mathrm{Nc}(\beta) = \mathrm{Nc}(\alpha \cup \beta)$.
Proof. Let $\alpha \cap \beta = \Lambda$. If $\gamma \in \mathrm{Nc}(\alpha) + \mathrm{Nc}(\beta)$, then by Thm.X.1.1, $\phi \in \mathrm{Nc}(\alpha).\theta \in \mathrm{Nc}(\beta).\phi \cap \theta = \Lambda.\phi \cup \theta = \gamma$. Then by Thm.XI.2.1, α sm ϕ and β sm θ. So by Thm.XI.1.12, corollary, $(\phi \cup \theta)$ sm $(\alpha \cup \beta)$. That is, γ sm $(\alpha \cup \beta)$. So $\gamma \in \mathrm{Nc}(\alpha \cup \beta)$ by Thm.XI.2.1. So

(1) $$\mathrm{Nc}(\alpha) + \mathrm{Nc}(\beta) \subseteq \mathrm{Nc}(\alpha \cup \beta).$$

Conversely, if $\gamma \in \mathrm{Nc}(\alpha \cup \beta)$, then $(\alpha \cup \beta)$ sm γ. Then

(2) $$R \in 1\text{–}1,$$

$\alpha \cup \beta = \mathrm{Arg}(R)$ and $\gamma = \mathrm{Val}(R)$. So by Thm.IX.4.13, Cor. 7, $\alpha \subseteq \mathrm{Arg}(R)$ and $\beta \subseteq \mathrm{Arg}(R)$. Hence by (2) and Thm.XI.1.2, α sm $(R``\alpha)$ and $\beta$ sm $(R``\beta)$.

Thus

(3) $$(R``\alpha) \in \mathrm{Nc}(\alpha)$$

(4) $$(R``\beta) \in \mathrm{Nc}(\beta).$$

Now suppose $(R``\alpha) \cap (R``\beta) \neq \Lambda$. Then $y \in R``\alpha$ and $y \in R``\beta$. Then $xRy.x \in \alpha$ and $zRy.z \in \beta$. So by (2), $x = z$, and so $x \in \beta$. Hence $x \in \alpha \cap \beta$, contrary to assumption. Thus

(5) $$(R``\alpha) \cap (R``\beta) = \Lambda.$$

By Ex.X.4.6, $(R``\alpha) \cup (R``\beta) = R``(\alpha \cup \beta)$. Then by Thm.X.4.26, Part I,

(6) $$\gamma = (R``\alpha) \cup (R``\beta).$$

Then by (3), (4), (5), and (6), $\gamma \in \mathrm{Nc}(\alpha) + \mathrm{Nc}(\beta)$. So by (1), $\mathrm{Nc}(\alpha) + \mathrm{Nc}(\beta) = \mathrm{Nc}(\alpha \cup \beta)$.

We now wish to prove that, if m and n are cardinal numbers, then so is $m + n$. The critical point is that, if α is a class with m members and β is a class with n members, then α and β may overlap, and so $\alpha \cup \beta$ may have fewer than $m + n$ members. Thus there seems no immediate way to get a class with $m + n$ members, and we must produce such a class to prove that $m + n$ is a cardinal number. This difficulty is avoided by noting that $\alpha \times 0$ has as many members as α, namely, m, and $\beta \times \{V\}$ has as many members as β, namely, n, and $\alpha \times 0$ and $\beta \times \{V\}$ do not overlap, so that $(\alpha \times 0) \cup (\beta \times \{V\})$ has $m + n$ members.

***Theorem XI.2.10.** $\vdash (m,n){:}m,n \in \text{NC}. \supset .m + n \in \text{NC}.$

Proof. Let $m,n \in \text{NC}$. Then

(1) $$m = \text{Nc}(\alpha),$$

(2) $$n = \text{Nc}(\beta).$$

Now, by Thm.XI.1.20, α sm $(\alpha \times 0)$ and β sm $(\beta \times \{V\})$. So by (1), (2), and Thm.XI.2.2, Part II,

(3) $$m = \text{Nc}(\alpha \times 0),$$

(4) $$n = \text{Nc}(\beta \times \{V\}).$$

Suppose $(\alpha \times 0) \cap (\beta \times \{V\}) \neq \Lambda$. Then $u \in \alpha \times 0$ and $u \in \beta \times \{V\}$. So $u = \langle x,y\rangle .x \in \alpha .y \in 0$ and $u = \langle w,v\rangle .w \in \beta .v \in \{V\}$. Hence $y = \Lambda$, $y = v$, and $v = V$. This contradicts Thm.IX.4.6, corollary. So

(5) $$(\alpha \times 0) \cap (\beta \times \{V\}) = \Lambda.$$

So by (3), (4), (5), and Thm.XI.2.9,

$$m + n = \text{Nc}((\alpha \times 0) \cup (\beta \times \{V\})).$$

Then by Thm.XI.2.2, Part I, $m + n \in \text{NC}$.

Corollary. $\vdash (n){:}n \in \text{NC}. \supset .n + 1 \in \text{NC}.$

***Theorem XI.2.11.** $\vdash \text{Nn} \subseteq \text{NC}.$

Proof. We shall prove

$$\vdash (n){:}n \in \text{Nn}. \supset .n \in \text{NC}$$

by "induction" on n. That is, we use Thm.X.1.13, taking $F(n)$ to be $n \in \text{NC}$. By Thm.XI.2.7, Cor. 1, we have $\vdash F(0)$. By Thm.XI.2.10, corollary,

$$\vdash (n){:}n \in \text{Nn}.F(n). \supset .F(n + 1).$$

Hence

$$\vdash (n){:}n \in \text{Nn}. \supset .F(n),$$

which is our theorem.

Corollary 1. $\vdash 2 \in \text{NC}.$

Corollary 2. $\vdash 3 \in \text{NC}.$

etc.

Thus we infer that every nonnegative integer is a cardinal number. Indeed the nonnegative integers are just the finite cardinal numbers, but we shall go into this question later.

Theorem XI.2.12. $\vdash (m,n){:}m,n \in \mathrm{NC}.m + 1 = n + 1. \supset .m = n.$

Proof. Assume $m,n \in \mathrm{NC}$ and $m + 1 = n + 1$. Then by Thm.XI.2.10, corollary, $m + 1 \in \mathrm{NC}$. So by rule C, $m + 1 = \mathrm{NC}(\gamma) = n + 1$. So $\gamma \in m + 1$ and $\gamma \in n + 1$. Then by Thm.X.1.16 and rule C

$$\theta \in m.\sim x \in \theta.\theta \cup \{x\} = \gamma.$$

$$\phi \in n.\sim y \in \phi.\phi \cup \{y\} = \gamma.$$

So by Thm.XI.1.13, θ sm ϕ. Now from $\theta \in \mathrm{m}$ and $\phi \in n$, we get $m = \mathrm{Nc}(\theta)$ and $n = \mathrm{Nc}(\phi)$ by Thm.XI.2.2, Part III. Also, from θ sm ϕ, we get $\mathrm{Nc}(\theta) = \mathrm{Nc}(\phi)$ by Thm.XI.2.2, Part II. Thus $m = n$.

Corollary. $\vdash (m,n){:}m,n \in \mathrm{Nn}.m + 1 = n + 1. \supset .m = n.$

This corollary is just the result assumed in Axiom scheme 13. Of course, we have used Axiom scheme 13 in the proof, but indirectly and only through Thms.X.2.7, X.2.8, and X.2.9. Hence, if these theorems can somehow be proved without the use of Axiom scheme 13, then we can dispense with Axiom scheme 13, since in the corollary just proved we have derived the result stated in Axiom scheme 13.

We now introduce the relations of greater and less between cardinal numbers. We define

$\leq_c$	for	$\hat{m}\hat{n}(\mathrm{E}\alpha,\beta).\alpha \in m.\beta \in n.\alpha \subseteq \beta.$
$\geq_c$	for	$\mathrm{Cnv}(\leq_c).$
$<_c$	for	$\leq_c - I.$
$>_c$	for	$\mathrm{Cnv}(<_c).$

$\leq_c$, $\geq_c$, $<_c$, and $>_c$ are all stratified and contain no free variables and so may be assigned any type.

In most cases, it will be clear from the context that we are dealing with cardinal numbers, and in such cases we shall omit the subscript c and write merely $\leq$, $\geq$, $<$, or $>$.

We commonly write $m \leq n \leq p$ for $m \leq n.n \leq p$, $m \leq n < p$ for $m \leq n.n < p$, $m = n < p$ for $m = n.n < p$, etc.

Theorem XI.2.13.

*I. $\vdash (m,n){:}m \leq n. \equiv .(\mathrm{E}\alpha,\beta).\alpha \in m.\beta \in n.\alpha \subseteq \beta.$

II. $\vdash (m,n){:}m \geq n. \equiv .n \leq m.$

III. $\vdash (m,n){:}m < n. \equiv .m \leq n.m \neq n.$

IV. $\vdash (m,n){:}m > n. \equiv .n < m.$

Theorem XI.2.14. $\vdash (n){:}n \neq \Lambda. \supset .n \leq n.$

Proof. Use Thm.IX.4.13, Cor. 3.

Corollary 1. $\vdash (n){:}n \in \mathrm{NC}. \supset .n \leq n.$

***Corollary 2.** $\vdash (m,n){:}.m,n \in \mathrm{NC}{:} \supset {:}m \leq n. \equiv .m < n.\mathbf{v}.m = n.$

Corollary 3. $\vdash (m,n){:}.m,n \in \mathrm{NC}{:} \supset {:}m \geq n. \equiv .m > n.\mathbf{v}.m = n.$

Proof of Corollaries 2 *and* 3. Use proof by cases with the cases $m = n$ and $m \neq n$.

Theorem XI.2.15. $\vdash (n){:}n \neq \Lambda. \supset .0 \leq n.$

Proof. Use Thm.IX.4.13, Cor. 5.

Corollary 1. $\vdash (n){:}n \neq \Lambda.n \neq 0. \supset .0 < n.$

Corollary 2. $\vdash (n){:}n \in \mathrm{NC}. \supset .0 \leq n.$

Corollary 3. $\vdash (n){:}n \in \mathrm{NC}.n \neq 0. \supset .0 < n.$

Theorem XI.2.16. $\vdash (n){:}n \neq \Lambda. \supset .n \leq \mathrm{Nc}(V).$

Proof. Use Thm.IX.4.13, Cor. 4.

Corollary. $\vdash (n){:}n \in \mathrm{NC}. \supset .n \leq \mathrm{Nc}(V).$

Thus we see that there is a least cardinal number, namely, 0, and a greatest cardinal number, namely, Nc(V). In intuitive mathematics, the latter result contradicts an alternative form of Cantor's theorem in the form $(\alpha).\mathrm{Nc}(\alpha) < \mathrm{Nc}(\mathrm{SC}(\alpha))$. Because of our stratification requirements, we only know how to prove this latter result with the hypothesis $\mathrm{Can}(\alpha)$ and thus have no contradiction with the result that Nc(V) is the greatest cardinal.

Theorem XI.2.17. $\vdash (\alpha).\mathrm{Nc}(\mathrm{USC}(\alpha)) < \mathrm{Nc}(\mathrm{SC}(\alpha)).$

Proof. By Thm.XI.2.1, Cor. 1, $\vdash \mathrm{USC}(\alpha) \in \mathrm{Nc}(\mathrm{USC}(\alpha))$ and $\vdash \mathrm{SC}(\alpha) \in \mathrm{Nc}(\mathrm{SC}(\alpha))$. Also by Thm.IX.6.18, Cor. 1, $\vdash \mathrm{USC}(\alpha) \subseteq \mathrm{SC}(\alpha)$. So $\vdash \mathrm{Nc}(\mathrm{USC}(\alpha)) \leq \mathrm{Nc}(\mathrm{SC}(\alpha))$. Our theorem now follows by Thm.XI.2.4.

Theorem XI.2.18. $\vdash (\alpha){:}\mathrm{Can}(\alpha). \supset .\mathrm{Nc}(\alpha) < \mathrm{Nc}(\mathrm{SC}(\alpha)).$

Proof. Combine Thm.XI.2.5 with Thm.XI.2.17.

Theorem XI.2.19. $\vdash (m,n){:}m + n \neq \Lambda. \supset .m \leq m + n.n \leq m + n.$

Proof. Let $m + n \neq \Lambda$. Then by rule C, $\alpha \in m + n$. So by rule C and Thm.X.1.1, $\beta \in m.\gamma \in n.\beta \cap \gamma = \Lambda.\beta \cup \gamma = \alpha$. So by Thm.IX.4.13, Cor. 7, $\beta \in m.\alpha \in m + n.\beta \subseteq \alpha$. So $m \leq m + n$. Similarly, $n \leq m + n$.

Corollary. $\vdash (m,n){:}m,n \in \mathrm{NC}. \supset .m \leq m + n.n \leq m + n.$

We now prove one of the most important properties of $\leq$, namely, the version of the Schröder-Bernstein theorem which is stated in terms of inequality of cardinal numbers.

****Theorem XI.2.20.** $\vdash (m,n){:}m,n \in \mathrm{NC}.m \leq n.n \leq m. \supset .m = n.$

Proof. Assume the hypothesis. Then by rule C

$$(1) \qquad \gamma \in m.\beta \in n.\gamma \subseteq \beta,$$

$$(2) \qquad \delta \in n.\alpha \in m.\delta \subseteq \alpha.$$

Then by Thm.XI.2.3, Part I, α sm γ and β sm δ. So by Thm.XI.1.15, α sm β. So by Thm.XI.2.3, Part II, $\beta \in m$. Hence $m \cap n \neq \Lambda$. So by Thm.XI.2.2, Part IV, $m = n$.

Corollary 1. $\vdash (m,n):m,n \in \text{NC}.m < n. \supset .\sim(n \leq m)$.
Corollary 2. $\vdash (m,n):m,n \in \text{NC}.n \leq m. \supset .\sim(m < n)$.
Corollary 3. $\vdash (m,n):m,n \in \text{NC}.n > m. \supset .\sim(n \leq m)$.
Corollary 4. $\vdash (m,n):m,n \in \text{NC}.m \geq n. \supset .\sim(m < n)$.
Theorem XI.2.21. $\vdash (m,n):.m,n \in \text{NC}: \supset :m < n. \equiv .m \leq n.\sim(n \leq m)$.
Proof. Assume $m,n \in \text{NC}$. Then by Thm.XI.2.13, Part III, and Thm. XI.2.20, Cor. 1

$$m < n. \supset .m \leq n.\sim(n \leq m).$$

Conversely, since $m = n. \supset .n \leq m$ by Thm.XI.2.14, Cor. 1, we get $\sim(n \leq m). \supset .m \neq n$, and so by Thm.XI.2.13, Part III,

$$m \leq n.\sim(n \leq m). \supset .m < n.$$

***Theorem XI.2.22.** $\vdash (m,n):.m,n \in \text{NC}: \supset :m \leq n. \equiv .(\text{E}p).p \in \text{NC}.n = m + p$.
Proof. Assume $m,n \in \text{NC}$. Then by Thm.XI.2.19, corollary, we can go from right to left in our equivalence. Now let $m \leq n$. By rule C, $\alpha \in m$. $\beta \in n.\alpha \subseteq \beta$. Hence by Thm.IX.4.13, Part III, $\beta = \alpha \cup \beta$, so that by Thm.IX.4.4, Part XIX, $\beta = \alpha \cup (\beta - \alpha)$. Also $\alpha \cap (\beta - \alpha) = \Lambda$. Also $(\beta - \alpha) \in \text{Nc}(\beta - \alpha)$. Hence $\beta \in m + \text{Nc}(\beta - \alpha)$ by Thm.X.1.1. However, $n \in \text{NC}$ and $(m + \text{Nc}(\beta - \alpha)) \in \text{NC}$, so that by Thm.XI.2.2, Part IV, $n = m + \text{Nc}(\beta - \alpha)$.
Theorem XI.2.23. $\vdash (m,n,p):m,n,p \in \text{NC}.m \leq n. \supset .m + p \leq n + p$.
Proof. Assume the hypothesis. Then by rule C and Thm.XI.2.22, $q \in \text{NC}.n = m + q$. So $n + p = (m + q) + p = m + (q + p) = m + (p + q) = (m + p) + q$. So by Thm.XI.2.22, $m + p \leq n + p$.
Theorem XI.2.24. $\vdash (n):n \in \text{NC}. \supset .n = 0.\text{v}.1 \leq n$.
Proof. Assume $n \in \text{NC}$. Then by rule C, $n = \text{Nc}(\alpha)$.
Case 1. $\alpha = \Lambda$. Then $n = 0$.
Case 2. $\alpha \neq \Lambda$. Then by rule C, $x \in \alpha$. So $\{x\} \subseteq \alpha$. As $\{x\} \in 1$ and $\alpha \in n$, we have $1 \leq n$.
Corollary. $\vdash (n):.n \in \text{NC}: \supset :n = 0.\text{v}.(\text{E}m).m \in \text{NC}.n = m + 1$.
***Theorem XI.2.25.** $\vdash (m,n,p):m,n,p \in \text{NC}.m \leq n.n \leq p. \supset .m \leq p$.
Proof. Assume the hypothesis. Then by Thm.XI.2.22 and rule C,

$$q_1 \in \text{NC}.n = m + q_1$$

$$q_2 \in \text{NC}.p = n + q_2.$$

So $q_1 + q_2 \in \text{NC}.p = m + (q_1 + q_2)$. So $m \leq p$.
Corollary 1. $\vdash (m_1,m_2,n_1,n_2):m_1,m_2,n_1,n_2 \in \text{NC}.m_1 \leq m_2.n_1 \leq n_2. \supset . m_1 + n_1 \leq m_2 + n_2$.
Proof. Use Thm.XI.2.23.
Corollary 2. $\vdash (m,n,p):m,n,p \in \text{NC}.m < n.n \leq p. \supset .m < p$.

Corollary 3. $\vdash (m,n,p):m,n,p \in \mathrm{NC}.m \leq n.n < p. \supset .m < p.$

Corollary 4. $\vdash (m,n,p):m,n,p \in \mathrm{NC}.m < n.n < p. \supset .m < p.$

The reader will observe that we now have the familiar properties of + and $\leq$ except for the statement that any two cardinal numbers are "comparable," to wit

$$(m,n):.m,n \in \mathrm{NC}: \supset :m < n.\mathbf{v}.m = n.\mathbf{v}.m > n.$$

So far as we know, there is no way to prove this without assuming the axiom of choice. We shall say more on this point in Chapter XV.

To put it otherwise, we have proved that NC is partially ordered by $\leq$, but we have not proved that it is simply ordered.

We now introduce multiplication of cardinals, and define

$$m \times_c n \qquad \text{for} \qquad \hat{\alpha}(\mathrm{E}\beta,\gamma).\beta \in m.\gamma \in n.\alpha \text{ sm } (\beta \times \gamma),$$

where α, β, and γ are variables which do not occur in m or n.

We shall usually omit the subscript c, letting the reader decide from the context whether $\alpha \times \beta$ or $m \times_c n$ is intended.

The free occurrences of variables in $m \times n$ are just those of m and n.

For stratification, m and n have to have the same type, which will be the type of $m \times n$.

Theorem XI.2.26. $\vdash (\alpha,m,n):.\alpha \in m \times_c n: \equiv :(\mathrm{E}\beta,\gamma).\beta \in m.\gamma \in n.\alpha \text{ sm } (\beta \times \gamma).$

Theorem XI.2.27. $\vdash (\beta,\gamma).\mathrm{Nc}(\beta) \times_c \mathrm{Nc}(\gamma) = \mathrm{Nc}(\beta \times \gamma).$

Proof. Let $\alpha \in \mathrm{Nc}(\beta) \times_c \mathrm{Nc}(\gamma)$. Then by rule C, $\beta_1 \in \mathrm{Nc}(\beta).\gamma_1 \in \mathrm{Nc}(\gamma).\alpha \text{ sm } (\beta_1 \times \gamma_1)$. Hence $\beta_1 \text{ sm } \beta$ and $\gamma_1 \text{ sm } \gamma$. So by Thm.XI.1.18, Part II, $(\beta_1 \times \gamma_1) \text{ sm } (\beta \times \gamma)$. So $\alpha \text{ sm } (\beta \times \gamma)$. Hence $\alpha \in \mathrm{Nc}(\beta \times \gamma)$. So

(1) $$\vdash \mathrm{Nc}(\beta) \times_c \mathrm{Nc}(\gamma) \subseteq \mathrm{Nc}(\beta \times \gamma).$$

Conversely, let $\alpha \in \mathrm{Nc}(\beta \times \gamma)$. So $\alpha \text{ sm } (\beta \times \gamma)$. However, $\beta \in \mathrm{Nc}(\beta)$ and $\gamma \in \mathrm{Nc}(\gamma)$. Hence $\alpha \in \mathrm{Nc}(\beta) \times_c \mathrm{Nc}(\gamma)$. Thus

(2) $$\vdash \mathrm{Nc}(\beta \times \gamma) \subseteq \mathrm{Nc}(\beta) \times_c \mathrm{Nc}(\gamma).$$

Corollary. $\vdash (m,n):m,n \in \mathrm{NC}. \supset .m \times n \in \mathrm{NC}.$

****Theorem XI.2.28.** $\vdash (m,n).m \times n = n \times m.$

Proof. By Thm. XI.1.17, $\vdash \alpha \text{ sm } (\beta \times \gamma). \equiv .\alpha \text{ sm } (\gamma \times \beta)$. So

$$\begin{aligned} \vdash (\mathrm{E}\beta,\gamma).\beta \in m.\gamma \in n.\alpha \text{ sm } (\beta \times \gamma) \\ . \equiv .(\mathrm{E}\beta,\gamma).\beta \in m.\gamma \in n.\alpha \text{ sm } (\gamma \times \beta) \\ . \equiv .(\mathrm{E}\gamma,\beta).\gamma \in n.\beta \in m.\alpha \text{ sm } (\gamma \times \beta). \end{aligned}$$

****Theorem XI.2.29.** $\vdash (m,n,p):m,n,p \in \mathrm{NC}. \supset .(m \times n) \times p = m \times (n \times p).$

Proof. Let $m,n,p \epsilon$ NC. Then by rule C, $m = \text{Nc}(\alpha)$, $n = \text{Nc}(\beta)$, $p = \text{Nc}(\gamma)$. Then by Thm.XI.2.27, $m \times n = \text{Nc}(\alpha \times \beta)$ and $n \times p = \text{Nc}(\beta \times \gamma)$. So by Thm.XI.2.27,

$$(m \times n) \times p = \text{Nc}((\alpha \times \beta) \times \gamma),$$

$$m \times (n \times p) = \text{Nc}(\alpha \times (\beta \times \gamma)).$$

But, by Thm.XI.1.19,

$$\text{Nc}((\alpha \times \beta) \times \gamma) = \text{Nc}(\alpha \times (\beta \times \gamma)).$$

****Theorem XI.2.30.** $\vdash (m,n,p){:}m,n,p \epsilon \text{NC}. \supset .(m + n) \times p = (m \times p) + (n \times p)$.

Proof. Let $m,n,p \epsilon$ NC. Then $m + n \epsilon$ NC. So by rule C, $m + n = \text{Nc}(\alpha)$, $p = \text{Nc}(\delta)$. Then $\alpha \epsilon m + n$, so that by Thm.XI.1.1 and rule C, $\beta \epsilon m.\gamma \epsilon n.\beta \cap \gamma = \Lambda.\beta \cup \gamma = \alpha$. So $m = \text{Nc}(\beta)$, $n = \text{Nc}(\gamma)$, $m + n = \text{Nc}(\beta \cup \gamma)$. Now by Thm.XI.2.27,

(1) $$(m + n) \times p = \text{Nc}((\beta \cup \gamma) \times \delta).$$

But by Thm.X.3.11,

(2) $$(\beta \cup \gamma) \times \delta = (\beta \times \delta) \cup (\gamma \times \delta)$$

$$(\beta \cap \gamma) \times \delta = (\beta \times \delta) \cap (\gamma \times \delta).$$

However, $\beta \cap \gamma = \Lambda$. So by Thm.X.2.12, Cor. 3, $(\beta \times \delta) \cap (\gamma \times \delta) = \Lambda$. Hence, by (1), (2), and Thm.XI.2.9,

(3) $$(m + n) \times p = \text{Nc}(\beta \times \delta) + \text{Nc}(\gamma \times \delta).$$

By Thm.XI.2.27, $m \times p = \text{Nc}(\beta \times \delta)$ and $n \times p = \text{Nc}(\gamma \times \delta)$. So

$$(m + n) \times p = (m \times p) + (n \times p).$$

***Theorem XI.2.31.** $\vdash (m,n,p){:}m,n,p \epsilon \text{NC}. \supset .m \times (n + p) = (m \times n) + (m \times p)$.

Proof. Let $m,n,p \epsilon$ NC. Then $m \times (n + p) = (n + p) \times m = (n \times m) + (p \times m) = (m \times n) + (m \times p)$.

Theorem XI.2.32. $\vdash (m){:}m \neq \Lambda. \supset .m \times 0 = 0$.

Proof. By Thm.XI.2.26,

$$\begin{aligned} \vdash \alpha \epsilon m \times 0. &\equiv .(\text{E}\beta,\gamma).\beta \epsilon m.\gamma \epsilon 0.\alpha \text{ sm } (\beta \times \gamma) \\ .&\equiv .(\text{E}\beta,\gamma).\beta \epsilon m.\gamma = \Lambda.\alpha \text{ sm } (\beta \times \gamma) \\ .&\equiv .(\text{E}\beta).\beta \epsilon m.\alpha \text{ sm } (\beta \times \Lambda). \end{aligned}$$

However, by Thm.X.2.12, Cor. 3, $\beta \times \Lambda = \Lambda$. So

$$\begin{aligned} \vdash \alpha \epsilon m \times 0. &\equiv .(\text{E}\beta).\beta \epsilon m.\alpha \text{ sm } \Lambda \\ .&\equiv .(\text{E}\beta).\beta \epsilon m.\alpha \epsilon 0 \end{aligned}$$

by Thm.XI.1.9, corollary. So if $m \neq \Lambda$, then $(E\beta)\ \beta \epsilon m$, and so

$$\vdash \alpha \epsilon m \times 0. \equiv .\alpha \epsilon 0.$$

Corollary. $\vdash (m):m \epsilon \mathrm{NC}. \supset .m \times 0 = 0.$

***Theorem XI.2.33.** $\vdash (m):m \epsilon \mathrm{NC}. \supset .m \times 1 = m.$

Proof. Let $m \epsilon \mathrm{NC}$. Then by rule C, $m = \mathrm{Nc}(\delta)$. Now by Thm.XI.2.26,

$$\begin{aligned} \alpha \epsilon m \times 1. &\equiv .(E\beta,\gamma).\beta \epsilon m.\gamma \epsilon 1.\alpha \text{ sm } (\beta \times \gamma) \\ .&\equiv .(E\beta,\gamma,x).\beta \text{ sm } \delta.\gamma = \{x\}.\alpha \text{ sm } (\beta \times \gamma) \\ .&\equiv .(E\beta,x).\beta \text{ sm } \delta.\alpha \text{ sm } (\beta \times \{x\}). \end{aligned}$$

But by Thm.XI.1.20,

$$\vdash \alpha \text{ sm } (\beta \times \{x\}). \equiv .\alpha \text{ sm } \beta.$$

So

$$\begin{aligned} \alpha \epsilon m \times 1. &\equiv .(E\beta,x).\beta \text{ sm } \delta.\alpha \text{ sm } \beta \\ .&\equiv .(E\beta).\beta \text{ sm } \delta.\alpha \text{ sm } \beta \\ .&\equiv .\alpha \text{ sm } \delta \\ .&\equiv .\alpha \epsilon \mathrm{Nc}(\delta) \\ .&\equiv .\alpha \epsilon m. \end{aligned}$$

Corollary 1. $\vdash (m):m \epsilon \mathrm{NC}. \supset .m \times 2 = m + m.$

Corollary 2. $\vdash (m):m \epsilon \mathrm{NC}. \supset .m \times 3 = m + m + m.$

Theorem XI.2.34. $\vdash (m,n):m,n \epsilon \mathrm{NC}.m \times n = 0. \supset .m = 0 \mathbf{v} n = 0.$

Proof. Let $m,n \epsilon \mathrm{NC}$ and $m \times n = 0$. Then by rule C, $m = \mathrm{Nc}(\alpha)$, $n = \mathrm{Nc}(\beta)$. Then by Thm.XI.2.27, $m \times n = \mathrm{Nc}(\alpha \times \beta)$. So $\alpha \times \beta \epsilon m \times n$. So $\alpha \times \beta \epsilon 0$. So $\alpha \times \beta = \Lambda$.

Case 1. $\alpha = \Lambda$. Then $m = \mathrm{Nc}(\Lambda) = 0$. So $m = 0 \mathbf{v} n = 0$.

Case 2. $\alpha \neq \Lambda$. Since $\alpha \times \Lambda = \Lambda$ (see Thm.X.2.12, Cor. 3), we have $\alpha \times \Lambda = \alpha \times \beta$. Then by Thm.X.4.4, corollary, Part II, $\beta = \Lambda$. So $n = \mathrm{Nc}(\Lambda) = 0$. So $m = 0 \mathbf{v} n = 0$.

This theorem is very useful. It is used to prove the corresponding result for real and complex numbers. This latter result is very widely used. One standard use occurs in solving equations. Thus to solve

$$x^2 - 4x + 3 = 0,$$

we factor the left side and write

$$(x - 3)(x - 1) = 0.$$

Then we infer that one of $x - 3$ or $x - 1$ must be zero, and hence that $x = 3$ or $x = 1$.

This is a standard routine, and its justification goes back to the theorem just proved.

Theorem XI.2.35. $\vdash (m,n,p):m,n,p \epsilon \mathrm{NC}.m \leq n. \supset .m \times p \leq n \times p.$

Proof. Assume $m,n,p \epsilon$ NC and $m \leq n$. Then by Thm.XI.2.22 and rule C, $q \epsilon \text{NC}.n = m + q$. Then $n \times p = (m + q) \times p = (m \times p) + (q \times p)$. So by Thm.XI.2.22, $m \times p \leq n \times p$.

Corollary. $\vdash (m_1,m_2,n_1,n_2):m_1,m_2,n_1,n_2 \;\epsilon\; \text{NC}.m_1 \leq m_2.n_1 \leq n_2. \supset . m_1 \times n_1 \leq m_2 \times n_2$.

Theorem XI.2.36. $\vdash (m,n):m,n \epsilon \text{NC}.n \neq 0. \supset .m \leq m \times n$.

Proof. Assume $m,n \epsilon$ NC and $n \neq 0$. Then by Thm.XI.2.24, $1 \leq n$. So by Thm.XI.2.35, $m \times 1 \leq m \times n$. Then by Thm.XI.2.33, $m \leq m \times n$.

Theorem XI.2.37. $\vdash \text{Nc(V)} \times \text{Nc(V)} = \text{Nc(V)}$.

Proof. By Thm.IX.4.6, corollary, $\vdash \text{V} \neq \Lambda$, so that by Thm.XI.2.7, Cor. 2, $\vdash \text{Nc(V)} \neq 0$. Hence, by Thm.XI.2.36, $\vdash \text{Nc(V)} \leq \text{Nc(V)} \times \text{Nc(V)}$. However, by Thm.XI.2.16, corollary, $\vdash \text{Nc(V)} \times \text{Nc(V)} \leq \text{Nc(V)}$. So by Thm.XI.2.20, $\vdash \text{Nc(V)} \times \text{Nc(V)} = \text{Nc(V)}$.

Corollary. $\vdash (\text{V} \times \text{V})$ sm V.

Proof. By Thm.XI.2.27, $\vdash \text{Nc(V)} \times \text{Nc(V)} = \text{Nc(V} \times \text{V)}$.

This corollary states

$$\vdash (\text{E}R).\text{V sm}_R\ (\text{V} \times \text{V}).$$

That is, the set of all objects is in one-to-one correspondence with the set of all ordered pairs. That is, there are exactly as many objects as there are pairs of objects. This sounds contradictory at first, but we shall learn that for many infinite classes α which occur in mathematics, α sm $(\alpha \times \alpha)$ is provable. This is one of the ways in which infinite classes can differ from finite classes.

We now define exponentiation of cardinal numbers. This is done in terms of $\alpha \wedge \beta$, as indicated in the preceding section. We define

$$m \wedge_c n \quad \text{for} \quad \hat{\gamma}(\text{E}\alpha,\beta).\text{USC}(\alpha) \;\epsilon\; m.\text{USC}(\beta) \;\epsilon\; n.\gamma \text{ sm } (\alpha \wedge \beta),$$

$$n^m \quad \text{for} \quad m \wedge_c n.$$

In the first of these, α, β, and γ are variables which do not occur in m or n.

We shall usually omit the subscript c, letting the reader decide from the context whether $\alpha \wedge \beta$ or $m \wedge_c n$ is intended. The notation n^m is unambiguous, since it always means $m \wedge_c n$.

The free occurrences of variables in $m \wedge n$ are just those of m and n.

For stratification, m and n have to have the same type, which will be the type of $m \wedge_c n$.

Note that this is not the same situation that holds for $\alpha \wedge \beta$, since $\alpha \wedge \beta$ is one type higher than the type of α and β. If exponentiation is to avoid type difficulties, n^m must have the same type as m and n. We arranged this by using $\text{USC}(\alpha) \;\epsilon\; m$ and $\text{USC}(\beta) \;\epsilon\; n$ instead of $\alpha \;\epsilon\; m$ and $\beta \;\epsilon\; n$ in the definition of $m \wedge_c n$. This leads to certain complexities in deriving the laws of exponents, but these complexities are not serious.

The notation $m \wedge n$ for n^m is motivated as follows. If

$$\sqrt[m]{n}$$

denotes

$$n^{1/m},$$

then it seems reasonable to use $m \wedge n$ for n^m.

It will be noted that $n^m = \Lambda$ unless $(E\alpha).USC(\alpha) \epsilon m$ and $(E\beta).USC(\beta) \epsilon n$. There are cardinal numbers m and n for which $n^m = \Lambda$, and these cardinal numbers fail to satisfy all the familiar laws of exponents. However, for all the cardinal numbers m which occur in ordinary mathematics, $(E\alpha).USC(\alpha) \epsilon m$ holds, and so all the usual laws of exponents hold for these cardinal numbers.

Theorem XI.2.38. $\vdash (\gamma,m,n):\gamma \epsilon n^m. \equiv .(E\alpha,\beta).USC(\alpha) \epsilon m.USC(\beta) \epsilon n. \gamma \text{ sm } (\alpha \wedge \beta)$.

Theorem XI.2.39. $\vdash (\alpha,\beta).Nc(USC(\alpha)) \wedge_c Nc(USC(\beta)) = Nc(\alpha \wedge \beta)$.

Proof. Since $\vdash USC(\alpha) \epsilon Nc(USC(\alpha))$ and $\vdash USC(\beta) \epsilon Nc(USC(\beta))$, it follows by Thm.XI.2.1, and Thm.XI.2.38, that $\vdash \gamma \epsilon Nc(\alpha \wedge \beta). \supset . \gamma \epsilon (Nc(USC(\alpha))) \wedge_c Nc(USC(\beta))$. That is,

(1) $$\vdash Nc(\alpha \wedge \beta) \subseteq Nc(USC(\alpha)) \wedge_c Nc(USC(\beta)).$$

Now let $\gamma \epsilon Nc(USC(\alpha)) \wedge_c Nc(USC(\beta))$. Then by Thm.XI.2.38 and rule C, $USC(\phi) \epsilon Nc(USC(\alpha))$, $USC(\theta) \epsilon Nc(USC(\beta))$, and $\gamma \text{ sm } (\phi \wedge \theta)$. Then by Thm.XI.2.1, and Thm.XI.1.33, we have $\phi \text{ sm } \alpha$ and $\theta \text{ sm } \beta$. Then by Thm.XI.1.23, corollary, $(\phi \wedge \theta) \text{ sm } (\alpha \wedge \beta)$. So $\gamma \text{ sm } (\alpha \wedge \beta)$. So $\gamma \epsilon Nc(\alpha \wedge \beta)$. Then by (1), our theorem follows.

As we said before, $n^m = \Lambda$ unless $(E\alpha).USC(\alpha) \epsilon m$ and $(E\beta).USC(\beta) \epsilon n$. So we devote a few theorems to conditions under which $(E\alpha).USC(\alpha) \epsilon m$.

Theorem XI.2.40. $\vdash 0 = Nc(USC(\Lambda))$.

Proof. By Thm.IX.6.12, Part IV, $\vdash \Lambda = USC(\Lambda)$. So $\vdash Nc(\Lambda) = Nc(USC(\Lambda))$. Then our theorem follows by Thm.XI.2.7.

Theorem XI.2.41. $\vdash (x).1 = Nc(USC(\{x\}))$.

Proof. By Thm.IX.6.16, $\vdash \{\{x\}\} = USC(\{x\})$. So $\vdash Nc(\{\{x\}\}) = Nc(USC(\{x\}))$. Then our theorem follows by Thm.XI.2.8.

Theorem XI.2.42. $\vdash (m):m^0 \neq \Lambda. \equiv .(E\alpha).USC(\alpha) \epsilon m$.

Proof. Suppose $m^0 \neq \Lambda$. Then $\gamma \epsilon m^0$, so that by Thm.XI.2.38, $(E\alpha).USC(\alpha) \epsilon m$. So

(1) $$\vdash m^0 \neq \Lambda. \supset .(E\alpha).USC(\alpha) \epsilon m.$$

Conversely, assume $(E\alpha).USC(\alpha) \epsilon m$. Then $USC(\alpha) \epsilon m$, and by Thm. XI.2.40, $USC(\Lambda) \epsilon 0$. So by Thm.XI.2.38, $(\Lambda \wedge \alpha) \epsilon m^0$. So

(2) $$\vdash (E\alpha).USC(\alpha) \epsilon m. \supset .m^0 \neq \Lambda.$$

Corollary. $\vdash (m){:}.m \in \mathrm{NC}{:} \supset {:}m^0 \neq \Lambda. \equiv .(\mathrm{E}\alpha).m = \mathrm{Nc}(\mathrm{USC}(\alpha))$.

Because of this theorem, we can (and often will) use the shorter notation $m^0 \neq \Lambda$ in place of the lengthier notation $(\mathrm{E}\alpha).\mathrm{USC}(\alpha) \in m$.

Theorem XI.2.43. $\vdash (m,n){:}.m,n \in \mathrm{NC}{:} \supset {:}(m + n)^0 \neq \Lambda. \equiv .m^0 \neq \Lambda. n^0 \neq \Lambda.$

Proof. Assume $(m + n)^0 \neq \Lambda$. Then $\mathrm{USC}(\alpha) \in m + n$ by Thm.XI.2.42. Then $\beta \in m.\gamma \in n.\beta \cap \gamma = \Lambda.\beta \cup \gamma = \mathrm{USC}(\alpha)$. By Thm.IX.4.13, Cor. 7, $\beta \subseteq \mathrm{USC}(\alpha)$ and $\gamma \subseteq \mathrm{USC}(\alpha)$. By Thm.IX.6.14, Cor. 2, $\beta = \mathrm{USC}(\phi)$, $\gamma = \mathrm{USC}(\theta)$. So $m^0 \neq \Lambda.n^0 \neq \Lambda$. Thus

(1) $$\vdash (m + n)^0 \neq \Lambda. \supset .m^0 \neq \Lambda.n^0 \neq \Lambda.$$

Conversely, assume $m,n \in \mathrm{NC}$, $m^0 \neq \Lambda$, $n^0 \neq \Lambda$. Then by Thm.XI.2.42, corollary, $m = \mathrm{Nc}(\mathrm{USC}(\beta))$, $n = \mathrm{Nc}(\mathrm{USC}(\gamma))$. By Thm.XI.1.20, $\beta \text{ sm } (\beta \times 0)$ and $\gamma \text{ sm } (\gamma \times \{\mathrm{V}\})$. Hence by Thm.XI.1.33, $m = \mathrm{Nc}(\mathrm{USC}(\beta \times 0))$ and $n = \mathrm{Nc}(\mathrm{USC}(\gamma \times \{\mathrm{V}\}))$. As in the proof of Thm.XI.2.10, we get $(\beta \times 0) \cap (\gamma \times \{\mathrm{V}\}) = \Lambda$. By Thm.IX.6.12, Parts I and IV, $\mathrm{USC}(\beta \times 0) \cap \mathrm{USC}(\gamma \times \{\mathrm{V}\}) = \Lambda$. By Thm.XI.2.9, $m + n = \mathrm{Nc}(\mathrm{USC}(\beta \times 0) \cup \mathrm{USC}(\gamma \times \{\mathrm{V}\}))$. Then by Thm.IX.6.12, Part II, $m + n = \mathrm{Nc}(\mathrm{USC}((\beta \times 0) \cup (\gamma \times \{\mathrm{V}\})))$. Then $(m + n)^0 \neq \Lambda$. So

(2) $$\vdash m,n \in \mathrm{NC}.{:} \supset {:}.m^0 \neq \Lambda.n^0 \neq \Lambda. \supset .(m + n)^0 \neq \Lambda.$$

Theorem XI.2.44. $\vdash (n){:}n \in \mathrm{Nn}. \supset .n^0 \neq \Lambda.$

Proof. We shall prove the theorem by induction on n. That is, we use Thm.X.1.13, taking $F(n)$ to be $n^0 \neq \Lambda$. By Thm.XI.2.40 and Thm.XI.2.42,

(1) $$\vdash F(0).$$

Assume $n \in \mathrm{Nn}.F(n)$. Then $n \in \mathrm{NC}.n^0 \neq \Lambda$ by Thm.XI.2.11. Also, by Thm.XI.2.41 and Thm.XI.2.42, $\vdash 1 \in \mathrm{NC}.1^0 \neq \Lambda$. So by Thm.XI.2.43, $(n + 1)^0 \neq \Lambda$. So

(2) $$\vdash (n){:}n \in \mathrm{Nn}.F(n). \supset .F(n + 1).$$

Corollary 1. $\vdash 0^0 \neq \Lambda.$
Corollary 2. $\vdash 1^0 \neq \Lambda.$
Corollary 3. $\vdash 2^0 \neq \Lambda.$
etc.

This result tells us that all finite cardinal numbers n have the property $n^0 \neq \Lambda$. Actually all cardinal numbers n of interest in mathematics have the property $n^0 \neq \Lambda$, so that for such numbers the usual laws of exponentiation hold.

Theorem XI.2.45. $\vdash (m,n){:}m,n \in \mathrm{NC}.m^0 \neq \Lambda.n^0 \neq \Lambda. \supset .(m \times n)^0 \neq \Lambda.$

Proof. Let $m,n \in \mathrm{NC}.m^0 \neq \Lambda.n^0 \neq \Lambda$. Then by Thm.XI.2.42, corollary,

$m = \mathrm{Nc}(\mathrm{USC}(\alpha))$, $n = \mathrm{Nc}(\mathrm{USC}(\beta))$. By Thm.XI.2.27, $m \times n = \mathrm{Nc}(\mathrm{USC}(\alpha) \times \mathrm{USC}(\beta))$. By Thm.XI.1.41, $m \times n = \mathrm{Nc}(\mathrm{USC}(\alpha \times \beta))$.

Theorem XI.2.46. $\vdash (m){:}m = \mathrm{Nc}(V).\supset .m^0 = \Lambda$.

Proof. Assume $m = \mathrm{Nc}(V)$ and $m^0 \neq \Lambda$. Then by Thm.XI.2.42, corollary, $m = \mathrm{Nc}(\mathrm{USC}(\alpha))$. Thus by Thm.IX.6.12, Cor. 2, and Thm. XI.2.13, Part I, $m \leq \mathrm{Nc}(1)$. However, by Thm.XI.2.16, corollary, $\mathrm{Nc}(1) \leq m$. So by Thm.XI.2.20, $m = \mathrm{Nc}(1)$. Hence V sm 1. By the definitions of 1 and Can(V), this is Can(V). Hence we have a contradiction with Thm.XI.1.8.

This theorem shows the falsity of

$$(n){:}n \in \mathrm{NC}.\supset .n^0 \neq \Lambda.$$

In conjunction with Thm.XI.2.44, we can infer

$$\vdash \sim\mathrm{Nc}(V) \in \mathrm{Nn},$$

so that not all cardinal numbers are finite.

We can also use this theorem to show the falsity of

$$(m,n){:}m,n \in \mathrm{NC}.(m \times n)^0 \neq \Lambda.\supset .m^0 \neq \Lambda.n^0 \neq \Lambda,$$

for we can take $m = \mathrm{Nc}(V)$, $n = 0$. Then we have $m \times n = 0$ by Thm. XI.2.32, corollary. Hence by Thm.XI.2.40 and Thm.XI.2.42, $(m \times n)^0 \neq \Lambda$. However, we have $m^0 = \Lambda$.

We shall show later how to prove the falsity of

$$(m,n){:}m,n \in \mathrm{NC}.m^0 \neq \Lambda.n^0 \neq \Lambda.\supset .(n^m)^0 \neq \Lambda.$$

Theorem XI.2.47. $\vdash (m,n){:}m^0 \neq \Lambda.n^0 \neq \Lambda.\equiv .n^m \neq \Lambda$.

Proof. Assume $m^0 \neq \Lambda.n^0 \neq \Lambda$. Then by Thm.XI.2.42, $\mathrm{USC}(\alpha) \in m$ and $\mathrm{USC}(\beta) \in n$. By Thm.XI.2.38, $(\alpha \wedge \beta) \in n^m$. Conversely, assume $n^m \neq \Lambda$. Then $\gamma \in n^m$, so that by Thm.XI.2.38, $(E\alpha).\mathrm{USC}(\alpha) \in m$ and $(E\beta).\mathrm{USC}(\beta) \in n$.

Theorem XI.2.48. $\vdash (m,n){:.}m,n \in \mathrm{NC}{:}\supset {:}m^0 \neq \Lambda.n^0 \neq \Lambda.\equiv .n^m \in \mathrm{NC}$.

Proof. By Thm.XI.2.47 and Thm.XI.2.2, Part VI,

(1) $$\vdash n^m \in \mathrm{NC}.\supset .m^0 \neq \Lambda.n^0 \neq \Lambda.$$

Assume $m,n \in \mathrm{NC}$ and $m^0 \neq \Lambda.n^0 \neq \Lambda$. Then by Thm.XI.2.42, corollary, $m = \mathrm{Nc}(\mathrm{USC}(\alpha))$ and $n = \mathrm{Nc}(\mathrm{USC}(\beta))$. By Thm.XI.2.39, $n^m = \mathrm{Nc}(\alpha \wedge \beta)$. So $n^m \in \mathrm{NC}$.

Corollary 1. $\vdash (m){:.}m \in \mathrm{NC}{:}\supset {:}m^0 \neq \Lambda.\equiv .m^0 \in \mathrm{NC}$.

Corollary 2. $\vdash (m){:}m,m^0 \in \mathrm{NC}.\supset .(E\alpha).m = \mathrm{Nc}(\mathrm{USC}(\alpha))$.

Corollary 3. $\vdash (m,n){:}m,n,m^0,n^0 \in \mathrm{NC}.\supset .n^m \in \mathrm{NC}$.

When we are dealing with an m which is a cardinal number, Cor. 1 gives us still another notation, $m^0 \in \mathrm{NC}$, for the important condition $(E\alpha)$. $\mathrm{USC}(\alpha) \in m$.

We now prove a series of theorems which will be recognized as the familiar laws of exponents, except for the occurrence of conditions such as $m^0 \epsilon$ NC in the hypotheses. As we have explained earlier, we have the condition $m^0 \epsilon$ NC satisfied for all m's of interest, and so have the usual laws of exponents for all such m's.

Theorem XI.2.49. $\vdash (m):m,m^0 \epsilon \mathrm{NC}. \supset .m^0 = 1.$

Proof. Assume $m,m^0 \epsilon$ NC. By Thm.XI.2.48, Cor. 2, $m = \mathrm{Nc}(\mathrm{USC}(\alpha))$. By Thm.XI.2.40 and Thm.XI.2.39, $m^0 = \mathrm{Nc}(\Lambda \wedge \alpha)$. By Thm.XI.1.24, $m^0 = \mathrm{Nc}(0)$. By Thm.XI.2.8, Cor. 1, $m^0 = 1$.

Theorem XI.2.50. $\vdash 0^0 = 1.$

Proof. By Thm.XI.2.40 and Thm.XI.2.42, $\vdash 0^0 \neq \Lambda$. Then by Thm. XI.2.7, Cor. 1, and Thm.XI.2.48, Cor. 1, $\vdash 0,0^0 \epsilon$ NC. Now use Thm. XI.2.49.

This result is in distinction to the case of 0^0 for real numbers, which is usually considered as undefined.

Theorem XI.2.51. $\vdash (m):m,m^0 \epsilon \mathrm{NC}.m \neq 0. \supset .0^m = 0.$

Proof. Assume $m,m^0 \epsilon$ NC, and $m \neq 0$. Then by Thm.XI.2.48, Cor. 2, $m = \mathrm{Nc}(\mathrm{USC}(\alpha))$. By Thm.XI.2.40 and Thm.XI.2.39, $0^m = \mathrm{Nc}(\alpha \wedge \Lambda)$. Now, since $\mathrm{USC}(\alpha) \epsilon m$ and $m \neq 0$, we get $\mathrm{USC}(\alpha) \neq \Lambda$ by Thm.XI.2.7, Cor. 4. By Thm.IX.6.12, Part IV, $\alpha \neq \Lambda$. Then by Thm.XI.1.25, $\alpha \wedge \Lambda = \Lambda$. So $0^m = \mathrm{Nc}(\Lambda) = 0$.

Theorem XI.2.52. $\vdash (m):m,m^0 \epsilon \mathrm{NC}. \supset .m^1 = m.$

Proof. Assume $m,m^0 \epsilon$ NC. By Thm.XI.2.48, Cor. 2, $m = \mathrm{Nc}(\mathrm{USC}(\alpha))$. Also, by Thm.XI.2.41, $1 = \mathrm{Nc}(\mathrm{USC}(0))$. By Thm.XI.2.39, $m^1 = \mathrm{Nc}(0 \wedge \alpha)$. However, by Thm.XI.1.38, $(0 \wedge \alpha)$ sm $\mathrm{USC}(\alpha)$. Hence $\mathrm{Nc}(0 \wedge \alpha) = \mathrm{Nc}(\mathrm{USC}(\alpha)) = m$. So $m^1 = m$.

Theorem XI.2.53. $\vdash (m):m,m^0 \epsilon \mathrm{NC}. \supset .1^m = 1.$

Proof. Similar to that of Thm.XI.2.52, except that Thm.XI.1.27 and Thm.XI.2.8 are used.

Theorem XI.2.54. $\vdash (m,n,p):m,n,p,m^0,(n + p)^0 \epsilon \mathrm{NC}. \supset .m^{n+p} = m^n \times m^p.$

Proof. Assume $m,n,p,m^0,(n + p)^0 \epsilon$ NC. Then $m = \mathrm{Nc}(\mathrm{USC}(\alpha))$ and $n + p = \mathrm{Nc}(\mathrm{USC}(\delta))$. Then $\mathrm{USC}(\delta) \epsilon n + p$, so that $\phi \epsilon n.\theta \epsilon p. \phi \cap \theta = \Lambda.\phi \cup \theta = \mathrm{USC}(\delta)$. By Thm.IX.6.14, Cor. 2, $\phi = \mathrm{USC}(\beta)$, $\theta = \mathrm{USC}(\gamma)$. Then $\mathrm{USC}(\beta) \epsilon n.\mathrm{USC}(\gamma) \epsilon p.\mathrm{USC}(\beta) \cap \mathrm{USC}(\gamma) = \Lambda. \mathrm{USC}(\beta) \cup \mathrm{USC}(\gamma) = \mathrm{USC}(\delta)$. Then by Thm.XI.2.2, Part III, $n = \mathrm{Nc}(\mathrm{USC}(\beta))$, $p = \mathrm{Nc}(\mathrm{USC}(\gamma))$, and by Thm.XI.2.39

$$m^{n+p} = \mathrm{Nc}(\delta \wedge \alpha),$$

$$m^n = \mathrm{Nc}(\beta \wedge \alpha),$$

$$m^p = \mathrm{Nc}(\gamma \wedge \alpha).$$

So by Thm.XI.2.27,

$$m^n \times m^p = \mathrm{Nc}((\beta \wedge \alpha) \times (\gamma \wedge \alpha)).$$

By Thm.IX.6.12, Parts I and II, $\mathrm{USC}(\beta \cap \gamma) = \Lambda$ and $\mathrm{USC}(\beta \cup \gamma) = \mathrm{USC}(\delta)$. As $\vdash \Lambda = \mathrm{USC}(\Lambda)$ by Thm.IX.6.2, Part IV, we get $\beta \cap \gamma = \Lambda$ and $\beta \cup \gamma = \delta$ by Thm.IX.6.11, Cor. 1. Then by Thm.XI.1.29, $(\delta \wedge \alpha)$ sm $((\beta \wedge \alpha) \times (\gamma \wedge \alpha))$. So $\mathrm{Nc}(\delta \wedge \alpha) = \mathrm{Nc}((\beta \wedge \alpha) \times (\gamma \wedge \alpha))$. Thus $m^{n+p} = m^n \times m^p$.

Theorem XI.2.55. $\vdash (m){:}m,m^0 \in \mathrm{NC}. \supset .m^2 = m \times m.$

Proof. By Thm.XI.2.11, Cor. 1, $\vdash 2 \in \mathrm{NC}$, and by Thm.XI.2.44, Cor. 3, $\vdash 2^0 \neq \Lambda$. Then by Thm.XI.2.48, Cor. 2, $\vdash 2,2^0 \in \mathrm{NC}$. Since $\vdash 2 = 1 + 1$, we have by Thm.XI.2.54,

$$\vdash m,m^0 \in \mathrm{NC}. \supset .m^2 = m^1 \times m^1.$$

However, by Thm.XI.2.52,

$$\vdash m,m^0 \in \mathrm{NC}. \supset .m^1 = m.$$

So our theorem follows.

Theorem XI.2.56. $\vdash (m,n,p){:}m,n,p,p^0,(m^n)^0 \in \mathrm{NC}. \supset .(m^n)^p = m^{n \times p}.$

Proof. Assume $m,n,p,p^0,(m^n)^0 \in \mathrm{NC}$. Then $p = \mathrm{Nc}(\mathrm{USC}(\gamma))$. Also, by Thm.XI.2.2, Part VI, $(m^n)^0 \neq \Lambda$. By Thm.XI.2.42, $\mathrm{USC}(\delta) \in m^n$. By Thm.XI.2.38, $\mathrm{USC}(\alpha) \in m$, $\mathrm{USC}(\beta) \in n$, and $(\beta \wedge \alpha)$ sm $\mathrm{USC}(\delta)$. Then by Thm.XI.1.30,

$$(1) \qquad \mathrm{Nc}(\gamma \wedge \delta) = \mathrm{Nc}((\gamma \times \beta) \wedge \alpha).$$

Now by Thm.XI.2.42, $m^0 \neq \Lambda$ and $n^0 \neq \Lambda$, so that by Thm.XI.2.48, $m^n \in \mathrm{NC}$. Then by Thm.XI.2.2, Part III, $m = \mathrm{Nc}(\mathrm{USC}(\alpha))$, $n = \mathrm{Nc}(\mathrm{USC}(\beta))$, and $m^n = \mathrm{Nc}(\mathrm{USC}(\delta))$. By Thm.XI.2.27, $p \times n = \mathrm{Nc}(\mathrm{USC}(\gamma) \times \mathrm{USC}(\beta))$. By Thm.XI.1.41, $p \times n = \mathrm{Nc}(\mathrm{USC}(\gamma \times \beta))$. By Thm.XI.2.39,

$$(m^n)^p = \mathrm{Nc}(\gamma \wedge \delta),$$

$$m^{p \times n} = \mathrm{Nc}((\gamma \times \beta) \wedge \alpha).$$

So by (1),

$$(m^n)^p = m^{p \times n}.$$

Then by Thm.XI.2.28,

$$(m^n)^p = m^{n \times p}.$$

Theorem XI.2.57. $\vdash (m,n,p){:}m,n,p,n^0,p^0 \in \mathrm{NC}.m \leq n. \supset .m^p \leq n^p.$

Proof. Assume the hypothesis. Then $n = \mathrm{Nc}(\mathrm{USC}(\beta))$, $p = \mathrm{Nc}(\mathrm{USC}(\gamma))$. Also, by Thm.XI.2.22, $q \in \mathrm{NC}.n = m + q$. Then $\mathrm{USC}(\beta) \in m + q$. So $\phi \in m.\theta \in q.\phi \cap \theta = \Lambda.\phi \cup \theta = \mathrm{USC}(\beta)$. By Thm.IX.6.14,

Cor. 2, $\alpha \subseteq \beta.\phi = \text{USC}(\alpha)$. Then $\text{USC}(\alpha) \in m$, so that by Thm.XI.2.2, Part III, $m = \text{Nc}(\text{USC}(\alpha))$. By Thm.XI.2.39,

$$m^p = \text{Nc}(\gamma \wedge \alpha)$$

$$n^p = \text{Nc}(\gamma \wedge \beta).$$

However, by Thm.XI.1.31, $(\gamma \wedge \alpha) \subseteq (\gamma \wedge \beta)$. Then by Thm.XI.2.13, Part I,

$$\text{Nc}(\gamma \wedge \alpha) \leq \text{Nc}(\gamma \wedge \beta).$$

So

$$m^p \leq n^p.$$

Theorem XI.2.58. $\vdash (m,n){:}m \in \text{NC}.m^n = 0. \supset .m = 0.$

Proof. Assume $m \in \text{NC}$ and $m^n = 0$. Then $\Lambda \in m^n$, so that by Thm. XI.2.38, $\text{USC}(\alpha) \in m.\text{USC}(\beta) \in n.\Lambda \text{ sm } (\beta \wedge \alpha)$. Then $(\beta \wedge \alpha) = \Lambda$ by Thm.XI.1.9, and by Thm.XI.1.32, $\alpha = \Lambda$. So $\text{USC}(\alpha) = \Lambda$, and $\Lambda \in m$. Then $m = 0$ by Thm.XI.2.7, Cor. 4.

Theorem XI.2.59. $\vdash (m,n,p){:}m,n,p,m^0,p^0 \in \text{NC}.n \leq p.m \neq 0. \supset . m^n \leq m^p.$

Proof. Assume the hypothesis. Then by Thm.XI.2.22, $q \in \text{NC}.p = n + q$. By Thm.XI.2.48, Cor. 2, and Thm.XI.2.42, corollary, $p^0 \neq \Lambda$. By Thm.XI.2.43, $n^0 \neq \Lambda.q^0 \neq \Lambda$. Also by Thm.XI.2.48, Cor. 1, $m^0 \neq \Lambda$. Then by Thm.XI.2.48, $m^n \in \text{NC}$, $m^q \in \text{NC}$. By Thm.XI.2.54,

(1) $$m^p = m^n \times m^q.$$

By Thm.XI.2.58, $m^q \neq 0$. So by Thm.XI.2.36,

(2) $$m^n \leq m^n \times m^q.$$

By (1) and (2), our theorem follows.

Theorem XI.2.60. $\vdash (m,n){:}m,n \in \text{NC}.m^n = 1. \supset .n = 0 \vee m = 1.$

Proof. Assume $m,n \in \text{NC}$ and $m^n = 1$. Then $m^n \neq \Lambda$, so that by Thm. XI.2.47, $m^0 \neq \Lambda$ and $n^0 \neq \Lambda$. By Thm.XI.2.48, Cor. 1, $m^0, n^0 \in \text{NC}$.

Case 1. $n = 0$. Then $n = 0 \vee m = 1$.

Case 2. $n \neq 0$. Then by Thm.XI.2.24,

(1) $$1 \leq n.$$

By Thm.XI.2.51, $m = 0 \supset m^n = 0$. So by Thm.IX.6.15, Cor. 2, $m \neq 0$. Hence by Thm.XI.2.24,

(2) $$1 \leq m.$$

Also, by (1) and Thm.XI.2.59, $m^1 \leq m^n$. Then by Thm.XI.2.52, $m \leq m^n$, so that

(3) $$m \leq 1.$$

By (2) and (3) and Thm.XI.2.20, $m = 1$, so that $n = 0 \mathbf{v} m = 1$.

Hence, in either case, $n = 0 \mathbf{v} m = 1$.

For most of the familiar classes α of mathematics, Can(α) holds. We now consider some of the special properties of Nc(α) when Can(α).

Theorem XI.2.61. $\vdash (m):.m \in \text{NC}: \supset :(\text{E}\alpha).\alpha \in m.\text{Can}(\alpha). \equiv .(\alpha).\alpha \in m \supset \text{Can}(\alpha)$.

Proof. Assume $m \in \text{NC}, (\text{E}\alpha).\alpha \in m.\text{Can}(\alpha)$, and $\beta \in m$. Then by rule C, $\alpha \in m.\text{Can}(\alpha)$. Then α sm β by Thm.XI.2.3, Part I. So Can(β) by Thm. XI.1.34. Thus

$$m \in \text{NC}, (\text{E}\alpha).\alpha \in m.\text{Can}(\alpha), \beta \in m \vdash \text{Can}(\beta).$$

So

$$m \in \text{NC}, (\text{E}\alpha).\alpha \in m.\text{Can}(\alpha) \vdash (\beta).\beta \in m \supset \text{Can}(\beta).$$

So

(1) $$m \in \text{NC} \vdash (\text{E}\alpha).\alpha \in m.\text{Can}(\alpha). \supset .(\alpha).\alpha \in m \supset \text{Can}(\alpha).$$

Conversely, assume $m \in \text{NC}$ and $(\alpha).\alpha \in m \supset \text{Can}(\alpha)$. By Thm.XI.2.2, Part VI, and rule C, $\alpha \in m$. So Can(α). So $(\text{E}\alpha).\alpha \in m.\text{Can}(\alpha)$.

Theorem XI.2.62. $\vdash (\alpha,m):m \in \text{NC}.\alpha \in m.\text{Can}(\alpha). \supset .\text{USC}(\alpha) \in m$.

Proof. Use Thm.XI.2.3, Part II, with the definition of Can(α).

Corollary. $\vdash (m):.m \in \text{NC}:(\text{E}\alpha).\alpha \in m.\text{Can}(\alpha): \supset :m^0 \neq \Lambda$.

Proof. Use Thm.XI.2.42.

Theorem XI.2.63. $\vdash (m,n):.m,n \in \text{NC}:(\text{E}\alpha).\alpha \in m.\text{Can}(\alpha):(\text{E}\alpha).\alpha \in n.\text{Can}(\alpha): \supset :n^m \in \text{NC}$.

Proof. Use Thm.XI.2.62, corollary, with Thm.XI.2.48.

Corollary. $\vdash (m):.m \in \text{NC}:(\text{E}\alpha).\alpha \in m.\text{Can}(\alpha): \supset :m^0 \in \text{NC}$.

Theorem XI.2.64. $\vdash (m,n):.m,n \in \text{NC}:(\text{E}\alpha).\alpha \in m.\text{Can}(\alpha):(\text{E}\alpha).\alpha \in n.\text{Can}(\alpha): \supset :(\text{E}\alpha).\alpha \in m + n.\text{Can}(\alpha)$.

Proof. Assume the hypothesis. Then $m + n \in \text{NC}$ by Thm.XI.2.10. Hence $\alpha \in m + n$ by Thm.XI.2.2, Part VI, and rule C. Then $\beta \in m.\gamma \in n.\beta \cap \gamma = \Lambda.\beta \cup \gamma = \alpha$. By Thm.XI.2.61, Can($\beta$) and Can($\gamma$). Then Can($\beta \cup \gamma$) by Thm.XI.1.39. Thus Can(α), so that $(\text{E}\alpha).\alpha \in m + n.\text{Can}(\alpha)$.

Theorem XI.2.65. $\vdash \text{Can}(\Lambda)$.

Proof. By Thm.IX.6.12, Part IV, $\vdash \Lambda$ sm USC(Λ).

Corollary. $\vdash (\text{E}\alpha).\alpha \in 0.\text{Can}(\alpha)$.

Theorem XI.2.66. $\vdash (x).\text{Can}(\{x\})$.

Proof. By Thm.XI.1.10, $\vdash \{x\}$ sm $\{\{x\}\}$. So by Thm.IX.6.16, $\vdash \{x\}$ sm USC($\{x\}$).

Corollary. $\vdash (\text{E}\alpha).\alpha \in 1.\text{Can}\ (\alpha)$.

Theorem XI.2.67. $\vdash (m):.m \in \text{NC}.(\text{E}\alpha).\alpha \in m.\text{Can}(\alpha): \supset :(\text{E}\alpha).\alpha \in m + 1.\text{Can}(\alpha)$.

Proof. Use Thm.XI.2.64 and Thm.XI.2.66, corollary.

Corollary 1. $\vdash (\mathrm{E}\alpha).\alpha \epsilon 2.\mathrm{Can}(\alpha)$.

Corollary 2. $\vdash (\mathrm{E}\alpha).\alpha \epsilon 3.\mathrm{Can}(\alpha)$.

etc.

One might think that by combining Thm.XI.2.65, corollary, and Thm.XI.2.67, one could prove

$$(n):n \epsilon \mathrm{Nn}. \supset .(\mathrm{E}\alpha).\alpha \epsilon n.\mathrm{Can}(\alpha)$$

by induction (Thm.X.1.13) on n. However, $(\mathrm{E}\alpha).\alpha \epsilon n.\mathrm{Can}(\alpha)$ is not stratified, and so one is not entitled to use Thm.X.1.13. As far as we know, the result in question cannot be proved. This seems a bit surprising, since we can prove each of

$$\vdash (\mathrm{E}\alpha).\alpha \epsilon 0.\mathrm{Can}(\alpha),$$
$$\vdash (\mathrm{E}\alpha).\alpha \epsilon 1.\mathrm{Can}(\alpha),$$
$$\vdash (\mathrm{E}\alpha).\alpha \epsilon 2.\mathrm{Can}(\alpha),$$

etc.

However, the distinction between proving each of the results just listed and proving

$$\vdash (n):n \epsilon \mathrm{Nn}. \supset .(\mathrm{E}\alpha).\alpha \epsilon n.\mathrm{Can}(\alpha)$$

is just the distinction between the use of induction to prove results about the symbolic logic and the use of induction within the symbolic logic.

Theorem XI.2.68. $\vdash (m,n)\text{:.}(\mathrm{E}\alpha).\alpha \epsilon m.\mathrm{Can}(\alpha):(\mathrm{E}\alpha).\alpha \epsilon n.\mathrm{Can}(\alpha): \supset : (\mathrm{E}\alpha).\alpha \epsilon m \times n.\mathrm{Can}(\alpha)$.

Proof. Assume the hypothesis. By rule C, $\alpha \epsilon m.\mathrm{Can}(\alpha)$ and $\beta \epsilon n.\mathrm{Can}(\beta)$. So by Thm.XI.2.26, $(\alpha \times \beta) \epsilon m \times n$, and by Thm.XI.1.42, $\mathrm{Can}(\alpha \times \beta)$.

Theorem XI.2.69. $\vdash (m,n)\text{:.}m,n \epsilon \mathrm{NC}:(\mathrm{E}\alpha).\alpha \epsilon m.\mathrm{Can}(\alpha):(\mathrm{E}\alpha).\alpha \epsilon n.\mathrm{Can}(\alpha): \supset :(\mathrm{E}\alpha).\alpha \epsilon n^m.\mathrm{Can}(\alpha)$.

Proof. Assume the hypothesis. By rule C, $\alpha \epsilon m.\mathrm{Can}(\alpha)$ and $\beta \epsilon n.\mathrm{Can}(\beta)$. By Thm.XI.2.62, $\mathrm{USC}(\alpha) \epsilon m$ and $\mathrm{USC}(\beta) \epsilon n$. So by Thm.XI.2.38, $(\alpha \wedge \beta) \epsilon n^m$, and by Thm.XI.1.45, $\mathrm{Can}(\alpha \wedge \beta)$.

Theorem XI.2.70. $\vdash (\alpha,m):m = \mathrm{Nc}(\mathrm{USC}(\alpha)). \supset .2^m = \mathrm{Nc}(\mathrm{SC}(\alpha))$.

Proof. Temporarily let A denote $\{\Lambda,\mathrm{V}\}$. By Thm.IX.4.6, corollary, and Thm.XI.1.16, Cor. 1, $\vdash A \epsilon 2$. So by Thm.XI.2.67, Cor. 1, and Thm.XI.2.61, $\vdash \mathrm{Can}(A)$. Then by Thm.XI.2.62, $\vdash \mathrm{USC}(A) \epsilon 2$. Hence, $\vdash 2 = \mathrm{Nc}(\mathrm{USC}(A))$. If now, $m = \mathrm{Nc}(\mathrm{USC}(\alpha))$, then by Thm.XI.2.39, $2^m = \mathrm{Nc}(\alpha \wedge A)$. However, by Thm.XI.1.28, $\mathrm{Nc}(\alpha \wedge A) = \mathrm{Nc}(\mathrm{SC}(\alpha))$. So $2^m = \mathrm{Nc}(\mathrm{SC}(\alpha))$.

We can now show the falsity of

$$(m,n):m,n \epsilon \mathrm{NC}.m^0 \neq \Lambda.n^0 \neq \Lambda. \supset .(n^m)^0 \neq \Lambda.$$

We merely take m to be Nc(USC(V)) and n to be 2. Then $\vdash m,n \epsilon$ NC. Also $\vdash m^0 \neq \Lambda$ by Thm.XI.2.42. Also $\vdash n^0 \neq \Lambda$ by Thm.XI.2.44, Cor. 3. However, $\vdash n^m =$ Nc(SC(V)) by Thm.XI.2.70, and so $\vdash n^m =$ Nc(V) by Thm.IX.6.19, Part II. So by Thm.XI.2.46, $\vdash (n^m)^0 = \Lambda$.

Theorem XI.2.71. $\vdash (m){:}m,m^0 \epsilon \text{NC}. \supset .m < 2^m$.

Proof. Assume $m,m^0 \epsilon$ NC. By Thm.XI.2.48, Cor. 2, $m = \text{Nc}(\text{USC}(\alpha))$. So by Thm.XI.2.70, $\text{Nc}(\text{SC}(\alpha)) = 2^m$. However, by Thm.XI.2.17, $m < \text{Nc}(\text{SC}(\alpha))$.

EXERCISES

XI.2.1. Prove:

(a) $\vdash \text{AV}(\leq_c) = \text{V} - 0$.
(b) $\vdash (\text{NC}\upharpoonleft\leq_c\upharpoonright\text{NC}) \epsilon$ Pord.

XI.2.2. Prove $\vdash \text{Nc}(1) < \text{Nc}(\text{V})$.

XI.2.3. Prove $\vdash (\alpha,\beta,\gamma){:.}\alpha \subseteq \beta.\gamma \neq \Lambda{:} \supset {:}(\text{E}\delta).(\alpha \wedge \gamma) \text{ sm } \delta.\delta \subseteq (\beta \wedge \gamma)$.

XI.2.4. Prove $\vdash (\alpha,\beta){:}\alpha \cap \beta = \Lambda. \supset .\text{Nc}(\text{USC}(\alpha)) + \text{Nc}(\text{USC}(\beta)) = \text{Nc}(\text{USC}(\alpha \cup \beta))$.

XI.2.5. Prove:

(a) $\vdash 2 \times 2 = 4$.
(b) $\vdash 2^2 = 4$.
(c) $\vdash 2^4 = 4^2$.

XI.2.6. Prove:

(a) $\vdash \text{Nc}(\text{V}) + \text{Nc}(\text{V}) = \text{Nc}(\text{V})$.
(b) $\vdash 2 \times \text{Nc}(\text{V}) = \text{Nc}(\text{V})$.

XI.2.7. Prove:

(a) $\vdash (m){:}m = \text{Nc}(\text{V}). \supset .m^2 = \Lambda$.
(b) $\vdash (m){:}m = \text{Nc}(\text{V}). \supset .m^2 \neq m \times m$.

XI.2.8. Prove $\vdash (\alpha,\beta){:}\text{Nc}(\alpha \cup \beta) = \text{Nc}(\alpha) + \text{Nc}(\beta - \alpha)$.

XI.2.9. Prove $\vdash (m){:}m \neq 0.m \epsilon \text{NC}. \supset .m \times \text{Nc}(\text{V}) = \text{Nc}(\text{V})$.

XI.2.10. Prove $\vdash (m,\alpha,x){:}m \epsilon \text{NC}.\alpha \cup \{x\} \epsilon m + 1.{\sim}x \epsilon \alpha. \supset .\alpha \epsilon m$.

XI.2.11. Prove $\vdash (\alpha,\beta).\text{Nc}(\alpha \cup \beta) + \text{Nc}(\alpha \cap \beta) = \text{Nc}(\alpha) + \text{Nc}(\beta)$.

XI.2.12. Prove $\vdash (R){:}R \epsilon \text{Funct}.\text{Nc}(\text{Val}(R)) < \text{Nc}(\text{Arg}(R)). \supset . (\text{E}x,y).x,y \epsilon \text{Arg}(R).x \neq y.R(x) = R(y)$. (*Hint.* If the conclusion is false, then $R \epsilon$ 1–1 and Arg(R) sm Val(R).) This is the basis of the pigeonhole principle.

3. Finite Classes and Mathematical Induction. We take the finite cardinals to be just the members of Nn. Then the infinite cardinals are just the members of NC − Nn. In Sec. 1 of Chapter X, we have given a number of properties of finite cardinals. Many more properties follow from the theorems of Sec. 2 of the present chapter because of Thm.XI.2.11, which says

$$\vdash \mathrm{Nn} \subseteq \mathrm{NC}.$$

Theorem XI.3.1. $\vdash \sim \mathrm{Nc}(\mathrm{V}) \in \mathrm{Nn}$.

Proof. Use Thms.XI.2.44 and XI.2.46.

Corollary. $\vdash \mathrm{NC} - \mathrm{Nn} \neq \Lambda$.

This theorem states that the universe is infinite. It would be the obvious form to take for an "axiom of infinity." It is equivalent to Axiom scheme 13, so that in effect we were assuming the axiom of infinity when we assumed Axiom scheme 13. In deducing the above theorem from Axiom scheme 13, we have proved half of the equivalence between Axiom scheme 13 and the axiom of infinity. For hints as to how to prove the other half of the equivalence, see Rosser, 1939.

Theorem XI.3.2. $\vdash (m,n,p){:}m \in \mathrm{Nn}.n,p \in \mathrm{NC}.m + n = m + p. \supset .n = p.$

Proof. Proof by induction on m (Thm.X.1.13). Let $F(x)$ be

$$(n,p){:}n,p \in \mathrm{NC}.x + n = x + p. \supset .n = p.$$

Then $\vdash F(0)$ by Thm.X.1.8. Assume $m \in \mathrm{Nn}$, $F(m)$, and $n,p \in \mathrm{NC}.(m + 1) + n = (m + 1) + p$. Then $(m + n) + 1 = (m + p) + 1$ by Thms. X.1.9 and X.1.11, corollary. By Thm.XI.2.12, $m + n = m + p$. So $n = p$ by $F(m)$. So we have proved $\vdash m \in \mathrm{Nn}.F(m). \supset .F(m + 1)$.

Corollary 1. $\vdash (m,n){:}m \in \mathrm{Nn}.n \in \mathrm{NC}.m + n = m. \supset .n = 0.$

Corollary 2. $\vdash (m,n){:}m \in \mathrm{Nn}.n \in \mathrm{NC}.n \neq 0. \supset .m + n \neq m.$

Corollary 3. $\vdash (m){:}m \in \mathrm{Nn}. \supset .m \neq m + 1.$

Corollary 4. $\vdash (m,n,p){:}m \in \mathrm{Nn}.n,p \in \mathrm{NC}.m + n \leq m + p. \supset .n \leq p.$

Proof. Use Thm.XI.2.22.

Corollary 5. $\vdash (m,n,p){:}m \in \mathrm{Nn}.n,p \in \mathrm{NC}.m + n < m + p. \supset .n < p.$

Corollary 6. $\vdash (m,n,p){:}m \in \mathrm{Nn}.n,p \in \mathrm{NC}.n < p. \supset .m + n < m + p.$

Proof. Use Thm.XI.2.23.

This theorem and its corollaries say in effect that, if one adds or subtracts the same finite cardinal to or from both sides of an equation or an inequality, the result is again an equation or an inequality with the same sense. This is not necessarily true for infinite cardinals. For instance, let $m = \mathrm{Nc}(\mathrm{V})$, $n = \mathrm{Nc}(\mathrm{V})$, and $p = 0$. Then $m + p = m$. Also, by Ex.XI.2.6, Part (a), $m + n = m$. So $m + n = m + p$, but $n \neq p$.

Theorem XI.3.3. $\vdash (m,n){:}m \in \mathrm{Nn}.n \in \mathrm{NC}.n \leq m. \supset .n \in \mathrm{Nn}.$

Proof. Proof by induction on m. Let $F(x)$ be

$$(n){:}n \in \mathrm{NC}.n \leq x. \supset .n \in \mathrm{Nn},$$

First assume $n \in \text{NC}.n \leq 0$. Then by Thm.XI.2.15, Cor. 2, and Thm. XI.2.20, $n = 0$. So $n \in \text{Nn}$. Hence

(1) $$\vdash F(0).$$

Now assume $m \in \text{Nn}$, $F(m)$, and $n \in \text{NC}.n \leq m + 1$. By Thm.XI.2.22,

$$p \in \text{NC}.m + 1 = n + p.$$

Also by Thm.XI.2.24, corollary,

$$p = 0.\mathbf{v}.(\text{E}q).q \in \text{NC}.p = q + 1.$$

Case 1. $p = 0$. Then $n = m + 1$, and so $n \in \text{Nn}$.

Case 2. $(\text{E}q).q \in \text{NC}.p = q + 1$. Then by rule C, $p = q + 1, m + 1 = n + q + 1$. By Thm.XI.2.12, $m = n + q$. Hence $n \leq m$, and by the hypothesis $F(m)$, we conclude $n \in \text{Nn}$.

In words, this theorem says that, if m is a finite cardinal, then any smaller cardinal is also finite. This is one of the important properties of finite cardinals in intuitive mathematics and so is one of the results which must be proved in the symbolic logic if we wish to justify our decision that Nn should be taken as the class of finite cardinals.

Theorem XI.3.4. $\vdash (m,n):.m,n \in \text{Nn}: \supset :n \leq m. \equiv .(\text{E}p).p \in \text{Nn}. m = n + p.$

Proof. Assume $m,n \in \text{Nn}$. Then by Thm.XI.2.22, we go from right to left easily. Conversely, assume $n \leq m$. Then by Thm.XI.2.22 and rule C, $p \in \text{NC}.m = n + p$. By Thm.XI.2.22, $p \leq m$. By Thm.XI.3.3, $p \in \text{Nn}$.

Theorem XI.3.5. $\vdash (m,n):.m,n \in \text{Nn}: \supset :n < m. \equiv .(\text{E}p).p \in \text{Nn}. m = n + p + 1.$

Proof. Assume $m,n \in \text{Nn}$ and $n < m$. Then

(1) $$m \neq n,$$

and by Thm.XI.3.4 and rule C,

(2) $$p \in \text{Nn}.m = n + p.$$

Then by (1), $p \neq 0$. So by Thm.X.1.7, $q \in \text{Nn}.p = q + 1$. So $q \in \text{Nn}. m = n + q + 1$.

Conversely, assume $m,n \in \text{Nn}$ and $(\text{E}p).p \in \text{Nn}.m = n + p + 1$. Then by rule C,

(3) $$p \in \text{Nn}.m = n + p + 1,$$

and by Thm.XI.3.4,

(4) $$n \leq m.$$

By Thm.XI.3.2, Cor. 2, and Thm.X.1.2, $n \neq n + p + 1$, and so by (3), $m \neq n$.

Corollary 1. $\vdash (m,n):.m,n \epsilon \text{Nn}: \supset :n < m. \equiv .n + 1 \leq m.$
Corollary 2. $\vdash (m):m \epsilon \text{Nn}. \supset .m < m + 1.$
Corollary 3. $\vdash (m,n):.m,n \epsilon \text{Nn}: \supset :n < m + 1. \equiv .n \leq m.$
Proof. By Cor. 1,

$$n < m + 1. \equiv .n + 1 \leq m + 1,$$

by Thm.XI.3.2, Cor. 4,

$$n + 1 \leq m + 1. \supset .n \leq m,$$

and by Thm.XI.2.23,

$$n \leq m. \supset .n + 1 \leq m + 1.$$

Theorem XI.3.6. $\vdash (m,n):.m \epsilon \text{Nn}.n \epsilon \text{NC}: \supset :m < n.\mathbf{v}.m = n.\mathbf{v}.m > n.$
Proof. Proof by induction on m. Let $F(x)$ be

$$(n):.n \epsilon \text{NC}: \supset :x < n.\mathbf{v}.x = n.\mathbf{v}.x > n.$$

By Thm.XI.2.15, Cor. 2, and Thm.XI.2.14, Cor. 2,

(1) $$\vdash F(0).$$

Assume $F(m)$, $m \epsilon \text{Nn}$, and $n \epsilon \text{NC}$. Then by $F(m)$,

(2) $$m < n.\mathbf{v}.m = n.\mathbf{v}.m > n.$$

Case 1. Assume $m < n$. Then

(3) $$m \neq n$$

and by Thm.XI.2.22,

(4) $$p \epsilon \text{NC}.n = m + p.$$

By (3) and (4), $p \neq 0$. By Thm.XI.2.24, corollary, $q \epsilon \text{NC}.p = q + 1$. By (4), $n = m + q + 1 = (m + 1) + q$. So $m + 1 \leq n$, and by Thm. XI.2.14, Cor. 2,

$$m + 1 < n.\mathbf{v}.m + 1 = n.$$

Case 2. Assume $m = n.\mathbf{v}.m > n$. By Thm.XI.2.14, Cor. 2, $n \leq m$. Also by Thm.XI.3.5, Cor. 2, $m < m + 1$. So by Thm.XI.2.25, Cor. 3, $n < m + 1$. That is, $m + 1 > n$.

By truth values,

$$\vdash P \supset R.Q \supset S. \supset .P\mathbf{v}Q \supset R\mathbf{v}S.$$

So, from (2) we get

$$m + 1 < n.\mathbf{v}.m + 1 = n.\mathbf{v}.m + 1 > n.$$

Corollary 1. $\vdash (m,n):m \epsilon \text{Nn}.n \epsilon \text{NC}.\sim(m < n). \supset .n \leq m.$
Corollary 2. $\vdash (m,n):m \epsilon \text{Nn}.n \epsilon \text{NC}.\sim(m < n). \supset .n \epsilon \text{Nn}.$

Proof. Use Thm.XI.3.3.

Corollary 3. $\vdash (m,n){:}m \in \text{Nn}.n \in \text{NC} - \text{Nn}. \supset .m < n.$

Proof. $\vdash n \in \text{NC} - \text{Nn}. \equiv .n \in \text{NC}.{\sim} n \in \text{Nn}.$

This last corollary tells us that each finite cardinal is less than each infinite cardinal, which is a familiar intuitive property.

****Theorem XI.3.7.** $\vdash (m,n){:.}m,n \in \text{Nn}{:} \supset {:}m < n.\text{v}.m = n.\text{v}.m > n.$

Proof. Use Thm.XI.3.6.

Corollary 1. $\vdash (m,n){:.}m,n \in \text{Nn}{:} \supset {:}{\sim}(m < n). \equiv .n \leq m.$

Proof. Combine the theorem with Thm.XI.2.20, Cor. 2.

Corollary 2. $\vdash (m,n){:.}m,n \in \text{Nn}{:} \supset {:}{\sim}(m \leq n). \equiv .n < m.$

This theorem tells us that any two finite cardinals are comparable. Also, the two corollaries are familiar and widely used properties of finite cardinals.

Theorem XI.3.8. $\vdash (m,n){:}m,n \in \text{Nn}. \supset .m \times n \in \text{Nn}.$

Proof. Proof by induction on n. Let $F(n)$ be

$$(m){:}m \in \text{Nn}. \supset .m \times n \in \text{Nn}.$$

By Thm.XI.2.32, Cor. 1,

$$\vdash F(0).$$

Assume $n \in \text{Nn}$, $F(n)$, and $m \in \text{Nn}$. Then $m \times n \in \text{Nn}$, and so by Thm. X.1.14, $(m \times n) + m \in \text{Nn}$. However, $(m \times n) + m = (m \times n) + (m \times 1) = m \times (n + 1)$. So $m \times (n + 1) \in \text{Nn}$. Thus

$$\vdash n \in \text{Nn}.F(n). \supset .F(n + 1).$$

This theorem tells us that the product of any two finite cardinals is a finite cardinal. This theorem has a partial converse, which we now state.

Theorem XI.3.9. $\vdash (m,n){:}m,n \in \text{NC}.n \neq 0.m \times n \in \text{Nn}. \supset .m \in \text{Nn}.$

Proof. Assume the hypothesis. Then by Thm.XI.2.36, $m \leq m \times n$. So by Thm.XI.3.3, $m \in \text{Nn}$.

Theorem XI.3.10. $\vdash (m,n,p){:}m,n,p \in \text{Nn}.m \neq 0.n < p. \supset .m \times n < m \times p.$

Proof. Assume the hypothesis. Then by Thm.X.1.7,

$$q \in \text{Nn}.m = q + 1.$$

Also by Thm.XI.3.5,

$$r \in \text{Nn}.p = n + r + 1.$$

So

$$\begin{aligned} m \times p &= m \times (n + r + 1) \\ &= (m \times n) + (m \times r) + m \\ &= (m \times n) + (m \times r) + (q + 1) \\ &= (m \times n) + ((m \times r) + q) + 1. \end{aligned}$$

So, by Thm.XI.3.5, $m \times n < m \times p$.

Theorem XI.3.11.

I. $\vdash (m,n,p)\colon.m,n,p \in \mathrm{Nn}.m \neq 0\colon \supset \colon n = p. \equiv .m \times n = m \times p.$

II. $\vdash (m,n,p)\colon.m,n,p \in \mathrm{Nn}.m \neq 0\colon \supset \colon n < p. \equiv .m \times n < m \times p.$

III. $\vdash (m,n,p)\colon.m,n,p \in \mathrm{Nn}.m \neq 0\colon \supset \colon n \leq p. \equiv .m \times n \leq m \times p.$

Proof of Part I. Assume $m,n,p \in \mathrm{Nn}.m \neq 0$ and $m \times n = m \times p$. By Thm.XI.3.7, $n < p.\mathbf{v}.n = p.\mathbf{v}.n > p$. If $n < p$, then $m \times n < m \times p$ by Thm.XI.3.10. Also, if $n > p$, then $m \times n > m \times p$ by Thm.XI.3.10. So $n = p$.

Proof of Part II. Similar.

Proof of Part III. Combine Parts I and II by Thm.XI.2.14, Cor. 2.

This theorem tells us that division is possible if the divisor is not zero, and that division of both sides of an equality or an inequality yields an equality or an inequality with the same sense.

We now prove that all the usual laws of exponents hold for finite cardinals without exception, and also that, if m and n are finite cardinals, then so is n^m.

Theorem XI.3.12. $\vdash (m)\colon m \in \mathrm{Nn}. \supset .m,m^0 \in \mathrm{NC}.$

Proof. Assume $m \in \mathrm{Nn}$. Then $m \in \mathrm{NC}$. Also, by Thm.XI.2.44, $m^0 \neq \Lambda$. Then by Thm.XI.2.48, Cor. 1, $m^0 \in \mathrm{NC}$.

Corollary 1. $\vdash (m)\colon m \in \mathrm{Nn}. \supset .m^0 = 1.$

Corollary 2. $\vdash (m)\colon m \in \mathrm{Nn}.m \neq 0. \supset .0^m = 0.$

Corollary 3. $\vdash (m)\colon m \in \mathrm{Nn}. \supset .m^1 = m.$

Corollary 4. $\vdash (m)\colon m \in \mathrm{Nn}. \supset .1^m = 1.$

Corollary 5. $\vdash (m,n,p)\colon m,n,p \in \mathrm{Nn}. \supset .m^{n+p} = m^n \times m^p.$

Corollary 6. $\vdash (m)\colon m \in \mathrm{Nn}. \supset .m^2 = m \times m.$

Corollary 7. $\vdash (m,n,p)\colon m,n,p \in \mathrm{Nn}.m \leq n. \supset .m^p \leq n^p.$

Corollary 8. $\vdash (m,n,p)\colon m,n,p \in \mathrm{Nn}.n \leq p.m \neq 0. \supset .m^n \leq m^p.$

Corollary 9. $\vdash (m)\colon m \in \mathrm{Nn}. \supset .m < 2^m.$

Theorem XI.3.13. $\vdash (m,n)\colon m,n \in \mathrm{Nn}. \supset .n^m \in \mathrm{Nn}.$

Proof. Proof by induction on m. Let $F(x)$ be

$$(n)\colon n \in \mathrm{Nn}. \supset .n^x \in \mathrm{Nn}.$$

By Thm.XI.3.12, Cor. 1,

$$\vdash F(0).$$

Assume $m \in \mathrm{Nn}$, $F(m)$, and $n \in \mathrm{Nn}$. Then $n^m \in \mathrm{Nn}$. So by Thm.XI.3.8, $n^m \times n \in \mathrm{Nn}$. However $n = n^1$ by Thm.XI.3.12, Cor. 3. So by Thm. XI.3.12, Cor. 5,

$$\begin{aligned} n^m \times n &= n^m \times n^1 \\ &= n^{m+1}. \end{aligned}$$

So $n^{m+1} \in \mathrm{Nn}$. Thus

$$\vdash m \in \mathrm{Nn}.F(m). \supset .F(m+1).$$

Corollary. $\vdash (m,n,p){:}m,n,p \in \text{Nn}. \supset .(m^n)^p = m^{n \times p}$.

Theorem XI.3.14. $\vdash (m,n,p){:}m,n,p \in \text{Nn}.m < n.p \neq 0. \supset .m^p < n^p$.

Proof. Assume $m,n,p \in \text{Nn}.m < n.p \neq 0$. We prove by induction on q the statement

$$(1) \qquad (q){:}q \in \text{Nn}. \supset .m^{q+1} < n^{q+1}.$$

Let $F(x)$ be

$$m^{x+1} < n^{x+1}.$$

Now $0 + 1 = 1$, so that $m^{0+1} = m^1 = m$ and $n^{0+1} = n^1 = n$. So $m^{0+1} < n^{0+1}$. That is,

$$F(0).$$

Now assume $q \in \text{Nn}$ and $F(q)$. Then $m^{q+1} < n^{q+1}$. However, $m^{(q+1)+1} = m^{q+1} \times m$ and $n^{(q+1)+1} = n^{q+1} \times n$. By Thm.XI.3.5,

$$r \in \text{Nn}.n^{q+1} = m^{q+1} + r + 1,$$

$$s \in \text{Nn}.n = m + s + 1.$$

So

$$\begin{aligned} n^{(q+1)+1} &= (m^{q+1} + r + 1) \times n \\ &= (m^{q+1} \times n) + (r \times n) + n \\ &= (m^{q+1} \times (m + s + 1)) + (r \times n) + m + s + 1 \\ &= (m^{q+1} \times m) + (m^{q+1} \times (s + 1)) + (r \times n) + m + s + 1 \\ &= m^{(q+1)+1} + ((m^{q+1} \times (s + 1)) + (r \times n) + m + s) + 1. \end{aligned}$$

So by Thm.XI.3.5,

$$m^{(q+1)+1} < n^{(q+1)+1}.$$

Thus

$$q \in \text{Nn}.F(q). \supset .F(q + 1).$$

So (1) is established. Now by $p \neq 0$ and Thm.X.1.7, $q \in \text{Nn}.p = q + 1$. So by (1), $m^p < n^p$.

Theorem XI.3.15.

I. $\vdash (m,n,p){:.}m,n,p \in \text{Nn}.p \neq 0{:} \supset {:}m = n. \equiv .m^p = n^p$.

II. $\vdash (m,n,p){:.}m,n,p \in \text{Nn}.p \neq 0{:} \supset {:}m < n. \equiv .m^p < n^p$.

III. $\vdash (m,n,p){:.}m,n,p \in \text{Nn}.p \neq 0{:} \supset {:}m \leq n. \equiv .m^p \leq n^p$.

Proof. Proof similar to that of Thm.XI.3.11.

Theorem XI.3.16. $\vdash (m,n,p){:}m,n,p \in \text{Nn}.2 \leq m.n < p. \supset .m^n < m^p$.

Proof. Assume the hypothesis. By Thm.XI.3.5, $q \in \text{Nn}.p = n + q + 1$. Then $m^p = m^n \times m^{q+1}$. Now $\vdash 1 < 2$, so that $1 < m$. Hence, by Thm. XI.3.14, $1^{q+1} < m^{q+1}$. So $1 < m^{q+1}$. Also, by Thm.XI.2.58, $m^n \neq 0$. Then, by Thm.XI.3.10, $m^n \times 1 < m^n \times m^{q+1}$. So $m^n < m^p$.

Theorem XI.3.17.
I. $\vdash (m,n,p):.m,n,p \in \text{Nn}.2 \leq m: \supset :n = p. \equiv .m^n = m^p.$
II. $\vdash (m,n,p):.m,n,p \in \text{Nn}.2 \leq m: \supset :n < p. \equiv .m^n < m^p.$
III. $\vdash (m,n,p):.m,n,p \in \text{Nn}.2 \leq m: \supset :n \leq p. \equiv .m^n \leq m^p.$
Proof. Similar to that of Thm.XI.3.11.

We have so far used induction only in the form

$$F(0),\ (n):n \in \text{Nn}.F(n). \supset .F(n+1) \vdash (n):n \in \text{Nn}. \supset .F(n).$$

We shall call this the principle of weak induction to distinguish it from a stronger form which we shall soon derive. We also say that it starts at zero. A form which starts at unity is in common use. Let temporarily

$$\text{PI} = \text{Nn} - \{0\},$$

so that PI is the class of all positive integers. Then the principle of weak induction starting at unity can be expressed as

$$F(1),\ (n):n \in \text{PI}.F(n). \supset .F(n+1) \vdash (n):n \in \text{PI}. \supset .F(n).$$

This is the form which is used to prove by induction such results as:

If n is a positive integer, then

$$1^2 + 2^2 + \cdots + n^2 = \frac{n(n+1)}{2}.$$

Actually, one can start a proof by induction at any integer. This is expressed in the following theorem, which is the general form of the principle of weak induction.

Theorem XI.3.18. Let m be a variable distinct from n, and let $F(x)$ be a stratified statement. Then $m \in \text{Nn},\ F(m),\ (n):n \in \text{Nn}.m \leq n.F(n). \supset . F(n+1) \vdash (n):n \in \text{Nn}.m \leq n. \supset .F(n).$

Proof. Define $G(x)$ to be $F(m+x)$. Then

$$\vdash F(m) \equiv G(0),$$

$$m \in \text{Nn} \vdash (n):n \in \text{Nn}.m \leq n.F(n). \supset .F(n+1).: \equiv :.(x):x \in \text{Nn}.G(x). \supset . G(x+1),$$

$$m \in \text{Nn} \vdash (n):n \in \text{Nn}.m \leq n. \supset .F(n).: \equiv :.(x):x \in \text{Nn}. \supset .G(x).$$

From these, our theorem follows readily by Thm.X.1.13.

As an illustration of the use of this for $m > 1$, we will prove:

If n is an integer ≥ 5, then

$$\frac{(2n)!}{(n!)^2} < 4^{n-1}.$$

Proof by induction on n. First, let $n = 5$. Then

$$\begin{aligned}\frac{(2n)!}{(n!)^2} &= \frac{6\cdot 7\cdot 8\cdot 9\cdot 10}{1\cdot 2\cdot 3\cdot 4\cdot 5}\\ &= 7\cdot 2\cdot 9\cdot 2\\ &= 4\cdot 63\\ &< 4\cdot 64 = 4^4 = 4^{n-1}.\end{aligned}$$

Now assume $n \geq 5$ and

$$\frac{(2n)!}{(n!)^2} < 4^{n-1}.$$

Then

$$\begin{aligned}\frac{(2(n+1))!}{((n+1)!)^2} &= \frac{(2n)!(2n+1)(2n+2)}{(n!)^2(n+1)^2}\\ &< \frac{(2n)!}{(n!)^2}\,\frac{(2n+2)(2n+2)}{(n+1)^2}\\ &< 4^{n-1}\cdot 4 = 4^{(n+1)-1}.\end{aligned}$$

In some of the theorems which will follow, we shall have rather complicated hypotheses and shall wish to write the theorems in a form which displays the hypotheses so that they are easily grasped by the eye. To do this, we shall often write the various statements of the hypothesis and conclusion on separate lines, separating them by the word "yield" to indicate $\vdash$. Often we may number some of the statements. Thus we might write Thm.XI.3.18 above in the alternative form

Theorem XI.3.18. Let m be a variable distinct from n, and let $F(x)$ be a stratified statement. Then

(1) $$m \in \mathrm{Nn},$$

(2) $$F(m),$$

(3) $$(n){:}n \in \mathrm{Nn}.m \leq n.F(n). \supset .F(n+1)$$

yield

$$(n){:}n \in \mathrm{Nn}.m \leq n. \supset .F(n).$$

In order to avoid having to insert trivial hypotheses such as the hypothesis that m and n are distinct, we shall agree that henceforth any variables appearing in theorems as distinct letters will be understood to be distinct.

We now consider strong induction. For simplicity, we first consider only the case in which the induction starts from zero. In weak induction, one assumes only $n \in \mathrm{Nn}$ and $F(n)$ and uses them to derive $F(n+1)$. In strong induction, one assumes each of $n \epsilon \mathrm{Nn}$, $F(0)$, $F(1)$, . . . , $F(n)$, and uses them to derive $F(n+1)$. With more assumptions, it is clearly easier to derive $F(n+1)$. Hence one can carry out proofs by strong induction in cases where weak induction would be inadequate.

We often hear the principle of strong induction (starting with zero) expressed in words as follows.

If $F(0)$, and if $F(n+1)$ follows whenever we have $F(x)$ for all $x \leq n$, then $F(n)$ for all n.

In symbols, the principle appears as follows.

(1) $$F(0)$$

(2) $$(n)::n \epsilon \mathrm{Nn}:.(x):x \epsilon \mathrm{Nn}.x \leq n. \supset .F(x).: \supset :.F(n+1)$$

yield

$$(n):n \epsilon \mathrm{Nn}. \supset .F(n).$$

We can generalize strong induction to start at any integer, and we prove the principle in this form.

Theorem XI.3.19. Let $F(x)$ be a stratified statement. Then

(1) $$m \epsilon \mathrm{Nn},$$

(2) $$F(m),$$

(3) $$(n)::n \epsilon \mathrm{Nn}.m \leq n:.(x):x \epsilon \mathrm{Nn}.m \leq x.x \leq n. \supset .F(x).: \supset :.F(n+1),$$

yield

$$(n):n \epsilon \mathrm{Nn}.m \leq n. \supset .F(n).$$

Proof. Assume the hypotheses, and in addition

(4) $$n \epsilon \mathrm{Nn}.m \leq n.$$

Define $G(n)$ to be

$$(x):x \epsilon \mathrm{Nn}.m \leq x.x \leq n. \supset .F(x).$$

Clearly, by (1), (2), and Thm.XI.2.20,

(5) $$G(m).$$

Lemma. $(p):p \epsilon \mathrm{Nn}.m \leq p.G(p). \supset .G(p+1).$

Proof. Assume

(i) $$p \epsilon \mathrm{Nn}.m \leq p,$$

(ii) $$G(p),$$

(iii) $$x \epsilon \mathrm{Nn}.m \leq x.x \leq p+1.$$

By (iii) and Thm.XI.2.14, Cor. 2, $x < p + 1 . \vee . x = p + 1$.

Case 1. $x < p + 1$. Then by Thm.XI.3.5, Cor. 3, $x \leq p$. So by (iii), (ii), and the definition of $G(p)$, we get $F(x)$.

Case 2. $x = p + 1$. Put (i) and (ii) into (3), and get $F(p + 1)$. Then $F(x)$.

So in either case, we get $F(x)$. Then, by the definition of $G(p + 1)$, our lemma follows.

By using Thm.XI.3.18 with (1), (5), and our lemma, we infer

$$(n):n \in \mathrm{Nn}.m \leq n. \supset .G(n).$$

So by (4), $G(n)$. Then by taking x to be n in $G(n)$ and using (4) and Thm.XI.2.14, Cor. 1, we infer $F(n)$.

Corollary. Let $F(x)$ be a stratified statement. Then

(1) $$F(0)$$

(2) $$(n)::n \in \mathrm{Nn}:.(x):x \in \mathrm{Nn}.x \leq n. \supset .F(x).: \supset :.F(n + 1)$$

yield

$$(n):n \in \mathrm{Nn}. \supset .F(n).$$

Proof. Take $m = 0$.

The principle of strong induction is sometimes stated in the alternative form:

Theorem XI.3.20. Let $F(x)$ be a stratified statement. Then

(1) $$m \in \mathrm{Nn},$$

(2) $$(n)::n \in \mathrm{Nn}.m \leq n:.(x):x \in \mathrm{Nn}.m \leq x.x < n. \supset .F(x).: \supset :.F(n)$$

yield

$$(n):n \in \mathrm{Nn}.m \leq n. \supset .F(n).$$

Proof. Assume the hypotheses.

Lemma 1. $(x).x \in \mathrm{Nn}.m \leq x.x < m. \supset .F(x)$.

Proof. Assume $x \in \mathrm{Nn}.m \leq x.x < m$. Then by (1) and Thm.XI.2.20, Cor. 1, $(m \leq x){\sim}(m \leq x)$. However, by truth values, $\vdash P{\sim}P. \supset .Q$. So $F(x)$.

Lemma 2. $(n)::n \in \mathrm{Nn}.m \leq n:.(x):x \in \mathrm{Nn}.m \leq x.x \leq n. \supset .F(x).: \supset :. F(n + 1)$.

Proof. Assume

(i) $$n \in \mathrm{Nn}.m \leq n$$

(ii) $$(x):x \in \mathrm{Nn}.m \leq x.x \leq n. \supset .F(x).$$

By (i),

$$n + 1 \in \mathrm{Nn}.m \leq n + 1,$$

and by (ii) and Thm.XI.3.5, Cor. 3,

$$(x):x \epsilon \mathrm{Nn}.m \leq x.x < n + 1. \supset .F(x).$$

Hence by taking n to be $n + 1$ in (2), we get $F(n + 1)$.

If we take n to be m in (2), and use (1), Thm.XI.2.14, Cor. 1, and Lemma 1, we get $F(m)$. Then by (1), Lemma 2, and Thm.XI.3.19, we deduce our theorem.

The form of the principle embodied in Thm.XI.3.20 has one less hypothesis than the form embodied in Thm.XI.3.19. However, in practice, the second hypothesis of Thm.XI.3.20 is usually just as difficult to prove as the second and third hypotheses of Thm.XI.3.19. Accordingly, Thm.XI.3.20 is very little used, and we include it mainly as a curiosity.

As an illustration of the use of strong induction, we cite the proofs of Thms.IV.5.2, VI.5.4, VI.6.3, VI.7.1, IX.2.4, IX.2.6, and others. In the proof of Thm.VI.7.2, Lemma A is proved by strong induction and Lemma D by weak induction. We now prove by strong induction a theorem whose proof by weak induction would be difficult.

****Theorem XI.3.21.** $\vdash (\alpha):.\alpha \subseteq \mathrm{Nn}.\alpha \neq \Lambda: \supset :(\mathrm{E}n):n \epsilon \alpha:(m).m \epsilon \alpha \supset n \leq m.$

Proof. Let $F(x)$ denote

$$x \epsilon \alpha: \supset :(\mathrm{E}n):n \epsilon \alpha:(m).m \epsilon \alpha \supset n \leq m.$$

We shall prove by strong induction (Thm.XI.3.19, corollary) that

$$\alpha \subseteq \mathrm{Nn} \vdash (x):x \epsilon \mathrm{Nn}. \supset .F(x).$$

Let us assume

(1) $$\alpha \subseteq \mathrm{Nn}.$$

By (1) and Thm.XI.2.15, Cor. 2, $(m).m \epsilon \alpha \supset 0 \leq m$. So

$$0 \epsilon \alpha: \supset :0 \epsilon \alpha:(m).m \epsilon \alpha \supset 0 \leq m.$$

Then

$$0 \epsilon \alpha: \supset :(\mathrm{E}n):n \epsilon \alpha:(m).m \epsilon \alpha \supset n \leq m.$$

That is,

(2) $$F(0).$$

Lemma. $(n)::n \epsilon \mathrm{Nn}:.(x):x \epsilon \mathrm{Nn}.x \leq n. \supset .F(x).: \supset :.F(n + 1).$

Proof. Assume

(i) $$n \epsilon \mathrm{Nn},$$

(ii) $$(x):x \epsilon \mathrm{Nn}.x \leq n. \supset .F(x),$$

(iii) $$n + 1 \epsilon \alpha.$$

Case 1. $(m).m \epsilon \alpha \supset n + 1 \leq m$. Then, by (iii),

$$(En):n \epsilon \alpha:(m).m \epsilon \alpha \supset n \leq m.$$

Case 2. $\sim(m).m \epsilon \alpha \supset n + 1 \leq m$. Then by duality and rule C, $m \epsilon \alpha.\sim(n + 1 \leq m)$. Then $m \epsilon$ Nn by (1), and so by (i) and Thm.XI.3.7, Cor. 2, $m < n + 1$. By Thm.XI.3.5, Cor. 3, $m \leq n$. Then $F(m)$ by (ii), and so, since $m \epsilon \alpha$,

$$(En):n \epsilon \alpha:(m).m \epsilon \alpha \supset n \leq m.$$

Hence this result holds in both cases, and our lemma is proved.

By (2) and our lemma and Thm.XI.3.19, corollary,

(3) $$\alpha \subseteq \text{Nn} \vdash (x):x \epsilon \text{Nn}. \supset .F(x).$$

We now prove our theorem. Assume $\alpha \subseteq$ Nn and $\alpha \neq \Lambda$. Then $x \epsilon \alpha$, and so $x \epsilon$ Nn. Then by (3), $(En):n \epsilon \alpha:(m).m \epsilon \alpha \supset n \leq m$.

Corollary. $\vdash (\alpha,z)::\alpha \subseteq \text{Nn}.\alpha \neq \Lambda.z = \iota x\ (x \epsilon \alpha:(y).y \epsilon \alpha \supset x \leq y).: \supset :. z \epsilon \alpha:(y).y \epsilon \alpha \supset z \leq y$.

Proof. Assume

(1) $$\alpha \subseteq \text{Nn}$$

and $\alpha \neq \Lambda$, and write $F(x)$ for $x \epsilon \alpha:(y).y \epsilon \alpha \supset x \leq y$. Then by our theorem,

$$(Ex).F(x).$$

Also by (1) and Thm.XI.2.20

$$(x,z):F(x).F(z). \supset .x = z.$$

Then by Thm.VII.2.1,

$$(E_1x).F(x).$$

Then by Thm.VIII.2.2,

$$F(\iota x\ F(x)).$$

If we now assume

$$z = \iota x\ (x \epsilon \alpha:(y).y \epsilon \alpha \supset x \leq y),$$

we are assuming $z = \iota x\ F(x)$, and we infer $F(z)$, which is our theorem.

In words, our theorem states that every nonempty set of nonnegative integers has a least member. The corollary states that in such case $\iota x\ (x \epsilon \alpha:(y).y \epsilon \alpha \supset x \leq y)$ is this least member.

Although we used the principle of strong induction to prove Thm.XI.3.21, the latter is more flexible and of wider application than the principle of strong induction. Indeed, any proof that could be carried out by use of strong induction could be carried out almost as simply by use of Thm. XI.3.21. We shall indicate the procedure, restricting attention to the case in which the induction starts with zero. Let us have given a stratified statement $F(x)$ with the properties

(A) $$F(0),$$

(B) $$(n)::n \in \mathrm{Nn}:.(x):x \in \mathrm{Nn}.x \leq n. \supset .F(x).: \supset :.F(n+1).$$

Let us prove

(C) $$(n):n \in \mathrm{Nn}. \supset .F(n)$$

by reductio ad absurdum. So we assume the dual of (C), and use rule C to infer

(D) $$p \in \mathrm{Nn}.{\sim}F(p).$$

We now denote

$$\hat{p}(p \in \mathrm{Nn}.{\sim}F(p))$$

by α. Then $\alpha \subseteq \mathrm{Nn}$, and by (D), $\alpha \neq \Lambda$. Hence by Thm.XI.3.21, there is a least m in α.

Case 1. $m = 0$. Since $m \in \alpha$, we have ${\sim}F(m)$ by the definition of α, and hence ${\sim}F(0)$, which contradicts (A).

Case 2. $m \neq 0$. Then there is an n such that $n \in \mathrm{Nn}.m = n + 1$. Since m is the least member of α, we have $(x):x \in \alpha. \supset .n < x$. That is, $(x):x \in \mathrm{Nn}. x \leq n. \supset .{\sim}\, x \in \alpha$. However, by the definition of α, ${\sim}\, x \in \alpha: \supset :x \in \mathrm{Nn}. \supset .F(x)$. So $(x):x \in \mathrm{Nn}.x \leq n. \supset .F(x)$. Then by (B), $F(n + 1)$. That is, $F(m)$, contradicting $m \in \alpha$.

Some mathematicians use Thm.XI.3.21 even in cases as indicated above where strong induction would avoid reductio ad absurdum and simplify the proof. However, there are many cases in which use of Thm.XI.3.21 yields a simpler proof than would result from the use of strong induction. Such a case would be the proof of the theorem that every integer greater than unity has a prime factor. One can easily prove this by strong induction, taking $m = 2$ in Thm.XI.3.19. For assume the theorem for all m with $2 \leq m \leq n$. If $n + 1$ has no factor f with $1 < f < n + 1$, then $n + 1$ is a prime, and has itself as a prime factor. If $n + 1$ has a factor f with $1 < f < n + 1$, then $2 \leq f \leq n$. Then f has a prime factor p, which must then divide $n + 1$. By use of Thm.XI.3.21, the proof is even quicker. For let $n \geq 2$. Then n is in the set of divisors of n which are greater than unity. Let f be the least such. Then f has no divisor g with $1 < g < f$, else g would be a smaller divisor of n. Thus f is a prime, and so n has the prime divisor f.

In this connection, it is instructive to compare the two proofs of unique factorization given by Hardy and Wright on pages 19 to 22. The first uses Thm.XI.3.21 (see the proof of Theorem 23 on page 20 of Hardy and Wright) and the second uses strong induction (see Sec. 2.11 of Hardy and Wright).

Another useful means of proving properties of integers is by means of the principle of infinite descent. This operates as follows. Let it be required to prove (C). We prove

(E) $(n):.n \epsilon \mathrm{Nn}.\sim F(n): \supset :(\mathrm{E}m).m < n.m \epsilon \mathrm{Nn}.\sim F(m).$

We then infer (C).

The original intuitive justification for this principle was to proceed by reductio ad absurdum. Suppose $\sim(n):n \epsilon \mathrm{Nn}. \supset .F(n)$. Then there is an integer n for which $\sim F(n)$. Then by (E), there is a smaller integer m for which $\sim F(m)$. Then by (E) again, there is a still smaller integer p for which $\sim F(p)$. Proceeding indefinitely in this fashion, we produce an infinite succession of smaller and smaller integers, all nonnegative. This cannot be.

It was this sort of intuitive justification which lead to the name "infinite descent." Often one shortens the phrase and refers to a proof which uses the principle of infinite descent merely as a "proof by descent."

Proof by descent is widely used in number theory. For an example, see Hardy and Wright, pages 190 to 193, 298, and others.

By means of Thm.XI.3.21, one can readily justify the principle of infinite descent. We do so in the following theorem.

Theorem XI.3.22. Let $F(x)$ be a stratified statement. Then

(1) $$m \epsilon \mathrm{Nn},$$

(2) $$(n):.n \epsilon \mathrm{Nn}.m \leq n.\sim F(n): \supset :(\mathrm{E}x).x < n.x \epsilon \mathrm{Nn}.m \leq x.\sim F(x),$$

yield

$$(n):n \epsilon \mathrm{Nn}.m \leq n. \supset .F(n).$$

Proof. Assume the hypothesis. Define α to be

$$\hat{n}(n \epsilon \mathrm{Nn}.m \leq n.\sim F(n)).$$

Then

(3) $$\alpha \subseteq \mathrm{Nn},$$

and by (2),

(4) $$(n):n \epsilon \alpha. \supset .(\mathrm{E}x).x \epsilon \alpha.x < n.$$

We wish to prove the theorem by reductio ad absurdum, to which end we assume

$$\sim(n):n \epsilon \mathrm{Nn}.m \leq n. \supset .F(n).$$

By duality, this gives $(\mathrm{E}n).n \epsilon \alpha$. Then $\alpha \neq \Lambda$. Hence by (3) and Thm. XI.3.21, $(\mathrm{E}n).n \epsilon \alpha.(m).m \epsilon \alpha \supset n \leq m$. By rule C and (4)

$$(m).m \in \alpha \supset n \leq m,$$

$$(\mathrm{E}x).x \in \alpha.x < n.$$

Then by rule C, $x \in \alpha$, $x < n$, and $n \leq x$. By Thm.XI.2.20, Cor. 1, we have a contradiction.

We now consider definition by induction. In its simplest version, this takes the following form. We set down the two conditions

(I) $$f(0) = a,$$

(II) $$f(n + 1) = g(f(n)),$$

where a is a specified constant and $g(x)$ is a specified function value of x, and f is a function which is supposedly being defined by (I) and (II). It is usual to say that (I) and (II) define $f(n)$ by induction on n.

The intuitive argument for supposing that (I) and (II) define a function f goes as follows. Certainly, (I) and (II) specify a unique value for $f(0)$, namely,

$$f(0) = a.$$

Then by putting $n = 0$ in (II), we specify a unique value for $f(1)$, namely,

$$f(1) = g(f(0)) = g(a).$$

Now we put $n = 1$ in (II) and specify a unique value for $f(2)$, namely,

$$f(2) = g(f(1)) = g(g(a)).$$

By proceeding in this manner, we specify $f(n)$ uniquely for any given nonnegative integer n. Moreover, it is clear that we have not specified a value for $f(x)$ if x is not a nonnegative integer. So we have specified a unique value for $f(n)$ when and only when n is a nonnegative integer. Thus we have defined a function f with $\mathrm{Arg}(f) = \mathrm{Nn}$.

The fallacy in the intuitive reasoning just presented is that this reasoning requires that we specify each of $f(0), f(1), f(2), \ldots$, in turn and then define f by collecting all the ordered pairs $\langle 0,f(0)\rangle, \langle 1,f(1)\rangle, \langle 2,f(2)\rangle, \ldots$, into a single assemblage. That is, we are required to define the infinite class f by listing its members. Clearly this is not humanly possible.

Thus the intuitive reasoning presented merely makes it plausible that (I) and (II) do define a function f.

Actually, (I) and (II) are circular in that (II) defines f in terms of f itself. In general a circular definition, in which we try to define a quantity in terms of itself, is not a legitimate definition. However, there are exceptional cases in which a circular definition is acceptable. A very familiar case from mathematics occurs with differential equations. It is well known that the two conditions

$$f(0) = 1$$

$$f'(x) = f(x)$$

define a unique function value $f(x)$ of real numbers x. Nevertheless the second condition is circular, since we cannot use it to obtain $f'(x)$ unless $f(x)$ is already known, and vice versa.

The standard method for legitimizing the use of differential equations, in spite of their feature of circularity, is to prove that under suitable conditions there is one and only one function satisfying a differential equation with boundary conditions. Then certainly the differential equation and boundary conditions can be considered as a definition of this unique function, regardless of the circularity of the differential equation.

We shall proceed similarly with definition by induction. We shall prove that under rather mild stratification conditions there is exactly one function f, with $\mathrm{Arg}(f) = \mathrm{Nn}$, which satisfies (I) and (II). Then, in spite of the circularity of (II), it is certainly acceptable to consider (I) and (II) as a definition of this unique function. Indeed we can then write a formula for this function, namely,

$$\iota f\ (f \in \mathrm{Funct}{:}.\mathrm{Arg}(f) = \mathrm{Nn}{:}.f(0) = a{:}.(n){:}n \in \mathrm{Nn}. \supset .f(n+1) = g(f(n))).$$

Before proceeding with the proof that (I) and (II) determine a unique function, we discuss certain general aspects of definition by induction.

As an illustration of definition by induction we cite Hardy's second proof of the Weierstrass theorem (see Hardy, 1947, page 139). In this, Hardy starts with an infinite set S on the real line contained in the closed interval PQ. Then he defines by induction on n the intervals I_n according to the following conditions:

(I) I_0 is PQ.

(II) Given I_n, we divide it into two equal parts. If the left-hand half contains an infinite number of points of S, then we take I_{n+1} to be the left-hand half. Otherwise we take I_{n+1} to be the right-hand part.

By using definition by cases, we can define a term $g(x)$ such that (II) can be written as

$$I_{n+1} = g(I_n).$$

Thus (I) and (II) give a clear case of defining I_n by induction on n.

In a slightly more general form of definition by induction, we write down the two conditions

(I) $$f(0) = a,$$

(III) $$f(n+1) = h(n, f(n)).$$

That is, we make $f(n+1)$ depend upon n as well as the previous value of $f(n)$. As an illustration of this, let us have given an arithmetical function value $r(n)$, and let us define

$$\sum_{m=0}^{n} r(m)$$

by induction on n. We write the conditions

(I) $$\sum_{m=0}^{0} r(m) = r(0),$$

(III) $$\sum_{m=0}^{n+1} r(m) = \left(\sum_{m=0}^{n} r(m) \right) + r(n+1).$$

Here the function value $f(n)$ to be defined by induction is

$$f(n) = \sum_{m=0}^{n} r(m)$$

and h is such that

$$h(n,f(n)) = f(n) + r(n+1).$$

That is,

$$h(x,y) = y + r(x+1).$$

In the instances cited so far, the form of definition by induction used has been analogous to proof by weak induction in that the function value $f(n+1)$ is specified in terms of at most one previous function value, namely, $f(n)$. As in the case of proof by induction, one need not necessarily start with zero, but can define $f(n)$ by writing

(I*) $$f(1) = a,$$

(II) $$f(n+1) = g(f(n)).$$

Clearly this defines $f(n)$ only for $n \geq 1$.

Analogous to proof by strong induction, there are versions of definition by induction in which the function value $f(n+1)$ is specified in terms of more than one preceding function value. There is a particularly important case, in which $f(n+1)$ is specified in terms of the two preceding function values, $f(n)$ and $f(n-1)$. This is illustrated by the definition of the convergents of a continued fraction. Given a continued fraction

$$\frac{1}{a_0 +}\,\frac{1}{a_1 +}\,\frac{1}{a_2 +}\cdots,$$

the numerator p_n and the denominator q_n of the nth convergent

$$\frac{p_n}{q_n}$$

are defined by

$$p_0 = 0$$
$$p_1 = 1$$
$$p_{n+1} = a_n p_n + p_{n-1},$$
$$q_0 = 1$$
$$q_1 = a_0$$
$$q_{n+1} = a_n q_n + q_{n-1}$$

(see Hardy and Wright, Chapter 10).

These are not genuinely different from the type of definition discussed earlier. If we let $f(n)$ be $\langle p_{n+1}, p_n \rangle$, then we can define $f(n)$ by induction on n by

(I) $$f(0) = \langle 1,0 \rangle,$$

(III) $$f(n+1) = \langle a_{n+1} Q_1(f(n)) + Q_2(f(n)), Q_1(f(n)) \rangle.$$

Then we can define p_n by writing

$$p_n = Q_2(f(n)).$$

However, there are cases, in strict analogy with proof by strong induction, in which $f(n+1)$ is specified in terms of all preceding function values, $f(0)$, $f(1)$, . . . , $f(n)$. This is used, for example, in the proof that every real number has a decimal expansion (see Hardy, 1947, pages 150 to 151). As an illustration, we shall give the details for the slightly simpler proof that every real number x with $0 < x \leq 1$ has a nonterminating binary expansion. The critical point in the proof is the definition by induction on n of the nth digit in the binary expansion of x. Let $f(n)$ be the nth digit after the binary point. (In dealing with binary expansions, the term "binary point" corresponds to the term "decimal point" in dealing with decimal expansions.) It is convenient to take $f(0) = 0$, which has the same effect as specifying that there are to be no digits to the left of the binary point. Given $f(0)$, $f(1)$, . . . , $f(n)$, we define $f(n+1)$ (which is the $(n+1)$st digit) as follows.

Case 1. If

$$2^{n+1}\left(x - \sum_{m=0}^{n} f(m)2^{-m}\right) \leq 1,$$

take $f(n+1)$ to be zero.

Case 2. Otherwise, take $f(n+1)$ to be 1.

This is a definition by strong induction since the value of $f(n+1)$ depends upon all the values $f(0)$, $f(1)$, . . . , $f(n)$, and not merely on the value

$f(n)$. We shall prove that this definition does indeed define a function f. Accepting this for the moment, it is clear that the value $f(n)$ must be either 0 or 1 for each positive integer n, and so can serve as the nth digit of a binary expansion. We readily prove by weak induction on n (using the fact that $0 < x \leq 1$), that for $0 \leq n$,

$$0 < x - \sum_{m=0}^{n} f(m)2^{-m} \leq 2^{-n}. \tag{XI.3.1}$$

From this follows

$$x = \lim_{n\to\infty} \sum_{m=0}^{n} f(m)2^{-m}, \tag{XI.3.2}$$

so that $f(n)$ is indeed the nth digit in the binary expansion of x. Moreover, this expansion is nonterminating, for if it were terminating, this would mean that there is an $N \geq 0$ such that

$$(n):n \in \mathrm{Nn}.n > N. \supset .f(n) = 0.$$

Then by (XI.3.2),

$$x = \sum_{m=0}^{N} f(m)2^{-m},$$

which contradicts (XI.3.1).

For a general formulation of definition by induction, which includes even the strong form in which $f(n+1)$ depends on all of $f(0)$, $f(1)$, . . . , $f(n)$, we write

$$f(0) = a, \tag{I}$$

$$f(n+1) = j(n,f). \tag{IV}$$

In order for this to define a function, we need the condition

(V) $(R,S,n)::R,S \in \mathrm{Funct}.\mathrm{Arg}(R) \subseteq \mathrm{Nn}.\mathrm{Arg}(S) \subseteq \mathrm{Nn}.n \in \mathrm{Nn}:.(m):$
$$m \in \mathrm{Nn}.m \leq n. \supset .R(m) = S(m).: \supset :.j(n,R) = j(n,S).$$

The effect of (V) is to say that the value of $j(n,f)$ does not involve all function values of f, but only the values $f(0)$, $f(1)$, . . . , $f(n)$. Thus, in effect, (IV) defines $f(n+1)$ in terms of $f(0)$, $f(1)$, . . . , $f(n)$.

Our earlier forms of definition by induction are included in the general form just stated. For if we write down

$$f(0) = a \tag{I}$$

$$f(n+1) = g(f(n)), \tag{II}$$

then in (IV) and (V), we can take $j(n,f)$ to be $g(f(n))$. Clearly (V) is satisfied. If we write down

(I) $$f(0) = a$$

(III) $$f(n + 1) = h(n,f(n)),$$

then analogously we take $j(n,f)$ to be $h(n,f(n))$ in (IV) and (V).

If we make a definition by induction using (I) and (II) or (I) and (III), we shall say that it is a definition by weak induction. If we use (I) and (IV), with (V) satisfied, we shall say that it is a definition by strong induction.

We have our choice of various schemes for proving the acceptability of definition by induction. One scheme is to wait until the next chapter after we have proved a very general theorem on definition by transfinite induction. Then we can justify definition by strong induction as a special case of definition by transfinite induction. Then definition by weak induction can be justified as a special case of definition by strong induction.

This scheme has a drawback. We need to use definition by weak induction in the treatment of denumerable classes in the next section. If we postpone a proof of the validity of definition by weak induction until the next chapter, we must similarly postpone portions of the theory of denumerable classes.

A second scheme is to justify definition by weak induction and then use definition by weak induction to justify definition by strong induction. This scheme has the drawback that using definition by weak induction to justify definition by strong induction is a lengthy and complicated process.

We shall adopt a compromise. We shall proceed now to justify definition by weak induction. Thus we shall have it available for use in the theory of denumerable classes. However, as we have no immediate need for definition by strong induction, we shall leave its justification until the next chapter, when we can treat it as a special case of definition by transfinite induction.

In justifying definition by weak induction, it clearly suffices to justify the form involving (I) and (III), since the form involving (I) and (II) is more special, resulting from taking $h(n,f(n))$ to be just $g(f(n))$. In our justification, we shall have need for the following hypothesis.

Hypothesis H_4. Let α, R, S, a, m, n, x, y, and z be distinct variables. Let $h(x,y)$ be a term in which neither of n, R, or S occurs. If A and B are terms, let $h(A,B)$ denote {Sub in $h(x,y)$: A for x, B for y}, where it shall be understood that the substitutions indicated cause no confusion.

We prove first that (I) and (III) can be satisfied by at most one function. We take the general case in which the induction starts at m instead of 0.

****Theorem XI.3.23.** Assume Hypothesis H_4. Then

(1) $$m \in \mathrm{Nn},$$

(2) $$\alpha = \hat{n}(n \in \mathrm{Nn}.m \leq n),$$

(3) $$R,S \in \mathrm{Funct},$$

(4) $$\mathrm{Arg}(R) = \mathrm{Arg}(S) = \alpha,$$

(5) $$R(m) = S(m) = a,$$

(6) $$(n):n \in \alpha. \supset .R(n+1) = h(n,R(n)),$$

(7) $$(n):n \in \alpha. \supset .S(n+1) = h(n,S(n)),$$

yield

$$R = S.$$

Proof. Assume the hypotheses. We shall use Thm.X.5.16. So we prove by weak induction on n that $(n):n \in \alpha. \supset .R(n) = S(n)$. So let $F(x)$ be $R(x) = S(x)$. By Thm.XI.3.18, it suffices to prove

(8) $$F(m)$$

and

(9) $$(n):n \in \alpha.F(n). \supset .F(n+1).$$

We get (8) from (5) and (9) from (6) and (7).

We remark that this theorem continues to hold if we replace a by any term with no free occurrences of n, since the theorem can be reduced to an implication by repeated use of the deduction theorem, and then one can use rule G with a, after which one can replace a by any term A by use of Axiom scheme 6 or Axiom scheme 8, provided that this replacement causes no confusion of bound variables. As there may be free occurrences of a in $h(x,y)$, one must assume that there are no free occurrences of n in A if one is to be sure of avoiding confusion.

We now prove that, under a simple stratification condition, (I) and (III) are satisfied by at least one function f, which must then be unique by the preceding theorem. The proof is motivated as follows. We are requiring

(I) $$f(m) = a,$$

(III) $$f(n+1) = h(n,f(n)) \qquad \text{for} \qquad n \geq m.$$

Thus we require

$$f(m) = a,$$

$$f(m+1) = h(m,a),$$

$$f(m+2) = h(m+1, h(m,a)),$$

etc.

That is, we wish f to consist of the following collection of ordered pairs:

$$\langle m,a\rangle,$$
$$\langle m+1,h(m,a)\rangle,$$
$$\langle m+2,h(m+1,h(m,a))\rangle,$$
etc.

Now we note that, if

$$S = \lambda xy(\langle x+1,h(x,y)\rangle),$$

then

$$S(\langle n,y\rangle) = \langle n+1,h(n,y)\rangle,$$

so that

$$S(\langle m,a\rangle) = \langle m+1,h(m,a)\rangle,$$
$$S(\langle m+1,h(m,a)\rangle) = \langle m+2,h(m+1,h(m,a))\rangle,$$
etc.

That is, we wish f to consist of the ordered pairs

$$\langle m,a\rangle,$$
$$S(\langle m,a\rangle),$$
$$S(S(\langle m,a\rangle)),$$
etc.

This can be accomplished by taking f to be

$$\mathrm{Clos}(\{\langle m,a\rangle\},xSz).$$

Accordingly, we prove our theorem by defining f so.

****Theorem XI.3.24.** Assume the Hypothesis H_4. Assume further that $R(n+1) = h(n,R(n))$ is stratified. Then

(1) $$m \in \mathrm{Nn},$$

(2) $$\alpha = \hat{n}(n \in \mathrm{Nn}.m \leq n),$$

(3) $$S = \lambda xy(\langle x+1,h(x,y)\rangle),$$

(4) $$R = \mathrm{Clos}(\{\langle m,a\rangle\},xSz)$$

yield

(5) $$R \in \mathrm{Funct},$$

(6) $$\mathrm{Arg}(R) = \alpha,$$

(7) $$R(m) = a,$$

(8) $$(n):n \in \alpha. \supset .R(n+1) = h(n,R(n)).$$

Proof. Assume the hypotheses. If $R(n + 1) = h(n,R(n))$ is stratified, then $x = y = h(x,y)$ is stratified. So by Thm.X.5.28,

$$(9) \qquad (x,y,z):\langle x,y\rangle Sz. \equiv .z = \langle x + 1,h(x,y)\rangle.$$

Then by Thm.X.4.34,

$$(10) \qquad \langle m,a\rangle \in R,$$

by Thm.X.4.35,

$$(11) \qquad (x,y):\langle x,y\rangle \in R. \supset .\langle x + 1,h(x,y)\rangle \in R,$$

by Thm.X.4.36,

$$(12) \qquad (\beta)::\langle m,a\rangle \in \beta:(w,z):w \in \beta.w \in R.wSz. \supset .z \in \beta.: \supset :.R \subseteq \beta,$$

and by Thm.X.4.37,

$$(13) \qquad (z):.z \in R: \equiv :z = \langle m,a\rangle.\mathbf{v}.(\mathrm{E}w).w \in R.wSz.$$

Let β be $\alpha \times \mathrm{V}$. Then by (1) and (2), $\langle m,a\rangle \in \beta$. Also, $w \in \beta. \supset .(\mathrm{E}x,y).x \in \alpha.w = \langle x,y\rangle$. So if $w \in \beta.w \in R.wSz$, then $x \in \alpha.\langle x,y\rangle Sz$. So by (1), (2), and (9), $x + 1 \in \alpha.z = \langle x + 1,h(x,y)\rangle$. Hence $z \in \beta$. Thus by (12), $R \subseteq \beta$. Thus

$$(14) \qquad R \in \mathrm{Rel},$$

$$(15) \qquad \mathrm{Arg}(R) \subseteq \alpha.$$

Let $F(x)$ be $x \in \mathrm{Arg}(R)$. By (10), $F(m)$. By (11), $(n):n \in \alpha.F(n). \supset .F(n + 1)$. So by Thm.XI.3.18, $(n):n \in \alpha. \supset .F(n)$. That is, $\alpha \subseteq \mathrm{Arg}(R)$. Then by (15), we have established (6).

By (9),

$$(16) \qquad (\mathrm{E}x,y).xRy.z = \langle x + 1,h(x,y)\rangle: \supset :(\mathrm{E}w).w \in R.wSz.$$

If $w \in R$, then by (14), $w = \langle x,y\rangle$. Consequently, by (9),

$$(\mathrm{E}w).w \in R.wSz: \supset :(\mathrm{E}x,y).xRy.z = \langle x + 1,h(x,y)\rangle.$$

So by (16) and (13),

$$(17) \qquad (z):.z \in R: \equiv :z = \langle m,a\rangle.\mathbf{v}.(\mathrm{E}x,y).xRy.z = \langle x + 1,h(x,y)\rangle.$$

Lemma. $(n):.n \in \alpha: \supset :(u,v):nRu.nRv. \supset .u = v.$

Proof. Proof by weak induction on n (Thm.XI.3.18). Let $F(n)$ be $(u,v):nRu.nRv. \supset .u = v$.

First we wish to prove $F(m)$. Assume mRu. Then by (17), $\langle m,u\rangle = \langle m,a\rangle.\mathbf{v}.(\mathrm{E}x,y).xRy.\langle m,u\rangle = \langle x + 1,h(x,y)\rangle$. If $xRy.\langle m,u\rangle = \langle x + 1,h(x,y)\rangle$, then $x \in \alpha$ by (6) and $m = x + 1$. From $x \in \alpha$ by (2), $m \leq x$. So $x + 1 \leq x$, contradicting Thm.XI.3.5, Cor. 2. Consequently $\langle m,u\rangle = \langle m,a\rangle$, and $u = a$. So we have shown $mRu. \supset .u = a$. Hence we conclude

(i) $$F(m).$$

Now assume $n \epsilon \alpha$, $F(n)$, and $(n + 1)Ru$. Then by (17), $\langle n + 1,u\rangle = \langle m,a\rangle.\mathbf{v}.(\mathrm{E}x,y).xRy.\langle n + 1,u\rangle = \langle x + 1,h(x,y)\rangle$. If we had $n + 1 = m$, we would get the contradiction $n + 1 \leq n$ from $n \epsilon \alpha$. So $xRy.\langle n + 1,u\rangle = \langle x + 1,h(x,y)\rangle$. By (6), $x \epsilon \alpha$. Also $n + 1 = x + 1$, $u = h(x,y)$, so that $n = x$. By this and xRy, we have nRy. By this and $F(n)$ and Thm. VII.2.1, $(\mathrm{E}_1 y).nRy$. So by Axiom scheme 11, $nRy. \equiv .y = R(n)$. So $y = R(n)$. But $x = n$ and $u = h(x,y)$. So $u = h(n,R(n))$. The net result of all the development since (i) is to show

$$n \epsilon \alpha.F(n) \vdash (n + 1)Ru. \supset .u = h(n,R(n)).$$

So

$$n \epsilon \alpha.F(n) \vdash F(n + 1).$$

Then by (i), our lemma follows.

Now by (14), (6), and our lemma, we establish (5).

By (10), mRa. Hence by (5), (6), and Thm.X.5.3, we establish (7).

Let $n \epsilon \alpha$. Then by (5), (6), and Thm.X.5.3, Cor. 1, $nR(R(n))$. Then by (11), $(n + 1)Rh(n,R(n))$. So by (5) and Thm.X.5.3, $R(n + 1) = h(n,R(n))$. Thus we establish (8).

The theorem continues to hold if we replace a by any term with no free occurrences of x, y, z, or n, for the same reasons which we gave after Thm.XI.3.23. We do not even need to require any stratification conditions for the term which we use for a.

Note that by (4), we can say that there is actually a term R which satisfies (5), (6), (7), and (8). Also, this term R contains occurrences of a and m as free variables, and also all free occurrences in $h(x,y)$ of variables other than x and y are free occurrences in R. Also R is stratified if $f(n + 1) = h(n,f(n))$ is stratified. Hence if any question should arise about free occurrences of variables, or about stratification, for the f defined by weak induction, we can assume the conditions stated above, since we know that there does exist a term R satisfying the conditions stated.

We can write another term which satisfies (5), (6), (7), and (8) and satisfies the various conditions about stratification and occurrences of free variables which we have just cited. This is

$$\iota R\ (R \epsilon \mathrm{Funct}:.\mathrm{Arg}(R) = \hat{n}(n \epsilon \mathrm{Nn}.m \leq n):.R(m) = a:.$$
$$(n):n \epsilon \mathrm{Nn}.m \leq n. \supset .R(n + 1) = h(n,R(n))).$$

It should be noted that by trivial variations we can justify definition by weak induction for other stratification conditions than those assumed in

Thm.XI.3.24. We shall not attempt to state the most general possible variation and the corresponding stratification condition, but shall show one simple variation. With this as a model, the reader can easily work out other variations.

Theorem XI.3.25. Assume Hypothesis H_4. Then

(1) $$m \in \text{Nn},$$

(2) $$\alpha = \hat{n}(n \in \text{Nn}.m \leq n),$$

(3) $$R,S \in \text{Funct},$$

(4) $$\text{Arg}(R) = \text{Arg}(S) = \text{USC}(\alpha),$$

(5) $$R(\{m\}) = S(\{m\}) = a,$$

(6) $$(n):n \in \alpha. \supset .R(\{n+1\}) = h(n,R(\{n\})),$$

(7) $$(n):n \in \alpha. \supset .S(\{n+1\}) = h(n,S(\{n\})),$$

yield
$$R = S.$$

Proof. Prove by induction on n that
$$(n):n \in \alpha. \supset .R(\{n\}) = S(\{n\}).$$

Theorem XI.3.26. Assume Hypothesis H_4. Assume further that $R(\{n+1\}) = h(n,R(\{n\}))$ is stratified. Then

(1) $$m \in \text{Nn},$$

(2) $$\alpha = \hat{n}(n \in \text{Nn}.m \leq n),$$

(3) $$S = \lambda xy(\langle\{(\iota v\ (x = \{v\})) + 1\},h(\iota v\ (x = \{v\}),y)\rangle),$$

(4) $$R = \text{Clos}(\{\langle\{m\},a\rangle\},xSz)$$

yield

(5) $$R \in \text{Funct},$$

(6) $$\text{Arg}(R) = \text{USC}(\alpha),$$

(7) $$R(\{m\}) = a,$$

(8) $$(n):n \in \alpha. \supset .R(\{n+1\}) = h(n,R(\{n\})).$$

Proof. We proceed as in the proof of Thm.XI.3.24.

Although we shall not give all proofs until the next chapter, we shall state here for convenient reference the theorems which justify definition by strong induction. We use the following hypothesis.

Hypothesis H_5. Let α, R, S, a, f, m, and n be distinct variables. Let $j(n,f)$ be a term not containing any occurrences of R or S. If A and B are terms, let $j(A,B)$ denote {Sub in $j(n,f)$: A for n, B for f}, where it shall be understood that the substitutions indicated cause no confusion.

Theorem XI.3.27. Assume Hypothesis H_5. Then

(1) $$m \in \text{Nn},$$

(2) $$\alpha = \hat{n}(n \in \text{Nn}.m \leq n),$$

(3) $$R,S \in \text{Funct},$$

(4) $$\text{Arg}(R) = \text{Arg}(S) = \alpha,$$

(5) $$R(m) = S(m) = a,$$

(6) $$(n){:}n \in \alpha. \supset .R(n+1) = j(n,R),$$

(7) $$(n){:}n \in \alpha. \supset .S(n+1) = j(n,S),$$

(8) $$(R,S,n){::}R,S \in \text{Funct}.\text{Arg}(R) \subseteq \alpha.\text{Arg}(S) \subseteq \alpha.n \in \alpha{:.}(x){:}x \in \alpha.x \leq n. \supset .R(x) = S(x).{:} \supset {:.}j(n,R) = j(n,S)$$

yield

$$R = S.$$

Proof. Assume the hypotheses. We shall use Thm.X.5.16. So we prove by strong induction on n that $(n){:}n \in \alpha. \supset .R(n) = S(n)$. So let $F(x)$ be $R(x) = S(x)$. By Thm.XI.3.19, it suffices to prove

(9) $$F(m)$$

and

(10) $$(n){::}n \in \alpha{:.}(x){:}x \in \alpha.x \leq n. \supset .F(x).{:} \supset {:.}F(n+1).$$

However, $F(m)$ follows by (5). By (3), (4), and (8),

$$(n){::}n \in \alpha{:.}(x){:}x \in \alpha.x \leq n. \supset .F(x).{:} \supset {:.}j(n,R) = j(n,S).$$

Then by (6) and (7), we infer (10).

THEOREM XII.2.12. Assume Hypothesis H_5. Assume further that $R(n+1) = j(n,R)$ is stratified. Then

(1) $$m \in \text{Nn},$$

(2) $$\alpha = \hat{n}(n \in \text{Nn}.m \leq n),$$

(3) $$(R,S,n){::}R,S \in \text{Funct}.\text{Arg}(R) \subseteq \alpha.\text{Arg}(S) \subseteq \alpha.n \in \alpha{:.}(x){:}x \in \alpha.x \leq n. \supset .R(x) = S(x).{:} \supset {:.}j(n,R) = j(n,S)$$

yield

$$(\mathrm{E}R)::R \in \mathrm{Funct}.\mathrm{Arg}(R) = \alpha.R(m) = a:.(n):n \in \alpha. \supset .R(n+1) = j(n,R).$$

If we should wish to prove this theorem with the means now at our disposal, we could proceed along the following lines. If R is the function to be defined, let R_n denote that portion of R which consists of the ordered pairs

$$\langle m,R(m)\rangle,$$
$$\langle m+1,R(m+1)\rangle,$$
$$\cdots\cdots\cdots\cdots\cdots$$
$$\langle m+n,R(m+n)\rangle.$$

We can build up the R_n's successively by the following scheme.

$$R_0 = \{\langle m,a\rangle\},$$
$$R_1 = R_0 \cup \{\langle m+1,j(m,R_0)\rangle\},$$
$$R_2 = R_1 \cup \{\langle m+2,j(m+1,R_1)\rangle\},$$
$$\text{etc.,}$$

and in general

$$R_{n+1} = R_n \cup \{\langle m+n+1,j(m+n,R_n)\rangle\}.$$

Thus the R_n's can be defined by weak induction on n. In fact, we can use Thm.XI.3.25 and Thm.XI.3.26 to define a function f such that $f(\{n\})$ is just our R_n. The conditions on f are

(I) $$f(\{0\}) = \{\langle m,a\rangle\},$$

(III) $$f(\{n+1\}) = f(\{n\}) \cup \{\langle m+n+1,j(m+n,f(\{n\}))\rangle\}.$$

Then in Thm.XI.3.25 and Thm.XI.3.26 we take a to be $\{\langle m,a\rangle\}$ and $h(x,y)$ to be

$$y \cup \{\langle m+x+1,j(m+x,y)\rangle\}.$$

Clearly the stratification conditions are satisfied, and so a function f is actually defined by (I) and (III) above. As we wish R to be the logical sum of all the R_n, we can now define

$$R = \hat{w}(\mathrm{E}n).n \in \mathrm{Nn}.w \in f(\{n\}).$$

We now turn to a study of finite and infinite classes. We define a finite class as a class whose cardinal number is finite, and an infinite class as a class whose cardinal number is infinite. This is achieved by the following definitions:

Fin	for	$\bigcup(\mathrm{Nn})$
Infin	for	$V - \mathrm{Fin}.$

Fin and Infin are stratified and contain no free variables and so may be assigned any type.

Theorem XI.3.28.

*I. $\vdash (\alpha){:}\alpha \epsilon \text{Fin}. \equiv .(\text{E}n).n \epsilon \text{Nn}.\alpha \epsilon n.$

II. $\vdash (\alpha){:}\alpha \epsilon \text{Infin}. \equiv .\sim \alpha \epsilon \text{Fin}.$

Corollary 1. $\vdash (\alpha){:}\alpha \epsilon \text{Fin}. \equiv .\text{Nc}(\alpha) \epsilon \text{Nn}.$

Corollary 2. $\vdash (\alpha){:}\alpha \epsilon \text{Infin}. \equiv .\text{Nc}(\alpha) \epsilon \text{NC} - \text{Nn}.$

Corollary 3. $\vdash \Lambda \epsilon \text{Fin}.$

Corollary 4. $\vdash (x).\{x\} \epsilon \text{Fin}.$

Corollary 5. $\vdash \text{V} \epsilon \text{Infin}.$

***Corollary 6.** $\vdash (\alpha,\beta){:}\alpha \epsilon \text{Fin}.\alpha \text{ sm } \beta. \supset .\beta \epsilon \text{Fin}.$

Corollary 7. $\vdash (\alpha,\beta){:}\alpha \epsilon \text{Infin}.\alpha \text{ sm } \beta. \supset .\beta \epsilon \text{Infin}.$

Theorem XI.3.29.

I. $\vdash (\alpha,\beta){:}\alpha \subset \beta.\alpha \epsilon \text{Fin}. \supset .\text{Nc}(\alpha) < \text{Nc}(\beta).$

II. $\vdash (\alpha,\beta){:}\alpha \subset \beta.\beta \epsilon \text{Fin}. \supset .\text{Nc}(\alpha) < \text{Nc}(\beta).$

Proof of I. Let $\alpha \subset \beta$ and $\alpha \epsilon$ Fin. Then by Thm.XI.2.13, Part I,

(1) $$\text{Nc}(\alpha) \leq \text{Nc}(\beta)$$

and by Thm.XI.3.28, Cor. 1,

(2) $$\text{Nc}(\alpha) \epsilon \text{Nn}.$$

Then by Thm.XI.2.13, Part III, it suffices to prove $\text{Nc}(\alpha) \neq \text{Nc}(\beta)$. This we do by reductio ad absurdum, to which end we assume

(3) $$\text{Nc}(\alpha) = \text{Nc}(\beta).$$

By Ex.XI.2.8, $\text{Nc}(\alpha \cup \beta) = \text{Nc}(\alpha) + \text{Nc}(\beta - \alpha)$. Then by Thm.IX.4.13, Part III, $\text{Nc}(\beta) = \text{Nc}(\alpha) + \text{Nc}(\beta - \alpha)$. So by (3), $\text{Nc}(\alpha) = \text{Nc}(\alpha) + \text{Nc}(\beta - \alpha)$. So by (2) and Thm.XI.3.2, Cor. 1, $\text{Nc}(\beta - \alpha) = 0$. Hence $\beta - \alpha = \Lambda$ by Thm.XI.2.7, Cor. 2. Then $\beta \subseteq \alpha$ by Thm.IX.4.13, Part II. However, from $\alpha \subset \beta$, we get $\sim(\beta \subseteq \alpha)$ by Thm.IX.4.19.

Proof of Part II. Similar.

Corollary 1. $\vdash (\alpha,\beta){:}\alpha \subset \beta.\alpha \epsilon \text{Fin}. \supset .\sim(\alpha \text{ sm } \beta).$

Proof. If α sm β, then $\text{Nc}(\alpha) = \text{Nc}(\beta)$ by Thm.XI.2.2, Part II.

Corollary 2. $\vdash (\alpha,\beta){:}\alpha \subset \beta.\beta \epsilon \text{Fin}. \supset .\sim(\alpha \text{ sm } \beta).$

Corollary 3. $\vdash (\alpha,\beta){:}\alpha \subset \beta.\alpha \text{ sm } \beta. \supset .\alpha \epsilon \text{Infin}.$

****Corollary 4.** $\vdash (\alpha,\beta){:}\alpha \subset \beta.\alpha \text{ sm } \beta. \supset .\beta \epsilon \text{Infin}.$

This theorem and its corollaries tell us that no finite class can be similar to a proper subset of itself, and that if any class is similar to a proper subset of itself then it is an infinite class. A sort of converse, to the effect that every infinite class is similar to a proper subclass of itself is widely quoted. We do not know how to prove this converse except by making use of the denumerable axiom of choice. As most mathematicians accept the denumerable axiom of choice without the slightest hesitation, they are able to conclude that a class is infinite if and only if it is similar to a proper subset of itself. However, for the present, we have only Thm.XI.3.29, Cor. 4.

Theorem XI.3.30. $\vdash \text{Nn sm Nn} - \{0\}$.

Proof. Define $R = \text{Nn}\upharpoonright\lambda x(x+1)$. Clearly

(1) $$\vdash \text{Arg}(R) = \text{Nn}.$$

Also, by Thm.XI.2.12, corollary,

(2) $$\vdash R \in 1\text{–}1.$$

By Thm.X.1.2 and Thm.X.1.5,

(3) $$\vdash \text{Val}(R) \subseteq \text{Nn} - \{0\}.$$

By Thm.X.1.7,

(4) $$\vdash \text{Nn} - \{0\} \subseteq \text{Val}(R).$$

Hence our theorem follows by Thm.XI.1.1, Part IV.

Corollary 1. $\vdash \text{Nn} \in \text{Infin}$.

Proof. By Thm.IX.4.21, $\vdash \text{Nn} - \{0\} \subset \text{Nn}$. So we use Thm.XI.3.29, Cor. 4.

Corollary 2. $\vdash \text{Nc(Nn)} \in \text{NC} - \text{Nn}$.

Corollary 3. $\vdash (n){:}n \in \text{Nn}. \supset .n < \text{Nc(Nn)}$.

Proof. Use Thm.XI.3.6, Cor. 3.

****Theorem XI.3.31.** $\vdash (\alpha,\beta){:}\alpha \subseteq \beta.\beta \in \text{Fin}. \supset .\alpha \in \text{Fin}$.

Proof. Assume $\alpha \subseteq \beta$ and $\beta \in \text{Fin}$. Then by Thm.XI.2.13, Part I, $\text{Nc}(\alpha) \leq \text{Nc}(\beta)$ and by Thm.XI.3.28, Cor. 1, $\text{Nc}(\beta) \in \text{Nn}$. So by Thm. XI.3.3, $\text{Nc}(\alpha) \in \text{Nn}$. Hence $\alpha \in \text{Fin}$.

Corollary 1. $\vdash (\alpha,\beta){:}\alpha \subseteq \beta.\alpha \in \text{Infin}. \supset .\beta \in \text{Infin}$.

Corollary 2. $\vdash (\alpha,\beta){:}\alpha \in \text{Fin}. \supset .\alpha \cap \beta \in \text{Fin}$.

Corollary 3. $\vdash (\alpha,\beta){:}\alpha \cap \beta \in \text{Infin}. \supset .\alpha \in \text{Infin}$.

Corollary 4. $\vdash (\alpha,\beta){:}\alpha \cup \beta \in \text{Fin}. \supset .\alpha \in \text{Fin}$.

Corollary 5. $\vdash (\alpha,\beta){:}\alpha \in \text{Infin}. \supset .\alpha \cup \beta \in \text{Infin}$.

Theorem XI.3.32. $\vdash (\alpha,\beta){:}\alpha,\beta \in \text{Fin}. \supset .\alpha \cup \beta \in \text{Fin}$.

Proof. Let $\alpha,\beta \in \text{Fin}$. Then by Thm.XI.3.31, Cor. 2, $\beta - \alpha \in \text{Fin}$. So $\text{Nc}(\alpha) \in \text{Nn}$, $\text{Nc}(\beta - \alpha) \in \text{Nn}$. Hence by Thm.X.1.14, $(\text{Nc}(\alpha) + \text{Nc}(\beta - \alpha)) \in \text{Nn}$. Then by Ex.XI.2.8, $\text{Nc}(\alpha \cup \beta) \in \text{Nn}$. So $\alpha \cup \beta \in \text{Fin}$.

Corollary 1. $\vdash (\alpha,\beta){:}.\alpha \cup \beta \in \text{Infin}{:} \supset {:}\alpha \in \text{Infin}.\mathbf{v}.\beta \in \text{Infin}$.

Corollary 2. $\vdash (\alpha,\beta){:}\alpha \cup \beta \in \text{Infin}.\alpha \in \text{Fin}. \supset .\beta \in \text{Infin}$.

Corollary 3. $\vdash (\alpha,\beta){:}\alpha \in \text{Infin}.\beta \in \text{Fin}. \supset .\alpha - \beta \in \text{Infin}$.

Proof. If $\alpha \in \text{Infin}$, then $\alpha \cup \beta \in \text{Infin}$ by Thm.XI.3.31, Cor. 5. So by Thm.IX.4.4, Part XIX, $(\alpha - \beta) \cup \beta \in \text{Infin}$. If $\beta \in \text{Fin}$, then $\alpha - \beta \in \text{Infin}$ by Cor. 2.

Corollary 4. $\vdash (\alpha,x){:}\alpha \in \text{Infin.} \supset .\alpha - \{x\} \in \text{Infin.}$

Theorem XI.3.33. $\vdash (\lambda){:}\lambda \in \text{Fin.}\lambda \subseteq \text{Fin.} \supset .\bigcup\lambda \in \text{Fin.}$

Proof. We prove by weak induction on n that

(1) $$\vdash (\lambda,n){:}n \in \text{Nn.}\lambda \in n.\lambda \subseteq \text{Fin.} \supset .\bigcup\lambda \in \text{Fin.}$$

Let $F(x)$ be

$$(\lambda){:}\lambda \in x.\lambda \subseteq \text{Fin.} \supset .\bigcup\lambda \in \text{Fin.}$$

By Ex.IX.5.1, Part (b), and Thm.XI.3.28, Cor. 3, $(\lambda){:}\lambda \in 0. \supset .\bigcup\lambda \in \text{Fin.}$ So

(2) $$\vdash F(0).$$

Assume $n \in \text{Nn}$, $F(n)$, and $\lambda \in n + 1$, $\lambda \subseteq \text{Fin}$. Then by Thm.X.1.16, $\mu \in n.\sim \alpha \in \mu.\lambda = \mu \cup \{\alpha\}$. Then $\mu \subseteq \lambda$, so that $\mu \subseteq \text{Fin}$, so that by $F(n)$,

(3) $$\bigcup\mu \in \text{Fin.}$$

Also $\alpha \in \lambda$, so that

(4) $$\alpha \in \text{Fin.}$$

By Thm.IX.6.9, Part VIII, $\bigcup\lambda = \alpha \cup \bigcup\mu$. Then by (3) and (4) and Thm.XI.3.32, $\bigcup\lambda \in \text{Fin}$. Thus we have

$$n \in \text{Nn}, F(n) \vdash F(n + 1).$$

So by (2), we conclude (1). From (1) by a simple transformation, we get

$$(\lambda){:}.(En).n \in \text{Nn.}\lambda \in n{:}\lambda \subseteq \text{Fin}{:} \supset {:}\bigcup\lambda \in \text{Fin.}$$

Our theorem now follows by Thm.XI.3.28, Part I.

This theorem tells us that the logical sum of any finite number of finite classes is finite.

Theorem XI.3.34. $\vdash (\alpha,n){:}n \in \text{Nn.}\alpha \in \text{Infin.} \supset .(E\beta).\beta \in n.\beta \subset \alpha.$

Proof. Assume $n \in \text{Nn}$, $\alpha \in \text{Infin}$. Then $\text{Nc}(\alpha) \in \text{NC} - \text{Nn}$. So by Thm.XI.3.6, Cor. 3, $n < \text{Nc}(\alpha)$. Then by Thm.XI.2.22, $\text{Nc}(\alpha) = n + p$. So $\alpha \in n + p$. Then $\beta \in n.\gamma \in p.\beta \cap \gamma = \Lambda.\beta \cup \gamma = \alpha$. So $\beta \subseteq \alpha$. If $\beta = \alpha$, then $n = \text{Nc}(\alpha)$ by Thm.XI.2.2, Part IV. So $\beta \neq \alpha$, and $\beta \subset \alpha$.

This theorem tells us that from any infinite class we may extract as large a finite class as we wish. Incidentally, by Thm.XI.3.32, Cor. 3, what remains is still infinite.

Theorem XI.3.35. $\vdash (\alpha,\beta){:}\alpha,\beta \in \text{Fin.} \supset .\alpha \times \beta \in \text{Fin.}$

Proof. Let $\alpha,\beta \in \text{Fin}$. Then $\text{Nc}(\alpha),\text{Nc}(\beta) \in \text{Nn}$. So by Thm.XI.3.8, $(\text{Nc}(\alpha) \times \text{Nc}(\beta)) \in \text{Nn}$. Then by Thm.XI.2.27, $\text{Nc}(\alpha \times \beta) \in \text{Nn}$. So $\alpha \times \beta \in \text{Fin}$.

Theorem XI.3.36. $\vdash (\alpha,\beta){:}\alpha \times \beta \in \text{Fin.} \supset .\beta \times \alpha \in \text{Fin.}$

Proof. Use Thm.XI.1.17 and Thm.XI.3.28, Cor. 6.

Theorem XI.3.37. $\vdash (\alpha,\beta):\beta \neq \Lambda.\alpha \times \beta \in \text{Fin}. \supset .\alpha \in \text{Fin}.$

Proof. If $\beta \neq \Lambda$ and $\alpha \times \beta \in \text{Fin}$, then $\text{Nc}(\beta) \neq 0$ by Thm.XI.2.7, Cor. 2, and $(\text{Nc}(\alpha) \times \text{Nc}(\beta)) \in \text{Nn}$ by Thm.XI.3.28, Cor. 1, and Thm. XI.2.27. So by Thm.XI.3.9, $\text{Nc}(\alpha) \in \text{Nn}$.

Corollary. $\vdash (\alpha,\beta):\alpha \neq \Lambda.\alpha \times \beta \in \text{Fin}. \supset .\beta \in \text{Fin}.$

Theorem XI.3.38. $\vdash (\alpha):\alpha \in \text{Fin}. \supset .\text{USC}(\alpha) \in \text{Fin}.$

Proof. We prove by weak induction on n that

(1) $$\vdash (\alpha,n):n \in \text{Nn}.\alpha \in n. \supset .\text{USC}(\alpha) \in \text{Fin}.$$

We let $F(x)$ be $(\alpha):\alpha \in x. \supset .\text{USC}(\alpha) \in \text{Fin}.$ By Thm.IX.6.12, Part IV, and Thm.XI.3.28, Cor. 3,

(2) $$\vdash F(0).$$

Assume $n \in \text{Nn}$, $F(n)$, and $\alpha \in n + 1$. Then by Thm.X.1.16, $\beta \in n. \sim x \in \beta.\alpha = \beta \cup \{x\}$. By $F(n)$, $\text{USC}(\beta) \in \text{Fin}$. So by Thm.XI.3.28,

(3) $$m \in \text{Nn},$$

(4) $$\text{USC}(\beta) \in m.$$

By Thm.IX.6.10, Part II,

(5) $$\sim\{x\} \in \text{USC}(\beta).$$

So by (4), (5), and Thm.X.1.16, $\text{USC}(\beta) \cup \{\{x\}\} \in m + 1$. Then by (3), $\text{USC}(\beta) \cup \{\{x\}\} \in \text{Fin}$. However, by Thm.IX.6.12, Part II, and Thm.IX.6.16, $\text{USC}(\alpha) = \text{USC}(\beta) \cup \{\{x\}\}$. So $\text{USC}(\alpha) \in \text{Fin}$. Thus we have shown

$$n \in \text{Nn}, F(n) \vdash F(n + 1).$$

So by (2), we conclude (1). By Thm.XI.3.28, our theorem follows from (1).

Theorem XI.3.39. $\vdash (\alpha):\text{USC}(\alpha) \in \text{Fin}. \supset .\alpha \in \text{Fin}.$

Proof. Since $\vdash 1 \in \text{Nn}$, we have $\vdash 1 \subseteq \text{Fin}$ by Thm.IX.5.5, Part II, and the definition of Fin. So by Thm.IX.6.12, Cor. 2, $\vdash \text{USC}(\alpha) \subseteq \text{Fin}$. Then by Thm.XI.3.33,

$$\vdash \text{USC}(\alpha) \in \text{Fin}. \supset .\bigcup(\text{USC}(\alpha)) \in \text{Fin}.$$

Our theorem follows by Thm.IX.6.11.

Corollary 1. $\vdash (\alpha):\alpha \in \text{Fin}. \equiv .\text{USC}(\alpha) \in \text{Fin}.$

Corollary 2. $\vdash (\alpha):\alpha \in \text{Infin}. \equiv .\text{USC}(\alpha) \in \text{Infin}.$

Theorem XI.3.40. $\vdash (\alpha,\beta):\alpha,\beta \in \text{Fin}. \supset .(\alpha \wedge \beta) \in \text{Fin}.$

Proof. Let $\alpha,\beta \in \text{Fin}$. Then $\text{USC}(\alpha),\text{USC}(\beta) \in \text{Fin}$. So $\text{Nc}(\text{USC}(\alpha))$, $\text{Nc}(\text{USC}(\beta)) \in \text{Nn}$. Then by Thm.XI.3.13, $(\text{Nc}(\text{USC}(\alpha)) \wedge_c \text{Nc}(\text{USC}(\beta))) \in \text{Nn}$. Then by Thm.XI.2.39, $\text{Nc}(\alpha \wedge \beta) \in \text{Nn}$.

Theorem XI.3.41. $\vdash (\alpha):\alpha \in \text{Fin}. \supset .\text{SC}(\alpha) \in \text{Fin}.$

Proof. Let $\alpha \in \text{Fin}$. Let $A = \{\Lambda,\text{V}\}$. Then $\vdash A \in 2$. So $\vdash A \in \text{Fin}$. Then by Thm.XI.3.40, $(\alpha \curlywedge A) \in \text{Fin}$. However, $\vdash \text{SC}(\alpha) \text{ sm } (\alpha \curlywedge A)$ by Thm.XI.1.28. So $\text{SC}(\alpha) \in \text{Fin}$ by Thm.XI.3.28, Cor. 6.

Theorem XI.3.42. $\vdash (\alpha):\text{SC}(\alpha) \in \text{Fin}. \supset .\alpha \in \text{Fin}.$

Proof. Let $\text{SC}(\alpha) \in \text{Fin}$. Then $\text{USC}(\alpha) \in \text{Fin}$ by Thm.XI.3.31 and Thm.IX.6.18, Cor. 1. So $\alpha \in \text{Fin}$ by Thm.XI.3.39.

Corollary 1. $\vdash (\alpha):\alpha \in \text{Fin}. \equiv .\text{SC}(\alpha) \in \text{Fin}.$

Corollary 2. $\vdash (\alpha):\alpha \in \text{Infin}. \equiv .\text{SC}(\alpha) \in \text{Infin}.$

Theorem XI.3.43. $\vdash (\alpha,n):n \in \text{Nn}.\alpha \in n. \supset .\text{USC}^2(\alpha) \text{ sm } \hat{x}(x \in \text{Nn}.x < n).$

Proof. Proof by weak induction on n. Let $F(n)$ denote $(\alpha):\alpha \in n. \supset . \text{USC}^2(\alpha) \text{ sm } \hat{x}(x \in \text{Nn}.x < n)$. By Thm.XI.2.15, Cor. 2, and Thm.XI.2.20, Cor. 2, we get

$$\vdash \hat{x}(x \in \text{Nn}.x < 0) = \Lambda$$

by Thm.IX.4.12, Part II. Thence we get

(1) $$\vdash F(0)$$

by Thm.IX.6.12, Part IV. Assume $n \in \text{Nn}$, $F(n)$, and $\alpha \in n + 1$. By Thm.X.1.16,

(2) $$\beta \in n.\sim z \in \beta.\alpha = \beta \cup \{z\}.$$

From $F(n)$, we get

(3) $$\text{USC}^2(\beta) \text{ sm } \hat{x}(x \in \text{Nn}.x < n).$$

By (2) and Thm.IX.6.6, Cor. 1, $\beta \cap \{z\} = \Lambda$. So by Thm.IX.6.12, Parts I and IV,

(4) $$\text{USC}^2(\beta) \cap \text{USC}^2(\{z\}) = \Lambda.$$

By (2) and Thm.IX.6.12, Part II,

(5) $$\text{USC}^2(\alpha) = \text{USC}^2(\beta) \cup \text{USC}^2(\{z\}).$$

By Thm.XI.2.13, Part III, $\vdash \sim(n < n)$. So $\vdash \sim n \in \hat{x}(x \in \text{Nn}.x < n)$. Then by Thm.IX.6.6, Cor. 1,

(6) $$\hat{x}(x \in \text{Nn}.x < n) \cap \{n\} = \Lambda.$$

By Thm.IX.6.16, $\text{USC}^2(\{z\}) = \{\{\{z\}\}\}$. So by Thm.XI.1.10,

(7) $$\vdash \text{USC}^2(\{z\}) \text{ sm } \{n\}.$$

Since $n \in \text{Nn}$, we have by Thm.XI.2.14, Cor. 2, and Thm.XI.3.5, Cor. 3,

$$\begin{aligned} y \in \hat{x}(x \in \text{Nn}.x < n) \cup \{n\}&: \\ &\equiv :y \in \text{Nn}.y < n.\mathbf{v}.y = n: \\ &\equiv :y \in \text{Nn}.y < n.\mathbf{v}.y \in \text{Nn}.y = n: \\ &\equiv :y \in \text{Nn}.y \leq n: \\ &\equiv :y \in \text{Nn}.y < n + 1: \\ &\equiv :y \in \hat{x}(x \in \text{Nn}.x < n + 1). \end{aligned}$$

So

(8) $$\hat{x}(x \in \text{Nn}.x < n) \cup \{n\} = \hat{x}(x \in \text{Nn}.x < n + 1).$$

By (3), (7), (4), (6), and Thm.XI.1.12, corollary,

$$(\text{USC}^2(\beta) \cup \text{USC}^2(\{z\})) \text{ sm } (\hat{x}(x \in \text{Nn}.x < n) \cup \{n\}).$$

So by (5) and (8),

$$\text{USC}^2(\alpha) \text{ sm } \hat{x}(x \in \text{Nn}.x < n + 1).$$

Corollary 1. $\vdash (n):n \in \text{Nn}. \supset .\hat{x}(x \in \text{Nn}.x < n) \in \text{Fin}.$

Proof. Let $n \in \text{Nn}$. Then by Thm.XI.2.2, Part VI, $\alpha \in n$. Then by Thm.XI.3.28, Part I, $\alpha \in \text{Fin}$. So by Thm.XI.3.38, $\text{USC}^2(\alpha) \in \text{Fin}$. Thence by Thm.XI.3.28, Cor. 6, $\hat{x}(x \in \text{Nn}.x < n) \in \text{Fin}$.

Corollary 2. $\vdash (n):n \in \text{Nn}. \supset .\hat{x}(x \in \text{Nn}.x \leq n) \in \text{Fin}.$

Proof. If $n \in \text{Nn}$, then

$$\hat{x}(x \in \text{Nn}.x \leq n) = \hat{x}(x \in \text{Nn}.x < n + 1)$$

by Thm.XI.3.5, Cor. 3. However, $n + 1 \in \text{Nn}$, so that $\hat{x}(x \in \text{Nn}.x < n + 1) \in \text{Fin}$ by Cor. 1.

We have seen (Thm.XI.3.21) that each nonempty set of finite cardinals has a least member. However, there are nonempty sets of finite cardinals with no greatest member; for example, Nn. For finite nonempty sets, the situation is different. Each nonempty finite set of finite cardinals has a greatest member as well as a least.

This is just a special case of the general result that each nonempty finite subset of a simply ordered set must have both a least and greatest member. Even more generally, each nonempty, finite subset of a partially ordered set must have a minimal element and a maximal element. We now prove this.

Theorem XI.3.44. $\vdash (\alpha,R):R \in \text{Pord}.\alpha \in \text{Fin}.\alpha \neq \Lambda.\alpha \subseteq \text{AV}(R). \supset . (\text{E}x).x \text{ min}_R\, \alpha.$

Proof. We prove by weak induction on n that

(1) $$(\alpha,R,n):R \in \text{Pord}.n \in \text{Nn}.\alpha \in n + 1.\alpha \subseteq \text{AV}(R). \supset .(\text{E}x).x \text{ min}_R\, \alpha.$$

We take $F(n)$ to be $(\alpha,R):R \in \text{Pord}.\alpha \in n + 1.\alpha \subseteq \text{AV}(R). \supset .(\text{E}x). x \text{ min}_R\, \alpha.$

Assume $R \epsilon \text{Pord}.\alpha \epsilon 1.\alpha \subseteq \text{AV}(R)$. Then $\alpha = \{y\}$. Then by the definition of the term, we readily get $y \min_R \alpha$. Thus we infer

$$(2) \qquad \vdash F(0).$$

Assume $n \epsilon \text{Nn}$, $F(n)$, and $R \epsilon \text{Pord}.\alpha \epsilon (n + 1) + 1.\alpha \subseteq \text{AV}(R)$. Then $\beta \epsilon n + 1.\sim y \epsilon \beta.\alpha = \beta \cup \{y\}$. Then $\beta \subseteq \alpha$, so that $\beta \subseteq \text{AV}(R)$, so that by $F(n)$,

$$(3) \qquad z \min_R \beta.$$

Case 1. yRz. Then $y \min_R \alpha$, for clearly $y \epsilon \alpha \cap \text{AV}(R)$, and if $w \epsilon \alpha \cap \text{AV}(R)$, then $\sim(w(R - I)y)$, for if $w(R - I)y$, then $w(R - I)z$ by Thm. X.6.5, Part VII, and $w \epsilon \beta \cap \text{AV}(R)$ by $\alpha = \beta \cup \{y\}$, and we have a contradiction with (3).

Case 2. $\sim(yRz)$. Then

$$(4) \qquad \sim(y(R - I)z).$$

Then $z \min_R \alpha$, for $z \epsilon \alpha \cap \text{AV}(R)$, and if $w \epsilon \alpha \cap \text{AV}(R)$, then either $w \epsilon \beta$, so that $\sim(w(R - I)z)$ by (3), or else $w = y$, so that $\sim(w(R - I)z)$ by (4).

Thus we have established (1). Now assume $R \epsilon \text{Pord}.\alpha \epsilon \text{Fin}.\alpha \neq \Lambda.$ $\alpha \subseteq \text{AV}(R)$. Then by Thm.XI.3.28, $m \epsilon \text{Nn}.\alpha \epsilon m$. Since $\alpha \neq \Lambda$, $m \neq 0$. Hence by Thm.X.1.7, $n \epsilon \text{Nn}.m = n + 1$. So $\alpha \epsilon n + 1$. Then by (1), our theorem follows.

Corollary 1. $\vdash (\alpha,R){:}R \epsilon \text{Pord}.\alpha \epsilon \text{Fin}.\alpha \neq \Lambda.\alpha \subseteq \text{AV}(R). \supset .(\text{E}x).$ $x \max_R \alpha$.

Proof. Use Thm.X.6.5, Part V.

Corollary 2. $\vdash (\alpha,R){:}R \epsilon \text{Sord}.\alpha \epsilon \text{Fin}.\alpha \neq \Lambda.\alpha \subseteq \text{AV}(R). \supset .(\text{E}x).$ $x \text{ least}_R\, \alpha$.

Proof. Use Thm.X.6.10, Part I.

Corollary 3. $\vdash (\alpha,R){:}R \epsilon \text{Sord}.\alpha \epsilon \text{Fin}.\alpha \neq \Lambda.\alpha \subseteq \text{AV}(R). \supset .(\text{E}x).$ $x \text{ greatest}_R\, \alpha$.

****Corollary 4.** $\vdash (\alpha){:}\alpha \subseteq \text{Nn}.\alpha \epsilon \text{Fin}.\alpha \neq \Lambda{:} \supset {:}(\text{E}n){:}n \epsilon \alpha{:}(m).m \epsilon \alpha \supset$ $m \leq n$.

Proof. Take R to be $\text{Nn} \upharpoonleft \leq_c \upharpoonright \text{Nn}$ in Cor. 3.

Theorem XI.3.45. $\vdash (\alpha){::}\alpha \subseteq \text{Nn}{:.}(n){:}n \epsilon \text{Nn}. \supset .(\text{E}x).x \epsilon \alpha.x > n.{:} \supset {:.}$ $\alpha \epsilon \text{Infin}$.

Proof. By Thm.XI.3.44, Cor. 4,

(1) $\vdash (\alpha){::}\alpha \subset \text{Nn}{:}\alpha \neq \Lambda{:.}\sim(\text{E}n){:}n \epsilon \alpha{:}(m).m \epsilon \alpha \supset m \leq n.{:} \supset {:.}\alpha \epsilon \text{Infin}.$

Now assume

$$(2) \qquad \alpha \subseteq \text{Nn}$$

$$(3) \qquad (n){:}n \epsilon \text{Nn}. \supset .(\text{E}x).x \epsilon \alpha.x > n.$$

By putting $n = 0$ in (3), we get $\alpha \neq \Lambda$. Also from (3) by duality and Thm.XI.3.7, Cor. 2, $\sim(\mathrm{E}n):n \in \alpha:(m).m \in \alpha \supset m \leq n$. So by (1), $\alpha \in$ Infin, and we infer our theorem.

An early use of this theorem was Euclid's proof that there are infinitely many primes. For given any n, the prime divisors of $(n!) + 1$ must be greater than n, so that there is a prime greater than n. Hence by the theorem above, the set of primes is infinite.

EXERCISES

XI.3.1. Prove:

(a) $\vdash (m,n):.m \in \mathrm{Nn}.n \in \mathrm{NC}: \supset :n \leq m. \equiv .(\mathrm{E}p).p \in \mathrm{Nn}.m = n + p.$
(b) $\vdash (m,n):.m \in \mathrm{Nn}.n \in \mathrm{NC}: \supset :n < m. \equiv .(\mathrm{E}p).p \in \mathrm{Nn}.m = n + p + 1.$

XI.3.2. Prove:

(a) $\vdash (m,n):m,n \in \mathrm{NC}.m \neq 0.n^m \in \mathrm{Nn}. \supset .n \in \mathrm{Nn}.$
(b) $\vdash (m,n):m,n \in \mathrm{NC}.2 \leq n.n^m \in \mathrm{Nn}. \supset .m \in \mathrm{Nn}.$
(c) $\vdash (m,n):m,n \in \mathrm{NC}.m \neq 0.2 \leq n.n^m \in \mathrm{Nn}. \supset .m,n \in \mathrm{Nn}.$

XI.3.3. Prove $\vdash (n):n \in \mathrm{Nn}. \supset .\hat{x}(x \in \mathrm{Nn}.x < n)$ sm $\hat{x}(x \in \mathrm{Nn}.x \neq 0.x \leq n)$.

XI.3.4. Prove that, if $F(x)$ is stratified, then $F(0),F(1),(n):n \in \mathrm{Nn}.F(n). \supset .F(n + 2) \vdash (n):n \in \mathrm{Nn}. \supset .F(n)$.

XI.3.5. Expose the flaw in the following incorrect proof. We wish to show that all members of any finite nonempty class α are the same. We prove this by weak induction on the number of members of α. When α has a single member, the result is obvious. Assume the result for all α's with n members, and let α have $n + 1$ members. Removing the last member of α, the remaining n members must all be the same by our assumption. Similarly, upon removing the first member of α, the remaining n members must all be the same. Hence the last member must be the same as the first m.

XI.3.6. Prove that, if a and b are specified constants and $h(x,y,z)$ is a specified function value of x, y, and z such that $x = y = z = h(x,y,z)$ is stratified, then there is a unique f such that

$$f \in \mathrm{Funct},$$

$$\mathrm{Arg}(f) = \mathrm{Nn},$$

$$f(0) = a,$$

$$f(1) = b,$$

$$(n):n \in \mathrm{Nn}. \supset .f(n + 2) = h(n,f(n),f(n + 1)).$$

XI.3.7. Prove $\vdash \mathrm{Nn}\urcorner \leq_c \ulcorner\mathrm{Nn} \in \mathrm{Word}$.

XI.3.8. Writing $m - n$ for $\iota p\ (p \in \mathrm{NC}.n + p = m)$, prove:

(a) $\vdash (m,n){:}m \in \mathrm{NC}.n \in \mathrm{Nn}.n \leq m.\ \supset .(m - n) + n = m.m - n \in \mathrm{NC}.$

(b) $\vdash (m,n,p){:}m,p \in \mathrm{NC}.n \in \mathrm{Nn}.n + p = m.\ \supset .p = m - n.$

(c) $\vdash (m,n){:}m \in \mathrm{NC}.n \in \mathrm{Nn}.\ \supset .(m + n) - n = m.$

(d) $\vdash (m,n,p){:}m,n \in \mathrm{NC}.p \in \mathrm{Nn}.p \leq n.\ \supset .(m + n) - p = m + (n - p).$

(e) $\vdash (m,n,p){:}m \in \mathrm{NC}.n,p \in \mathrm{Nn}.n \leq m + p.p \leq n.\ \supset .m - (n - p) = (m + p) - n.$

(f) $\vdash (m,n,p){:}m \in \mathrm{NC}.n,p \in \mathrm{Nn}.p \leq m.\ \supset .(m + n) - (n + p) = m - p.$

(g) $\vdash (m,n,p){:}m \in \mathrm{NC}.n,p \in \mathrm{Nn}.n + p \leq m.\ \supset .m - (n + p) = (m - n) - p.$

(h) $\vdash (m,n){:}m \in \mathrm{NC}.n \in \mathrm{Nn}.n \leq m.\ \supset .m - n \leq m.$

(i) $\vdash (m,n,p){:}m \in \mathrm{NC}.n,p \in \mathrm{Nn}.n \leq m.\ \supset .(m \times p) - (n \times p) = (m - n) \times p.$

(j) $\vdash (m){:}m \in \mathrm{Nn}.\ \supset .m - m = 0.$

XI.3.9. Writing $Q(m \div n)$ for $\iota q\ (q \in \mathrm{NC}.n \times q \leq m.m < n \times (q + 1))$, and $R(m \div n)$ for $m - (n \times Q(m \div n))$, prove:

(a) $\vdash (m,n){:}m,n \in \mathrm{Nn}.n \neq 0.\ \supset .Q(m \div n) \in \mathrm{Nn}.n \times Q(m \div n) \leq m.\ m < n \times (Q(m \div n) + 1).$

(b) $\vdash (m,n,q){:}m,n \in \mathrm{Nn}.q \in \mathrm{NC}.n \times q \leq m.m < n \times (q + 1).\ \supset .\ q = Q(m \div n).$

(c) $\vdash (m,n){:}m,n \in \mathrm{Nn}.n \neq 0.\ \supset .R(m \div n) \in \mathrm{Nn}.m = (n \times Q(m \div n)) + R(m \div n).$

(d) $\vdash (m,n){:}m,n \in \mathrm{Nn}.n \neq 0.\ \supset .0 \leq R(m \div n).R(m \div n) < n.$

(e) $\vdash (m,n){:}m,n \in \mathrm{Nn}.n \neq 0.\ \supset .Q((m \times n) \div n) = m.R((m \times n) \div n) = 0.$

(f) $\vdash (m){:}m \in \mathrm{Nn}.m \neq 0.\ \supset .Q(m \div m) = 1.$

(g) $\vdash (m,n){:}m,n,p \in \mathrm{Nn}.n \neq 0.R(m \div n) = 0.\ \supset .Q((m + p) \div n) = Q(m \div n) + Q(p \div n).$

(h) $\vdash (m,n,p){:}m,n,p \in \mathrm{Nn}.n \neq 0.p \leq m.\ \supset .n^{m-p} = Q((n^m) \div (n^p)).$

(i) $\vdash (m,n,p){:}m,n,p \in \mathrm{Nn}.n \neq 0.m = n \times p.\ \supset .p = Q(m \div n).$

XI.3.10. Let us define

$$\sum_{x=m}^{n} f(x)$$

by weak induction on n, according to the conditions

$$\sum_{x=m}^{m} f(x) = f(m),$$

$$\sum_{x=m}^{n+1} f(x) = f(n + 1) + \sum_{x=m}^{n} f(x).$$

Prove that, if $x = f(x)$ is stratified, then:

(a) $\vdash (m,n,p):m,n,p \in \text{Nn}.m \leq n.n < p. \supset . \sum_{x=m}^{p} f(x) = \sum_{x=m}^{n} f(x) + \sum_{x=n+1}^{p} f(x).$

(b) $\vdash (m,n,p):m,n,p \in \text{Nn}.m \leq n. \supset . \sum_{x=m}^{n} f(x) = \sum_{x=m+p}^{n+p} f(x - p).$

(c) $\vdash (m,n,p)::m,n \in \text{Nn}.p \in \text{NC}.m \leq n:.(x):x \in \text{Nn}.m \leq x.x \leq n. \supset .f(x) \in \text{NC}.: \supset :.p \times \left(\sum_{x=m}^{n} f(x)\right) = \sum_{x=m}^{n} (p \times f(x)).$

XI.3.11. Let us define $n!$ by weak induction on n, according to the conditions

$$0! = 1,$$

$$(n + 1)! = (n + 1) \times (n!).$$

Let us define

$$\binom{n}{m} \quad \text{as} \quad Q((n!) \div ((m!) \times ((n - m)!))).$$

Prove:

(a) $\vdash (n):n \in \text{Nn}. \supset .\binom{n}{n} = 1.$

(b) $\vdash (m,n):m,n \in \text{Nn}.m \leq n. \supset .(m!) \times ((n - m)!) \times \binom{n}{m} = n!$

(*Hint.* Use weak induction on n. If (b) is assumed for n and if $m < n$, then

$$((m + 1)!) \times ((n - m)!) \times \left(\binom{n}{m} + \binom{n}{m + 1}\right)$$
$$= ((m + 1) \times (n!)) + ((n - m) \times (n!))$$
$$= (n + 1)!)$$

(c) $\vdash (m,n):m,n \in \text{Nn}.m + 1 \leq n. \supset .\binom{n}{m} + \binom{n}{m + 1} = \binom{n + 1}{m + 1}.$

(*Hint.* Use the same algebraic relation as in the hint for (b).)

(d) $\vdash (x,y,n):x,y \in \text{NC}.n \in \text{Nn}. \supset .(x + y)^n = \sum_{m=0}^{n} \binom{n}{m} x^m y^{n-m}.$

(*Hint.* Use weak induction on n.)

XI.3.12. Prove Thm.XII.2.12. (*Hint.* Define S by

$$S(\{0\}) = \{\langle m,a\rangle\},$$

$(n):n \epsilon \text{Nn.} \supset .S(\{n+1\}) = S(\{n\}) \cup \{\langle m+n+1, j(m+n, S(\{n\}))\rangle\}$

(see Thm.XI.3.26). Also define

$$R = \hat{w}(\text{E}n).n \epsilon \text{Nn}.w \epsilon S(\{n\}).$$

Assuming the hypothesis of Thm.XII.2.12, prove the following lemmas:

1. $(n):n \epsilon \text{Nn.} \supset .\text{Arg}(S(\{n\})) = \hat{x}(x \epsilon \text{Nn}.m \leq x.x \leq m+n).$
2. $(n):n \epsilon \text{Nn.} \supset .S(\{n\}) \epsilon \text{Funct.}$
3. $(n):n \epsilon \text{Nn.} \supset .m(S(\{n\}))a.$
4. $(n,p):n,p \epsilon \text{Nn.} \supset .(m+n+1)(S(\{n+p+1\}))j(m+n, S(\{n\})).$
5. $(y):mRy. \equiv .y = a.$
6. $(n):.n \epsilon \text{Nn}: \supset :(y):(m+n+1)Ry. \equiv .y = j(m+n, S(\{n\})).$
7. $\text{Arg}(R) = \alpha.$
8. $R \epsilon \text{Funct.}$
9. $R(m) = a.$
10. $(n):.n \epsilon \text{Nn}: \supset :(x):x \epsilon \alpha.x \leq m+n. \supset .R(x) = (S(\{n\}))(x).$
11. $(n):n \epsilon \alpha. \supset .R(n+1) = j(n,R).)$

XI.3.13. If $\alpha, \beta_1, \beta_2, \ldots$ are as in the discussion between Thms.IX.5.15 and IX.5.16, show how to define a function R such that

$$R(0) = \alpha$$
$$R(1) = \beta_1$$
$$R(2) = \beta_2$$
$$\text{etc.}$$

With this R, prove $\vdash \text{Clos}(\alpha,P) = \bigcup\{R(n) \mid n \epsilon \text{Nn}\}$. Explain why this may be interpreted as

$$\text{Clos}(\alpha,P) = \alpha \cup \beta_1 \cup \beta_2 \cup \cdots.$$

XI.3.14. Prove $\vdash (\alpha)::\alpha \subseteq \text{Nn.}: \supset :.(n):n \epsilon \text{Nn.} \supset .(\text{E}x).x \epsilon \alpha.x > n: \equiv : (n):n \epsilon \text{Nn.} \supset .(\text{E}x).x \epsilon \alpha.x \geq n.$

XI.3.15. Give an intuitive proof that each real number x with $0 < x \leq 1$ can be uniquely expanded in a nonterminating ternary expansion (every digit of the expansion is either a 0, 1, or 2) with no digits to the left of the ternary point.

XI.3.16. Prove:

(a) $\vdash (\lambda):\bigcup\lambda \epsilon \text{Fin.} \equiv .\lambda \epsilon \text{Fin}.\lambda \subseteq \text{Fin.}$
(*Hint.* Show that $\vdash \lambda \subseteq \text{SC}(\bigcup\lambda)$.)
(b) $\vdash (\alpha)::\alpha \epsilon \text{Infin.}: \equiv :.(n):n \epsilon \text{Nn.} \supset .(\text{E}\beta).\beta \subseteq \alpha.\beta \epsilon n.$

Throughout the remaining exercises, assume the "four" Hausdorff axioms, and use the notation of Sec. 8 of Chapter IX.

XI.3.17. Prove:

(a) $(\lambda):\lambda \epsilon \text{Fin}.\lambda \subseteq \text{OS}. \supset .\bigcap\lambda \epsilon \text{OS}.$
(b) $(\lambda):\lambda \epsilon \text{Fin}.\lambda \subseteq \text{CS}. \supset .\bigcup\lambda \epsilon \text{CS}.$

(*Hint.* Proceed as in the proof of Thm.XI.3.33.)

XI.3.18. Prove $(\alpha,x):\sim x \epsilon \alpha.\alpha \epsilon \text{Fin}. \supset .(\text{E}\beta).\beta \epsilon H(x).\alpha \cap \beta = \Lambda.$ (*Hint.* Use weak induction on $\text{Nc}(\alpha)$.)

XI.3.19. Prove $(\alpha,x):.x \epsilon \alpha': \equiv :(\beta):x \epsilon \beta.\beta \epsilon \text{OS}. \supset .\beta \cap \alpha \epsilon \text{Infin}.$ (*Hint.* If $x \epsilon \alpha'$, $x \epsilon \beta.\beta \epsilon \text{OS}$, and $\beta \cap \alpha \epsilon \text{Fin}$, choose γ_1 with $\gamma_1 \epsilon H(x).\gamma_1 \subseteq \beta$. Then $\alpha \cap (\gamma_1 - \{x\}) \epsilon \text{Fin}$. So by the preceding exercise, there is a γ_2 with $\gamma_2 \epsilon H(x).\gamma_2 \cap (\alpha \cap (\gamma_1 - \{x\})) = \Lambda$. Choose γ_3 with $\gamma_3 \epsilon H(x).\gamma_3 \subseteq \gamma_1 \cap \gamma_2$. Then $x \epsilon \gamma_3.\gamma_3 \epsilon \text{OS}.(\gamma_3 - \{x\}) \cap \alpha = \Lambda$, contradicting $x \epsilon \alpha'$.)

XI.3.20. Prove $(\alpha):\alpha \epsilon \text{Fin}. \supset .\alpha' = \Lambda.$

We say that a set of sets, λ, covers a set, α, if $\alpha \subseteq \bigcup\lambda$.

We say that a Hausdorff space is compact if, whenever λ is a set of open sets which covers Σ, then it has a finite subset which covers Σ. This would be expressed in symbols as follows:

$$(\lambda):\lambda \subseteq \text{OS}.\bigcup\lambda = \Sigma. \supset .(\text{E}\mu).\mu \subseteq \lambda.\mu \epsilon \text{Fin}.\bigcup\mu = \Sigma.$$

XI.3.21. Prove that a Hausdorff space is compact if and only if $\bigcap\lambda \neq \Lambda$ whenever λ is a set of closed sets and $\bigcap\mu \neq \Lambda$ for every finite subset of λ. That is,

$$(\lambda):\lambda \subseteq \text{OS}.\bigcup\lambda = \Sigma. \supset .(\text{E}\mu).\mu \subseteq \lambda.\mu \epsilon \text{Fin}.\bigcup\mu = \Sigma:: \equiv ::(\lambda)::\lambda \subseteq \text{CS}:. (\mu):\mu \epsilon \text{Fin}.\mu \subseteq \lambda. \supset .\bigcap\mu \neq \Lambda.: \supset :.\bigcap\lambda \neq \Lambda.$$

XI.3.22. Prove that, if a Hausdorff space is compact, then every infinite set has a limit point. That is,

$$(\lambda):\lambda \subseteq \text{OS}.\bigcup\lambda = \Sigma. \supset .(\text{E}\mu).\mu \subseteq \lambda.\mu \epsilon \text{Fin}.\bigcup\mu = \Sigma.: \supset :.(\alpha):\alpha \epsilon \text{Infin}. \supset .\alpha' \neq \Lambda.$$

(*Hint.* Let the space be compact and assume $\alpha \epsilon \text{Infin}$ and $\alpha' = \Lambda$. Put $\lambda = \hat{\beta}(\beta \epsilon \text{OS}.\beta \cap \alpha \epsilon \text{Fin})$. By Ex.XI.3.19, $\bigcup\lambda = \Sigma$. So $\mu \subseteq \lambda.\mu \epsilon \text{Fin}.\bigcup\mu = \Sigma$. So $\alpha \cap \bigcup\mu = \alpha$. However, $\alpha \cap \bigcup\mu = \bigcup\{\alpha \cap \gamma \mid \gamma \epsilon \mu\}$. Since $\mu \epsilon \text{Fin}$, we get $\{\alpha \cap \gamma \mid \gamma \epsilon \mu\} \epsilon \text{Fin}$. Also, since $\mu \subseteq \hat{\beta}(\beta \epsilon \text{OS}.\beta \cap \alpha \epsilon \text{Fin})$, we get $\{\alpha \cap \gamma \mid \gamma \epsilon \mu\} \subseteq \text{Fin}$. So $\alpha \epsilon \text{Fin}$, and we have a contradiction.)

4. Denumerable Classes. We shall define a denumerable class as one which can be put into one-to-one correspondence with the nonnegative integers. That is, we say that α is denumerable if and only if α sm Nn.

We say that α is countable if α is either finite or denumerable. Specifically, we define

Den	for	Nc(Nn)
Count	for	Fin $\cup$ Den.

Both Den and Count are stratified and have no free variables, and hence may be assigned any type. It will be noted that Den is a cardinal number. When thinking of it in this sense, it is standard mathematical usage to denote it by $\aleph_0$. As this is often very awkward typographically, we shall use the simpler Den in all cases.

From an intuitive point of view, a class α is denumerable if and only if its members can be arranged in a well-ordered linear sequence with a first member but no last member, and such that every member but the first has an immediate predecessor in the sequence. For if they can be so arranged, we can attach a subscript zero to the first, a subscript unity to the next, a subscript "two" to the next, etc. We then have set up a one-to-one correspondence between the members of α and of Nn. Conversely, given such a pairing of the members of α and Nn, we can arrange the members of α in a sequence by writing down first the one paired with zero, then the one paired with unity, then the one paired with "two", etc. In intuitive mathematics, one often puts the above ideas in evidence by referring to α as consisting of $x_0, x_1, x_2, \ldots$.

In the symbolic logic, we do not have available this idea of arranging the members of a set in a linear sequence. Instead, we have to use the notion of the set being similar to Nn. This is adequate for the purpose, as we shall show by deriving the familiar theorems on denumerable sets.

If a set is merely countable, one can still arrange the members in a sequence, but the sequence may terminate, whereas if the set is denumerable, the sequence must be nonterminating.

The usage which we have adopted for "denumerable" and "countable" is not universal. Many mathematicians treat "denumerable" and "countable" as synonymous. Some of these mathematicians use both words in our sense of "denumerable," and some use both words in our sense of "countable." However, our usage has sanction (see Kershner and Wilcox), and we know of no case where it is reversed.

Some authors use the word "enumerable." Most commonly it is used in our sense of "denumerable" (see Townsend, 1928), but occasionally it is used in our sense of "countable."

Theorem XI.4.1.

I. $\vdash (\alpha):\alpha \in \text{Den}. \equiv .\alpha \text{ sm Nn}.$

II. $\vdash (\alpha):\alpha \in \text{Den}.\alpha \text{ sm } \beta. \supset .\beta \in \text{Den}.$

III. $\vdash (\alpha,\beta):\alpha,\beta \in \text{Den}. \supset .\alpha \text{ sm } \beta.$

IV. $\vdash (\alpha):\alpha \in \text{Count}. \equiv .\alpha \in \text{Fin} \vee \alpha \in \text{Den}.$

V. $\vdash (\alpha,\beta):\alpha \in \text{Count}.\alpha \text{ sm } \beta. \supset .\beta \in \text{Count}.$

Corollary 1. $\vdash (\alpha):\alpha \in \text{Den}. \equiv .\alpha \text{ sm Nn} - \{0\}.$

Corollary 2. $\vdash \Lambda \in \text{Count}.$

Corollary 3. $\vdash (x).\{x\} \in \text{Count}.$

Corollary 4. $\vdash (\alpha):\alpha \in \text{Den}. \supset .\alpha \in \text{Infin}.$

Theorem XI.4.2. $\vdash (\alpha)::\alpha \subseteq \text{Nn}:.(\text{E}n):n \in \text{Nn}.(x).x \in \alpha \supset x \leq n.: \supset :. \alpha \in \text{Fin}.$

Proof. Assume $\alpha \subseteq \text{Nn}$ and $(\text{E}n):n \in \text{Nn}.(x).x \in \alpha \supset x \leq n.$ Then $n \in \text{Nn}$ and $\alpha \subseteq \hat{x}(x \in \text{Nn}.x \leq n)$. Then by Thm.XI.3.43, Cor. 2, and Thm.XI.3.31, $\alpha \in \text{Fin}$.

Corollary. $\vdash (\alpha)::\alpha \subseteq \text{Nn}:.(\text{E}n):n \in \text{Nn}.(x).x \in \alpha \supset x < n.: \supset :. \alpha \in \text{Fin}.$

We now show that any unbounded set of integers is denumerable and indeed can be enumerated in the obvious fashion, namely, by numbering the members in increasing order, starting with the least.

****Theorem XI.4.3.** $\vdash (\alpha)::\alpha \subseteq \text{Nn}:.(n):n \in \text{Nn}. \supset .(\text{E}x).x \in \alpha.x > n.: \supset :. (\text{E}R):.\text{Nn sm}_R\ \alpha:.(m,n):.m,n \in \text{Nn}: \supset :m < n. \equiv .R(m) < R(n).$

Proof. Assume

(1) $$\alpha \subseteq \text{Nn}$$

(2) $$(n):n \in \text{Nn}. \supset .(\text{E}x).x \in \alpha.x > n.$$

Now by Thm.XI.3.24 there is an R such that

(3) $$R \in \text{Funct},$$

(4) $$\text{Arg}(R) = \text{Nn},$$

(5) $$R(0) = \iota y\ (y \in \alpha:(z):z \in \alpha. \supset .y \leq z),$$

(6) $$(n):n \in \text{Nn}. \supset .R(n+1) = \iota y\ (y > R(n):.y \in \alpha:.(z):z > R(n).z \in \alpha. \supset .y \leq z).$$

Lemma 1. $R(0) \in \alpha:(z):z \in \alpha. \supset .R(0) \leq z.$

Proof. By (2), $\alpha \neq \Lambda$. So our lemma follows by (1), (5), and Thm. XI.3.21, corollary.

Lemma 2. $(n)::n \in \text{Nn}.R(n) \in \alpha.: \supset :.R(n+1) > R(n):.R(n+1) \in \alpha:. (z):z > R(n).z \in \alpha. \supset .R(n+1) \leq z.$

Proof. Take β to be $\hat{y}(y > R(n).y \in \alpha)$. Then by (6),

(i) $$(n):n \in \text{Nn}. \supset .R(n+1) = \iota y\ (y \in \beta:(z):z \in \beta. \supset .y \leq z).$$

Now assume $n \in \text{Nn}$ and $R(n) \in \alpha$. Then $R(n) \in \text{Nn}$, so that by (2), $\beta \neq \Lambda$. Also, by (1), $\beta \subseteq \text{Nn}$, so that by Thm.XI.3.21, corollary, and (i)

$$R(n+1) \in \beta:(z):z \in \beta. \supset .R(n+1) \leq z.$$

By the definition of β, our lemma follows.

Lemma 3. $\mathrm{Val}(R) \subseteq \alpha$.

Proof. Using Lemma 1 and Lemma 2, we can prove by weak induction on n that

$$(n){:}n \in \mathrm{Nn}. \supset .R(n) \in \alpha.$$

Now let $y \in \mathrm{Val}(R)$. Then nRy. So $n \in \mathrm{Nn}$ by (4). Also $y = R(n)$ by Thm.X.5.3. Thus $y \in \alpha$.

Lemma 4. $(m,n){:}m,n \in \mathrm{Nn}. \supset .R(m) < R(m + n + 1)$.

Proof. We use weak induction on n. By Lemma 2, our lemma holds when $n = 0$. Now assume the lemma for n and let $n \in \mathrm{Nn}$. Then $R(m) < R(m + n + 1)$. Also by Lemma 2, $R(m + n + 1) < R(m + (n + 1) + 1)$. Likewise, by Lemma 3, $R(m)$, $R(m + n + 1)$, and $R(m + (n + 1) + 1)$ are all in α, and hence all in Nn. So by Thm.XI.2.25, Cor. 4, $R(m) < R(m + (n + 1) + 1)$.

Lemma 5. $R \in 1\text{–}1$.

Proof. Let $mRy.nRy$. Then by (4), $m,n \in \mathrm{Nn}$, and by Thm.X.5.3, $R(m) = y = R(n)$. By Thm.XI.3.7, $m < n.\mathsf{v}.m = n.\mathsf{v}.m > n$. If $m < n$, then by Lemma 4 and Thm.XI.3.5, $R(m) < R(n)$, which is a contradiction. If $m > n$, we get a similar contradiction. So $m = n$.

Lemma 6. $(m){:}m \in \mathrm{Nn}. \supset .m \leq R(m)$.

Proof. Proof by weak induction on m. Clearly $0 \leq R(0)$ by Lemma 3. Let $m \leq R(m)$. By Lemma 2, $R(m) < R(m + 1)$. So $m < R(m + 1)$, whence $m + 1 \leq R(m + 1)$ by Thm.XI.3.5, Cor. 1.

Lemma 7. $\alpha \subseteq \mathrm{Val}(R)$.

Proof. Proof by reductio ad absurdum. Assume $\sim(\alpha \subseteq \mathrm{Val}(R))$. Then by duality and rule C, $x \in \alpha.\sim x \in \mathrm{Val}(R)$. Let $\gamma = \hat{y}(y \in \alpha.\sim y \in \mathrm{Val}(R))$. Then γ has a least member z, so that by Thm.XI.3.21,

(i) $$z \in \alpha.\sim z \in \mathrm{Val}(R)$$

(ii) $$(y){:}y \in \alpha.\sim y \in \mathrm{Val}(R). \supset .z \leq y.$$

Then by (ii) and Thm.XI.3.7, Cor. 2,

(iii) $$(y){:}y \in \alpha.y < z. \supset .y \in \mathrm{Val}(R).$$

Now by Lemma 6, $R(z) \geq z$. Hence $(m){:}m \in \hat{n}(n \in \mathrm{Nn}.R(n) < z). \supset . m < z$ by Lemma 4. So

(iv) $$\hat{n}(n \in \mathrm{Nn}.R(n) < z) \in \mathrm{Fin}$$

by Thm.XI.4.2. By Lemma 1 and (i), $R(0) \leq z$. However, $R(0) \in \mathrm{Val}(R)$, so that by (i), $R(0) \neq z$. So $R(0) < z$. Thus $0 \in \hat{n}(n \in \mathrm{Nn}.R(n) < z)$. So $\hat{n}(n \in \mathrm{Nn}.R(n) < z) \neq \Lambda$. Thus, by (iv) and Thm.XI.3.44, Cor. 4, there is a greatest n in $\hat{n}(n \in \mathrm{Nn}.R(n) < z)$. Call this w, so that

(v) $$w \,\epsilon\, \text{Nn}.R(w) < z$$

(vi) $$(m):m \,\epsilon\, \text{Nn}.R(m) < z. \supset .m \leq w.$$

Then by (vi)

(vii) $$R(w + 1) \geq z.$$

By (v), Lemma 2, and Lemma 3, $(m):R(w) < m.m \,\epsilon\, \alpha. \supset .R(w + 1) \leq m$. Then by (v) and (i), $R(w + 1) \leq z$. Combining with (vii) gives $R(w + 1) = z$. However, $R(w + 1) \,\epsilon\, \text{Val}(R)$. So $z \,\epsilon\, \text{Val}(R)$, and we have a contradiction by (i). This completes the proof of our lemma.

Lemma 8. $(m,n):.m,n \,\epsilon\, \text{Nn}: \supset :m < n. \equiv .R(m) < R(n)$.

Proof. By Lemma 4,

(i) $$(m,n):m,n \,\epsilon\, \text{Nn}.m < n. \supset .R(m) < R(n).$$

Now let $m,n \,\epsilon\, \text{Nn}.R(m) < R(n)$. If $m > n$ we get a contradiction by (i), and if $m = n$ we get $R(m) = R(n)$, which is also a contradiction. So $m < n$ by Thm.XI.3.7.

By the definition of $\text{Nn sm}_R\, \alpha$, we can derive our theorem from Lemma 5, (4), Lemma 3, Lemma 7, and Lemma 8.

Corollary. $\vdash (\alpha)::\alpha \subseteq \text{Nn}:.(n):n \,\epsilon\, \text{Nn}. \supset .(Ex).x \,\epsilon\, \alpha.x > n.: \supset :.\alpha \,\epsilon\, \text{Den}$.

Theorem XI.4.4. $\vdash (\alpha):\alpha \subseteq \text{Nn}. \supset .\alpha \,\epsilon\, \text{Count}$.

Proof. Assume $\alpha \subseteq \text{Nn}$.

Case 1. $(En):n \,\epsilon\, \text{Nn}.(x).x \,\epsilon\, \alpha \supset x \leq n$. Then $\alpha \,\epsilon\, \text{Fin}$ by Thm.XI.4.2. So $\alpha \,\epsilon\, \text{Count}$.

Case 2. $\sim(En):n \,\epsilon\, \text{Nn}.(x).x \,\epsilon\, \alpha \supset x \leq n$. Then by Thm.XI.3.7, Cor. 2, and duality, $(n):n \,\epsilon\, \text{Nn}. \supset .(Ex).x \,\epsilon\, \alpha.x > n$. Then $\alpha \,\epsilon\, \text{Den}$ by Thm.XI.4.3, corollary. So $\alpha \,\epsilon\, \text{Count}$.

Corollary. $\vdash (\alpha,\beta):\alpha \,\epsilon\, \text{Den}.\beta \subseteq \alpha. \supset .\beta \,\epsilon\, \text{Count}$.

Proof. Assume $\alpha \,\epsilon\, \text{Den}.\beta \subseteq \alpha$. Then $\text{Nc}(\alpha) = \text{Den}$. Also $\text{Nc}(\beta) \leq \text{Nc}(\alpha)$. So $p \,\epsilon\, \text{NC}.\text{Nc}(\alpha) = \text{Nc}(\beta) + p$. That is, $\text{Den} = \text{Nc}(\beta) + p$. So $\text{Nn} \,\epsilon\, \text{Nc}(\beta) + p$. Then $\gamma \,\epsilon\, \text{Nc}(\beta).\delta \,\epsilon\, p.\gamma \cap \delta = \Lambda.\gamma \cup \delta = \text{Nn}$. Then $\gamma \text{ sm } \beta.\gamma \subseteq \text{Nn}$. Then $\gamma \,\epsilon\, \text{Count}$ and so $\beta \,\epsilon\, \text{Count}$.

Theorem XI.4.5.

I. $\vdash \text{Den} \,\epsilon\, \text{NC} - \text{Nn}$.

II. $\vdash (n):n \,\epsilon\, \text{Nn}. \supset .n < \text{Den}$.

Proof. These are just Cor. 2 and Cor. 3 of Thm.XI.3.30.

Theorem XI.4.6. $\vdash (n):n \,\epsilon\, \text{NC}.n < \text{Den}. \supset .n \,\epsilon\, \text{Nn}$.

Proof. Assume $n \,\epsilon\, \text{NC}$ and $n < \text{Den}$. Then $p \,\epsilon\, \text{NC}.\text{Den} = n + p$. So $\text{Nn} \,\epsilon\, n + p$. Then $\alpha \,\epsilon\, n.\beta \,\epsilon\, p.\alpha \cap \beta = \Lambda.\alpha \cup \beta = \text{Nn}$. So $\alpha \subseteq \text{Nn}$. Then $\alpha \,\epsilon\, \text{Count}$ by Thm.XI.4.4. If $\alpha \,\epsilon\, \text{Den}$, then $n = \text{Den}$ by Thm.XI.2.2, Part IV, which would contradict $n < \text{Den}$. So $\sim \alpha \,\epsilon\, \text{Den}$. Hence $\alpha \,\epsilon\, \text{Fin}$. Hence $\text{Nc}(\alpha) \,\epsilon\, \text{Nn}$ by Thm.XI.3.28, Cor. 1. But $n = \text{Nc}(\alpha)$ by Thm.XI.2.2, Part III.

Corollary 1. $\vdash (\alpha){:}\alpha \in \text{Fin}. \equiv .\text{Nc}(\alpha) < \text{Den}.$

Corollary 2. $\vdash (\alpha){:}\alpha \in \text{Count}. \equiv .\text{Nc}(\alpha) \leq \text{Den}.$

Corollary 3. $\vdash (\alpha,\beta){:}\alpha \in \text{Den}.\alpha \subseteq \beta.\beta \in \text{Count}. \supset .\beta \in \text{Den}.$

Proof. From the hypothesis we get $\text{Nc}(\alpha) = \text{Den}$, $\text{Nc}(\alpha) \leq \text{Nc}(\beta)$, $\text{Nc}(\beta) \leq \text{Den}$. Then by Thm.XI.2.20, $\text{Nc}(\beta) = \text{Den}$, so that $\beta \in \text{Den}$.

Theorem XI.4.7. $\vdash (\alpha){:.}\alpha \in \text{Fin}: \equiv :(\text{E}n).n \in \text{Nn}.\alpha \text{ sm } \hat{m}(m \in \text{Nn}. m \neq 0.m \leq n).$

Proof. By Thm.XI.3.43, Cor. 1, and Ex.XI.3.3, we easily go from right to left. Now assume $\alpha \in \text{Fin}$. Then $\text{Nc}(\alpha) \in \text{Nn}$. Then by Thms.XI.2.44 and XI.2.42, $\text{USC}(\beta) \in \text{Nc}(\alpha)$. So $\text{USC}(\beta) \text{ sm } \alpha$ by Thm.XI.2.1. Then $\beta \in \text{Fin}$ by Thm.XI.3.28, Cor. 6, and Thm.XI.3.39. Repeating for β the reasoning we carried out for α gives us $\text{USC}(\gamma) \text{ sm } \beta$. Then by Thm. XI.1.33, $\text{USC}^2(\gamma) \text{ sm } \alpha$. Then by Thm.XI.3.43, $\alpha \text{ sm } \hat{x}(x \in \text{Nn}.x < \text{Nc}(\gamma))$. We conclude the theorem by use of Ex.XI.3.3.

Corollary. $\vdash (\alpha){:.}\alpha \in \text{Count}: \equiv :(\text{E}\beta).\beta \subseteq \text{Nn}.\alpha \text{ sm } \beta.$

Proof. We go from right to left by Thm.XI.4.4. Conversely, let $\alpha \in \text{Count}$. If $\alpha \in \text{Fin}$, we use the theorem just proved. If $\alpha \in \text{Den}$, take β to be Nn.

Theorem XI.4.8. $\vdash (R){:}R \in \text{Funct}.\text{Arg}(R) \subseteq \text{Nn}. \supset .\text{Val}(R) \in \text{Count}.$

Proof. Assume

(1) $$R \in \text{Funct}$$

(2) $$\text{Arg}(R) \subseteq \text{Nn}.$$

Let

(3) $$S = \hat{x}\hat{y}(xRy{:}(z).zRy \supset x \leq z).$$

Obviously

(4) $$S \in \text{Funct}.$$

Let $uSy.vSy$. Then by (2), $u,v \in \text{Nn}$. Also by (3)

$$(z).zRy \supset u \leq z$$

$$(z).zRy \supset v \leq z.$$

Taking z to be v in the first of these, and u in the second gives $u \leq v$ and $v \leq u$, so that $u = v$. So

(5) $$S \in 1\text{–}1.$$

Obviously

(6) $$\text{Val}(S) \subseteq \text{Val}(R).$$

Now let $y \in \text{Val}(R)$. Then uRy. Hence $\hat{x}(xRy) \neq \Lambda$. Also by (2),

$\hat{x}(xRy) \subseteq \text{Nn}$. So by Thm.XI.3.21, there is a least x in $\hat{x}(xRy)$, so that $xRy{:}(z).zRy \supset x \leq z$. That is xSy. Thus $y \in \text{Val}(S)$. So by (6)

$$\text{(7)} \qquad \text{Val}(S) = \text{Val}(R).$$

By (5), (7), and Thm.XI.1.1, Part IV, Arg(S) sm Val(R). But by (3) and (2), $\text{Arg}(S) \subseteq \text{Nn}$. So by Thm.XI.4.4, $\text{Arg}(S) \in \text{Count}$. Hence $\text{Val}(R) \in \text{Count}$.

Theorem XI.4.9. $\vdash \text{Den} \times \text{Den} = \text{Den}$.

Proof. By Thm.XI.1.20,

$$\text{(1)} \qquad \vdash (\text{Nn} \times \{0\}) \in \text{Den}.$$

By Thm.X.3.12, Part II,

$$\text{(2)} \qquad \vdash (\text{Nn} \times \{0\}) \subseteq (\text{Nn} \times \text{Nn}).$$

Let

$$\text{(3)} \qquad R = \hat{u}\hat{v}((\text{E}x,y).x,y \in \text{Nn}.u = ((x + y) \times (x + y + 1)) + x. \\ v = \langle x,y \rangle).$$

Clearly

$$\text{(4)} \qquad \vdash \text{Arg}(R) \subseteq \text{Nn}.$$

$$\text{(5)} \qquad \vdash R \in \text{Rel}.$$

Let $uRv.uRw$. Then $x,y \in \text{Nn}.u = ((x + y) \times (x + y + 1)) + x.$ $v = \langle x,y \rangle$ and $x',y' \in \text{Nn}.u = ((x' + y') \times (x' + y' + 1)) + y'.w = \langle x',y' \rangle$. Write temporarily $z = x + y$, $z' = x' + y'$. Then $(z \times (z + 1)) + x = u = (z' \times (z' + 1)) + x'$. By Thm.XI.3.7, $z < z'.\mathbf{v}.z = z'.\mathbf{v}.z > z'$.

Case 1. $z < z'$. Then by Thm.XI.3.5, $n \in \text{Nn}.z' = z + n + 1$. Then

$$\begin{aligned} z' \times (z' + 1) &= (z + n + 1) \times ((z + n + 1) + 1) \\ &= (z + (n + 1)) \times ((z + 1) + (n + 1)) \\ &= (z \times (z + 1)) + (z \times (n + 1)) \\ &\qquad + ((n + 1) \times (z + 1)) + ((n + 1) \times (n + 1)) \\ &= (z \times (z + 1)) + (z \times (n + n + 2)) + ((n + 2) \times (n + 1)). \end{aligned}$$

By Thm.XI.2.35, $z \times (n + n + 2) \geq z \times 1$, so that $z \times (n + n + 2) \geq z$. Also

$$(n + 2) \times (n + 1) = (n \times n) + (n \times 3) + 2,$$

so that $(n + 2) \times (n + 1) \geq 2$. Then by Thm.XI.2.25, Cor. 1,

$$\begin{aligned} z' \times (z' + 1) &\geq (z \times (z + 1)) + z + 2 \\ &> (z \times (z + 1)) + z. \end{aligned}$$

Now, since $z = x + y$, we have $z \geq x$ by Thm.XI.2.19, corollary. So $z' \times (z' + 1) > (z \times (z + 1)) + x$. Then $(z' \times (z' + 1)) + x' > (z \times (z + 1)) + x$. This contradicts $(z \times (z + 1)) + x = (z' \times (z' + 1)) + x'$.

Case 2. $z > z'$. In this case we get a similar contradiction.

So $z = z'$. Then $z \times (z + 1) = z' \times (z' + 1)$. So from $(z \times (z + 1)) + x = (z' \times (z' + 1)) + x'$ we get $x = x'$ by Thm.XI.3.2. Since $z = x + y$ and $z' = x' + y'$, we have $x + y = x' + y'$, whence $y = y'$ by Thm.XI.3.2, since $x = x'$. Then $v = \langle x,y \rangle = \langle x',y' \rangle = w$. So

(6) $$\vdash R \in \text{Funct}.$$

By (4), (6), and Thm.XI.4.8, $\vdash \text{Val}(R) \in \text{Count}$. However, obviously $\vdash \text{Val}(R) = (\text{Nn} \times \text{Nn})$. So

(7) $$\vdash (\text{Nn} \times \text{Nn}) \in \text{Count}.$$

Now by (1), (2), (7), and Thm.XI.4.6, Cor. 3, we get $\vdash (\text{Nn} \times \text{Nn}) \in \text{Den}$. Then

$$\vdash \text{Nc}(\text{Nn} \times \text{Nn}) = \text{Den}.$$

So by Thm.XI.2.27

$$\vdash \text{Den} \times \text{Den} = \text{Den}.$$

Our proof of this is essentially the same as the familiar intuitive proof, which proceeds by arranging the members of Nn $\times$ Nn in a sequence as follows: $\langle 0,0 \rangle, \langle 0,1 \rangle, \langle 1,0 \rangle, \langle 0,2 \rangle, \langle 1,1 \rangle, \langle 2,0 \rangle, \langle 0,3 \rangle, \langle 1,2 \rangle, \langle 2,1 \rangle, \langle 3,0 \rangle, \langle 0,4 \rangle, \ldots$. In this sequence, pairs $\langle x,y \rangle$ are put ahead of pairs $\langle x',y' \rangle$ if $x + y < x' + y'$.

Theorem XI.4.10. $\vdash (m):m \in \text{Nn}.m \neq 0. \supset .m \times \text{Den} = \text{Den}.$

Proof. Let $m \in \text{Nn}.m \neq 0$. Then $n \in \text{Nn}.m = n + 1$. So $1 \leq m$. Then by Thm.XI.2.35

(1) $$(1 \times \text{Den}) \leq (m \times \text{Den}).$$

Also by Thm.XI.4.5, Part II, $m \leq \text{Den}$. So

(2) $$(m \times \text{Den}) \leq (\text{Den} \times \text{Den}).$$

However, $\vdash \text{Den} = (1 \times \text{Den})$ and $\vdash (\text{Den} \times \text{Den}) = \text{Den}$. So by Thm.XI.2.20 and (1) and (2), our theorem follows.

Corollary 1. $\vdash 2 \times \text{Den} = \text{Den}.$

Corollary 2. $\vdash \text{Den} + \text{Den} = \text{Den}.$

Theorem XI.4.11. $\vdash (m):m \in \text{Nn}. \supset .m + \text{Den} = \text{Den}.$

Proof. We have $\vdash 0 \leq m \leq \text{Den}$. Hence, by Cor. 2 of Thm.XI.4.10,

$$\vdash \text{Den} = 0 + \text{Den} \leq m + \text{Den} \leq \text{Den} + \text{Den} = \text{Den}.$$

****Theorem XI.4.12.** $\vdash \text{Can}(\text{Nn}).$

Proof. Put

(1) $R = \hat{x}\hat{z}(x \epsilon \text{Nn}:(\text{E}\alpha,\beta,y).\alpha \epsilon x.\beta \epsilon y.y \epsilon \text{Nn}.z = \{y\}.\alpha \text{ sm USC}(\beta))$.

Lemma 1. $\vdash R \epsilon 1\text{–}1$.

Proof. Clearly $R \epsilon$ Rel. Now let $xRz.xRz'$. Then $x \epsilon$ Nn, and $\alpha \epsilon x.\beta \epsilon y.y \epsilon \text{Nn}.z = \{y\}.\alpha$ sm USC(β), and $\alpha' \epsilon x.\beta' \epsilon y'.y' \epsilon \text{Nn}.z' = \{y'\}.\alpha'$ sm USC(β'). Then by Thm.XI.2.3, Part I, α sm α'. So USC(β) sm USC(β'). Then β sm β' by Thm.XI.1.33. So Nc(β) = Nc(β') by Thm. XI.2.2, Part II. Also y = Nc(β) and y' = Nc(β') by Thm.XI.2.2, Part III. Thus $y = y'$. Then $z = \{y\} = \{y'\} = z'$. Consequently

$$\vdash R \epsilon \text{Funct}.$$

Analogously, we show

$$\vdash \breve{R} \epsilon \text{Funct}.$$

Lemma 2. $\vdash$ Arg(R) = Nn.

Proof. It is obvious that $\vdash$ Arg(R) $\subseteq$ Nn. Let $x \epsilon$ Nn. Then $\alpha \epsilon x$ by Thm.XI.2.2, Part VI. Also USC(β) ϵx by Thm.XI.2.44 and Thm.XI.2.42. Then α sm USC(β) by Thm.XI.2.3, Part I. Also USC(β) ϵ Fin, since USC(β) $\epsilon x.x \epsilon$ Nn. So $\beta \epsilon$ Fin by Thm.XI.3.39. Thus $\beta \epsilon y.y \epsilon$ Nn. Hence $xR\{y\}$. So $x \epsilon$ Arg(R).

Lemma 3. $\vdash$ Val(R) = USC(Nn).

Proof. It is obvious that $\vdash$ Val(R) $\subseteq$ USC(Nn). Let $z \epsilon$ USC(Nn). Then $z = \{y\}.y \epsilon$ Nn. So $\beta \epsilon y$. Then $\beta \epsilon$ Fin, so that USC(β) ϵ Fin by Thm.XI.3.38. Accordingly, USC(β) $\epsilon x.x \epsilon$ Nn. Then xRz, so that $z \epsilon$ Val(R).

Our theorem now follows by (1), (2), (3), Thm.XI.1.1, Part IV, and the definition of Can(Nn).

Corollary 1. $\vdash (\text{Den})^0 \neq \Lambda$.

Proof. Use Thm.XI.2.62, corollary.

Corollary 2. $\vdash (\text{Den})^0 \epsilon$ NC.

Proof. Use Thm.XI.2.48, Cor. 1.

Corollary 3. $\vdash (\text{Den})^0 = 1$.

Corollary 4. $\vdash 0^{\text{Den}} = 0$.

Corollary 5. $\vdash (\text{Den})^1 = \text{Den}$.

Corollary 6. $\vdash 1^{\text{Den}} = 1$.

Corollary 7. $\vdash (\text{Den})^2 = \text{Den} \times \text{Den}$.

Corollary 8. $\vdash 2^{\text{Den}} = \text{Nc(SC(Nn))}$.

Corollary 9. $\vdash \text{Den} < 2^{\text{Den}}$.

Corollary 10. $\vdash$ Can(SC(Nn)).

Proof. Use Thm.XI.1.37.

Corollary 11. $\vdash (\alpha):\alpha \epsilon \text{Den}. \equiv .\text{USC}(\alpha) \epsilon \text{Den}$.

Corollary 12. $\vdash (\alpha):\alpha \epsilon \text{Count}. \equiv .\text{USC}(\alpha) \epsilon \text{Count}$.

Corollary 13. $\vdash (\alpha):\alpha \epsilon \text{Den}. \supset .\text{Can}(\alpha)$.

Proof. Use Thm.XI.2.61.

We have remarked earlier that, although we cannot prove Can(α) for general classes α, it is a property which seems intuitively obvious. Hence we should be able to prove Can(α) for the familiar classes which appear in mathematics. We have now done so for the familiar class Nn, and thus for all denumerable classes.

Theorem XI.4.13. $\vdash (m):m \in \text{Nn}.m \neq 0. \supset .(\text{Den})^m = \text{Den}.$

Proof. We prove by weak induction on n that

$$\vdash (n):n \in \text{Nn}. \supset .(\text{Den})^{n+1} = \text{Den}.$$

If $n = 0$, we use Thm.XI.4.12, Cor. 5. Assume $(\text{Den})^{n+1} = \text{Den}$. Then by Thm.XI.4.12, Cor. 2, Thm.XI.3.12, and Thm.XI.2.54,

$$\begin{aligned}(\text{Den})^{(n+1)+1} &= (\text{Den})^{(n+1)} \times (\text{Den})^1 \\ &= \text{Den} \times \text{Den} \\ &= \text{Den}\end{aligned}$$

by Thm.XI.4.9.

Theorem XI.4.14.

I. $\vdash (\alpha,\beta):\alpha,\beta \in \text{Den}. \supset .\alpha \cup \beta \in \text{Den}.$

II. $\vdash (\alpha,\beta):\alpha,\beta \in \text{Count}. \supset .\alpha \cup \beta \in \text{Count}.$

Proof of Part I. Assume $\alpha,\beta \in$ Den. Then Nc(α) = Den. Also $\beta - \alpha \subseteq \beta$. So by Thm.XI.4.4, corollary, $\beta - \alpha \in$ Count. Then by Thm.XI.4.6, Cor. 2, Nc($\beta - \alpha$) $\leq$ Den. Now by Ex.XI.2.8, Nc($\alpha \cup \beta$) = Nc(α) + Nc($\beta - \alpha$). But by Thm.XI.2.23,

$$\begin{aligned}\text{Nc}(\alpha) + \text{Nc}(\beta - \alpha) &= \text{Den} + \text{Nc}(\beta - \alpha) \\ &\leq \text{Den} + \text{Den}.\end{aligned}$$

So by Thm.XI.4.10, Cor. 2,

(1) $$\text{Nc}(\alpha \cup \beta) \leq \text{Den}.$$

Now Den = Nc(α) $\leq$ Nc(α) + Nc($\beta - \alpha$) = Nc($\alpha \cup \beta$). So

(2) $$\text{Den} \leq \text{Nc}(\alpha \cup \beta).$$

So Nc($\alpha \cup \beta$) = Den, and $\alpha \cup \beta \in$ Den.

Proof of Part II. Similar.

A generalized form of this says that if one has any nonnull finite class of denumerable classes, then the totality of all their elements is likewise denumerable. Similarly for countable classes.

Theorem XI.4.15.

I. $\vdash (\lambda):\lambda \neq \Lambda.\lambda \in \text{Fin}.\lambda \subseteq \text{Den}. \supset .\bigcup\lambda \in \text{Den}.$

II. $\vdash (\lambda):\lambda \in \text{Fin}.\lambda \subseteq \text{Count}. \supset .\bigcup\lambda \in \text{Count}.$

Proof of Part I. We proceed analogously to the proof of Thm.XI.3.33 to prove $\vdash (\lambda,n):n \in \text{Nn}.\lambda \in n + 1.\lambda \subseteq \text{Den}. \supset .\bigcup\lambda \in \text{Den}.$

Proof of Part II. Similar.

One hears widely quoted an even stronger result to the effect that, if one has a denumerable class of denumerable classes, then the totality of all their elements is likewise denumerable. The intuitive proof proceeds as follows. Let λ be the class, and $\alpha_0, \alpha_1, \alpha_2, \ldots$ its members. Now let the members of α_n be $x_{0,n}, x_{1,n}, x_{2,n}, \ldots$. By pairing $x_{m,n}$ with $\langle m,n\rangle$, we establish a one-to-one correspondence between $\bigcup\lambda$ and $\mathrm{Nn} \times \mathrm{Nn}$. Then by Thm.XI.4.9, $\bigcup\lambda \in \mathrm{Den}$.

Unfortunately, the proof just given involves the axiom of choice. Indeed, we know of no proof of this result which does not involve the axiom of choice. Hence we must defer a proof of this result until Chapter XIV. Meanwhile we now prove the nearest equivalents that we know how to prove with the axioms now at our disposal.

Theorem XI.4.16. Let R_n be a term, containing free occurrences of n, which is stratified and has type one higher than the type of n. Then:

I. $\vdash (n){:}n \in \mathrm{Nn}. \supset .R_n \in \mathrm{Funct.Arg}(R_n) \subseteq \mathrm{Nn}.{:} \supset {:}.\bigcup\{\mathrm{Val}(R_n) \mid n \in \mathrm{Nn}\} \in \mathrm{Count}$.

II. $\vdash (n){:}n \in \mathrm{Nn}. \supset .R_n \in \mathrm{Funct.Arg}(R_n) \subseteq \mathrm{Nn}{:}.(\mathrm{E}n).n \in \mathrm{Nn.Val}(R_n) \in \mathrm{Den}{::} \supset {::}\bigcup\{\mathrm{Val}(R_n) \mid n \in \mathrm{Nn}\} \in \mathrm{Den}$.

Proof of I. Assume

(1) $$(n){:}n \in \mathrm{Nn}. \supset .R_n \in \mathrm{Funct.Arg}(R_n) \subseteq \mathrm{Nn}.$$

By Thm.XI.4.9, there is an S such that

(2) $$S \in 1\text{–}1.\mathrm{Arg}(S) = \mathrm{Nn.Val}(S) = \mathrm{Nn} \times \mathrm{Nn}.$$

Now define W as

(3) $$W = \hat{x}\hat{y}(x \in \mathrm{Nn}{:}(\mathrm{E}m,n).xS\langle m,n\rangle.m \in \mathrm{Arg}(R_n).y = R_n(m)).$$

Clearly

(4) $$\vdash \mathrm{Arg}(W) \subseteq \mathrm{Nn}.$$

Let $xWy.xWz$. Then $xS\langle m,n\rangle.y = R_n(m)$ and $xS\langle u,v\rangle.z = R_v(u)$. So $\langle m,n\rangle = \langle u,v\rangle$ by (2). So $m = u$ and $n = v$. So $y = z$. Thus

(5) $$W \in \mathrm{Funct}.$$

Then by Thm.XI.4.8

(6) $$\mathrm{Val}(W) \in \mathrm{Count}.$$

Since $\mathrm{Val}(S) = \mathrm{Nn} \times \mathrm{Nn}$ by (2), we readily deduce by (3) that

(7) $$\mathrm{Val}(W) \subseteq \bigcup\{\mathrm{Val}(R_n) \mid n \in \mathrm{Nn}\}.$$

Conversely, let $y \in \bigcup\{\mathrm{Val}(R_n) \mid n \in \mathrm{Nn}\}$. Then by rule C, $y \in \alpha.\alpha \in \{\mathrm{Val}(R_n) \mid n \in \mathrm{Nn}\}$. By rule C again, $y \in \alpha.n \in \mathrm{Nn}.\alpha = \mathrm{Val}(R_n)$. So

$n \in \mathrm{Nn}.y \in \mathrm{Val}(R_n)$. Thus $n \in \mathrm{Nn}.m \in \mathrm{Arg}(R_n).m(R_n)y$. Then by (1), $m,n \in \mathrm{Nn}.m \in \mathrm{Arg}(R_n).y = R_n(m)$. By (2), there is an x such that $x \in \mathrm{Nn}$. $xS\langle m,n\rangle$. Then xWy, and $y \in \mathrm{Val}(W)$. Thus, by (7),

$$\mathrm{Val}(W) = \bigcup\{\mathrm{Val}(R_n) \mid n \in \mathrm{Nn}\}.$$

Then our theorem follows by (6).

Proof of II. Assume

$$(1) \qquad (n){:}n \in \mathrm{Nn}. \supset .R_n \in \mathrm{Funct}.\mathrm{Arg}(R_n) \subseteq \mathrm{Nn},$$

$$(2) \qquad (\mathrm{E}n).n \in \mathrm{Nn}.\mathrm{Val}(R_n) \in \mathrm{Den}.$$

By (1) and Part I,

$$(3) \qquad \bigcup\{\mathrm{Val}(R_n) \mid n \in \mathrm{Nn}\} \in \mathrm{Count}.$$

However, we easily show

$$(n){:}n \in \mathrm{Nn}. \supset .\mathrm{Val}(R_n) \subseteq \bigcup\{\mathrm{Val}(R_n) \mid n \in \mathrm{Nn}\}.$$

So by (2),

$$\mathrm{Val}(R_n) \in \mathrm{Den}{:}\mathrm{Val}(R_n) \subseteq \bigcup\{\mathrm{Val}(R_n) \mid n \in \mathrm{Nn}\}.$$

Then by (3), our theorem follows from Thm.XI.4.6, Cor. 3.

Theorem XI.4.17. Let R_n be a term which is stratified. Then:

I. $\vdash (n){:}n \in \mathrm{Nn}. \supset .R_n \in \mathrm{Funct}.\mathrm{Arg}(R_n) \subseteq \mathrm{Nn}.{:} \supset {:}.\bigcup\{\mathrm{Val}(R_n) \mid n \in \mathrm{Nn}\} \in \mathrm{Count}.$

II. $\vdash (n){:}n \in \mathrm{Nn}. \supset .R_n \in \mathrm{Funct}.\mathrm{Arg}(R_n) \subseteq \mathrm{Nn}{:}.(\mathrm{E}n).n \in \mathrm{Nn}.\mathrm{Val}(R_n) \in \mathrm{Den}{::} \supset {::}\bigcup\{\mathrm{Val}(R_n) \mid n \in \mathrm{Nn}\} \in \mathrm{Den}.$

Proof. We shall illustrate the procedure which would be used in case R_n contains free occurrences of n and has type one lower than n. It will be clear that the proof for any other type difference between R_n and n would be similar, as would the case where R_n contains no free occurrences of n. By Thm.XI.4.12, there are U and W such that

$$(1) \qquad U \in 1\text{–}1.\mathrm{Arg}(U) = \mathrm{Nn}.\mathrm{Val}(U) = \mathrm{USC}(\mathrm{Nn}).$$

$$(2) \qquad W \in 1\text{–}1.\mathrm{Arg}(W) = \mathrm{Nn}.\mathrm{Val}(W) = \mathrm{USC}(\mathrm{Nn}).$$

Define S_n so that

$$(3) \qquad S_n = \hat{x}\hat{y}((\mathrm{E}u,v).x(R_u)y.uU\{v\}.vW\{n\}).$$

Then S_n satisfies the conditions set on R_n in the hypothesis of Thm. XI.4.16. Also, by (1), (2), and (3) one easily shows that

$$\bigcup\{\mathrm{Val}(R_n) \mid n \in \mathrm{Nn}\} = \bigcup\{\mathrm{Val}(S_n) \mid n \in \mathrm{Nn}\}.$$

We now prove that the set of all finite subsets of Nn is denumerable. The usual intuitive proof is to show that there is a single null subset, a denumerable number of unit subsets, a denumerable number of subsets with two members, ... By combining all these, we get all finite subsets as the null set plus the totality of members of a denumerable set of denumerable sets, which is then denumerable by a well-known theorem. As we said above, we shall not have this well-known theorem until Chapter XIV, after assuming the axiom of choice. However, by modifying the reasoning a bit, we can manage by use of the weaker Thm.XI.4.17.

Theorem XI.4.18. $\vdash (\mathrm{SC}(\mathrm{Nn}) \cap \mathrm{Fin}) \in \mathrm{Den}$.

Proof. By Thm.XI.4.9 there is an S such that

(1) $$S \in 1\text{–}1.\mathrm{Arg}(S) = \mathrm{Nn}.\mathrm{Val}(S) = \mathrm{Nn} \times \mathrm{Nn}.$$

By Thm.XI.4.12 there is a T such that

(2) $$T \in 1\text{–}1.\mathrm{Arg}(T) = \mathrm{Nn}.\mathrm{Val}(T) = \mathrm{USC}(\mathrm{Nn}).$$

By Thm.XI.3.24, there is a W such that

(3) $$W \in \mathrm{Funct},$$

(4) $$\mathrm{Arg}(W) = \mathrm{Nn},$$

(5) $$W(0) = T,$$

(6) $$(n){:}n \in \mathrm{Nn}. \supset .W(n+1) = \hat{x}\hat{y}(x \in \mathrm{Nn}{:} \\ (\mathrm{E}r,s).xS\langle r,s\rangle.y = (W(n))(r) \cup T(s)).$$

It will turn out that, in effect, $W(n)$ is a function which enumerates all nonnull subsets of Nn with $n + 1$ or fewer members.

Lemma 1. $(n){:}n \in \mathrm{Nn}. \supset .W(n) \in \mathrm{Funct}.\mathrm{Arg}(W(n)) = \mathrm{Nn}.$

Proof. Proof by weak induction on n. Clearly the result holds for $n = 0$ by (5). Assume the result for n, and let $n \in \mathrm{Nn}$. By (6) and (1),

(i) $$\mathrm{Arg}(W(n+1)) = \mathrm{Nn}.$$

Now let $x(W(n+1))y.x(W(n+1))z$. Then $x \in \mathrm{Nn}$, $xS\langle r,s\rangle.y = (W(n))(r) \cup T(s)$, and $xS\langle r',s'\rangle.z = (W(n))(r') \cup T(s')$. So by (1), $\langle r,s\rangle = \langle r',s'\rangle$. So $r = r'$, $s = s'$. Then $y = z$. So

(ii) $$W(n+1) \in \mathrm{Funct}.$$

Lemma 2. $\mathrm{Val}(W(0)) \in \mathrm{Den}$.

Proof. Use (5), (2), and Thm.XI.4.12.

Lemma 3. $0 \cup \bigcup\{\mathrm{Val}(W(n)) \mid n \in \mathrm{Nn}\} \in \mathrm{Den}$.

Proof. Temporarily let α denote $\bigcup\{\mathrm{Val}(W(n)) \mid n \in \mathrm{Nn}\}$. By Thm. XI.4.17, Part II, $\alpha \in \mathrm{Den}$.

Case 1. $\Lambda \in \alpha$. Then by Thm.IX.6.5, Cor. 2, $0 \cup \alpha \in \mathrm{Den}$.

Case 2. $\sim \Lambda \in \alpha$. Then by Thm.IX.6.6, Cor. 1, $0 \cup \alpha \in 1 + \mathrm{Den}$. So by Thm.XI.4.11, $0 \cup \alpha \in \mathrm{Den}$.

Lemma 4. $(n){:}n \in \text{Nn}. \supset .\text{Val}(W(n)) \subseteq \text{SC}(\text{Nn}) \cap \text{Fin}.$

Proof. Proof by weak induction on n. By (5), (2), and Thm.IX.6.18, Cor. 1, $\text{Val}(W(0)) \subseteq \text{SC}(\text{Nn})$. Also by (5), (2), and Thm.XI.3.28, Cor. 4, $\text{Val}(W(0)) \subseteq \text{Fin}$. So by Thm.IX.4.18, Part I, our lemma holds when $n = 0$. So assume $n \in \text{Nn}$ and $\text{Val}(W(n)) \subseteq \text{SC}(\text{Nn}) \cap \text{Fin}$. If $y \in \text{Val}(W(n+1))$, then by (6), (5), (1), and Lemma 1, $r \in \text{Arg}(W(n))$, $s \in \text{Arg}(W(0))$, $y = (W(n))(r) \cup (W(0))(s)$. So by Lemma 1, $(W(n))(r) \in \text{Val}(W(n))$ and $(W(0))(s) \in \text{Val}(W(0))$. So by our lemma for 0 and n, $(W(n))(r),(W(0))(s) \in \text{SC}(\text{Nn}) \cap \text{Fin}$. Then by Thm.XI.3.32, $y \in \text{SC}(\text{Nn}) \cap \text{Fin}$.

Lemma 5. $0 \cup \bigcup\{\text{Val}(W(n)) \mid n \in \text{Nn}\} \subseteq \text{SC}(\text{Nn}) \cap \text{Fin}.$

Proof. Use Thm.XI.3.28, Cor. 3, to get $0 \subseteq \text{SC}(\text{Nn}) \cap \text{Fin}$. Use Thm.IX.5.8, Part II, and Lemma 4 to get $\bigcup\{\text{Val}(W(n)) \mid n \in \text{Nn}\} \subseteq \text{SC}(\text{Nn}) \cap \text{Fin}$.

Lemma 6. $(\alpha,m){:}m \in \text{Nn}.\alpha \in m + 1.\alpha \subseteq \text{Nn}. \supset .(\text{E}n).n \in \text{Nn}.\alpha \in \text{Val}(W(n)).$

Proof. Proof by weak induction on m. First let $\alpha \in 0 + 1.\alpha \subseteq \text{Nn}$. Then $\alpha \in \text{USC}(\text{Nn})$. So by (2) and (5), $\alpha \in \text{Val}(W(0))$. So our lemma holds for $m = 0$. Now assume the lemma for m and let $m \in \text{Nn}$, $\alpha \in (m+1)+1$, $\alpha \subseteq \text{Nn}$. Then $\beta \in m + 1. \sim x \in \beta.\beta \cup \{x\} = \alpha$. Then $\beta \subseteq \alpha$, so that $\beta \subseteq \text{Nn}$. So by our lemma, $n \in \text{Nn}.\beta \in \text{Val}(W(n))$. So $r \in \text{Nn}.\beta = (W(n))(r)$ by Lemma 1. Also $x \in \alpha$, so that $x \in \text{Nn}$. Then by (2), $s \in \text{Nn}.\{x\} = T(s)$. Finally by (1), $z \in \text{Nn}.zS\langle r,s\rangle$. So $z \in \text{Nn}.zS\langle r,s\rangle.\alpha = (W(n))(r) \cup T(s)$. So $z(W(n+1))\alpha$. Thus $\alpha \in \text{Val}(W(n+1))$.

Lemma 7. $\text{SC}(\text{Nn}) \cap \text{Fin} \subseteq 0 \cup \bigcup\{\text{Val}(W(n)) \mid n \in \text{Nn}\}.$

Proof. Let $\alpha \in \text{SC}(\text{Nn}) \cap \text{Fin}$. Then $\alpha \subseteq \text{Nn}$ and $p \in \text{Nn}.\alpha \in p$.

Case 1. $p = 0$. Then $\alpha \in 0$, so that

$$\alpha \in 0 \cup \bigcup\{\text{Val}(W(n)) \mid n \in \text{Nn}\}.$$

Case 2. $p \neq 0$. Then $m \in \text{Nn}.p = m + 1$. Then by Lemma 6, $n \in \text{Nn}. \alpha \in \text{Val}(W(n))$. So $(\text{E}\beta).\alpha \in \beta.\beta = \text{Val}(W(n)).n \in \text{Nn}$. Thus $(\text{E}\beta).\alpha \in \beta. \beta \in \{\text{Val}(W(n)) \mid n \in \text{Nn}\}$. Then $\alpha \in \bigcup\{\text{Val}(W(n)) \mid n \in \text{Nn}\}$. Thus

$$\alpha \in 0 \cup \bigcup\{\text{Val}(W(n)) \mid n \in \text{Nn}\}.$$

Our theorem now follows by Lemma 3, Lemma 5, and Lemma 7.

EXERCISES

XI.4.1. Prove $\vdash (R){:}R \in \text{Funct}.\text{Arg}(R) \in \text{Count}. \supset .\text{Val}(R) \in \text{Count}.$

XI.4.2. Formalize the following intuitive proof that the positive rational numbers are denumerable. In particular, show what has to be done if the positive rational number

$$\frac{m+1}{n+1}$$

has type one higher than the types of m and n. (*Hint.* Use Thm.XI.4.12.)

Proof. Given any ordered pair $\langle m,n \rangle$ with $m,n \in \text{Nn}$, we can obtain a unique positive rational number, namely,

$$\frac{m+1}{n+1},$$

and every positive rational number can be so obtained. Thus there is a function R with $\text{Arg}(R) = \text{Nn} \times \text{Nn}$ and $\text{Val}(R) =$ the set of positive rational numbers. Then by Ex.XI.4.1, the positive rational numbers are countable. However, there is a denumerable subset of the positive rational numbers.

XI.4.3. Using the fact that the positive rational numbers are denumerable, prove that all the rational numbers are denumerable.

We refer to a point (x,y) in the plane as a rational point if both its coordinates, x and y, are rational numbers.

XI.4.4. Prove that there is a denumerable number of rational points in the plane.

XI.4.5. Prove that the set of circles with a rational radius and a rational center is denumerable.

XI.4.6. Prove:

(a) $\vdash (\alpha,\beta){:}\alpha \subseteq \beta.\beta \in \text{Count}. \supset .\alpha \in \text{Count}.$
(b) $\vdash (\alpha,\beta){:}\alpha,\beta \in \text{Den}. \supset .\alpha \times \beta \in \text{Den}.$
(c) $\vdash \text{Nn} \times \text{USC}(\text{Nn}) \in \text{Den}.$

XI.4.7. A number is said to be even if it is divisible by 2. That is, we put

$$\text{Even} \quad \text{for} \quad \hat{m}((\text{E}n).n \in \text{Nn}.m = 2 \times n).$$

Prove $\vdash \text{Even} \in \text{Den}.$

XI.4.8. Prove $\vdash \hat{m}((\text{E}n).n \in \text{Nn}.m = n^2) \in \text{Den}.$

XI.4.9. Prove $\vdash \text{Den} < \text{Nc}(\text{SC}(\text{Nn}) \cap \text{Infin}).$

XI.4.10. Prove $\vdash (\text{SC}(\text{Nn}) \cap \text{Infin}) \text{ sm } \text{SC}(\text{Nn}).$

XI.4.11. Prove $\vdash 2^{\text{Den}} < \text{Nc}(\text{V}).$

XI.4.12. Prove $\vdash (R){:}R \in \text{Rel}.R \in \text{Count}. \supset .(\text{E}S).S \in \text{Funct}.\text{Arg}(R) = \text{Arg}(S).S \subseteq R.$

XI.4.13. Prove $\vdash (n){:}.n \in \text{NC}{:} \supset {:}\text{Den} \leq n. \equiv .n = \text{Den} + n.$ (*Hint.* Use Thm.XI.4.10, Cor.2.)

XI.4.14. Prove $\vdash (\alpha){:}.\text{Den} \leq \text{Nc}(\alpha){:} \supset {:}(\text{E}\beta).\beta \subset \alpha.\beta \text{ sm } \alpha.$ (*Hint.* Use Ex.XI.4.13.)

XI.4.15. Prove $\vdash (\alpha){:}.(\text{E}\beta).\beta \subset \alpha.\beta \text{ sm } \alpha{:} \supset {:}\text{Den} \leq \text{Nc}(\alpha).$ (*Hint.*

Let $\alpha \text{ sm}_R\, \beta . \beta \subset \alpha$. Choose x in $\alpha - \beta$. Define f by $f(0) = x$, $f(n+1) = R(f(x))$. Then $f \in 1\text{–}1$ and $\text{Val}(f) \subseteq \alpha$.)

XI.4.16. Prove that every open set in the plane is the sum of a countable number of interiors of circles. (*Hint.* Prove that the interiors of circles with rational radii and rational centers constitute a set of neighborhoods for the plane. Then use Ex.XI.4.5 and Thm.IX.8.11.)

This result is called the Lindelöf theorem.

5. The Cardinal Number of the Continuum. We now consider the cardinal number of all real numbers. Since the real numbers can be put into one-to-one correspondence with the points of a line, the cardinal number of all real numbers is also the cardinal number of all points on a line. Hence this cardinal number is commonly called the cardinal number of the continuum.

The cardinal number of the continuum is also the cardinal number of all positive real numbers less than or equal to unity. In turn, one can set up a one-to-one correspondence between the real numbers x with $0 < x \leq 1$ and the nonterminating binary expansions with no digits to the left of the binary point. The proof of this is sketched on pages 408 to 409 of this text. Accordingly, one can define the cardinal number of the continuum as the cardinal number of all nonterminating binary expansions with no digits to the left of the binary point. We do so.

Each such binary expansion determines a function R with $\text{Arg}(R) = \text{Nn} - \{0\}$ and $\text{Val}(R) \subseteq \{0,1\}$, since one merely defines $R(n)$ to be the nth digit in the expansion. Conversely, given a function R with $\text{Arg}(R) = \text{Nn} - \{0\}$ and $\text{Val}(R) \subseteq \{0,1\}$, we can define a binary expansion by taking $R(n)$ to be the nth digit. So we identify binary expansions with functions R such that $\text{Arg}(R) = \text{Nn} - \{0\}$ and $\text{Val}(R) \subseteq \{0,1\}$. Such a binary expansion is nonterminating if $(n){:}n \in \text{Nn}. \supset .(\text{E}m).m \in \text{Nn}.m > n. R(m) = 1$. Accordingly, we define

PI	for	$\text{Nn} - \{0\}$,
NTBX	for	$\hat{R}(R \in \text{Funct}.\text{Arg}(R) = \text{PI}.\text{Val}(R) \subseteq \{0,1\}{:}(n){:}$ $n \in \text{Nn}. \supset .(\text{E}m).m \in \text{Nn}.m > n.R(m) = 1)$,
c	for	$\text{Nc}(\text{NTBX})$.

Then PI is the class of positive integers, NTBX is the class of nonterminating binary expansions, and c is the cardinal number of the continuum. Each of PI, NTBX, and c is stratified, and contains no free variables, and so may be assigned any type.

Some writers use $\aleph$ for c.

Theorem XI.5.1.

I. $\vdash (n){:}n \in \text{PI}. \equiv .n \in \text{Nn}.n \neq 0$.

II. $\vdash (n):n \epsilon \text{PI}. \equiv .(\text{E}m).m \epsilon \text{Nn}.n = m + 1.$
III. $\vdash \text{PI} \epsilon \text{Den}.$

Proof of Part III. Use Thm.XI.3.30.

Theorem XI.5.2. $\vdash (R)::R \epsilon \text{NTBX}.: \equiv :.R \epsilon \text{Funct}.\text{Arg}(R) = \text{PI}.\text{Val}(R) \subseteq \{0,1\}:(n):n \epsilon \text{Nn}. \supset .(\text{E}m).m \epsilon \text{Nn}.m > n.R(m) = 1.$

Theorem XI.5.3.

I. $\vdash (\alpha):\alpha \epsilon c. \equiv .\alpha \text{ sm NTBX}.$
II. $\vdash (\alpha,\beta):\alpha \epsilon c.\alpha \text{ sm } \beta. \supset .\beta \epsilon c.$
III. $\vdash (\alpha,\beta):\alpha,\beta \epsilon c. \supset .\alpha \text{ sm } \beta.$

Theorem XI.5.4. $\vdash \text{Den} \leq c.$

Proof. Put

(1) $$R_n = \hat{x}\hat{y}(x \epsilon \text{PI}:x < n.y = 0.\text{v}.x \geq n.y = 1).$$

(2) $$\alpha = \{R_n \mid n \epsilon \text{PI}\}.$$

Clearly

(3) $$\vdash (n):n \epsilon \text{PI}. \supset .R_n \epsilon \text{NTBX}.$$

(4) $$\vdash \alpha \subseteq \text{NTBX}.$$

Put

(5) $$S = \hat{x}\hat{y}((\text{E}z).z \epsilon \text{PI}.x = \{z\}.y = R_z).$$

Then clearly

(6) $$\vdash S \epsilon \text{Funct}.$$

(7) $$\vdash \text{Arg}(S) = \text{USC}(\text{PI}).$$

(8) $$\vdash \text{Val}(S) = \alpha.$$

Let $uSy.vSy$. Then $z \epsilon \text{PI}.u = \{z\}.y = R_z$ and $w \epsilon \text{PI}.v = \{w\}.y = R_w$. Then $R_z = R_w$ and $z < w.\text{v}.z = w.\text{v}.z > w$. If $z < w$, then $\langle z,0\rangle \epsilon R_w$ but $\sim \langle z,0\rangle \epsilon R_z$ by (1), contradicting $R_z = R_w$. Similarly, we have a contradiction if $z > w$. So $z = w$. So $u = v$. Thus by (6)

(9) $$\vdash S \epsilon 1\text{–}1.$$

Then by (9), (7), and (8),

(10) $$\vdash \text{USC}(\text{PI}) \text{ sm } \alpha.$$

However, by Thm.XI.3.30 and Thm.XI.1.33,

(11) $$\vdash \text{USC}(\text{Nn}) \text{ sm USC}(\text{PI}).$$

Also, by Thm.XI.4.12,

(12) $$\vdash \text{Nn sm USC}(\text{Nn}).$$

So by (10), (11), and (12),

(13) $$\vdash \mathrm{Nc}(\alpha) = \mathrm{Den}.$$

Also by Thm.XI.2.13, Part I, together with (4),

(14) $$\vdash \mathrm{Nc}(\alpha) \leq c.$$

From (13) and (14), our theorem follows.

Corollary 1. $\vdash c \in \mathrm{NC} - \mathrm{Nn}$.

Proof. If $c \in \mathrm{Nn}$, we get a contradiction by Thm.XI.4.5, Part II.

Corollary 2. $\vdash c = \mathrm{Den} + c$.

Proof. By the theorem, $p \in \mathrm{NC}.c = \mathrm{Den} + p$. Then by Thm.XI.4.10, Cor. 2, $c = (\mathrm{Den} + \mathrm{Den}) + p = \mathrm{Den} + (\mathrm{Den} + p) = \mathrm{Den} + c$.

****Theorem XI.5.5.** $\vdash c = 2^{\mathrm{Den}}$.

Proof. Put

(1) $$\alpha = \hat{R}(R \in \mathrm{Funct}.\mathrm{Arg}(R) = \mathrm{PI}.\mathrm{Val}(R) \subseteq \{0,1\}:$$
$$(\mathrm{E}n):n \in \mathrm{Nn}:(m):m \in \mathrm{Nn}.m > n. \supset .R(m) = 0).$$

Clearly

(2) $$\vdash \alpha \cap \mathrm{NTBX} = \Lambda.$$

(3) $$\vdash \alpha \cup \mathrm{NTBX} \subseteq (\mathrm{PI} \wedge \{0,1\}).$$

Lemma 1. $\vdash (\mathrm{PI} \wedge \{0,1\}) \subseteq \alpha \cup \mathrm{NTBX}$.

Proof. Let $R \in \mathrm{PI} \wedge \{0,1\}$. Then by Thm.XI.1.21, Part II,

(i) $$R \in \mathrm{Funct}.\mathrm{Arg}(R) = \mathrm{PI}.\mathrm{Val}(R) \subseteq \{0,1\}.$$

Case 1. $(n):n \in \mathrm{Nn}. \supset .(\mathrm{E}m).m \in \mathrm{Nn}.m > n.R(m) = 1$. Then $R \in \mathrm{NTBX}$.

Case 2. $\sim(n):n \in \mathrm{Nn}. \supset .(\mathrm{E}m).m \in \mathrm{Nn}.m > n.R(m) = 1$. Then by duality, $(\mathrm{E}n):n \in \mathrm{Nn}:(m):m \in \mathrm{Nn}.m > n. \supset .R(m) \neq 1$. However, $\vdash n \in \mathrm{Nn}.m \in \mathrm{Nn}.m > n. \supset .m \in \mathrm{PI}$. So by (i), $n \in \mathrm{Nn}.m \in \mathrm{Nn}.m > n. \supset . R(m) = 0.\mathsf{v}.R(m) = 1$. Hence $R \in \alpha$.

Lemma 2. $\vdash \mathrm{Nc}(\alpha) + c = 2^{\mathrm{Den}}$.

Proof. By (2), (3), Lemma 1, and Thm.XI.2.9, $\vdash \mathrm{Nc}(\alpha) + c = \mathrm{Nc}(\mathrm{PI} \wedge \{0,1\})$. So by Thm.XI.2.39,

(i) $$\vdash \mathrm{Nc}(\alpha) + c = \mathrm{Nc}(\mathrm{USC}(\mathrm{PI})) \wedge \mathrm{Nc}(\mathrm{USC}(\{0,1\})).$$

Now by Thm.XI.2.67, Cor. 1, and Thm.XI.2.61, $\vdash \mathrm{Nc}(\mathrm{USC}(\{0,1\})) = \mathrm{Nc}(\{0,1\})$. So

(ii) $$\vdash \mathrm{Nc}(\mathrm{USC}(\{0,1\})) = 2.$$

By Thm.XI.3.30 and Thm.XI.1.33, $\vdash \mathrm{Nc}(\mathrm{USC}(\mathrm{PI})) = \mathrm{Nc}(\mathrm{USC}(\mathrm{Nn}))$, and by Thm.XI.4.12, $\vdash \mathrm{Nc}(\mathrm{USC}(\mathrm{Nn})) = \mathrm{Den}$. So

$$\vdash \mathrm{Nc}(\alpha) + c = 2^{\mathrm{Den}}.$$

Lemma 3. $\vdash \alpha \ \mathrm{sm}\ (\mathrm{SC(Nn)} \cap \mathrm{Fin})$.

Proof. We put

$$W = \hat{R}\hat{\beta}(R \in \alpha . \beta = \hat{n}(n \in \mathrm{Nn}.R(n+1) = 1)).$$

Clearly

(i) $$\vdash W \in \mathrm{Funct}.$$

(ii) $$\vdash \mathrm{Arg}(W) = \alpha.$$

(iii) $$\vdash \mathrm{Val}(W) \subseteq \mathrm{SC(Nn)}.$$

Let $RW\beta . SW\beta$. Then $R,S \in \mathrm{Funct}.\mathrm{Arg}(R) = \mathrm{PI} = \mathrm{Arg}(S)$, $\mathrm{Val}(R) \subseteq \{0,1\}$, $\mathrm{Val}(S) \subseteq \{0,1\}, \hat{n}(n \in \mathrm{Nn}.R(n+1) = 1) = \beta = \hat{n}(n \in \mathrm{Nn}.S(n+1) = 1)$. We wish to prove $R = S$ by means of Thm.X.5.16. So let $x \in \mathrm{PI}$. Then $n \in \mathrm{Nn}.x = n + 1$.

Case 1. $n \in \beta$. Then $R(x) = R(n+1) = 1 = S(n+1) = S(x)$.

Case 2. $\sim n \in \beta$. Then $R(x) \neq 1$ and $S(x) \neq 1$. But $\mathrm{Val}(R) \subseteq \{0,1\}$ and $\mathrm{Val}(S) \subseteq \{0,1\}$. So $R(x) = 0 = S(x)$.

Thus $R = S$. So by (i),

(iv) $$\vdash W \in 1\text{–}1.$$

Now let $\beta \in \mathrm{Val}(W)$. Then $R \in \alpha$ and $(n):n \in \beta . \equiv .n \in \mathrm{Nn}.R(n+1) = 1$. By $R \in \alpha$, we know that $n \in \mathrm{Nn}:(m):m \in \mathrm{Nn}.m > n. \supset .R(m) = 0$. So $(m):m \in \mathrm{Nn}.m > n. \supset .\sim m \in \beta$. Thus $(m):m \in \beta \supset m \leq n$. Then by Thm.XI.4.2, $\beta \in \mathrm{Fin}$. Thus, by (iii),

(v) $$\vdash \mathrm{Val}(W) \subseteq \mathrm{SC(Nn)} \cap \mathrm{Fin}.$$

Now let $\beta \in \mathrm{SC(Nn)} \cap \mathrm{Fin}$.

Case 1. $\beta = \Lambda$. If we put $R = \mathrm{PI} \upharpoonright \lambda x(0)$, then clearly $RW\beta$, so that $\beta \in \mathrm{Val}(W)$.

Case 2. $\beta \neq \Lambda$. Then by Thm.XI.3.44, Cor. 4, $n \in \mathrm{Nn}$ and $(m):m \in \beta \supset m \leq n$. Now define

$$R = \hat{x}\hat{y}((\mathrm{E}z):z \in \mathrm{Nn}.x = z + 1:z \in \beta.y = 1.\mathbf{v}.\sim z \in \beta.y = 0).$$

Clearly $R \in \mathrm{Funct}.\mathrm{Arg}(R) = \mathrm{PI}.\mathrm{Val}(R) \subseteq \{0,1\}.(m):m \in \mathrm{Nn}.m > n + 1. \supset .R(m) = 0$. So $R \in \alpha$. Also, $\beta = \hat{n}(n \in \mathrm{Nn}.R(n+1) = 1)$. So $RW\beta$. Thus, in this case also $\beta \in \mathrm{Val}(W)$.

Thus we have

(vi) $$\vdash \mathrm{SC(Nn)} \cap \mathrm{Fin} \subseteq \mathrm{Val}(W).$$

Then our lemma follows by (iv), (ii), (v), and (vi).

Now by Lemma 3 and Thm.XI.4.18, $\vdash \alpha \epsilon$ Den. So $\vdash \text{Nc}(\alpha) = \text{Den}$. So by Lemma 2, $\vdash \text{Den} + c = 2^{\text{Den}}$. Then by Thm.XI.5.4, Cor. 2, our theorem follows.

Corollary 1. $\vdash \text{Den} < c$.

Proof. Use Thm.XI.4.12, Cor. 9.

Corollary 2. $\vdash c = \text{Nc}(\text{SC}(\text{Nn}))$.

Proof. Use Thm.XI.4.12, Cor. 8.

Corollary 3. $\vdash c^0 \neq \Lambda$.

Proof. Use Thm.XI.4.12, Cor. 10, and Thm.XI.2.62, corollary.

Corollary 4. $\vdash c^0 \epsilon \text{NC}$.

Corollary 5. $\vdash c^0 = 1$.

Corollary 6. $\vdash 0^c = 0$.

Corollary 7. $\vdash c^1 = c$.

Corollary 8. $\vdash 1^c = 1$.

Corollary 9. $\vdash c^2 = c \times c$.

Corollary 10. $\vdash 2^c = \text{Nc}(\text{SC}^2(\text{Nn}))$.

Corollary 11. $\vdash c < 2^c$.

Corollary 12. $\vdash (\alpha){:}\alpha \epsilon c. \equiv .\text{USC}(\alpha) \epsilon c$.

Corollary 13. $\vdash (\alpha){:}\alpha \epsilon c. \supset .\text{Can}(\alpha)$.

Theorem XI.5.6. $\vdash c = c^{\text{Den}}$.

Proof. By the preceding theorem $\vdash c = 2^{\text{Den}}$. Then by Thm.XI.4.9, $\vdash c = 2^{\text{Den}\times\text{Den}}$. Then by Thm.XI.2.56, $\vdash c = (2^{\text{Den}})^{\text{Den}}$. Hence $\vdash c = c^{\text{Den}}$.

Corollary 1. $\vdash (m){:}m \epsilon \text{Nn}.m \neq 0. \supset .c = c^m$.

Proof. If $m \epsilon \text{Nn}.m \neq 0$, then $1 \leq m < \text{Den}$. So by Thm.XI.2.52, $c^1 \leq c^m \leq c^{\text{Den}}$.

Corollary 2. $\vdash (\alpha){:}\alpha \epsilon c. \supset .c = \text{Nc}(\text{Nn} \curlywedge \alpha)$.

Proof. Let $\alpha \epsilon c$. Then by Thm.XI.5.5, Cor. 12, $c = \text{Nc}(\text{USC}(\alpha))$. Also, by Thm.XI.4.12, Cor. 11, $\vdash \text{Den} = \text{Nc}(\text{USC}(\text{Nn}))$. So $c = \text{Nc}(\text{USC}(\text{Nn})) \curlywedge \text{Nc}(\text{USC}(\alpha))$. Then by Thm.XI.2.39, $c = \text{Nc}(\text{Nn} \curlywedge \alpha)$.

Theorem XI.5.7.

I. $\vdash (\text{Den})^{\text{Den}} = c$.

II. $\vdash (m){:}m \epsilon \text{Nn}.2 \leq m. \supset .m^{\text{Den}} = c$.

Proof of Part I. We have $\vdash 2 < \text{Den} < c$. So by Thm.XI.2.57, $\vdash 2^{\text{Den}} \leq (\text{Den})^{\text{Den}} \leq c^{\text{Den}}$. But $\vdash c = 2^{\text{Den}}$ and $\vdash c = c^{\text{Den}}$.

Proof of Part II. Similar.

Theorem XI.5.8. $\vdash c = c \times c$.

Proof. We can take $m = 2$ in Thm.XI.5.6, Cor. 1. Alternatively, we can note that $\vdash c = 2^{\text{Den}} = 2^{\text{Den}+\text{Den}} = 2^{\text{Den}} \times 2^{\text{Den}} = c \times c$.

Corollary 1. $\vdash c = \text{Den} \times c$.

Corollary 2. $\vdash (m){:}m \epsilon \text{Nn}.m \neq 0. \supset .c = m \times c$.

This theorem tells us that there are as many ordered pairs $\langle x,y \rangle$ of real numbers x and y as there are real numbers. If we pair the ordered pairs

$\langle x,y\rangle$ with the points in the plane of which x and y are the coordinates, we infer that there are exactly as many points in the real plane as in the real line. Alternatively, we can pair $\langle x,y\rangle$ with the complex number $x + iy$ and infer that there are exactly as many complex numbers as real numbers.

Let us now take α to be the class of all complex numbers in Cor. 2 of Thm.XI.5.6. Each member of $\mathrm{Nn} \wedge \alpha$ is a function R with $\mathrm{Arg}(R) = \mathrm{Nn}$ and $\mathrm{Val}(R) \subseteq \alpha$. That is, $R(0)$, $R(1)$, $R(2)$, . . . constitute a sequence of complex numbers. That is, $\mathrm{Nn} \wedge \alpha$ is the class of all sequences of complex numbers. So there are as many sequences of complex numbers as there are real numbers.

Let us look at a fixed point z_0. Each function which is analytic in the neighborhood of z_0 determines a sequence of complex numbers, namely, the coefficients of the Taylor series expansion of the function at the point. So the number of functions analytic in the neighborhood of z_0 is no greater than the number of real numbers. Nor is it less, as one can see by considering the constant analytic functions whose constant value is a real number. So there are c functions which are analytic in the neighborhood of z_0. Since there are c points z_0, there is a temptation to infer that the total number of analytic functions is less than or equal to $c \times c$, and hence that there are c analytic functions, since $\vdash c = c \times c$. However, this inference seems to require the axiom of choice, and we postpone discussion of it until Chapter XIV.

Theorem XI.5.9. $\vdash c = c + c$.

Proof. Take $m = 2$ in Cor. 2 of Thm.XI.5.8.

Corollary 1. $\vdash c = \mathrm{Den} + c$.

Corollary 2. $\vdash (m){:}m \in \mathrm{Nn}. \supset .c = m + c$.

We defined c as the cardinal number of all nonterminating binary expansions with no digits to the left of the binary point. On pages 408 and 409, we sketched a proof that these are as numerous as the real numbers x with $0 < x \leq 1$. So there are c such numbers. If, momentarily, we write p for the cardinal number of the real numbers x with $0 < x < 1$, then clearly $p + 1 = c$. However, $c = c + 1$. So $p + 1 = c + 1$, so that by Thm. XI.2.12, $p = c$. If now we pair the real numbers y with $1 < y$ with the real numbers x with $0 < x < 1$ by writing $y = 1/x$, we infer that there are p y's. So the totality of positive real numbers has the cardinal number $p + 1 + p$ which is $p + c$ or $c + c$ or c. So there are c positive reals. Thus there are also c negative reals. Counting in zero, we get $c + 1 + c$ reals altogether, or exactly c real numbers.

Thus c is the cardinal number of all real numbers, and hence c is the cardinal number of all points on a line. Thus c is the cardinal number of the linear continuum. Then, as noted above, c is also the cardinal number of the plane continuum.

EXERCISES

XI.5.1. Prove that not every nonterminating binary expansion can be the expansion of a rational number. (*Hint.* Use Ex.XI.4.2.)

XI.5.2. Prove that c is the cardinal number of all nonterminating ternary expansions in which no 1 occurs, and which have no digits to the left of the ternary point.

Ternary expansions of this sort are just the ternary expansions of points of the famous Cantor middle-third set (except the left end point of the set. See Titchmarsh, 1939, Sec. 10.291, where this set is called the Cantor ternary set).

XI.5.3. Prove $\vdash 2^c < \mathrm{Nc}(V)$.

XI.5.4. Prove that c is the cardinal number of the possible positions of a plane figure in the plane. (*Hint.* A position is uniquely determined by a point and an angle.)

XI.5.5. Prove that there are c real functions, f, of real numbers which are defined only at rational points. (*Hint.* Let $r_0, r_1, r_2, \ldots$ be the rational numbers. For each f of the kind in question define a sequence R of real numbers as follows:

$$R(n) = f(r_n) \text{ if } r_n \in \mathrm{Arg}(f) \text{ and } f(r_n) \leq 0.$$

$$R(n) = f(r_n) + 1 \text{ if } r_n \in \mathrm{Arg}(f) \text{ and } f(r_n) > 0.$$

$$R(n) = \tfrac{1}{2} \text{ if } \sim r_n \in \mathrm{Arg}(f).)$$

XI.5.6. Prove that there are c real functions of real numbers which are continuous in the entire plane. (*Hint.* Each such function is uniquely determined by its values at the rational points.)

XI.5.7. Prove that c is the cardinal number of all real functions of real numbers, f, such that for each such f there is a circle such that f is continuous and defined exactly on the interior of the circle. (We say that f is defined on α if $\mathrm{Arg}(f) = \alpha$.)

XI.5.8. Prove that there are c open sets in the plane. (*Hint.* Let α be an open set. Enumerate the interiors of circles with rational radii and rational centers. Call them $I_0, I_1, I_2, \ldots$. By strong induction, define a function g such that $g(0)$ is the first I_n which lies wholly inside α if $\alpha \neq \Lambda$, and $g(0) = \Lambda$ if $\alpha = \Lambda$, and $g(n+1) =$ the first I_n which lies wholly inside α and has a point in common with $\alpha - \bigcup\{g(m) \mid m \in \mathrm{Nn}.m \leq n\}$ if the latter set is not null, and $g(n+1) = \Lambda$ otherwise. Then $\mathrm{Arg}(g) - 0$ is a unique subset of the I's.)

XI.5.9. Prove that there are c open sets on the line. (*Hint.* Each open set α on the line determines a unique open set in the plane, namely, $\alpha \times R$, where R is the set of all reals.)

XI.5.10. Prove that c is the cardinal number of all real functions of real numbers, f, such that for each such f there is an open set α such that f is continuous and defined exactly on α. (*Hint.* By the construction of Ex.XI.5.8, each open set α determines a unique sequence g such that every value $g(n)$ is either Λ or an I. Then the construction of Ex.XI.5.5 determines a unique sequence of reals for each $g(n)$. Thus for each α there is a unique sequence of sequences of reals. But by Cor. 2 of Thm.XI.5.6, there are c sequences of sequences of reals.)

XI.5.11. Prove $\vdash 2^c = c^c$.

XI.5.12. Prove that there are 2^c real functions of real numbers.

XI.5.13. Let J be the set of real numbers x with $0 \leq x \leq 1$ and let K be the set of rational numbers in J. Prove that there are 2^c subsets of J which include K.

XI.5.14. Prove that there are 2^c real functions of real numbers which are continuous at all points at which they are defined. (*Hint.* For each subset in Ex.XI.5.13 we can get a continuous function, namely, the function which is defined to be zero at exactly the points of this subset.)

XI.5.15. Prove that each class of nonoverlapping open sets is a countable class. (*Hint.* Each nonempty open set contains a rational number. Then pair each nonempty set of the class with the first rational which it contains.)

6. Applications. Many of the theorems of the present chapter are important theorems in their own right, particularly those on the arithmetic of finite cardinals. The various principles of proof by induction and definition by induction are widely used. Besides the illustrations already noted, we shall give two more instances of definition by induction.

The so-called "sieve of Eratosthenes" (see Hardy and Wright, pages 3 to 4) for discovering the primes is such an instance. We first define S_1 as $\text{Nn} - \{0,1\}$. Then we get S_{n+1} from S_n by removing from S_n all multiples of the least member of S_n. Clearly, this is an inductive definition of S_n. Then the nth prime, p_n, is just the least member of S_n. For any specified finite N, one can follow the inductive definition of S_n in order actually to list all members of $S_n \cap \hat{m}(m \in \text{Nn}.m \leq N)$. One can then read off the values of p_n below the point where $p_n > N$. This, with refinements, is the construction that has been used to construct large tables of prime numbers.

In Ex.XI.5.2 we gave an explicit definition of the Cantor middle-third set. Important properties of this set are most easily proved if the set is defined by a process involving definition by induction. A typical intuitive definition of the Cantor middle-third set is as follows.

Divide the interval (0,1) into three equal parts, and remove the interior of the middle part. Next subdivide each of the two remaining parts into three equal parts, and remove the interiors of the middle parts of each of them; and repeat this process indefinitely. Let E be the set of points which remain.

This definition can be formalized as follows. Let S_0 be the set of real numbers x with $0 \leq x \leq 1$. Then construct S_{n+1} from S_n by removing the interiors of the middle thirds of all intervals occurring in S_n. This gives an inductive definition of S_n. Finally we set $\mathrm{E} = \bigcap\{S_n \mid n \in \mathrm{Nn}\}$.

The ideas of finiteness, countability, and noncountability have constant usage in topology. We have indicated certain of these uses in Ex.XI.3.17 to Ex.XI.3.22, inclusive. By use of Ex.XI.3.19, we can get a simpler proof of Thm.IX.8.12, as follows. Let $x \in \alpha''$. If now $x \in \beta.\beta \in \mathrm{OS}$, then there is a y with $y \in \alpha'.y \in \beta$. So by Ex.XI.3.19, $\beta \cap \alpha \in \mathrm{Infin}$. This proof is probably given more often than the proof which we gave for Thm.IX.8.12.

Actually limit points, x, of a set α, are often classified according to the cardinality of $\beta \cap \alpha$. In particular, we say that x is a point of condensation (Verdichtungspunkt) if

$$(\beta):x \in \beta.\beta \in \mathrm{OS}. \supset .\sim(\beta \cap \alpha \in \mathrm{Count}).$$

After Ex.XI.3.20, we gave the definition of compactness for a Hausdorff space (in older writings this is called bicompactness). A set α in a Hausdorff space is called countably compact if every infinite subset of α has a limit point in α (in older writings the "countably" is omitted). If α is Σ itself, we say that the space is countably compact. In Ex.XI.3.22, we proved that every compact space is countably compact.

The so-called first and second countability axioms for Hausdorff spaces (see Lefschetz, 1942, page 6) impose the conditions of being countable on certain important sets. In particular, the second countability axiom says that there is a countable set of neighborhoods which is equivalent to the given set of neighborhoods in the sense of Ex.IX.8.5. By use of the axiom of choice (see Chapter XIV), one can show that, if a Hausdorff space is countably compact and satisfies the second countability axiom, then it is compact. By taking the set of neighborhoods in the plane to be the set of circles with rational centers and rational radii (see Ex.XI.4.5), we can show that the plane is a Hausdorff space satisfying the second countability axiom.

We say that a Hausdorff space is separable if there is a countable set which has at least one member in common with each open set. In symbols:

$$(\mathrm{E}\alpha):\alpha \in \mathrm{Count}:(\beta):\beta \in \mathrm{OS}. \supset .\alpha \cap \beta \neq \Lambda.$$

By using the axiom of choice, one can show that a Hausdorff space is separable if it satisfies the second countability axiom. By taking α to be the set of rational points in the plane, we see that the plane is a separable Hausdorff space.

There is not uniform usage with regard to the word "separable." Some writers call a space separable if and only if it satisfies the second countability axiom. Other writers express this by saying that the space is completely separable or perfectly separable.

Actually, the ideas of compactness, separability, satisfaction of countability axioms, etc., are commonly defined in an analogous fashion for rather more general spaces in which only a weaker form of Hausdorff's fourth axiom is assumed.

Many of these topological ideas carry over into analysis and are reflected as theorems having to do with the cardinality of sets. Thus the theorem of Weierstrass, to the effect that any infinite set contained in a closed interval of the line has a limit point in the interval, is merely a statement that any such closed interval is a countably compact Hausdorff space. Incidentally, the usual proof given for Weierstrass's theorem (see Hardy, 1947, page 32) is an interesting example of the use of the ideas of finite and infinite sets.

Another theorem of analysis which reflects a topological idea is the Heine-Borel theorem, to the effect that, if a bounded closed set on the line is covered by a set λ of open sets, then it is covered by a finite subset of λ. This says in effect that any nonempty bounded closed set is a compact Hausdorff space.

The proof of the Heine-Borel theorem is sufficiently illustrative of the ideas of this chapter that we now sketch it in some detail. Let us have the bounded closed set α, covered by the set λ of open sets. That is, $\lambda \subseteq \mathrm{OS}.$ $\alpha \subseteq \bigcup\lambda$. We dismiss the trivial case where $\alpha = \Lambda$, and take a and b to be, respectively, the greatest lower bound and least upper bound of α. By the boundedness of α, a and b exist, and by the closure of α, a and b are in α. Moreover, a and b bound α so that $(x){:}x \in \alpha. \supset .a \leq x \leq b$.

Now define β as the set of all points x of α such that some finite subset of λ covers all points of α in the closed interval (a,x). That is,

$$\beta = \hat{x}(x \in \alpha{::}(\mathrm{E}\mu){:.}\mu \subseteq \lambda{:}\mu \in \mathrm{Fin}{:}$$
$$(y){:}y \in \alpha.a \leq y \leq x. \supset .y \in \bigcup\mu).$$

Clearly a is in β. We define L as the set of all numbers which are less than or equal to some member of β and R as the set of all numbers which are greater than all members of β. Clearly a is in L, and every number greater than b is in R. So by the Dedekind theorem (see Hardy, 1947, page 301), L and R constitute a Dedekind cut which determines a number z in the interval (a,b) such that

(i) $$(\varepsilon){:}\varepsilon > 0. \supset .(\mathrm{E}y).y \in \beta.z - \varepsilon \leq y \leq z,$$

(ii) $$(y){:}y > z. \supset .\sim y \in \beta.$$

By (i), z is a limit point of β, and hence of α, since $\beta \subseteq \alpha$. But α is closed, so that $z \in \alpha$. Then z is in some member γ of λ, and since γ is an open set, some neighborhood $\hat{w}(z - \varepsilon < w < z + \varepsilon)$ of z is included in γ. That is,

$$\text{(iii)} \qquad (w):z - \varepsilon < w < z + \varepsilon. \supset .w \in \gamma.$$

We first show that z is in β. By (i), there is a y with $y \in \beta.z - \varepsilon \leq y \leq z$. Then by the definition of β, some finite subset μ of λ covers that part of α in the interval (a,y). By (iii), γ covers that part of α in the interval (y,z), except perhaps the point y. So, together, μ and γ cover that part of α in the entire interval (a,z). That is, the finite set $\mu \cup \{\gamma\}$ covers all points of α in the closed interval (a,z). This, with $z \in \alpha$ and the definition of β, gives $z \in \beta$. Furthermore, z must be b, for if not, one can get a contradiction as follows.

Case 1. Let there be a w in α with $z < w < z + \varepsilon$ and $w \leq b$. Then by (iii), γ covers the interval (z,w). So the finite set $\mu \cup \{\gamma\}$ covers the points of α in the interval (a,w). Then w is in β, contradicting (ii).

Case 2. Let there be no such w. Then $z + \varepsilon \leq b$. Take v to be the greatest lower bound of the closed set consisting of those members of α in the closed interval $(z + \varepsilon,b)$. Then there are no members of α between z and v. Also v is in some δ of λ. Then $\mu \cup \{\gamma\} \cup \{\delta\}$ covers all points of α in the closed interval (a,v). Then v is in β, contradicting (ii).

Since z is b, we have those points of α in the interval (a,b) covered by the finite set $\mu \cup \{\gamma\}$, and our theorem is proved.

There occur from time to time other cases in analysis in which there is interest in whether a set is finite or infinite, such as Picard's theorems (Titchmarsh, 1939, pages 282 to 283), or in which this point is relevant in a proof (see Lemma 1 on page 356 of Titchmarsh, 1939).

A rather startling result concerning the use of finite and infinite is given by Visser (see Visser, 1937). The basic theorem used by Visser is a special case of a result given earlier by Ramsey (see Ramsey, 1930).

We need hardly warn the reader that the use of ∞ in such places as

$$\lim_{y \to 0} \left(\frac{1}{y}\right) = \infty,$$

$$\int_0^\infty e^{-y}\, dy = 1,$$

etc., has nothing to do with the notion of infinite set but is concerned with a limiting process involving a number which is unbounded.

In the theory of Lebesgue measure and Lebesgue integration (see Titchmarsh, 1939, Chapter X to Chapter XII, inclusive), the notion of denumerable classes plays a central role. Indeed, the exterior measure of a set E is defined by essentially the following device. Choose denumerable sets, λ, of open intervals such that no two members of λ overlap and λ covers E. One can easily attach a number, $m(\lambda)$, to each such λ which is properly described as the sum of the lengths of the members of λ. Then the exterior measure of E is the greatest lower bound of the $m(\lambda)$ for all λ of the sort in question.

Finally, in the theory of general point sets on the line, or in the plane, theorems dealing with cardinality are numerous. For example, if α is a set of real numbers and $\alpha = \alpha'$, then $\mathrm{Nc}(\alpha) = c$ (see Townsend, 1928, page 48).

EXERCISE

XI.6.1. Prove the Heine-Borel theorem in the plane.

CHAPTER XII

ORDINAL NUMBERS

1. Ordinal Similarity. When two classes are similar, they have the same number of elements, and conversely. With ordered sets, the interest is usually in whether they have the same kind of order; that is, whether they are ordinally similar. To be ordinally similar, they must not merely be similar. One must be able to make their elements correspond in such a way that the order relation between elements in one set is "preserved" by the correspondence when we pass over to the other set. To be painfully explicit, if a precedes b in one set, then the element corresponding to a must precede the element corresponding to b in the second set, and vice versa.

As we consistently deal with the ordering relations rather than with the ordered sets, we define ordinal similarity between the ordering relations rather than between the ordered sets. Ordinal similarity between ordering relations necessarily entails ordinal similarity between the ordered sets determined by the ordering relations. So we define

$P \text{ smor}_R\ Q$ for $P,Q \in \text{Rel}:\text{AV}(P) \text{ sm}_R \text{ AV}(Q):(x,y).xPy \supset (R(x))Q(R(y)):(x,y).xQy \supset (\breve{R}(x))P(\breve{R}(y)).$

smor for $\hat{P}\hat{Q}(\text{E}R).P \text{ smor}_R\ Q.$

For stratification of $P \text{ smor}_R\ Q$ it is necessary and sufficient that $P = Q = R$ be stratified. The term smor is stratified and contains no free variables and so may be assigned any type.

Note that P and Q need not be ordering relations to be ordinally similar. However, ordinal similarity is of interest mainly between ordering relations.

Theorem XII.1.1.

I. $\vdash \exists(\text{smor})$.

II. $\vdash \text{smor} \in \text{Rel}$.

III. $\vdash (P,Q):P \text{ smor } Q. \equiv .(\text{E}R).P \text{ smor}_R\ Q.$

★IV. $\vdash (P,Q)::P \text{ smor } Q.: \equiv :.(\text{E}R):.P,Q \in \text{Rel}:\text{AV}(P) \text{ sm}_R \text{ AV}(Q):(x,y). xPy \supset (R(x))Q(R(y)):(x,y).xQy \supset (\breve{R}(x))P(\breve{R}(y)).$

Theorem XII.1.2. $\vdash (P):P \in \text{Rel}. \supset .P \text{ smor } P.$

Proof. Take R to be $\text{AV}(P)\upharpoonright I$ in Thm.XII.1.1, Part IV.

Corollary 1. $\vdash \text{Arg(smor)} = \text{Val(smor)} = \text{AV(smor)} = \text{Rel}.$

Corollary 2. $\vdash \text{smor} \in \text{Ref}.$

Theorem XII.1.3. $\vdash (P,Q,R,S):S = \breve{R}.P \text{ smor}_R\, Q. \supset .Q \text{ smor}_S\, P.$

****Corollary 1.** $\vdash (P,Q):P \text{ smor } Q. \supset .Q \text{ smor } P.$

Corollary 2. $\vdash$ smor ϵ Sym.

Theorem XII.1.4. $\vdash (P_1,P_2,P_3,R,S,T):T = R|S.P_1 \text{ smor}_R\, P_2. P_2 \text{ smor}_S\, P_3. \supset .P_1 \text{ smor}_T\, P_3.$

****Corollary 1.** $\vdash (P,Q,R):P \text{ smor } Q.Q \text{ smor } R. \supset .P \text{ smor } R.$

Corollary 2. $\vdash$ smor ϵ Trans.

Corollary 3. $\vdash$ smor ϵ Equiv.

Theorem XII.1.5. $\vdash (P,Q)::P,Q \epsilon \text{ Rel}: \supset :P \text{ smor } Q. \equiv .\text{RUSC}(P) \text{ smor RUSC}(Q).$

Proof. If P smor$_R$ Q and $S = \text{RUSC}(R)$, then RUSC(P) smor$_S$ RUSC(Q). Conversely, let $P,Q \epsilon$ Rel and RUSC(P) smor$_S$ RUSC(Q). Take

$$R = \hat{x}\hat{y}(\{x\}S\{y\}).$$

Then P smor$_R$ Q.

Theorem XII.1.6. $\vdash (P,Q):P \text{ smor } Q.P \epsilon \text{ Ref}. \supset .Q \epsilon \text{ Ref}.$

Proof. Let P smor Q and $P \epsilon$ Ref. Then by Thm.XII.1.1, Part IV, and Thm.XI.1.1, Part IV, $P,Q \epsilon$ Rel, $R \epsilon$ 1–1, AV(P) = Arg(R), AV(Q) = Val(R), and $(x,y).xPy \supset (R(x))Q(R(y))$. Now let $x \epsilon$ AV(Q). Then $x \epsilon$ Val(R). So by Thm.X.5.3, Cor. 5, $\breve{R}(x) \epsilon$ Arg(R). Then $\breve{R}(x) \epsilon$ AV(P), so that $(\breve{R}(x))P(\breve{R}(x))$. Then $(R(\breve{R}(x)))Q(R(\breve{R}(x)))$. Then by Thm. X.5.20, Part II, xQx.

Theorem XII.1.7. $\vdash (P,Q):P \text{ smor } Q.P \epsilon \text{ Trans}. \supset .Q \epsilon \text{ Trans}.$

Proof. As in the proof of Thm.XII.1.6, let P smor$_R$ Q and $P \epsilon$ Trans. If now, $xQy.yQz$, then $(\breve{R}(x))P(\breve{R}(y)).(\breve{R}(y))P(\breve{R}(z))$. So $(\breve{R}(x))P(\breve{R}(z))$. Then $(R(\breve{R}(x)))Q(R(\breve{R}(z)))$. Then xQz.

Corollary. $\vdash (P,Q):P \text{ smor } Q.P \epsilon \text{ Qord}. \supset .Q \epsilon \text{ Qord}.$

Theorem XII.1.8. $\vdash (P,Q):P \text{ smor } Q.P \epsilon \text{ Antisym}. \supset .Q \epsilon \text{ Antisym}.$

Corollary. $\vdash (P,Q):P \text{ smor } Q.P \epsilon \text{ Pord}. \supset .Q \epsilon \text{ Pord}.$

Theorem XII.1.9.

I. $\vdash (P,Q,R)::P \text{ smor}_R\, Q: \supset :(x,\beta).x \text{ least}_P\, \beta \supset R(x) \text{ least}_Q\, R``\beta:$
$(x,\beta).x \text{ least}_Q\, \beta \supset \breve{R}(x) \text{ least}_P\, \breve{R}``\beta.$

II. $\vdash (P,Q,R)::P \text{ smor}_R\, Q: \supset :(x,\beta).x \text{ min}_P\, \beta \supset R(x) \text{ min}_Q\, R``\beta:$
$(x,\beta).x \text{ min}_Q\, \beta \supset \breve{R}(x) \text{ min}_P\, \breve{R}``\beta.$

Proof of Part I. Assume P smor$_R$ Q and x least$_P$ β. Then $x \epsilon$ AV(P). Then $R(x) \epsilon (R``\beta) \cap \text{AV}(Q)$ by Thm.X.5.15 and Thm.X.5.3, Cor. 4. Now let $z \epsilon (R``\beta) \cap \text{AV}(Q)$. Then $\breve{R}(z) \epsilon (\breve{R}``R``\beta) \cap \text{AV}(P)$. But, by Thm. X.5.22, Cor. 1, $\breve{R}``R``\beta = \beta \cap \text{AV}(P)$. So $\breve{R}(z) \epsilon \beta \cap \text{AV}(P)$. Then, by the definition of x least$_P$ β, $xP(\breve{R}(z))$. So $(R(x))Q(R(\breve{R}(z)))$. Then $(R(x))Qz$.

Thus we have proved $(x,\beta).x \text{ least}_P\, \beta \supset R(x) \text{ least}_Q\, R``\beta$. The proof of $(x,\beta).x \text{ least}_Q\, \beta \supset \breve{R}(x) \text{ least}_P\, \breve{R}``\beta$ proceeds similarly.

Proof of Part II. Similar.

Theorem XII.1.10. $\vdash (P,Q):P$ smor $Q.P \in$ Connex. $\supset .Q \in$ Connex.

Corollary. $\vdash (P,Q):P$ smor $Q.P \in$ Sord. $\supset .Q \in$ Sord.

Theorem XII.1.11. $\vdash (P,Q,R):P$ smor_R $Q. \supset .\breve{P}$ smor_R $\breve{Q}$.

Theorem XII.1.12. $\vdash (P,Q,R,S,\alpha):P$ smor_R $Q.S = \alpha\upharpoonleft R. \supset .(\alpha\upharpoonleft P\upharpoonright\alpha)$ smor_S $((R``\alpha)\upharpoonleft Q\upharpoonright(R``\alpha))$.

Theorem XII.1.13. $\vdash (P,Q,R,x):P$ smor_R $Q.x \in \text{AV}(P). \supset .R``\hat{z}(z(P - I)x) = \hat{z}(z(Q - I)(R(x)))$.

****Corollary 1.** $\vdash (P,Q,R,S,x,y):P$ smor_R $Q.x \in \text{AV}(P).S = (\hat{z}(z(P - I)x))\upharpoonleft R.y = R(x). \supset .(\text{seg}_x P)$ smor_S $(\text{seg}_y Q)$.

Corollary 2. $\vdash (P,Q,x):P$ smor $Q.x \in \text{AV}(P). \supset .(\text{E}y).y \in \text{AV}(Q).(\text{seg}_x P)$ smor $(\text{seg}_y Q)$.

****Theorem XII.1.14.** $\vdash (P,Q):P$ smor $Q.P \in$ Word. $\supset .Q \in$ Word.

Theorems XII.1.5 to XII.1.14 inclusive seem to establish the fact that ordinal similarity between two relations is possible only in case they have similar order properties.

EXERCISES

XII.1.1. Prove:

(a) $\vdash (P,Q):P$ smor $Q.P \in$ Sym. $\supset .Q \in$ Sym.
(b) $\vdash (P,Q):P$ smor $Q.P \in$ Equiv. $\supset .Q \in$ Equiv.

XII.1.2. Prove $\vdash (P):P$ smor $\Lambda. \equiv .P = \Lambda$.

XII.1.3. Prove:

(a) $\vdash (x,y).\{\langle x,x\rangle\}$ smor $\{\langle y,y\rangle\}$.
(b) $\vdash (x,P):P$ smor $\{\langle x,x\rangle\}. \supset .(\text{E}y).P = \{\langle y,y\rangle\}$.

XII.1.4. Prove $\vdash (P,x):P \in$ Rel. $\supset .P$ smor $(\hat{y}\hat{z}(\text{E}u,v).uPv.y = \langle x,u\rangle.z = \langle x,v\rangle)$.

XII.1.5. Let $P +_s Q$ stand for

$$\hat{x}\hat{y}(xPy.\vee.x \in \text{AV}(P).y \in \text{AV}(Q).\vee.xQy).$$

Prove:

(a) $\vdash (P,Q):P,Q \in$ Ref. $\supset .P +_s Q \in$ Ref.
(b) $\vdash (P,Q):\text{AV}(P) \cap \text{AV}(Q) = \Lambda.P,Q \in$ Trans. $\supset .P +_s Q \in$ Trans.
(c) $\vdash (P,Q):\text{AV}(P) \cap \text{AV}(Q) = \Lambda.P,Q \in$ Antisym. $\supset .P +_s Q \in$ Antisym.
(d) $\vdash (P,Q):P,Q \in$ Connex. $\supset .P +_s Q \in$ Connex.
(e) $\vdash (P,Q):\text{AV}(P) \cap \text{AV}(Q) = \Lambda.P,Q \in$ Word. $\supset .P +_s Q \in$ Word.
(f) $\vdash (P,Q,R,S):P$ smor $Q.R$ smor $S.\text{AV}(P) \cap \text{AV}(R) = \Lambda.\text{AV}(Q) \cap \text{AV}(S) = \Lambda. \supset .(P +_s R)$ smor $(Q +_s S)$.
(g) $\vdash (P,Q):\text{AV}(P) \cap \text{AV}(Q) = \Lambda.x$ least_Q $\text{AV}(Q). \supset .P = \text{seg}_x(P +_s Q)$.
(h) $\vdash (P,Q,R).((P +_s Q) +_s R) = (P +_s (Q +_s R))$.
(i) $\vdash (P).P +_s \Lambda = P = \Lambda +_s P$.

XII.1.6. Let $P \times_s Q$ stand for

$$\hat{x}\hat{y}(\mathrm{E}u,v,w,z){:}u,w \in \mathrm{AV}(P){:}v,z \in \mathrm{AV}(Q){:}$$
$$x = \langle u,v\rangle{:}y = \langle w,z\rangle{:}v(Q - I)z.\mathbf{v}.v = z.uPw.$$

Prove:

(a) $\vdash (P,Q){:}P,Q \in \mathrm{Word}. \supset .P \times_s Q \in \mathrm{Word}.$
(b) $\vdash (P,Q,R){:}((P \times_s Q) \times_s R) \text{ smor } (P \times_s (Q \times_s R)).$
(c) $\vdash (P,Q,R){:}P \times_s (Q +_s R) = (P \times_s Q) +_s (P \times_s R).$
(d) $\vdash (P).P \times_s \Lambda = \Lambda = \Lambda \times_s P.$
(e) $\vdash (P,x){:}P \in \mathrm{Rel}. \supset .P \text{ smor } (\{\langle x,x\rangle\} \times_s P).$
(f) $\vdash (P,x){:}P \in \mathrm{Rel}. \supset .P \text{ smor } (P \times_s \{\langle x,x\rangle\}).$

2. Well-ordering Relations. We shall define ordinal numbers as equivalence classes of well-ordering relations with respect to smor. Before doing so, we wish to establish some special properties of well-ordering relations.

It turns out that there is a unique basic structure for all well-ordered sets, and any given well-ordered set is in effect just an initial segment of this basic structure. To put it another way, if one starts with a first element (and every nonempty well-ordered set must have a first element, by the descending-chain condition) and builds up a well-ordered set by adding further elements (and there is always a unique "next" element if one has not finished, again by the descending-chain condition), one must follow a fixed pattern. If one takes a "few" elements, one will not go far along the basic structure. If one takes "many" elements, one will go far along the basic structure. Thus different sets may extend to different points on the basic structure, but as far as both extend, they must follow the same pattern.

Removal of initial elements from this basic structure may not produce any essential difference. Thus Nn and Nn $-$ $\{0\}$ are well-ordered sets with the same order type, although Nn $-$ $\{0\}$ is got by removing the first element of Nn. However, if one starts at the beginning of this basic structure and proceeds to different points, one gets different order types. This is the essential import of the next two theorems.

****Theorem XII.2.1.** $\vdash (P,Q,y){:}P \in \mathrm{Word}.Q \subseteq \mathrm{seg}_y P.y \in \mathrm{AV}(P). \supset .\sim (P \text{ smor } Q).$

Proof. Proof by reductio ad absurdum. Assume

(1) $$P \in \mathrm{Word},$$

(2) $$Q \subseteq \mathrm{seg}_y P,$$

(3) $$y \in \mathrm{AV}(P),$$

(4) $$P \text{ smor}_R\, Q.$$

Now define f by weak induction so that

(5) $$f(0) = y,$$

(6) $$(n):n \in \text{Nn}. \supset .f(n+1) = R(f(n)).$$

Lemma 1. $(n):n \in \text{Nn}. \supset .f(n) \in \text{AV}(P)$.

Proof. Proof by weak induction. Clearly our lemma is valid for $n = 0$. Assume $f(n) \in \text{AV}(P)$. Then by (4), $R(f(n)) \in \text{AV}(Q)$. Then by (6) and (2), $f(n+1) \in \text{AV}(P)$.

Lemma 2. $(n):n \in \text{Nn}. \supset .(f(n+1))(P - I)(f(n))$.

Proof. Proof by weak induction on n. By (3) and (4), $R(y) \in \text{AV}(Q)$. Then by Thm.X.6.12, Part 3, and (2), $(R(y))(P - I)y$. Thus $(f(1))(P - I)(f(0))$, and our lemma holds for $n = 0$.

Assume $(f(n+1))(P - I)(f(n))$. Then by Lemma 1 and (4), $(R(f(n+1)))Q(R(f(n)))$. That is, by (6), $(f((n+1)+1))Q(f(n+1))$. Then $(f((n+1)+1))P(f(n+1))$ by (2). Also, if $R(f(n+1)) = R(f(n))$, then $f(n+1) = f(n)$ by $R \in 1\text{–}1$. So $(f((n+1)+1))(P - I)(f(n+1))$.

By Lemma 1, $\text{Val}(f) = \text{Val}(f) \cap \text{AV}(P)$. Then by (5), (3), and Thm. X.6.14, Part II, there is a least x in $\text{Val}(f)$. That is,

(7) $$x \in \text{Val}(f),$$

(8) $$(w):w \in \text{Val}(f). \supset .xPw.$$

Then by (7), there is an n with $n \in \text{Nn}.x = f(n)$. Then $f(n+1) \in \text{Val}(f)$. So by (8), $(f(n))P(f(n+1))$. On the other hand, $(f(n+1))(P - I)(f(n))$ by Lemma 2. Then, since $P \in \text{Antisym}$ by (1), we get a contradiction by Thm.X.6.4, Part V. Thus our theorem follows.

From this theorem it follows that, if one terminates a well-ordered series at two different places, the resulting series are ordinally dissimilar. We express this precisely in the next theorem.

Theorem XII.2.2. $\vdash (P,x,y):P \in \text{Word}.x,y \in \text{AV}(P).(\text{seg}_x P) \text{ smor } (\text{seg}_y P). \supset .x = y.$

Proof. Proof by reductio ad absurdum. Assume the hypothesis and $x \neq y$. Put $Q = \text{seg}_x P$ and $R = \text{seg}_y P$. Then

(1) $$Q \text{ smor } R.$$

Since $x,y \in \text{AV}(P)$ and $P \in \text{Connex}$, $xPy.\text{v}.yPx$.

Case 1. xPy. Then $x(P - I)y$, so that $x \in \text{AV}(R)$ by Thm.X.6.12, Part III. Then $\text{seg}_x R = \text{seg}_x P$ by Thm.X.6.13, corollary. That is, $\text{seg}_x R = Q$. But $R \in \text{Word}$ by Thm.X.6.14, Part V, so that we get a contradiction by Thm.XII.2.1.

Case 2. yPx. One derives a similar contradiction.

If two well-ordered sets are ordinally similar, they must extend equally far along the basic structure. Moreover, there must be a unique order-preserving correspondence between them, namely, that one which puts into correspondence the elements which are equally far along the basic structure.

Theorem XII.2.3. $\vdash (P,Q):P,Q \in \text{Word}.P \text{ smor } Q. \supset .(\text{E}_1R).P \text{ smor}_R\, Q.$

Proof. Assume $P,Q \in$ Word and P smor Q. Then, by the definition of smor, there must be an R such that $P \text{ smor}_R\, Q$. To prove that R is unique, let also $P \text{ smor}_S\, Q$ and $R \neq S$. Then by Thm.X.5.16 and duality, there is an x such that $x \in \text{Arg}(R)$, $x \in \text{Arg}(S)$, $R(x) \neq S(x)$. Let $y = R(x)$, $z = S(x)$, $T = \breve{R}|S$. Then by Thm.XII.1.4, $Q \text{ smor}_T\, Q$. Also, by Thm.X.5.20, Part II, $T(y) = S(\breve{R}(R(x))) = S(x) = z$. Then by Thm.XII.1.13, Cor. 1, $(\text{seg}_y Q)$ smor $(\text{seg}_z Q)$. Then by Thm.XII.2.2, $y = z$, and we have a contradiction.

Of two well-ordered sets, we say that the first is shorter than the second if the first is ordinally similar to an initial segment of the second. Or, putting the definition in terms of well-ordering relations, we define

$$\text{sr} \qquad \text{for} \qquad \hat{P}\hat{Q}(P,Q \in \text{Word}:(\text{E}x).x \in \text{AV}(Q).P \text{ smor } (\text{seg}_x Q)).$$

Clearly sr is stratified, and as it has no free variables, it may be assigned any type.

Theorem XII.2.4.

I. $\vdash \exists(\text{sr})$.

II. $\vdash \text{sr} \in \text{Rel}$.

III. $\vdash (P,Q):.P \text{ sr } Q: \equiv :P,Q \in \text{Word}:(\text{E}x).x \in \text{AV}(Q).P \text{ smor } (\text{seg}_x Q).$

IV. $\vdash (P,x):P \in \text{Word}.x \in \text{AV}(P). \supset .(\text{seg}_x P) \text{ sr } P.$

V. $\vdash (P,Q,R):P \text{ smor } Q.Q \text{ sr } R. \supset .P \text{ sr } R.$

Theorem XII.2.5. $\vdash (P).\sim(P \text{ sr } P).$

Proof. Take Q to be $\text{seg}_x P$ in Thm.XII.2.1.

Theorem XII.2.6. $\vdash (P,Q,R):P \text{ sr } Q.Q \text{ smor } R. \supset .P \text{ sr } R.$

Proof. Let P sr Q and Q smor R. Then $P,Q \in$ Word, $x \in \text{AV}(Q).P$ smor $(\text{seg}_x Q)$, and $Q \text{ smor}_S\, R$. Then $R \in$ Word by Thm.XII.1.14. Also, if we put $y = S(x)$, then $y \in \text{AV}(R)$, and by Thm.XII.1.13, Cor. 1, $(\text{seg}_x Q)$ smor $(\text{seg}_y R)$. Then P smor $(\text{seg}_y R)$.

Theorem XII.2.7. $\vdash (P,Q,R):P \text{ sr } Q.Q \text{ sr } R. \supset .P \text{ sr } R.$

Proof. Let P sr $Q.Q$ sr R. Then $y \in \text{AV}(R).Q$ smor $(\text{seg}_y R)$. Then by Thm.XII.2.6, P sr $(\text{seg}_y R)$. Thus $x \in \text{AV}(\text{seg}_y R).P$ smor $(\text{seg}_x(\text{seg}_y R))$. Then by Thm.X.6.13, corollary, P smor $(\text{seg}_x R)$. Also $x \in \text{AV}(R)$ by Thm. X.6.12, Part III.

Corollary 1. $\vdash (P,Q)\sim(P \text{ sr } Q.Q \text{ sr } P).$

Proof. Use Thm.XII.2.5.

Corollary 2. $\vdash (P,Q):P \text{ sr } Q. \supset .\sim(Q \text{ sr } P).$

Theorem XII.2.8. $\vdash (P):.P \in \text{Word}: \supset :(x,y):x(P - I)y. \equiv .x,y \in \text{AV}(P).$ $(\text{seg}_x P) \text{ sr } (\text{seg}_y P).$

Proof. Let $P \in$ Word.

First, let $x(P - I)y$. Then $x,y \in \mathrm{AV}(P)$. Also, $\mathrm{seg}_x P \in \mathrm{Word}$ and $\mathrm{seg}_y P \in \mathrm{Word}$. Likewise $x \in \mathrm{AV}(\mathrm{seg}_y P)$. Also, $\mathrm{seg}_x P = \mathrm{seg}_x(\mathrm{seg}_y P)$. Then $(\mathrm{seg}_x P)$ sr $(\mathrm{seg}_y P)$.

Conversely, let $x,y \in \mathrm{AV}(P)$ and $(\mathrm{seg}_x P)$ sr $(\mathrm{seg}_y P)$. Then $z \in \mathrm{AV}(\mathrm{seg}_y P)$ and $(\mathrm{seg}_x P)$ smor $(\mathrm{seg}_z(\mathrm{seg}_y P))$. Then $z(P - I)y$ and $\mathrm{seg}_z(\mathrm{seg}_y P) = \mathrm{seg}_z P$. Thus $x,z \in \mathrm{AV}(P)$ and $(\mathrm{seg}_x P)$ smor $(\mathrm{seg}_z P)$. Then $x = z$ by Thm.XII.2.2. Thus $x(P - I)y$.

We wish to show that, if one has given two well-ordered sets, then either they are ordinally similar, or one is shorter. We shall base the proof on the possibility of definition by transfinite induction. It is not necessary to use the possibility of definition by transfinite induction (see Rosser, 1942), but we wish to prove this possibility anyhow, and we now do so.

Definition by transfinite induction is a generalization of definition by strong induction. In both, we define a function f with $\mathrm{Arg}(f) = \alpha$. In strong induction, α is $\hat{n}(n \in \mathrm{Nn}.m \leq n)$, but in transfinite induction, α is any well-ordered set; say $\alpha = \mathrm{AV}(P)$, where P is a well-ordering relation. In both cases, we define $f(x)$ in terms of the values of f for elements of α which precede x. Speaking loosely, we define the value $f(x)$ in terms of the earlier values of f. Since y precedes x if and only if $y(P - I)x$, the values of f earlier than $f(x)$ are just the values of $(\hat{y}(y(P - I)x))\rceil f$. So we define $f(x)$ in terms of $(\hat{y}(y(P - I)x))\rceil f$. More generally, we let the value of $f(x)$ depend on both x and $(\hat{y}(y(P - I)x))\rceil f$. That is, given a term $j(x,f)$, we require a function f such that $\mathrm{Arg}(f) = \alpha$ and

$$f(x) = j(x,(\hat{y}(y(P - I)x))\rceil f).$$

We shall now show that, under proper stratification conditions, there is a unique f satisfying these conditions. We use the following hypothesis.

Hypothesis H_6. Let $p(x,P)$ denote $\hat{y}(y(P - I)x)$. Let P, R, S, x, f be distinct variables. Let $j(x,f)$ be a term not containing any occurrences of R or S. If A and B are terms, let $j(A,B)$ denote $\{\mathrm{Sub\ in\ } j(x,f){:}\ A \text{ for } x, B \text{ for } f\}$, where it shall be understood that the substitutions indicated cause no confusion.

Theorem XII.2.9. Assume Hypothesis H_6. Then

(1) $$P \in \mathrm{Word},$$

(2) $$R,S \in \mathrm{Funct},$$

(3) $$\mathrm{Arg}(R) = \mathrm{Arg}(S) = \mathrm{AV}(P),$$

(4) $$(x){:}x \in \mathrm{AV}(P). \supset .R(x) = j(x,p(x,P)\rceil R),$$

(5) $$(x){:}x \in \mathrm{AV}(P). \supset .S(x) = j(x,p(x,P)\rceil S)$$

yield

$$R = S.$$

Proof. Proof by reductio ad absurdum. Assume the hypotheses and also $R \neq S$. By Thm.X.5.16, there is an x with $x \in \mathrm{AV}(P).R(x) \neq S(x)$. So by Thm.X.6.14,

$$(6) \qquad y \in \mathrm{AV}(P).R(y) \neq S(y),$$

and $(z):z \in \mathrm{AV}(P).R(z) \neq S(z). \supset .yPz$. So by Thm.X.6.4, Part V,

$$(7) \qquad (z):z \in \mathrm{AV}(P).z(P - I)y. \supset .R(z) = S(z).$$

Let $u(p(y,P)\upharpoonright R)v$. Then $u \in p(y,P).uRv$. So $u(P - I)y.v = R(u)$. So by (7), $u(P - I)y.v = S(u)$, and by (3), $u \in \mathrm{Arg}(S)$. Then $u \in p(y,P).uSv$, and finally $u(p(y,P)\upharpoonright S)v$. Conversely, we can go from $u(p(y,P)\upharpoonright S)v$ to $u(p(y,P)\upharpoonright R)v$. Thus

$$p(y,P)\upharpoonright R = p(y,P)\upharpoonright S.$$

Then by (6), (4), and (5), $R(y) = S(y)$, and we have a contradiction by (6).

Theorem XII.2.10. Assume Hypothesis H_6. Assume further that $R(x) = j(x,p(x,P)\upharpoonright R)$ is stratified. Then $\vdash (P)::P \in \mathrm{Word}.: \supset :.(y):.$ $y \in \mathrm{AV}(P): \supset :(\mathrm{E}R):R \in \mathrm{Funct}:\mathrm{Arg}(R) = \hat{z}(zPy):(x):xPy. \supset .R(x) = j(x,p(x,P)\upharpoonright R)$.

Proof. Proof by reductio ad absurdum. Assume that

$$(1) \qquad P \in \mathrm{Word}$$

and that the conclusion is false. Then by Thm.X.6.14, Part II, there is a y such that

$$(2) \qquad y \in \mathrm{AV}(P),$$

$$(3) \qquad \sim(\mathrm{E}R):R \in \mathrm{Funct}:\mathrm{Arg}(R) = \hat{z}(zPy):(x):xPy. \supset .R(x) = j(x,p(x,P)\upharpoonright R),$$

and if corresponding results hold for any w, then yPw. Then by Thm. X.6.4, Part V,

$$(4) \qquad (w):.w(P - I)y: \supset :(\mathrm{E}R):R \in \mathrm{Funct}:\mathrm{Arg}(R) = \hat{z}(zPw):(x):xPw. \supset .R(x) = j(x,p(x,P)\upharpoonright R).$$

Put

$$(5) \qquad W = \hat{R}(\mathrm{E}w):.w(P - I)y:R \in \mathrm{Funct}:\mathrm{Arg}(R) = \hat{z}(zPw):(x):xPw. \supset .R(x) = j(x,p(x,P)\upharpoonright R).$$

$$(6) \qquad S = \bigcup W.$$

Lemma 1. $(R_1,R_2,\beta):R_1,R_2 \in W.\beta \subseteq \mathrm{Arg}(R_1) \cap \mathrm{Arg}(R_2). \supset .\beta\upharpoonright R_1 = \beta\upharpoonright R_2$.

Proof. Let $R_1,R_2 \in W$. Then for $i = 1$ and $i = 2$, $w_i(P - I)y:R_i \in$

Funct:Arg(R_i) $= \hat{z}(zPw_i)$:(x):xPw_i. $\supset$.$R_i(x) = j(x,p(x,P)\upharpoonright R_i)$. By $P \epsilon$ Connex, we may say without loss of generality that w_1Pw_2. Then Arg(R_1) $\subseteq$ Arg(R_2). Putting Arg$(R_1)\upharpoonright P \upharpoonright$Arg$(R_1)$, R_1, and Arg$(R_1)\upharpoonright R_2$ for P, R, and S in Thm.XII.2.9 gives $R_1 =$ Arg$(R_1)\upharpoonright R_2$. Then our lemma follows by Thm.X.4.11, Part V.

Lemma 2. (R_1,R_2,u,v_1,v_2):$R_1,R_2 \epsilon W.uR_1v_1.uR_2v_2. \supset .v_1 = v_2$.

Proof. Put $\beta =$ Arg$(R_1) \cap$ Arg(R_2). Then from the hypothesis of the lemma, $u(\beta\upharpoonright R_1)v_1.u(\beta\upharpoonright R_2)v_2$. Thus, by Lemma 1, $u(\beta\upharpoonright R_1)v_2$. But by (5), $\beta\upharpoonright R_1 \epsilon$ Funct. So $v_1 = v_2$.

Lemma 3. (R,u,v_1,v_2):$R \epsilon W.uRv_1.uSv_2. \supset .v_1 = v_2$.

Proof. If uSv_2, then by (6), $R_2 \epsilon W.uR_2v_2$. Then $v_1 = v_2$ by Lemma 2.

Lemma 4. $S \epsilon$ Funct.

Proof. Obvious by (6) and Lemma 2.

Lemma 5. Arg$(S) = p(y,P)$.

Proof. If uSv, then $R \epsilon W$ and $u \epsilon$ Arg(R). So $w(P - I)y.uPw$. Then $u \epsilon p(y,P)$ by Thm.X.6.5, Part VI. Conversely, let $u \epsilon p(y,P)$. Then $u(P - I)y$, so that by (4) there is an R in W with Arg$(R) = \hat{z}(zPu)$. So $u \epsilon$ Arg(R), and hence $u \epsilon$ Arg(S) by (6).

Lemma 6. (R,β):$R \epsilon W.\beta \subseteq$ Arg(R). $\supset .\beta\upharpoonright R = \beta\upharpoonright S$.

Proof. Let $R \epsilon W.\beta \subseteq$ Arg(R). If $u(\beta\upharpoonright R)v$, then $u \epsilon \beta.uRv$. Then by (6), $u \epsilon \beta.uSv$. So $u(\beta\upharpoonright S)v$. If $u(\beta\upharpoonright S)v$, then $u \epsilon \beta.uSv$. But $\beta \subseteq$ Arg(R). So uRw. Then $v = w$ by Lemma 3. So uRv, and finally $u(\beta\upharpoonright R)v$.

Lemma 7. (x):$x(P - I)y. \supset .S(x) = j(x,p(x,P)\upharpoonright S)$.

Proof. Use (5), (6), Lemma 3, Lemma 5, and Lemma 6.

Now put

(7) $$R = S \cup \{\langle y,j(y,S)\rangle\}.$$

Then

(8) $$R \epsilon \text{ Funct},$$

(9) $$\text{Arg}(R) = \hat{z}(zPy),$$

(10) $$S = p(y,P)\upharpoonright R,$$

(11) $$(x):xPy. \supset .R(x) = j(x,p(x,P)\upharpoonright R).$$

Then by (3), we have a contradiction.

****Theorem XII.2.11.** Assume Hypothesis H_6. Assume further that $R(x) = j(x,p(x,P)\upharpoonright R)$ is stratified. Then $\vdash (P)$::$P \epsilon$ Word.: $\supset$:.(ER): $R \epsilon$ Funct:Arg$(R) =$ AV(P):(x):$x \epsilon$ AV(P). $\supset .R(x) = j(x,p(x,P)\upharpoonright R)$.

Proof. Assume

(1) $$P \epsilon \text{ Word}.$$

Define

(2) $$W = \hat{R}(\mathrm{E}y){:}.y \in \mathrm{AV}(P){:}R \in \mathrm{Funct}{:}\mathrm{Arg}(R)$$
$$= \hat{z}(zPy){:}(x){:}xPy. \supset .R(x) = j(x,p(x,P)\upharpoonright R).$$

(3) $$S = \bigcup W.$$

As in the proof of Thm.XII.2.10, we prove seven lemmas. Lemma 5 will be $\mathrm{Arg}(S) = \mathrm{AV}(P)$. Then our theorem will follow from Lemmas 4, 5, and 7 by taking R to be S.

Theorem XII.2.12. Assume Hypothesis H_5. Assume further that $R(n+1) = j(n,R)$ is stratified. Then

(1) $$m \in \mathrm{Nn},$$

(2) $$\alpha = \hat{n}(n \in \mathrm{Nn}.m \leq n),$$

(3) $$(R,S,n){::}R,S \in \mathrm{Funct}.\mathrm{Arg}(R) \subseteq \alpha.\mathrm{Arg}(S) \subseteq \alpha.n \in \alpha{:}.$$
$$(x){:}x \in \alpha.x \leq n. \supset .R(x) = S(x).{:} \supset {:}.j(n,R) = j(n,S)$$

yield

$$(\mathrm{E}R){::}R \in \mathrm{Funct}.\mathrm{Arg}(R) = \alpha.R(m) = a{:}.(n){:}n \in \alpha. \supset .R(n+1) = j(n,R).$$

Proof. Assume the hypotheses. In Thm.XII.2.11, put

$$P = (\alpha \upharpoonright \leq_c \restriction \alpha)$$

and take $j(x,f)$ to be

$$\iota y\ (x = m.y = a{:}\mathbf{v}{:}(\mathrm{E}n){:}n \in \alpha.x = n + 1.y = j(n,f)).$$

Then we infer that there is an R such that

$$R \in \mathrm{Funct},$$

$$\mathrm{Arg}(R) = \alpha,$$

$$R(m) = a,$$

(4) $$(n){:}n \in \alpha. \supset .R(n+1) = j(n,(\hat{x}(x \in \alpha.x \leq n))\upharpoonright R).$$

Now let $n \in \alpha$ and

$$S = (\hat{x}(x \in \alpha.x \leq n))\upharpoonright R.$$

Then clearly $R,S \in \mathrm{Funct}.\mathrm{Arg}(R) \subseteq \alpha.\mathrm{Arg}(S) \subseteq \alpha.n \in \alpha{:}.(x){:}x \in \alpha.x \leq n. \supset .R(x) = S(x)$. So by (3), $j(n,R) = j(n,S)$. Then by (4), $R(n+1) = j(n,R)$. Thus our theorem is proved.

By analogous proofs, one can prove analogues of Thms.XII.2.9 to XII.2.12 satisfying other stratification conditions. Thus if $R(\{x\}) =$

$j(x, \mathrm{USC}(p(x,P))\upharpoonright R)$ is stratified and $P \in$ Word, then one can infer that there is a unique R such that

$$R \in \mathrm{Funct},$$

$$\mathrm{Arg}(R) = \mathrm{USC}(\mathrm{AV}(P)),$$

$$(x):x \in \mathrm{AV}(P). \supset .R(\{x\}) = j(x,\mathrm{USC}(p(x,P))\upharpoonright R).$$

Just in passing, we note that there is a principle of proof by transfinite induction. It is a generalization of Thm.XI.3.20. It is seldom used, since in most instances it is nearly as easy to carry out the proof of the principle for the particular case at hand as to apply the principle. The principle is embodied in the following theorem.

Theorem XII.2.13. Assume that $F(x)$ is stratified. Then

(1) $$P \in \mathrm{Word},$$

(2) $$(x)::x \in \mathrm{AV}(P):.(y):y(P - I)x. \supset .F(y).: \supset :.F(x)$$

yield

$$(x):x \in \mathrm{AV}(P). \supset .F(x).$$

Proof. Proof by reductio ad absurdum. Assume the hypotheses and $\sim(x):x \in \mathrm{AV}(P). \supset .F(x)$. Then by Thm.X.6.14, Part II, there is an x such that

(3) $$x \in \mathrm{AV}(P),$$

(4) $$\sim F(x),$$

and $(y):y \in \mathrm{AV}(P).\sim F(y). \supset .xPy$. Then by Thm.X.6.4, Part V, $(y):y(P - I)x. \supset .F(y)$. Then by (3) and (2), $F(x)$. Thus we have a contradiction by (4).

We return to our unfinished business, which consists of proving the following theorem.

****Theorem XII.2.14.** $\vdash (P,Q):.P,Q \in \mathrm{Word}: \supset :P \text{ sr } Q.\mathbf{v}.P \text{ smor } Q.\mathbf{v}.Q \text{ sr } P.$

Proof. Let

(1) $$P,Q \in \mathrm{Word}.$$

Let $p(x,P)$ denote $\hat{y}(y(P - I)x)$. By Thm.XII.2.11, there is an R such that

(2) $$R \in \mathrm{Funct},$$

(3) $$\mathrm{Arg}(R) = \mathrm{AV}(P),$$

(4) $$(x):x \in \mathrm{AV}(P). \supset .R(x) = \iota y\ (y \text{ least}_Q\ (\mathrm{AV}(Q) - \mathrm{Val}(p(x,P)\upharpoonright R))).$$

Write

(5) $$B(x) = \text{Val}(p(x,P)|R),$$

(6) $$C(x) = \text{AV}(Q) - B(x).$$

Then we can rewrite (4) as

(4) $$(x):x \epsilon \text{AV}(P). \supset .R(x) = \iota y\ (y \text{ least}_Q\ C(x)).$$

Lemma 1. $\text{AV}(Q) - \text{Val}(R) \neq \Lambda. \supset .P \text{ sr } Q.$

Proof. Assume $\text{AV}(Q) - \text{Val}(R) \neq \Lambda$. Since $B(x) \subseteq \text{Val}(R)$ by (5), it follows by (6) that $(x):x \epsilon \text{AV}(P). \supset .C(x) \neq \Lambda$. So by (4) and Thm. X.6.14, Part II,

(i) $$(x):x \epsilon \text{AV}(P). \supset .R(x) \text{ least}_Q\ C(x).$$

Also there is a w such that

(ii) $$w \text{ least}_Q\ (\text{AV}(Q) - \text{Val}(R)).$$

Then by Thm.X.6.4, Part V,

(iii) $$(x):x(Q - I)w. \supset .x \epsilon \text{Val}(R).$$

Now let $x \epsilon \text{Val}(R)$. Then by (2) and (3), $x = R(y).y \epsilon \text{AV}(P)$. So by (i), $x \epsilon \text{AV}(Q)$. Then by (ii), $x \neq w$. Also, since $w \epsilon (\text{AV}(Q) - \text{Val}(R))$ by (ii), and since $(\text{AV}(Q) - \text{Val}(R)) \subseteq C(x)$ by (5) and (6), we get $w \epsilon C(x)$. Then by (i), $(R(y))Qw$. Thus $x(Q - I)w$. So we have shown $x \epsilon \text{Val}(R). \supset .x(Q - I)w$. Then by (iii), $(x):x(Q - I)w. \equiv .x \epsilon \text{Val}(R)$. Thus by Thm.X.6.12, Part III,

(iv) $$\text{AV}(\text{seg}_w Q) = \text{Val}(R).$$

Let $x,y \epsilon \text{AV}(P).R(x) = R(y).x \neq y$. Without loss of generality, we can take yPx. Then $y(P - I)x$. So by (5), $R(y) \epsilon B(x)$, and by (6), $\sim R(y) \epsilon C(x)$. But by (i), $R(x) \epsilon C(x)$. So we have a contradiction. Thus

(v) $$(x,y):x,y \epsilon \text{AV}(P).R(x) = R(y). \supset .x = y.$$

If now $xRz.yRz$, then by (3), $x,y \epsilon \text{AV}(P)$. Also $R(x) = z = R(y)$. So by (v), $x = y$. Thus by (2),

(vi) $$R \epsilon 1\text{–}1.$$

Now let xPy. Then by (3), (2), and (i), $R(y) \epsilon \text{AV}(Q)$. Also $\sim(y(P - I)x)$ by Thm.X.6.4, Part V. So $\sim R(y) \epsilon B(x)$ by (5) and (v). Thus $R(y) \epsilon C(x)$ by (6). Then by (i), $(R(x))Q(R(y))$. Also $R(x),R(y) \epsilon \text{Val}(R)$. Then by (iv) and Thm.X.6.12, Part III, $R(x),R(y) \epsilon p(w,Q)$. Then $(R(x))(\text{seg}_w Q)(R(y))$. Thus

(vii) $$(x,y):xPy. \supset .(R(x))(\text{seg}_w Q)(R(y)).$$

Let $x(\text{seg}_w Q)y$. Then by (iv), $x,y \in \text{Val}(R)$. So by (vi) and (3), $\breve{R}(x), \breve{R}(y) \in \text{AV}(P)$. So $(\breve{R}(x))P(\breve{R}(y)) \vee (\breve{R}(y))P(\breve{R}(x))$. If $(\breve{R}(y))P(\breve{R}(x))$, then $(R(\breve{R}(y)))Q(R(\breve{R}(x)))$ by (vii). Thus yQx. Then $x = y$ since $Q \in \text{Antisym}$. Then $(\breve{R}(x))P(\breve{R}(y))$ since $P \in \text{Ref}$. Thus, in both cases, $(\breve{R}(x))P(\breve{R}(y))$. So

(viii) $$(x,y):x(\text{seg}_w Q)y. \supset .(\breve{R}(x))P(\breve{R}(y)).$$

Now by (1), (vi), (3), (iv), (vii), (viii), and Thm.XII.1.1, P smor $(\text{seg}_w Q)$. Also by (ii), $w \in \text{AV}(Q)$. So P sr Q.

Lemma 2. $(\text{E}x):x \in \text{AV}(P).C(x) = \Lambda.: \supset :.Q \text{ sr } P$.

Proof. Assume the hypothesis and let x be the least element of $\text{AV}(P)$ such that $C(x) = \Lambda$. Then

(i) $$x \in \text{AV}(P),$$

(ii) $$C(x) = \Lambda,$$

(iii) $$(y):y \in \text{AV}(P).y(P - I)x. \supset .C(y) \neq \Lambda.$$

Put

(iv) $$\alpha = p(x,P),$$

(v) $$S = \alpha \rceil R.$$

By (4) and (iii),

(vi) $$(y):y \in \alpha. \supset .R(y) \text{ least}_Q\, C(y).$$

By (3)

(vii) $$\text{Arg}(S) = \alpha = \text{AV}(\text{seg}_x P).$$

By (5), (iv), and (v), $B(x) = \text{Val}(S)$. Then by (6) and (ii), $\text{AV}(Q) \subseteq \text{Val}(S)$. Also, by (vi), $\text{Val}(S) \subseteq \text{AV}(Q)$. So

(viii) $$\text{Val}(S) = \text{AV}(Q).$$

By (2), $S \in \text{Funct}$. Thus we can reason from (vi) as we reasoned from (i) in the proof of Lemma 1 to infer

(ix) $$(y,z):y,z \in \text{Arg}(\text{seg}_x P).S(y) = S(z). \supset .y = z,$$

(x) $$S \in 1\text{–}1,$$

(xi) $$(y,z):y(\text{seg}_x P)z. \supset .(S(y))Q(S(z)),$$

(xii) $$(y,z):yQz. \supset .(\breve{S}(y))(\text{seg}_x P)(\breve{S}(z)).$$

Then our lemma follows.

Lemma 3. $\text{AV}(Q) - \text{Val}(R) = \Lambda :.(x):x \in \text{AV}(P). \supset .C(x) \neq \Lambda :: \supset :: P \text{ smor } Q$.

Proof. Assume

(i) $$\mathrm{AV}(Q) - \mathrm{Val}(R) = \Lambda,$$

(ii) $$(x){:}x \in \mathrm{AV}(P). \supset .C(x) \neq \Lambda.$$

Then by (4),

(iii) $$(x){:}x \in \mathrm{AV}(P). \supset .R(x) \text{ least}_Q\ C(x).$$

By (i), $\mathrm{AV}(Q) \subseteq \mathrm{Val}(R)$, and by (iii) and (3), $\mathrm{Val}(R) \subseteq \mathrm{AV}(Q)$. So

(iv) $$\mathrm{Val}(R) = \mathrm{AV}(Q).$$

We can now reason from (iii) as we reasoned from (i) in the proof of Lemma 1 to infer

(v) $$(x,y){:}x,y \in \mathrm{AV}(P).R(x) = R(y). \supset .x = y,$$

(vi) $$R \in 1\text{–}1,$$

(vii) $$(x,y){:}xPy. \supset .(R(x))Q(R(y)),$$

(viii) $$(x,y){:}xQy. \supset .(\breve{R}(x))P(\breve{R}(y)).$$

Thus our lemma follows.

Now our theorem follows since at least one of the hypotheses of Lemmas 1, 2, or 3 must hold.

EXERCISES

XII.2.1. Prove $\vdash (P,Q){:}P \text{ sr } Q. \supset .\mathrm{Nc}(\mathrm{AV}(P)) \leq \mathrm{Nc}(\mathrm{AV}(Q))$.

XII.2.2. Prove $\vdash (P,Q){::}P,Q \in \text{Word}.{:} \supset {:}.P \text{ sr } Q.\mathbf{v}.P \text{ smor } Q{:} \equiv {:} (x){:}x \in \mathrm{AV}(P). \supset .(\mathrm{E}y).y \in \mathrm{AV}(Q).(\mathrm{seg}_x P) \text{ smor } (\mathrm{seg}_y Q)$. (*Hint.* To go from left to right, use Thm.XII.1.13, Cor. 1, and Thm.X.6.13, corollary. To go from right to left, assume the right side and Q sr P and get a contradiction by Thm.XII.2.1. Then use Thm.XII.2.14.)

XII.2.3. Prove $\vdash (P,Q){::}P \text{ sr } Q.\mathbf{v}.P \text{ smor } Q{:}Q \text{ sr } P.\mathbf{v}.Q \text{ smor } P.{:} \supset {:}. P \text{ smor } Q$.

XII.2.4. Prove $\vdash (P){::}P \in \text{Word}.{:} \supset {:}.(x,y){:}.xPy{:} \equiv {:}x,y \in \mathrm{AV}(P){:} (\mathrm{seg}_x P) \text{ sr } (\mathrm{seg}_y P).\mathbf{v}.(\mathrm{seg}_x P) \text{ smor } (\mathrm{seg}_y P)$.

XII.2.5. Prove:

(a) $\vdash \text{Word}\rceil\text{smor} = \text{smor}\upharpoonright\text{Word} = \text{Word}\rceil\text{smor}\upharpoonright\text{Word}$.
(b) $\vdash \text{Word}\rceil\text{smor} \in \text{Equiv}$.
(c) $\vdash \mathrm{Arg}(\text{Word}\rceil\text{smor}) = \mathrm{Val}(\text{Word}\rceil\text{smor}) = \mathrm{AV}(\text{Word}\rceil\text{smor}) = \text{Word}$.

XII.2.6. Prove $\vdash (x).\Lambda \text{ sr } \{\langle x,x\rangle\}$.

XII.2.7. Prove $\vdash (P,Q){:}Q \in \text{Word}.P \subseteq Q.\ \supset .\sim(Q \text{ sr } P)$. (*Hint.* Let Q smor$_R$ (seg$_x P$). Then define f by

$$f(0) = x,$$

$$(n){:}n \in \text{Nn}.\ \supset .f(n+1) = R(f(n)),$$

and proceed to a contradiction as in the proof of Thm.XII.2.1.)

XII.2.8. Using the definitions of Exs.XII.1.5 and XII.1.6, prove

(a) $\vdash (P,x){:}P \in \text{Word}.\sim x \in \text{AV}(P).\ \supset .P \text{ sr } (P +_s \{\langle x,x\rangle\})$.

(b) $\vdash (P,Q,R){:}P \in \text{Word}.Q \text{ sr } R.\text{AV}(P) \cap \text{AV}(Q) = \Lambda.\text{AV}(P) \cap \text{AV}(R) = \Lambda.\ \supset .(P +_s Q) \text{ sr } (P +_s R)$.

(c) $\vdash (P,Q,R){:}P \in \text{Word}.P \neq \Lambda.Q \text{ sr } R.\ \supset .(P \times_s Q) \text{ sr } (P \times_s R)$.

(d) $\vdash (P,Q,R){:}P,Q,R \in \text{Word}.\text{AV}(P) \cap \text{AV}(Q) = \Lambda.\text{AV}(P) \cap \text{AV}(R) = \Lambda.(P +_s Q) \text{ smor } (P +_s R).\ \supset .Q \text{ smor } R$.

(e) $\vdash (P,Q){:}.P,Q \in \text{Word}{:}\ \supset {:}P \text{ sr } Q. \equiv .(\text{E}R).R \in \text{Word}.\text{AV}(P) \cap \text{AV}(R) = \Lambda.R \neq \Lambda.Q \text{ smor } P +_s R$.

3. Elementary Properties of Ordinal Numbers. Since P smor Q expresses the fact that P and Q have the same order structure, we can define the order of P or Q by abstraction with respect to the equivalence relation smor. The technical name for the order of P, or the order determined by P, is the "order type" of P. Thus we can have the order type of the continuum, which is the equivalence class with respect to smor of the relation $\leq$ for real numbers. Similarly there is the order type of the rationals, the order type of the integers, the order type of the positive integers (namely, the order type of sequences), etc.

In the present section we shall restrict attention to the order types of well-ordered sets. Such order types are called ordinal numbers. So we define the ordinal number No(P) of a well-ordering relation P by abstraction with respect to Word⌉smor, namely,

$$\text{No}(P) \quad \text{for} \quad (\text{Word}\rceil\text{smor})``\{P\}.$$

Clearly No(P) is stratified if and only if P is stratified, and must have type one higher than the type of P if it is stratified.

We have taken No(P) to be the equivalence class of P relative to Word⌉smor. If P is a well-ordering relation, we shall have $P \in \text{No}(P)$. Otherwise $\text{No}(P) = \Lambda$.

We now define the set of ordinal numbers as the set of equivalence classes with respect to Word⌉smor, namely,

$$\text{NO} \quad \text{for} \quad \text{EqC}(\text{Word}\rceil\text{smor}).$$

NO is stratified, and has no free variables, and so may be assigned any type.

Theorem XII.3.1.

I. $\vdash (P):P \epsilon \mathrm{No}(P). \equiv .P \epsilon \mathrm{Word}.$

II. $\vdash (P):P \epsilon \mathrm{Word}. \equiv .\mathrm{No}(P) \neq \Lambda.$

III. $\vdash (P,Q):.P,Q \epsilon \mathrm{Word}: \supset :Q \epsilon \mathrm{No}(P). \equiv .P \text{ smor } Q.$

IV. $\vdash (P,Q):Q \epsilon \mathrm{No}(P). \equiv .P \text{ smor } Q.P,Q \epsilon \mathrm{Word}.$

Corollary 1. $\vdash (P,Q):P \epsilon \mathrm{No}(Q). \equiv .Q \epsilon \mathrm{No}(P).$

Corollary 2. $\vdash (P,Q,R):P,Q \epsilon \mathrm{No}(R). \supset .P \text{ smor } Q.$

Corollary 3. $\vdash (P,Q,R):P \epsilon \mathrm{No}(R).P \text{ smor } Q. \supset .Q \epsilon \mathrm{No}(R).$

Corollary 4. $\vdash (P,Q):Q \epsilon \mathrm{No}(P). \equiv .P \text{ smor } Q.P \epsilon \mathrm{Word}.$

Since $\vdash \mathrm{Word}\upharpoonright\mathrm{smor} \epsilon \mathrm{Equiv}$, we can apply the theorems of Sec. 7 of Chapter X to get the following theorem.

Theorem XII.3.2.

I. $\vdash (\phi):.\phi \epsilon \mathrm{NO}: \equiv :(\mathrm{E}P).P \epsilon \mathrm{Word}.\phi = \mathrm{No}(P).$

II. $\vdash (P,Q):P \epsilon \mathrm{Word}.P \text{ smor } Q. \equiv .P,Q \epsilon \mathrm{Word}.\mathrm{No}(P) = \mathrm{No}(Q).$

III. $\vdash (\phi):.\phi \epsilon \mathrm{NO}: \supset :(P):P \epsilon \phi. \equiv .\phi = \mathrm{No}(P).$

IV. $\vdash (\phi,\theta):\phi,\theta \epsilon \mathrm{NO}.\phi \cap \theta \neq \Lambda. \supset .\phi = \theta.$

V. $\vdash (P):P \epsilon \mathrm{Word}. \supset .(\mathrm{E}_1\phi).\phi \epsilon \mathrm{NO}.P \epsilon \phi.$

VI. $\vdash (\phi):\phi \epsilon \mathrm{NO}. \supset .\phi \neq \Lambda.$

Corollary 1. $\vdash (P,Q):.P,Q \epsilon \mathrm{Word}: \supset :P \text{ smor } Q. \equiv .\mathrm{No}(P) = \mathrm{No}(Q).$

Corollary 2. $\vdash (P):P \epsilon \mathrm{Word}. \equiv .\mathrm{No}(P) \epsilon \mathrm{NO}.$

Corollary 3. $\vdash (P,\phi):P \epsilon \phi.\phi \epsilon \mathrm{NO}. \supset .P \epsilon \mathrm{Word}.$

Theorem XII.3.3.

I. $\vdash (P,Q,\phi):\phi \epsilon \mathrm{NO}.P,Q \epsilon \phi. \supset .P \text{ smor } Q.$

II. $\vdash (P,Q,\phi):\phi \epsilon \mathrm{NO}.P \epsilon \phi.P \text{ smor } Q. \supset .Q \epsilon \phi.$

We now introduce the relations of greater and less between ordinal numbers. We define

$<_0$	for	$\hat{\phi}\hat{\theta}(\mathrm{E}P,Q).P \text{ sr } Q.\phi = \mathrm{No}(P).\theta = \mathrm{No}(Q),$
$>_0$	for	$\mathrm{Cnv}(<_0),$
$\leq_0$	for	$<_0 \cup (\mathrm{NO}\upharpoonright I),$
$\geq_0$	for	$\mathrm{Cnv}(\leq_0).$

The terms $<_0$, $>_0$, $\leq_0$, $\geq_0$ are all stratified and contain no free variables and so may be assigned any type.

In any case where it is clear from the context that we are dealing with $<_0$, $>_0$, $\leq_0$, and $\geq_0$ instead of $<_c$, $>_c$, $\leq_c$, and $\geq_c$, we shall omit the subscript.

We commonly write $\phi \leq \theta \leq \psi$ for $\phi \leq \theta.\theta \leq \psi$, $\phi \leq \theta < \psi$ for $\phi \leq \theta.\theta < \psi$, $\phi = \theta < \psi$ for $\phi = \theta.\theta < \psi$, etc.

Theorem XII.3.4.

I. $\vdash (\phi,\theta):.\phi < \theta: \equiv :(\mathrm{E}P,Q).P \text{ sr } Q.\phi = \mathrm{No}(P).\theta = \mathrm{No}(Q).$

II. $\vdash (\phi,\theta):\phi > \theta. \equiv .\theta < \phi.$

III. $\vdash (\phi,\theta):.\phi \leq \theta: \equiv :\phi < \theta.\mathbf{v}.\phi = \theta.\phi \epsilon \mathrm{NO}.$

IV. $\vdash (\phi,\theta):\phi \geq \theta. \equiv .\theta \leq \phi.$

Corollary. $\vdash (\phi){:}\phi \in \mathrm{NO}. \supset .\phi \leq \phi.$

Theorem XII.3.5. $\vdash (\phi).{\sim}(\phi < \phi).$

Proof. Use Thm.XII.2.5.

Corollary. $\vdash (\phi,\theta){:}\phi < \theta. \equiv .\phi \leq \theta.\phi \neq \theta.$

Theorem XII.3.6. $\vdash (\phi,\theta,\psi){:}\phi < \theta.\theta < \psi. \supset .\phi < \psi.$

Proof. Use Thm.XII.2.7.

Corollary 1. $\vdash (\phi,\theta,\psi){:}\phi \leq \theta.\theta < \psi. \supset .\phi < \psi.$

Corollary 2. $\vdash (\phi,\theta,\psi){:}\phi < \theta.\theta \leq \psi. \supset .\phi < \psi.$

Corollary 3. $\vdash (\phi,\theta,\psi){:}\phi \leq \theta.\theta \leq \psi. \supset .\phi \leq \psi.$

Corollary 4. $\vdash (\phi,\theta){:}\phi < \theta. \supset .{\sim}(\theta < \phi).$

Proof. Use Thm.XII.3.5.

Corollary 5. $\vdash (\phi,\theta){:}\phi < \theta. \supset .{\sim}(\theta \leq \phi).$

Corollary 6. $\vdash (\phi,\theta){:}\theta \leq \phi. \supset .{\sim}(\phi < \theta).$

Theorem XII.3.7. $\vdash (\phi,\theta){:}\phi \leq \theta.\theta \leq \phi. \supset .\phi = \theta.$

Proof. From $\theta \leq \phi$, we get ${\sim}(\phi < \theta)$ by Thm.XII.3.6, Cor. 6. So $\phi = \theta$ by Thm.XII.3.4, Part III.

Theorem XII.3.8. $\vdash (\phi,\theta){:.}\phi,\theta \in \mathrm{NO}{:} \supset {:}\phi < \theta.\mathbf{v}.\phi = \theta.\mathbf{v}.\phi > \theta.$

Proof. Use Thm.XII.2.14.

Corollary 1. $\vdash (\phi,\theta){:.}\phi,\theta \in \mathrm{NO}{:} \supset {:}\phi \leq \theta.\mathbf{v}.\theta \leq \phi.$

Corollary 2. $\vdash (\phi,\theta){:.}\phi,\theta \in \mathrm{NO}{:} \supset {:}\phi < \theta. \equiv .{\sim}(\theta \leq \phi).$

Corollary 3. $\vdash (\phi,\theta){:.}\phi,\theta \in \mathrm{NO}{:} \supset {:}\theta \leq \phi. \equiv .{\sim}(\phi < \theta).$

Theorem XII.3.9. $\vdash (P,\phi){:.}\phi < \mathrm{No}(P){:} \supset {:}(\mathrm{E}y).y \in \mathrm{AV}(P).\phi = \mathrm{No}(\mathrm{seg}_y P).$

Proof. Use Thm.XII.2.4, Part III.

Theorem XII.3.10. $\vdash (P,x){:}P \in \mathrm{Word}.x \in \mathrm{AV}(P). \supset .\mathrm{No}(\mathrm{seg}_x P) < \mathrm{No}(P).$

Proof. Use Thm.XII.2.4, Part IV.

Theorem XII.3.11. $\vdash (P,x,y){:.}P \in \mathrm{Word}{:}x,y \in \mathrm{AV}(P){:} \supset {:}x(P - I)y. \equiv .\mathrm{No}(\mathrm{seg}_x P) < \mathrm{No}(\mathrm{seg}_y P).$

Proof. Use Thm.XII.2.8.

Corollary. $\vdash (P,x,y){:.}P \in \mathrm{Word}{:}x,y \in \mathrm{AV}(P){:} \supset {:}yPx. \equiv .\mathrm{No}(\mathrm{seg}_y P) \leq \mathrm{No}(\mathrm{seg}_x P).$

Proof. By Ex.X.6.6, Part (c), $x(P - I)y. \equiv .{\sim}(yPx)$, and by Thm. XII.3.8, Cor. 2, $\mathrm{No}(\mathrm{seg}_x P) < \mathrm{No}(\mathrm{seg}_y P). \equiv .{\sim}(\mathrm{No}(\mathrm{seg}_y P) \leq \mathrm{No}(\mathrm{seg}_x P)).$

Theorem XII.3.12.

I. $\vdash \mathrm{AV}(\leq_0) = \mathrm{NO}.$

II. $\vdash \leq_0 \in \mathrm{Sord}.$

Proof of Part I. By Thm.XII.3.4, Part I, and Thm.XII.2.4, Part III, $\vdash \phi < \theta. \supset .\phi,\theta \in \mathrm{NO}.$ So by Thm.XII.3.4, Part III, $\vdash \mathrm{AV}(\leq_0) \subseteq \mathrm{NO}.$ By Thm.XII.3.4, corollary, $\vdash \mathrm{NO} \subseteq \mathrm{AV}(\leq_0).$

Proof of Part II. Use Thm.XII.3.4, corollary, Thm.XII.3.6, Cor. 3, Thm.XII.3.7, and Thm.XII.3.8, Cor. 1.

**Theorem XII.3.13. $\vdash (P,\phi):P \epsilon \phi.\phi \epsilon \text{NO}. \supset .\text{RUSC}^2(P) \text{ smor } (\text{seg}_\phi \leq_0)$.

Proof. Assume

$$(1) \qquad P \epsilon \phi,$$

$$(2) \qquad \phi \epsilon \text{NO}.$$

Define

$$(3) \qquad R = \hat{x}\hat{\theta}(\text{E}y).y \epsilon \text{AV}(P).x = \{\{y\}\}.\theta = \text{No}(\text{seg}_y P).$$

By Thm.IX.6.10, Cor. 3, and Thm.X.4.29, Part III,

$$(4) \qquad \text{Arg}(R) = \text{AV}(\text{RUSC}^2(P)).$$

By (1), (2), and Thm.XII.3.2, Cor. 3,

$$(5) \qquad P \epsilon \text{Word}.$$

By (1), (2), and Thm.XII.3.2, Part III,

$$(6) \qquad \phi = \text{No}(P).$$

Let $\theta \epsilon \text{Val}(R)$. Then by (3), $y \epsilon \text{AV}(P).\theta = \text{No}(\text{seg}_y P)$. So by Thm. XII.3.10, $\theta < \phi$. Then by Thm.XII.3.5, corollary, $\theta(\leq - I)\phi$. Thus $\theta \epsilon \text{AV}(\text{seg}_\phi \leq)$. Conversely, let $\theta \epsilon \text{AV}(\text{seg}_\phi \leq)$. Then $\theta < \phi$. Then by Thm.XII.3.9, $y \epsilon \text{AV}(P).\theta = \text{No}(\text{seg}_y P)$. Thus $\theta \epsilon \text{Val}(R)$. So

$$(7) \qquad \text{Val}(R) = \text{AV}(\text{seg}_\phi \leq).$$

Clearly $R \epsilon \text{Funct}$. Let $xR\theta.uR\theta$. Then $y \epsilon \text{AV}(P).x = \{\{y\}\}.\theta = \text{No}(\text{seg}_y P)$, and $v \epsilon \text{AV}(P).u = \{\{v\}\}.\theta = \text{No}(\text{seg}_v P)$. Then $(\text{seg}_y P)$ smor $(\text{seg}_v P)$ by Thm.X.6.14, Part V, and Thm.XII.3.2, Part II. Then $y = v$ by Thm.XII.2.2. So $x = u$. Thus

$$(8) \qquad R \epsilon 1\text{–}1.$$

Let $x(\text{RUSC}^2(P))u$. Then $x = \{\{y\}\}.u = \{\{v\}\}.yPv$. Then by Thm. XII.3.11, corollary, $\text{No}(\text{seg}_y P) \leq \text{No}(\text{seg}_v P)$. By (3), $R(x) = \text{No}(\text{seg}_y P)$ and $R(u) = \text{No}(\text{seg}_v P)$. Thus $R(x) \leq R(u)$. Then by (7), $(R(x))(\text{seg}_\phi \leq)(R(u))$. So

$$(9) \qquad (x,u):x(\text{RUSC}^2(P))u. \supset .(R(x))(\text{seg}_\phi \leq)(R(u)).$$

Let $\theta(\text{seg}_\phi \leq)\psi$. Then $\theta < \phi.\psi < \phi.\theta \leq \psi$. By Thm.XII.3.9, $y \epsilon \text{AV}(P).\theta = \text{No}(\text{seg}_y P)$ and $v \epsilon \text{AV}(P).\psi = \text{No}(\text{seg}_v P)$. Since $\theta \leq \psi$, we have yPv by Thm.XII.3.11, corollary. By (3), $\breve{R}(\theta) = \{\{y\}\}$ and $\breve{R}(\psi) = \{\{v\}\}$. So by Thm.X.3.16, corollary, $(\breve{R}(\theta))(\text{RUSC}^2(P))(\breve{R}(\psi))$. Thus

$$(10) \qquad (\theta,\psi):\theta(\text{seg}_\phi \leq)\psi. \supset .(\breve{R}(\theta))(\text{RUSC}^2(P))(\breve{R}(\psi)).$$

By Thm.XII.1.1, Part IV, our theorem follows from (8), (4), (7), (9), and (10).

Corollary. $\vdash (\phi):.\phi \epsilon \text{NO}: \supset :(P):P \epsilon \phi. \equiv .\text{RUSC}^2(P) \text{ smor } (\text{seg}_\phi \leq_0)$.

Proof. Let $\phi \epsilon$ NO and $\text{RUSC}^2(P)$ smor $(\text{seg}_\phi \leq)$. Then by Thm. XII.3.2, Parts I and III, $Q \epsilon \phi$. By the theorem, $\text{RUSC}^2(Q)$ smor $(\text{seg}_\phi \leq)$. So $\text{RUSC}^2(P)$ smor $\text{RUSC}^2(Q)$. Then P smor Q by Thm.XII.1.5. Finally $P \epsilon \phi$ by Thm.XII.3.3, Part II.

In order to carry out the proof above, the formula defining R must be stratified with x and θ having the same type. If we should try to prove

(A) $$(P,\phi):P \epsilon \phi.\phi \epsilon \text{NO}. \supset .P \text{ smor } (\text{seg}_\phi \leq)$$

in a similar fashion, we would have to define $R = \hat{x}\hat{\theta}(x \epsilon \text{AV}(P).\theta = \text{No}(\text{seg}_x P))$. However, the formula involved in this case cannot be stratified with x and θ having the same type, and so we do not know how to prove that such an R exists. Accordingly, we do not know how to prove the statement (A). In the classical theory of ordinals, there were no inhibitions about the definition of relations by unstratified statements. Hence, in the classical theory of ordinals, one does prove (A), and indeed it is a key theorem in the classical theory of ordinals. In many of the cases in which (A) is used in the classical theory of ordinals, we can use Thm. XII.3.13 instead. However, we cannot do so in all cases, so that apparently the classical theory of ordinals contains results which we cannot prove. This is just as well, because one of the results which can be proved by (A) in the classical theory of ordinals is the Burali-Forti paradox. We are apparently spared this because of inability to prove (A).

In intuitive mathematics, it appears obvious that P smor $\text{RUSC}(P)$, because we merely have to pair x with $\{x\}$ for every x in $\text{AV}(P)$. However, this procedure involves defining a relation by an unstratified statement in a way which we do not know how to do. Actually, if we knew how to prove P smor $\text{RUSC}(P)$ for general P, we would get $\text{RUSC}(P)$ smor $\text{RUSC}^2(P)$, so that we could get P smor $\text{RUSC}^2(P)$. Then we could get (A) from Thm.XII.3.13. Thus it appears unlikely that we can prove P smor $\text{RUSC}(P)$ for general P. Nevertheless, we shall prove this for various of the familiar P's of everyday mathematics.

We now prove the key theorem in the theory of ordinal numbers.

****Theorem XII.3.14.** $\vdash \leq_0 \epsilon$ Word.

Proof. Let $\beta \cap \text{NO} \neq \Lambda$. Then $\phi \epsilon \beta \cap \text{NO}$.

Case 1. $(\theta):\theta \epsilon \beta \cap \text{NO}. \supset .\sim(\theta < \phi)$. Then $\phi \text{ min}_\leq \beta$.

Case 2. $\sim(\theta):\theta \epsilon \beta \cap \text{NO}. \supset .\sim(\theta < \phi)$. Then there is a θ such that $\theta \epsilon \beta \cap \text{NO}.\theta < \phi$. Then $\theta \epsilon \text{AV}(\text{seg}_\phi \leq)$, so that

(1) $$\beta \cap \text{AV}(\text{seg}_\phi \leq) \neq \Lambda.$$

By Thm.XII.3.2, Part I and Part III, $P \epsilon$ Word.$P \epsilon \phi$. Then RUSC$^2(P)$ ϵ Word by Thm.X.6.15, Part V, and RUSC$^2(P)$ smor (seg$_\phi \leq$) by Thm. XII.3.13. Thus (seg$_\phi \leq$) ϵ Word by Thm.XII.1.14. Then by (1), there is a ψ such that ψ min$_R$ β, where we write R for seg$_\phi \leq$. Then we show ψ min$_\leq$ β without difficulty.

Thus in either case, we find a minimal element in β.

Not only do we not know how to prove the statement (A), we can even prove it to be false.

Theorem XII.3.15. $\vdash \sim(P,\phi):P \epsilon \phi.\phi \epsilon$ NO. $\supset .P$ smor (seg$_\phi \leq$).

Proof. Proof by reductio ad absurdum. Assume

(1) $$(P,\phi):P \epsilon \phi.\phi \epsilon \text{NO}. \supset .P \text{ smor } (\text{seg}_\phi \leq).$$

Now put $\phi = \text{No}(\leq)$. By Thm.XII.3.14 and Thm.XII.3.1, Part I, $\leq \epsilon \phi$, and by Thm.XII.3.2, Part I, $\phi \epsilon$ NO. So by (1), $\leq$ smor (seg$_\phi \leq$). Taking P to be $\leq$, Q to be seg$_\phi \leq$, and x to be ϕ in Thm.XII.2.1 gives a contradiction.

In the classical theory of ordinals, where statement (A) is provable, the above result leads to a contradiction which is known as the Burali-Forti paradox.

EXERCISES

Define:

0_0	for	No(Λ).
1_0	for	No($\{\langle\Lambda,\Lambda\rangle\}$).
$\phi +_0 \theta$	for	$\hat\psi(\text{E}P,Q):P \epsilon \phi.Q \epsilon \theta.\psi$ smor $((\{\langle\Lambda,\Lambda\rangle\} \times_s P) +_s (\{\langle\text{V},\text{V}\rangle\} \times_s Q))$.
$\phi \times_0 \theta$	for	$\hat\psi(\text{E}P,Q):P \epsilon \phi.Q \epsilon \theta.\psi$ smor $(P \times_s Q)$.

XII.3.1. Prove:

(a) $\vdash 0_0 = 0$.
(b) $\vdash 0 \epsilon$ NO.
(c) $\vdash (\phi):\phi \epsilon$ NO. $\supset .0 \leq \phi$.
(d) $\vdash (\phi):\phi \epsilon$ NO. $\supset .0 +_0 \phi = \phi = \phi +_0 0$.
(e) $\vdash (\phi):\phi \epsilon$ NO. $\supset .0 \times_0 \phi = 0 = \phi \times_0 0$.

XII.3.2. Prove:

(a) $\vdash 1_0 \epsilon$ NO.
(b) $\vdash (\phi):\phi \epsilon$ NO. $\supset .1_0 \times_0 \phi = \phi = \phi \times_0 1_0$.
(c) $\vdash (\phi):\phi \epsilon$ NO. $\supset .\phi +_0 1_0 \epsilon$ NO.
(d) $\vdash (\phi):\phi \epsilon$ NO. $\supset .\phi < \phi +_0 1_0$.
(e) $\vdash (\phi):.\phi \epsilon$ NO: $\supset :(\text{E}\theta).\theta \epsilon$ NO.$\phi < \theta$.

Thus there is no greatest ordinal.

XII.3.3. Prove:

(a) $\vdash (\phi,\theta){:}\phi,\theta \in \mathrm{NO}. \supset .\phi +_0 \theta \in \mathrm{NO}.$
(b) $\vdash (\phi,\theta,\psi){:}\phi,\theta,\psi \in \mathrm{NO}. \supset .(\phi +_0 \theta) +_0 \psi = \phi +_0 (\theta +_0 \psi).$
(c) $\vdash (\phi,\theta,\psi){:}\phi,\theta,\psi \in \mathrm{NO}.\theta < \psi. \supset .(\phi +_0 \theta) < (\phi +_0 \psi).$
(d) $\vdash (\phi,\theta){:.}\phi,\theta \in \mathrm{NO}{:} \supset {:}\phi < \theta. \equiv .(\mathrm{E}\psi).\psi \in \mathrm{NO}.\psi \neq 0.\theta = \phi +_0 \psi.$
(e) $\vdash (\phi,\theta){:.}\phi,\theta \in \mathrm{NO}{:} \supset {:}\phi \leq \theta. \equiv .(\mathrm{E}\psi).\psi \in \mathrm{NO}.\theta = \phi +_0 \psi.$
(f) $\vdash (\phi,\theta,\psi){:}\phi,\theta,\psi \in \mathrm{NO}.\phi +_0 \theta = \phi +_0 \psi. \supset .\theta = \psi.$

XII.3.4. Prove:

(a) $\vdash (\phi,\theta){:}\phi,\theta \in \mathrm{NO}. \supset .\phi \times_0 \theta \in \mathrm{NO}.$
(b) $\vdash (\phi,\theta,\psi){:}\phi,\theta,\psi \in \mathrm{NO}. \supset .(\phi \times_0 \theta) \times_0 \psi = \phi \times_0 (\theta \times_0 \psi).$
(c) $\vdash (\phi,\theta,\psi){:}\phi,\theta,\psi \in \mathrm{NO}. \supset .\phi \times_0 (\theta +_0 \psi) = (\phi \times_0 \theta) +_0 (\phi \times_0 \psi).$
(d) $\vdash (\phi,\theta,\psi){:}\phi,\theta,\psi \in \mathrm{NO}.\phi \neq 0.\theta < \psi. \supset .(\phi \times_0 \theta) < (\phi \times_0 \psi).$

XII.3.5. Prove that $\vdash (R){:.}R \in \mathrm{Funct}.\mathrm{Arg}(R) = \mathrm{NO}.\mathrm{Val}(R) \subseteq \mathrm{USC}^2(\mathrm{V}){:} \supset {:}(\mathrm{E}\phi,\theta).\phi,\theta \in \mathrm{NO}.\phi \neq \theta.R(\phi) = R(\theta)$. (*Hint.* Suppose the conclusion false. Then $R \in 1\text{–}1$, and we can define a well-ordering relation P with $\leq \mathrm{smor}_R\ \mathrm{RUSC}^2(P)$. Then, if $\phi = \mathrm{No}(P)$, we have $\mathrm{RUSC}^2(P)$ smor $(\mathrm{seg}_\phi \leq)$, which leads to a contradiction.)

XII.3.6. Prove that, if $B(\alpha)$ is a term such that $x = B(\{x\})$ is stratified, then there is a term $A(\phi)$ such that $\phi = \{\{A(\phi)\}\}$ is stratified and

$$\vdash (\phi){:}\phi \in \mathrm{NO}. \supset .A(\phi) = B(\{A(\theta) \mid \theta < \phi\}).$$

(*Hint.* This is essentially a special case of Thm.XII.2.11 with different stratification conditions.)

XII.3.7. With $A(\phi)$ and $B(\alpha)$ as in the preceding exercise, prove

$$\vdash (\mathrm{E}\phi,\theta).\phi,\theta \in \mathrm{NO}.\phi \neq \theta.A(\phi) = A(\theta).$$

(*Hint.* Use Ex.XII.3.5.)

XII.3.8. Prove that, if $B(\alpha)$ and $C(x)$ are terms such that $x = B(\{x\})$ and $x = C(x)$ are stratified, then there is a term $A(\phi)$ such that $\phi = \{\{A(\phi)\}\}$ is stratified and

$$\vdash (\phi){:.}\phi \in \mathrm{NO}.\sim(\mathrm{E}\theta).\theta \in \mathrm{NO}.\phi = \theta +_0 1_0{:} \supset {:}A(\phi) = B(\{A(\theta) \mid \theta < \phi\}).$$

$$\vdash (\phi){:}\phi \in \mathrm{NO}. \supset .A(\phi +_0 1_0) = C(A(\phi)).$$

XII.3.9. With $A(\phi)$, $B(\alpha)$, and $C(x)$ as in the preceding exercise, prove $\vdash (\mathrm{E}\theta,\phi).\phi,\theta \in \mathrm{NO}.\phi \neq \theta.A(\phi) = A(\theta)$.

4. The Cardinal Number Associated with an Ordinal Number. We define

$$\omega \quad \text{for} \quad \text{No}(\text{Nn}\rceil \leq_c \lceil\text{Nn}).$$

Clearly ω is stratified and may be assigned any type.

Theorem XII.4.1.

I. $\vdash (\text{Nn}\rceil \leq_c \lceil\text{Nn}) \in \omega$.

II. $\vdash \omega \in \text{NO}$.

Proof. Use Ex.XI.3.7.

Theorem XII.4.2.

I. $\vdash (\text{Nn}\rceil \leq_c \lceil\text{Nn})$ smor $\text{RUSC}(\text{Nn}\rceil \leq_c \lceil\text{Nn})$.

II. $\vdash (\text{seg}_\omega \leq) \in \omega$.

III. $\vdash \hat{\phi}(\phi < \omega) \in \text{Den}$.

Proof of Part I. Write

(1) $$P = \text{Nn}\rceil \leq_c \lceil\text{Nn},$$

(2) $$Q = \text{RUSC}(P).$$

By Ex.XI.3.7 and Thm.X.6.15, Part V, $\vdash P,Q \in$ Word. Then by Thm. XII.2.14, P sr $Q.\mathbf{v}.P$ smor $Q.\mathbf{v}.Q$ sr P.

Case 1. Let P sr Q. Then $x \in \text{AV}(Q).P$ smor $(\text{seg}_x Q)$. So by Thm. X.4.29, Part III, $y \in \text{Nn}.x = \{y\}$. Then by Thm.X.6.15, Part VII, $\text{seg}_x Q = \text{RUSC}(\text{seg}_y P)$. Then by Thm.X.4.29, Part III, $\text{AV}(\text{seg}_x Q) = \text{USC}(\text{seg}_y P) = \text{USC}(\hat{m}(m \in \text{Nn}.m < y))$. But by Thm.XII.1.1, Part IV, $\text{AV}(P)$ sm $\text{AV}(\text{seg}_x Q)$. Thus $\dot{\text{N}}\text{n}$ sm $\text{USC}(\hat{m}(m \in \text{Nn}.m < y))$. By Thm.XI.3.43, Cor. 1, and Thm.XI.3.38, $\text{USC}(\hat{m}(m \in \text{Nn}.m < y)) \in \text{Fin}$. Then $\text{Nn} \in \text{Fin}$, contradicting Thm.XI.3.30, Cor. 1.

Case 2. Let Q sr P. In this case we get a similar contradiction.

So P smor Q.

Proof of Part II. Take P and Q as in the proof of Part I. By Part I and Thm.XII.1.5, $\text{RUSC}(P)$ smor $\text{RUSC}(Q)$. That is, Q smor $\text{RUSC}^2(P)$. So by Part I, P smor $\text{RUSC}^2(P)$. But by Thm.XII.3.13, $\text{RUSC}^2(P)$ smor $(\text{seg}_\omega \leq)$. Thus P smor $(\text{seg}_\omega \leq)$. Then by Thm.XII.3.3, Part II, $(\text{seg}_\omega \leq) \in \omega$.

Proof of Part III. In the preceding proof, we had P smor $(\text{seg}_\omega \leq)$. Then $\text{AV}(P)$ sm $\text{AV}(\text{seg}_\omega \leq)$ by Thm.XII.1.1, Part IV. So Nn sm $\hat{\phi}(\phi < \omega)$.

We refer to the number of ordinals less than ϕ as the cardinal number associated with ϕ. That is, we define

$$\text{Card}(\phi) \quad \text{for} \quad \text{Nc}(\hat{\theta}(\theta < \phi)).$$

Clearly $\text{Card}(\phi)$ is stratified if and only if ϕ is stratified, and if stratified has type two higher than ϕ.

Part III of the last theorem could be written

$$\vdash \mathrm{Card}(\omega) = \mathrm{Den}.$$

Theorem XII.4.3.

I. $\vdash (\phi,\theta){:}\phi \leq \theta. \supset .\mathrm{Card}(\phi) \leq \mathrm{Card}(\theta)$.

II. $\vdash (\phi,\theta){:.}\phi,\theta \in \mathrm{NO}{:} \supset {:}\mathrm{Card}(\phi) < \mathrm{Card}(\theta).\mathbf{v}.\mathrm{Card}(\phi) = \mathrm{Card}(\theta).\mathbf{v}.$ $\mathrm{Card}(\phi) > \mathrm{Card}(\theta)$.

Proof of Part I. If $\phi \leq \theta$, then by Thm.XI.3.6, Cor. 2, $(\hat{\psi}(\psi < \phi)) \subseteq (\hat{\psi}(\psi < \theta))$. Then we use Thm.XI.2.13, Part I.

Proof of Part II. Let $\phi,\theta \in \mathrm{NO}$. Then by Thm.XII.3.8, Cor. 1, $\phi \leq \theta.\mathbf{v}.\theta \leq \phi$.

Theorem XII.4.4.

I. $\vdash \mathrm{Den} < \mathrm{Nc}(\mathrm{NO})$.

II. $\vdash (E\phi){:}\phi \in \mathrm{NO}.\mathrm{Card}(\phi) > \mathrm{Den}$.

Proof of Part I. By Thm.XII.4.2, Part III, and Thm.XI.2.13, Part I,

(1) $$\vdash \mathrm{Den} \leq \mathrm{Nc}(\mathrm{NO}).$$

We now prove by reductio ad absurdum that $\vdash \mathrm{Den} \neq \mathrm{Nc}(\mathrm{NO})$. So assume $\mathrm{Den} = \mathrm{Nc}(\mathrm{NO})$. Then NO sm Nn. However, by Thm.XI.4.12 and Thm.XI.1.33, Nn sm USC(Nn) and USC(Nn) sm $\mathrm{USC}^2(\mathrm{Nn})$. Then NO sm $\mathrm{USC}^2(\mathrm{Nn})$, so that there is an R such that

(2) $$\mathrm{USC}^2(\mathrm{Nn})\ \mathrm{sm}_R\ \mathrm{NO}.$$

Now define

(3) $$P = \hat{m}\hat{n}(m,n \in \mathrm{Nn}.R(\{\{m\}\}) \leq R(\{\{n\}\})).$$

We get $\mathrm{AV}(P) = \mathrm{Nn}$, by Thm.XII.3.4, corollary. Then we easily get

(4) $$\mathrm{RUSC}^2(P)\ \mathrm{smor} \leq_0.$$

Then by Thm.XII.3.14 and Thm.XII.1.14, $\mathrm{RUSC}^2(P) \in \mathrm{Word}$. So $P \in \mathrm{Word}$ by Thm.X.6.15, Part V. Put $\phi = \mathrm{No}(P)$. Then $\phi \in \mathrm{NO}$ by Thm.XII.3.2, Part I, and $P \in \phi$ by Thm.XII.3.2, Part III. Then $\mathrm{RUSC}^2(P)$ smor $(\mathrm{seg}_\phi \leq)$ by Thm.XII.3.13. So by (4), $(\mathrm{seg}_\phi \leq)$ smor $\leq$. This is a contradiction by Thm.XII.2.1.

Proof of Part II. By Part I and Thm.XI.4.6, Cor. 2,

(1) $$\vdash \sim \mathrm{NO} \in \mathrm{Count}.$$

Let $\phi = \mathrm{No}(\leq_0)$. By Thm.XII.4.3, Part II, $\mathrm{Card}(\phi) \leq \mathrm{Card}(\omega).\mathbf{v}.$ $\mathrm{Card}(\phi) > \mathrm{Card}(\omega)$.

Case 1. $\mathrm{Card}(\phi) \leq \mathrm{Card}(\omega)$. But $\mathrm{Card}(\omega) = \mathrm{Den}$ by Thm.XII.4.2, Part III. Thus

(2) $$\hat{\theta}(\theta < \phi) \in \mathrm{Count}$$

by Thm.XI.4.6, Cor. 2. By Thm.XII.3.13, $\mathrm{RUSC}^2(\leq_0)$ smor $(\mathrm{seg}_\phi \leq)$. Then $\mathrm{USC}^2(\mathrm{NO})$ sm $\hat{\theta}(\theta < \phi)$ by Thm.XII.1.1, Part IV. Then by (2) and Thm.XI.4.1, Part V, $\mathrm{USC}^2(\mathrm{NO}) \in$ Count. Finally, by Thm.XI.4.12, Cor. 12, NO $\in$ Count, and we have a contradiction by (1).

This leaves only the possibility $\mathrm{Card}(\phi) > \mathrm{Card}(\omega)$. That is, $\mathrm{Card}(\phi) >$ Den by Thm.XII.4.2, Part III.

From Part II and Thm.XII.3.14, there is a least ordinal ϕ with $\mathrm{Card}(\phi) >$ Den. This is often called Ω. So we define

$$\Omega \quad \text{for} \quad \iota\psi\ (\psi \text{ least}_\leq \hat{\phi}(\phi \in \mathrm{NO}.\mathrm{Card}(\phi) > \mathrm{Den})).$$

Theorem XII.4.5.

I. $\vdash \Omega \in \mathrm{NO}$.

II. $\vdash \mathrm{Card}(\Omega) > \mathrm{Den}$.

III. $\vdash (\phi){:}\phi < \Omega. \supset .\mathrm{Card}(\phi) \leq \mathrm{Den}$.

IV. $\vdash (\phi){:}\phi \in \mathrm{NO}.\mathrm{Card}(\phi) \leq \mathrm{Den}. \supset .\phi < \Omega$.

V. $\vdash \omega < \Omega$.

Proof. By Thm.XII.3.14 and Thm.XII.4.4, Part II,

$$\vdash \Omega \text{ least}_\leq \hat{\phi}(\phi \in \mathrm{NO}.\mathrm{Card}(\phi) > \mathrm{Den}).$$

Then Parts I and II follow, as well as

$$(\phi){:}\phi < \Omega. \supset .\sim(\mathrm{Card}(\phi) > \mathrm{Den}).$$

Since Den $= \mathrm{Card}(\omega)$, we get Part III by Thm.XII.4.3, Part II.

Proof of Part IV. Assume $\phi \in$ NO and $\sim(\phi < \Omega)$. Then $\Omega \leq \phi$ by Thm.XII.3.8, Cor. 3. So $\mathrm{Card}(\Omega) \leq \mathrm{Card}(\phi)$ by Thm.XII.4.3, Part I. Then Den $< \mathrm{Card}(\phi)$ by Part II, so that $\sim(\mathrm{Card}(\phi) \leq \mathrm{Den})$.

Proof of Part V. Use Part IV and Thm.XII.4.2, Part III.

It is common to refer to the ordinals less than ω as ordinals of the first class, and to ordinals greater than or equal to ω but less than Ω as ordinals of the second class.

A common notation is to write ω_0 for ω and ω_1 for Ω. Also $\aleph_1$ for $\mathrm{Card}(\Omega)$. The conjecture that $\mathrm{Card}(\Omega) = c$ is known as the continuum hypothesis.

Theorem XII.4.6.

I. $\vdash (\mathrm{seg}_\Omega \leq)$ smor $\mathrm{RUSC}(\mathrm{seg}_\Omega \leq)$.

II. $\vdash \mathrm{Can}(\hat{\theta}(\theta < \Omega))$.

III. $\vdash (\mathrm{seg}_\Omega \leq) \in \Omega$.

Proof of Part I. This goes like the proof of Part I of Thm.XII.4.2. Put

$$P = \mathrm{seg}_\Omega \leq, \tag{1}$$

$$Q = \mathrm{RUSC}(P). \tag{2}$$

Then P sr $Q.\mathbf{v}.P$ smor $Q.\mathbf{v}.Q$ sr P.

Case 1. Let P sr Q. Then $x \in \mathrm{AV}(Q).P$ smor $(\mathrm{seg}_x Q)$. Thus $\phi < \Omega$,

$x = \{\phi\}$, and AV($\text{seg}_x Q$) = USC($\text{seg}_\phi P$) = USC($\hat{\theta}(\theta < \phi)$). So $\hat{\theta}(\theta < \Omega)$ sm USC($\hat{\theta}(\theta < \phi)$). However, by Thm.XII.4.5, Part III, and Thm.XI.4.6, Cor. 2, $\hat{\theta}(\theta < \phi) \epsilon$ Count. So USC($\hat{\theta}(\theta < \phi)$) ϵ Count. Thus we have a contradiction by Thm.XII.4.5, Part II.

Case 2. Let Q sr P. Proceed similarly.

So P smor Q.

Proof of Part II. By Part I, ($\hat{\theta}(\theta < \Omega)$) sm USC($\hat{\theta}(\theta < \Omega)$).

Proof of Part III. Let $P \epsilon \Omega$ and $Q = \text{seg}_\Omega \leq$. Then by Thm.XII.3.13, $\text{RUSC}^2(P)$ smor Q. However, by Part I, Q smor RUSC(Q). Then by Thm.XII.1.5, RUSC(Q) smor $\text{RUSC}^2(Q)$. Then $\text{RUSC}^2(P)$ smor $\text{RUSC}^2(Q)$. Then P smor Q by Thm.XII.1.5. Then $Q \epsilon \Omega$ by Thm.XII.3.3, Part II.

In Part II we have proved Can(α) for another well-known class of everyday mathematics.

The reader who is familiar with the classical theory of ordinals will recognize that we have proved the standard basic properties of Ω (though not always by the standard proofs) except the theorem that every denumerable set of ordinals of the second class has a bound in the second class. The proof of this seems to depend on the denumerable axiom of choice and must be postponed until Chapter XIV.

EXERCISES

XII.4.1. Prove $\vdash (\phi):.\phi \epsilon \text{NO}: \supset :\phi < \omega. \equiv .(\text{E}\theta).\theta < \omega.\phi = \text{No}(\text{seg}_\theta \leq)$. (*Hint.* Use Thm.XII.4.2, Part II.)

XII.4.2. Prove $\vdash (P,\phi):.P \epsilon \phi.\phi \epsilon \text{NO}: \supset :\phi < \omega. \equiv .\text{AV}(P) \epsilon \text{Fin}$.

XII.4.3. Prove $\vdash (\phi):.\phi \epsilon \text{NO}: \supset :\phi < \omega. \equiv .\text{No}(\text{seg}_\phi \leq) < \omega$.

XII.4.4. Prove $\vdash (\phi):.\phi \epsilon \text{NO}: \supset :\phi < \omega. \equiv .\text{Card}(\phi) \epsilon \text{Nn}$. (*Hint.* Use the two preceding exercises.)

XII.4.5. Prove $\vdash (\phi):.\phi \epsilon \text{NO}: \supset :\phi < \Omega. \equiv .(\text{E}\theta).\theta < \Omega.\phi = \text{No}(\text{seg}_\theta \leq)$. (*Hint.* Use Thm.XII.4.6, Part III.)

XII.4.6. Prove $\vdash (P,\phi):P \epsilon \phi.\phi < \Omega. \supset .\text{AV}(P) \epsilon \text{Count}$. (*Hint.* By Thm.XII.3.13, $\text{USC}^2(\text{AV}(P))$ sm $\hat{\theta}(\theta < \phi)$. So $\text{USC}^2(\text{AV}(P)) \epsilon$ Count by Thm.XII.4.5, Part III.)

XII.4.7. Prove $\vdash (P,\phi):P \epsilon \phi.\phi \epsilon \text{NO}.\text{AV}(P) \epsilon \text{Count}. \supset .\phi < \Omega$. (*Hint.* Use Thm.XII.3.13 and Thm.XII.4.5, Part IV.)

XII.4.8. Prove $\vdash (\phi):.\phi \epsilon \text{NO}: \supset :\phi < \Omega. \equiv .\text{No}(\text{seg}_\phi \leq) < \Omega$. (*Hint.* Use the two preceding exercises.)

XII.4.9. Prove $\vdash (\alpha)(\text{E}P).P \epsilon \text{Word}.\alpha = \text{AV}(P).: \supset :.(m,n):m,n \epsilon \text{NC}. \supset .m < n.\text{v}.m = n.\text{v}.m > n$. (*Hint.* Let $\alpha \epsilon m$, $\beta \epsilon n$, $\alpha = \text{AV}(P)$. $P \epsilon$ Word, $\beta = \text{AV}(Q).Q \epsilon$ Word. Then use Thm.XII.2.14 and Ex.XII.2.1.)

XII.4.10. Prove $\vdash (\alpha,\beta)::\beta = \hat{\phi}(\text{E}P,\gamma):P \epsilon \text{Word}.\gamma \subseteq \alpha.\gamma \text{ sm AV}(P).\phi = \text{No}(P).: \supset :.\sim(\text{Nc}(\beta) \leq \text{Nc}(\text{USC}^2(\alpha)))$. (*Hint.* If $\text{Nc}(\beta) \leq$

$\mathrm{Nc}(\mathrm{USC}^2(\alpha))$, then there is a γ with β sm $\mathrm{USC}^2(\gamma).\gamma \subseteq \alpha$. Then the well-ordering relation $\leq$ on β induces a well-ordering relation P with $(\beta\rceil \leq \lceil\beta)$ smor $\mathrm{RUSC}^2(P)$ and $\gamma = \mathrm{AV}(P)$. Then $\mathrm{No}(P) \,\epsilon\, \beta$. Also if we put $\phi = \mathrm{No}(P)$, then $(\mathrm{seg}_\phi \leq)$ smor $\mathrm{RUSC}^2(P)$, so that $(\mathrm{seg}_\phi \leq)$ smor $(\beta\rceil \leq \lceil\beta)$. As $(\mathrm{seg}_\phi \leq) = \mathrm{seg}_\phi(\beta\rceil \leq \lceil\beta)$, we get a contradiction.)

Note. Thm.XII.4.4, Part I, is essentially a special case of the result stated here, and the proof of Thm.XII.4.4, Part I, is a special case of the proof indicated here.

XII.4.11. Prove $\vdash (m,n){:}m,n \,\epsilon\, \mathrm{NC}. \supset .m < n.\mathsf{v}.m = n.\mathsf{v}.m > n.: \supset :. (\alpha)(\mathrm{E}P).P \,\epsilon\, \mathrm{Word}.\alpha = \mathrm{AV}(P)$. (*Hint.* Take β as in Ex.XII.4.10. Then by hypothesis, there is a γ with α sm $\gamma.\mathrm{USC}^2(\gamma) \subseteq \beta$. As β is well ordered by $\leq$, we get a well-ordering of γ, and hence of α.)

XII.4.12. Prove:

(a) $\vdash \mathrm{Card}(\Omega) < \mathrm{Nc}(\mathrm{NO})$.
(b) $\vdash (\mathrm{E}\phi).\phi \,\epsilon\, \mathrm{NO}.\mathrm{Card}(\phi) > \mathrm{Card}(\Omega)$.

Define ω_2 as the least ordinal ϕ such that $\mathrm{Card}(\phi) > \mathrm{Card}(\Omega)$.

XII.4.13. Prove:

(a) $\vdash \omega_2 \,\epsilon\, \mathrm{NO}$.
(b) $\vdash \mathrm{Card}(\omega_2) > \mathrm{Card}(\Omega)$.
(c) $\vdash (\phi){:}\phi < \omega_2. \supset .\mathrm{Card}(\phi) \leq \mathrm{Card}(\Omega)$.
(d) $\vdash (\phi){:}\phi \,\epsilon\, \mathrm{NO}.\mathrm{Card}(\phi) \leq \mathrm{Card}(\Omega). \supset .\phi < \omega_2$.
(e) $\vdash \Omega < \omega_2$.

XII.4.14. Prove:

(a) $\vdash (\phi){:}\phi = \omega_2. \supset .(\mathrm{seg}_\phi \leq)$ smor $\mathrm{RUSC}(\mathrm{seg}_\phi \leq)$.
(b) $\vdash \mathrm{Can}(\hat\theta(\theta < \omega_2))$.
(c) $\vdash (\phi){:}\phi = \omega_2. \supset .(\mathrm{seg}_\phi \leq) \,\epsilon\, \phi$.

XII.4.15. Prove $\vdash \mathrm{Den} \leq \mathrm{Nc}(\hat\theta(\omega \leq \theta < \Omega))$. (*Hint.* Prove $\vdash (\hat\theta(\mathrm{E}\phi){:} \phi < \omega.\theta = \omega +_0 \phi) \,\epsilon\, \mathrm{Den}$.)

XII.4.16. Prove $\vdash \mathrm{Card}(\Omega) = \mathrm{Nc}(\hat\theta(\omega \leq \theta < \Omega))$.

XII.4.17. Prove $\vdash (\phi,\theta){:}\mathrm{Card}(\theta) < \mathrm{Card}(\phi). \supset .\theta < \phi$.

XII.4.18. Prove $\vdash (\alpha){::}\alpha \,\epsilon\, \mathrm{Fin}{:}(\theta){:}\theta \,\epsilon\, \alpha. \supset .\theta < \Omega.: \supset :.(\mathrm{E}\phi){:}\phi < \Omega{:} (\theta){:}\theta \,\epsilon\, \alpha. \supset .\theta < \phi$.

5. Applications. The applications of ordinal numbers are less common than formerly. In topology, it is customary to assume that all classes can be well ordered. That is,

$$(\alpha)(\mathrm{E}P).P \,\epsilon\, \mathrm{Word}.\alpha = \mathrm{AV}(P).$$

Using this, many theorems were proved by transfinite induction and many definitions were made by transfinite induction. Nowadays, use is commonly made of the more convenient results known as Zorn's lemmas (see Chapter XIV), and the use of ordinal numbers and well-ordered sets has diminished. However, because this theory is well known to the older generation of mathematicians, many illustrations and counterexamples are based on it, and it does not seem likely that it will ever fall into complete disuse.

CHAPTER XIII

COUNTING

1. Preliminaries. We prove easily:

Theorem XIII.1.1.

I. $\vdash \hat{m}(m \in \text{Nn}.0 < m \leq 0) \in 0$.

II. $\vdash (n):n \in \text{Nn}.\hat{m}(m \in \text{Nn}.0 < m \leq n) \in n. \supset .\hat{m}(m \in \text{Nn}.0 < m \leq n + 1) \in n + 1$.

Corollary 1. $\vdash \hat{m}(m \in \text{Nn}.0 < m \leq 1) \in 1$.

Corollary 2. $\vdash \hat{m}(m \in \text{Nn}.0 < m \leq 2) \in 2$.

Corollary 3. $\vdash \hat{m}(m \in \text{Nn}.0 < m \leq 3) \in 3$.

etc.

It would appear to be a simple matter of proof by induction to prove

(A) $$(n):n \in \text{Nn}. \supset .\hat{m}(m \in \text{Nn}.0 < m \leq n) \in n.$$

However, the statement in question is not stratified and we apparently have no means of proving it. We can prove each particular instance with $n = 0, 1, 2, 3, \ldots$ (see the corollaries to Thm.XIII.1.1), since this involves only an induction about our formal logic in the intuitive logic. This is not the same as an induction in the formal logic, which is what we need to infer (A) from Thm.XIII.1.1, and for which (A) would have to be a stratified statement.

If $\alpha \in \text{Fin}$, then by Thm.XI.3.28, Part I, there is an n with

(B) $$n \in \text{Nn}.\alpha \in n.$$

By Thm.XI.4.7, there is also an n with

(C) $$n \in \text{Nn}.\alpha \text{ sm } \hat{m}(m \in \text{Nn}.0 < m \leq n).$$

One would expect that these two n's should be the same, but unless we can prove (A), it does not seem possible to prove that the two n's are the same. If we have any explicit n, such as $0, 1, 2, 3, \ldots$, then we can use the corollaries to Thm.XIII.1.1 to infer that the n's of (B) and (C) are the same. However, for arbitrary n, we apparently have no procedure for identifying the two n's of (B) and (C).

Theorem XIII.1.2.

I. $\vdash (\alpha):\alpha \in 0. \supset .\text{Can}(\alpha)$.

II. $\vdash (n)::n \in \text{Nn}:.(\alpha):\alpha \in n. \supset .\text{Can}(\alpha).: \supset :.(\alpha):\alpha \in n + 1. \supset .\text{Can}(\alpha)$.

Proof. Use Thm.XI.2.65 for Part I, and Thm.XI.2.67 and Thm. XI.2.61 for Part II.

Corollary 1. $\vdash (\alpha){:}\alpha \in 1. \supset .\mathrm{Can}(\alpha)$.

Corollary 2. $\vdash (\alpha){:}\alpha \in 2. \supset .\mathrm{Can}(\alpha)$.

Corollary 3. $\vdash (\alpha){:}\alpha \in 3. \supset .\mathrm{Can}(\alpha)$.

etc.

We have here a completely analogous situation. It would appear that we should be able to prove

$$\text{(D)} \qquad (n){:.}n \in \mathrm{Nn}{:} \supset {:}(\alpha){:}\alpha \in n. \supset .\mathrm{Can}(\alpha),$$

but this is unstratified and we know no way to prove it.

Actually, (A) and (D) are equivalent, so that, if either could be proved, then the other could be deduced. This is proved in the next two theorems.

Theorem XIII.1.3. $\vdash (n){:.}n \in \mathrm{Nn}{:} \supset {:}(\alpha){:}\alpha \in n. \supset .\mathrm{Can}(\alpha){::} \supset {::}(n){:}$ $n \in \mathrm{Nn}. \supset .\hat{m}(m \in \mathrm{Nn}.0 < m \leq n) \in n$.

Proof. Assume the hypothesis and $n \in \mathrm{Nn}$. Then there is an α with $\alpha \in \mathrm{Nn}$, and so $\mathrm{Can}(\alpha)$. That is, α sm $\mathrm{USC}(\alpha)$. Then $\mathrm{USC}(\alpha)$ sm $\mathrm{USC}^2(\alpha)$, so that $\mathrm{USC}^2(\alpha)$ sm α. Then by Thm.XI.3.43, α sm $\hat{m}(m \in \mathrm{Nn}.m < n)$. Then by Ex.XI.3.3, α sm $\hat{m}(m \in \mathrm{Nn}.0 < m \leq n)$. Thus $\hat{m}(m \in \mathrm{Nn}.$ $0 < m \leq n) \in n$ by Thm.XI.2.3, Part II.

Theorem XIII.1.4. $\vdash (n){:}n \in \mathrm{Nn}. \supset .\hat{m}(m \in \mathrm{Nn}.0 < m \leq n) \in n{::} \supset {::}$ $(n){:.}n \in \mathrm{Nn}{:} \supset {:}(\alpha){:}\alpha \in n. \supset .\mathrm{Can}(\alpha)$.

Proof. Assume the hypothesis and $n \in \mathrm{Nn}$ and $\alpha \in n$. Then by Ex. XI.3.3 and Thm.XI.3.43, $\mathrm{USC}^2(\alpha)$ sm $\hat{m}(m \in \mathrm{Nn}.0 < m \leq n)$, and by the hypothesis and Thm.XI.2.3, Part I, α sm $\hat{m}(m \in \mathrm{Nn}.0 < m \leq n)$. So

$$(1) \qquad \alpha \text{ sm } \mathrm{USC}^2(\alpha).$$

By Thm.XI.3.28, $\alpha \in \mathrm{Fin}$, so that by Thm.XI.3.38, $\mathrm{USC}(\alpha) \in \mathrm{Fin}$. Hence $m \in \mathrm{Nn}.\mathrm{USC}(\alpha) \in m$. By Thm.XI.3.7, $m < n.\mathsf{v}.m = n.\mathsf{v}.m > n$.

Case 1. $m < n$. Then by Thm.XI.3.5, $p \in \mathrm{Nn}.n = m + p + 1$. So $\beta \in m.\gamma \in p + 1.\beta \cap \gamma = \Lambda.\beta \cup \gamma = \alpha$. Then

$$(2) \qquad \beta \subseteq \alpha,$$

and by Thm.XI.2.3, Part I, β sm $\mathrm{USC}(\alpha)$. Then $\mathrm{USC}(\beta)$ sm $\mathrm{USC}^2(\alpha)$, so that by (1), $\mathrm{USC}(\beta)$ sm α. Then

$$(3) \qquad \mathrm{Nc}(\mathrm{USC}(\beta)) = n$$

by Thm.XI.2.3, Part II. By (2) and Thm.IX.6.12, Part V, $\mathrm{USC}(\beta) \subseteq \mathrm{USC}(\alpha)$. So by Thm.XI.2.13, Part I, $\mathrm{Nc}(\mathrm{USC}(\beta)) \leq m$. Then by (3), $n \leq m$, and we have a contradiction.

Case 2. $m > n$. Then we get a similar contradiction by using Thm. IX.6.14, Cor. 2.

Thus we have left only the case $m = n$. Then α sm USC(α), so that Can(α).

EXERCISES

XIII.1.1. Prove $\vdash (\phi){:}\phi < \omega. \supset .(\text{seg}_\phi \leq) \in \phi.{:} \equiv {:}.(P,\phi){:}P \in \phi.\phi < \omega. \supset .$ P smor RUSC(P).

XIII.1.2. Prove $\vdash (\phi){:}\phi < \Omega. \supset .(\text{seg}_\phi \leq) \in \phi.{:} \equiv {:}.(P,\phi){:}P \in \phi.\phi < \Omega. \supset .$ P smor RUSC(P).

2. The Axiom of Counting. We have defined Nn in such a way that, if $n \in$ Nn, one would expect to express the fact that α has n members by the statement

(A) $$\alpha \in n.$$

In actual practice, one determines the number of members of α by counting it. That is, one points successively at members of α and says "one", "two", "three", ... If one says "n" when one points at the final member of α, one then says that α has n members. By the act of pointing at members of α and simultaneously enunciating the names of positive integers, we set up a one-to-one correspondence between the members of α and the positive integers less than or equal to n. That is, we establish empirically that

(B) $$\alpha \text{ sm } \hat{m}(m \in \text{Nn}.0 < m \leq n).$$

Thus, in actual practice, it is condition (B) that is taken as the definition of α having n members. The theorems of mathematics which have to do with counting are all based on (B). Thus if we wish to reproduce such theorems in our symbolic logic, we have to arrange that (B) holds whenever α has n members.

In this situation, we have two alternatives. One is to abandon (A) completely and adopt (B) as the definition of α having n members. This would be quite awkward with the approach which we have made to cardinal numbers. Also, it is intuitively obvious that (A) should hold whenever (B) does, and vice versa.

The other alternative, which we adopt, is to retain (A) as the definition of α having n members, and to ensure that (A) and (B) will be equivalent. This we do by adopting the axiom of counting:

Axiom scheme 14. The following statement, and each statement got from it by prefixing some set of universal quantifiers, is an axiom:

$$(n){:}n \in \text{Nn}. \supset .\hat{m}(m \in \text{Nn}.0 < m \leq n) \in n.$$

****Theorem XIII.2.1.** $\vdash (\alpha,n){:}.n \in \text{Nn}{:} \supset {:}\alpha \in n. \equiv .\alpha \text{ sm } \hat{m}(m \in \text{Nn}.0 < m \leq n).$

Proof. Use Thm.XI.2.3.

Theorem XIII.2.2. $\vdash (\alpha,n):\alpha \in n.n \in \text{Nn}. \supset .\text{Can}(\alpha)$.

Proof. Use Thm.XIII.1.4.

****Corollary.** $\vdash (\alpha):\alpha \in \text{Fin}. \supset .\text{Can}(\alpha)$.

With this corollary, we can assert Can(α) for those α's which occur with reasonable frequency in everyday mathematics. Indeed, we can say more than this. From an intuitive point of view, it would seem obvious that one could pair the members x of α, respectively, with the members $\{x\}$ of USC(α). We say that α is strongly Cantorian if this can be done, namely,

$$\text{stCan}(\alpha) \quad \text{for} \quad (\text{E}R):\alpha \text{ sm}_R \text{ USC}(\alpha):(x,y):xRy. \supset .y = \{x\}.$$

Theorem XIII.2.3. $\vdash \text{stCan}(\text{Nn})$.

Proof. Put

(1) $$P = \text{Nn}\upharpoonleft \leq_c \restriction\text{Nn},$$

(2) $$Q = \text{RUSC}(P).$$

By Thm.XII.4.2, Part I, there is an R such that

(3) $$P \text{ smor}_R\ Q.$$

Let xRy. Then $x \in \text{Nn}.y \in \text{USC(Nn)}$. So $z \in \text{Nn}.y = \{z\}$. Also by Thm. XII.1.13, Cor. 1, $(\text{seg}_x P)$ smor $(\text{seg}_y Q)$. Then $\text{AV}(\text{seg}_x P)$ sm $\text{AV}(\text{seg}_y Q)$. That is, $\hat{m}(m \in \text{Nn}.m < x)$ sm $\text{USC}(\hat{m}(m \in \text{Nn}.m < z))$. But $\hat{m}(m \in \text{Nn}. m < z) \in \text{Fin}$ by Thm.XI.3.43, Cor. 1. Then $\text{Can}(\hat{m}(m \in \text{Nn}.m < z))$ by Thm.XIII.2.2, corollary. So $\hat{m}(m \in \text{Nn}.m < x)$ sm $\hat{m}(m \in \text{Nn}.m < z)$. If $x < z$, then $\hat{m}(m \in \text{Nn}.m < z)$ is similar to a proper subset of itself, contrary to Thm.XI.3.29, Cor. 2. If $x > z$, we get a similar contradiction. Then $x = z$ by Thm.XI.3.7. So $y = \{x\}$.

Thus Nn is strongly Cantorian. So, indeed, are the other familiar classes of mathematics, as we show below.

Theorem XIII.2.4. $\vdash (\alpha,\beta):\text{stCan}(\alpha).\alpha \text{ sm } \beta. \supset .\text{stCan}(\beta)$.

Proof. Let $\alpha \text{ sm}_R \text{ USC}(\alpha)$ and $(x,y):xRy. \supset .y = \{x\}$. Let also $\beta \text{ sm}_S\ \alpha$. Put $T = S|R|\text{Cnv}(\text{RUSC}(S))$. Then by Ex.X.5.17, $T \in 1\text{–}1$ and $(x,y):xTy. \supset .y = \{x\}$. Also, one proves easily that $\text{Arg}(T) = \beta$ and $\text{Val}(T) = \text{USC}(\beta)$.

Theorem XIII.2.5. $\vdash (\alpha,\beta):\text{stCan}(\alpha).\beta \subseteq \alpha. \supset .\text{stCan}(\beta)$.

Proof. Obvious.

Theorem XIII.2.6. $\vdash (\alpha):\alpha \in \text{Count}. \supset .\text{stCan}(\alpha)$.

Proof. Let $\alpha \in$ Count. Then by Thm.XI.4.7, corollary, $\beta \subseteq \text{Nn}.\alpha \text{ sm } \beta$. Then from Thm.XIII.2.3, we get stCan(β) by Thm.XII.2.5, and thence stCan(α) by Thm.XII.2.4.

Theorem XIII.2.7. $\vdash (\alpha):\text{stCan}(\alpha). \supset .\text{stCan}(\text{SC}(\alpha))$.

Proof. Let $\alpha \text{ sm}_R \text{ USC}(\alpha)$ and $(x,y):xRy. \supset .y = \{x\}$. Define $S = \hat{\beta}\hat{\gamma}(\beta \subseteq \alpha.(\text{E}\delta).R``\beta = \text{USC}(\delta).\gamma = \{\delta\})$. Since $R``\beta = \text{USC}(\beta)$ if $\beta \subseteq \alpha$, it is clear that $\text{SC}(\alpha) \text{ sm}_S \text{ USC}(\text{SC}(\alpha))$ and $(\beta,\gamma):\beta S\gamma. \supset .\gamma = \{\beta\}$.

Corollary. $\vdash (\alpha):\alpha \in c. \supset .\text{stCan}(\alpha)$.

Proof. Use Thm.XI.5.5, Cor. 2.

Theorem XIII.2.8. $\vdash (P):P \in \text{Rel}.\text{stCan}(\text{AV}(P)). \supset .P \text{ smor RUSC}(P)$.

Proof. Let $\text{AV}(P) \text{ sm}_R \text{ USC}(\text{AV}(P))$, and $(x,y):xRy. \supset .y = \{x\}$. Then clearly $P \text{ smor}_R \text{ RUSC}(P)$ if $P \in \text{Rel}$.

Theorem XIII.2.9. $\vdash \text{stCan}(\hat{\theta}(\theta < \Omega))$.

Proof. Put

(1) $$P = \text{seg}_\Omega \leq,$$

(2) $$Q = \text{RUSC}(P).$$

By Thm.XII.4.6, Part I, there is an R such that

(3) $$P \text{ smor}_R\ Q.$$

Let $\phi R\alpha$. Then $\phi < \Omega.\theta < \Omega.\alpha = \{\theta\}$. Also by Thm.XII.1.13, Cor. 1, $(\text{seg}_\phi P) \text{ smor } (\text{seg}_\alpha Q)$. But $\text{seg}_\alpha Q = \text{RUSC}(\text{seg}_\theta P)$ by Thm.X.6.15, Part VII. Now $\text{AV}(\text{seg}_\theta P) \in \text{Count}$ by Thm.XII.4.5, Part III. So $(\text{seg}_\theta P)$ smor $\text{RUSC}(\text{seg}_\theta P)$ by Thm.XIII.2.6 and Thm.XIII.2.8. Then $(\text{seg}_\phi P)$ smor $(\text{seg}_\theta P)$. Hence $\phi = \theta$ by Thm.XII.2.2, so that $\alpha = \{\phi\}$.

EXERCISES

XIII.2.1. Prove $\vdash (\alpha):\text{stCan}(\alpha). \equiv .\text{stCan}(\text{USC}(\alpha))$.
XIII.2.2. With ω_2 as in Ex.XII.4.13, prove $\vdash \text{stCan}(\hat{\theta}(\theta < \omega_2))$.
XIII.2.3. Prove $\vdash (\phi):\phi < \Omega. \supset .(\text{seg}_\phi \leq) \in \phi$.

3. The Pigeonhole Principle. If one has a pigeonhole desk with n pigeonholes, and one has $n + 1$ bills filed in these pigeonholes, at least one pigeonhole must have two or more bills in it.

Put more abstractly, let α have m members and λ have n members. If $\alpha \subseteq \bigcup\lambda$ and $m > n$, then at least one member of λ must have more than one member in common with α. That is,

$$(\text{E}\beta):\beta \in \lambda.\sim (\alpha \cap \beta) \in 0 \cup 1.$$

Here α is the class of bills, and λ is the class of pigeonholes (speaking roughly).

To prove the principle in this form requires the axiom of choice, as far as we know. Actually, in all applications that we know of, it is assumed further that λ is disjoint. That is,

$$(\alpha,\beta):\alpha,\beta \in \lambda.\alpha \neq \beta. \supset .\alpha \cap \beta = \Lambda.$$

In words, no two members of λ overlap. In terms of pigeonholes, no bill is put in two pigeonholes at once.

To the best of our knowledge, the principle is used only when $\lambda \epsilon$ Fin. So we prove the theorem for this case only, although a more general theorem could be proved.

****Theorem XIII.3.1.**

(1) $$\mathrm{Nc}(\lambda) < \mathrm{Nc}(\alpha),$$

(2) $$\alpha \subseteq \bigcup\lambda,$$

(3) $$\lambda \in \mathrm{Fin},$$

(4) $$(\beta,\gamma):\beta,\gamma \in \lambda.\beta \neq \gamma. \supset .\beta \cap \gamma = \Lambda$$

yield

$$(\mathrm{E}\beta):\beta \in \lambda.\sim (\alpha \cap \beta) \in 0 \cup 1.$$

Proof. Assume the hypotheses. Define

(5) $$R = \hat{\beta}\hat{\gamma}(\mathrm{E}x).x \in \alpha.\beta = \{x\}.x \in \gamma.\gamma \in \lambda.$$

By (4),

(6) $$R \in \mathrm{Funct}.$$

Also by (2),

(7) $$\mathrm{Arg}(R) = \mathrm{USC}(\alpha).$$

Also clearly

(8) $$\mathrm{Val}(R) \subseteq \lambda.$$

Case 1. $\alpha \in$ Infin. Then by (7) and Thm.XI.3.39, Cor. 2, Arg(R) ϵ Infin. Also by (3), (8), and Thm.XI.3.31, Val(R) ϵ Fin. So by Thm.XI.3.28, Cor. 1 and Cor. 2, and Thm.XI.3.6, Cor. 3, $\mathrm{Nc}(\mathrm{Val}(R)) < \mathrm{Nc}(\mathrm{Arg}(R))$.

Case 2. $\alpha \in$ Fin. Then by Thm.XIII.2.2, corollary, Can(α). So by (7), $\mathrm{Nc}(\mathrm{Arg}(R)) = \mathrm{Nc}(\alpha)$. Then by (1) and (7), $\mathrm{Nc}(\mathrm{Val}(R)) < \mathrm{Nc}(\mathrm{Arg}(R))$.

So in either case, $\mathrm{Nc}(\mathrm{Val}(R)) < \mathrm{Nc}(\mathrm{Arg}(R))$. Then by Ex.XI.2.12, $(\mathrm{E}\beta,\gamma):\beta,\gamma \in \mathrm{Arg}(R).\beta \neq \gamma.R(\beta) = R(\gamma)$. Then by (5), $x,y \in \alpha.x \neq y.$ $R(\{x\}) = R(\{y\})$. But by (5), $x \in R(\{x\}).R(\{x\}) \in \lambda$ and $y \in R(\{y\}).$ $R(\{y\}) \in \lambda$.

Note. We have refrained from using the results of this chapter in subsequent chapters, so that anyone who does not find the axiom of counting congenial may dispense with it at the loss of no more than the theorems of the second and third sections of the present chapter.

4. Applications. In number theory, most theorems dealing with the number of integers having a given property depend intrinsically upon counting them, and so depend on the axiom of counting. The prime number theorem, concerning the number of primes less than or equal to x is such a theorem. To illustrate how this comes about, one could look at the proof of Thm. 20 on page 17 of Hardy and Wright, where a lower bound is obtained for the number of primes less than or equal to x. The crucial step is where they say that there are at most x/p^2 numbers divisible by p^2 and not exceeding x. If we write $n = [x/p^2]$, the numbers in question are $1 \times p^2, 2 \times p^2, \ldots, n \times p^2$. Clearly this set of numbers is in one-to-one correspondence with $\hat{m}(m \in \text{Nn}.0 < m \leq n)$. So by Axiom scheme 14, there are n such numbers.

The same type of reasoning appears at crucial points in Landau, 1927, for instance, on page 194.

In an analogous fashion, theorems involving the number of zeros of a function go back to the axiom of counting. For instance, the theorem (Titchmarsh, 1939, page 115) that

$$\frac{1}{2\pi i}\int_C \frac{f'(z)}{f(z)}\,dz$$

equals the number of zeros of $f(z)$ inside C minus the number of poles inside C if $f(z)$ is meromorphic inside and on C.

Results on the number of permutations and combinations of sets of elements also stem from the axiom of counting.

The pigeonhole principle is used directly in various parts of mathematics. For examples, see the proofs given in Sec. 11.3 and Sec. 11.12 of Hardy and Wright.

Since much of the classical theory of cardinals and ordinals is based on the assumption $(\alpha).\text{stCan}(\alpha)$, one can get many of the classical theorems in these domains by confining attention to those cardinals n such that

$$n \in \text{NC}:(\text{E}\alpha).\alpha \in n.\text{stCan}(\alpha)$$

and to those ordinals ϕ such that

$$\phi \in \text{NO}:(\text{E}P).P \in \phi.\text{stCan}(\text{AV}(P)).$$

CHAPTER XIV

THE AXIOM OF CHOICE

1. The General Axiom of Choice. Mathematical opinion on the axiom of choice is not unanimous. Indeed there are many shades of opinion. We shall illustrate some of these by an imaginary conversation between three mathematicians, X, Y, and Z. (In Sierpinski, 1928, pages 103 to 109, various mathematicians holding divergent opinions are cited by name and their opinions actually quoted. There is also an extensive discussion in Zermelo, 1908, first paper.)

"It is of course obvious," said Y, "that every infinite set contains a denumerable subset. For choose an element of the set and call it x_0. Infinitely many elements remain. Choose another and call it x_1. Still, infinitely many elements remain. Indeed, when x_n has been chosen, infinitely many elements remain, and we can choose another and call it x_{n+1}. So we can choose $x_0, x_1, x_2, \ldots$, which form a denumerable subset."

"Oh, come now," protested X. "How much time do you think you have available for all this choosing? At your death you would still be choosing x_{n+1}."

"I didn't say that I personally could choose the set," returned Y. "I merely said it is there. Given a being who could choose the elements with no waste of time, he could choose the entire set in one second by choosing x_0 in half a second, x_1 in a quarter of a second, x_2 in an eighth of a second, and so on."

"There you go with that infernal 'and so on' again," objected X. "Just when you get to the critical point in a proof, you say 'and so on' and wave your hands, and I'm supposed to be satisfied. I thought you were supposed to prove things, and not appeal to the hypothetical abilities of a mythical being. You're doing theology, not mathematics."

Z broke in.

"As a matter of fact, it's perfectly clear that your original set can be well ordered. Why stop when you have chosen denumerably many elements? Go right on choosing, attaching ordinal numbers as subscripts, until you have exhausted the set. Then you will have it well ordered."

"You've exhausted me," complained X.

"Wait a minute," said Y. "If your set is uncountably infinite, then one must make an uncountable infinity of choices. Adding up the time intervals for each choice gives an infinite time for the entire process."

Z responded: "You are assuming a finite length of time for each choice, even though the time may be made as short as desired for each individual choice. But why should a choice take any time at all? I hypothecate a being who can perform a choice in no time at all. Then the entire well ordering takes him no time at all."

"The perfect reductio ad absurdum," grumbled X.

Thus it went far into the night, with none of X, Y, or Z retreating from his respective position. These positions are as follows.

X's position: Any finite number of choices is permissible, but not an infinite number.

Y's position: A denumerable number of choices is permissible, but not any larger number.

Z's position: Any number of choices is permissible.

Among actual mathematicians, perhaps a majority would applaud X's position, certainly some agree with Y, and others (who perhaps constitute a minority) agree wholeheartedly with Z. However, many mathematicians who would like to espouse the positions of X or Y find that this would leave them with no means of proof for certain theorems which they need in their research. Accordingly, they accept the position of Z, but with reluctance and a hope that someone will one day find proofs of their key theorems which do not involve an infinity of choices. Thus it comes about that we find papers written in which all the results of the paper depend on a theorem whose only known proof involves an infinity of choices; nevertheless, throughout the paper the author is careful to avoid the use of an infinity of choices.

A very complicating factor in the situation is that use of an infinite number of choices is often concealed by a plausible-sounding exposition. Witness our "proof," after Thm.XI.4.15, that the members of a denumerable set of denumerable sets are denumerable. The reasoning sounds entirely plausible, but it conceals a denumerable number of choices (we shall consider this point later with some care). Such implicit uses of an infinity of choices are so ingrained in the classical writings that it is rather hard to be sure which of the classical theorems have been proved without recourse to an infinity of choices. Presumably one could review the entire background of the discipline in which one wishes to work and check the status of the relevant theorems. However, this is a colossal task. Moreover, some of the uses of an infinity of choices are concealed under such extremely plausible arguments that it is very hard to be sure of ferreting them all out. Thus many mathematicians accept the position of Z out of sheer desperation, although they have no sympathy with it and some even find it repugnant.

Under the circumstances, there is nothing for us to do but indicate how one could introduce into symbolic logic an equivalent of making an infinity of choices. Then those who wish or feel forced to use an infinity of choices on occasion will at least have a mechanical equivalent thereof (which will not necessarily be any more palatable).

A prior question is that of making a single choice. This has been discussed at length in Sec. 7 of Chapter VI. Use of rule C is the mechanical equivalent of a single act of choice. Since we require that each demonstration be of finite length, we are thus entitled to make any finite number of choices but not an infinite number. Thus up to now our position has been strictly that of X.

It is interesting that justification for an infinity of choices can now be furnished by a suitable axiom. This axiom will be such that it will obviously take care of the simplest instance of an infinity of choices, and a succession of theorems will show that indeed it takes care of all cases.

Suppose we have an infinite class λ of sets α such that each α of λ is nonnull and no two α's from λ have a member in common. Then each α contains at least one x, and this x is not in any other α of λ. In such a circumstance, it seems almost indisputable that there should be a set of x's with precisely one x from each α of λ. Certainly, if one permits an infinity of choices, one can show that there is such a set of x's by simply choosing an x from each α. However, there seems no other way to infer the existence of such a set of x's in general.

In the symbolic logic, our basic tool for inferring the existence of classes is Axiom scheme 12. To use it in the present case, one must find a stratified statement $F(x)$ such that $F(x)$ is true if and only if x is in some α of λ and $F(y)$ is false for all other y's of this α. For an arbitrary λ, we know no way to write down such a $F(x)$.

Alternatively, one might try to infer the existence of such a set of x's by reductio ad absurdum, but so far no one has succeeded in this.

Thus it appears that, if we wish generally to be able to infer the existence of such a set of x's, we must state an axiom to that effect. Such an axiom would take the form:

$$(\lambda)::(\alpha):\alpha \in \lambda. \supset .\alpha \neq \Lambda:.(\alpha,\beta):\alpha,\beta \in \lambda.\alpha \neq \beta. \supset .$$

$$\alpha \cap \beta = \Lambda.: \supset :.(\mathrm{E}\gamma)(\alpha):\alpha \in \lambda. \supset .(\mathrm{E}_1 x).x \in \alpha \cap \gamma.$$

This is known as the "axiom of choice."

A significant consideration concerns the cardinality of λ. Thus if the additional hypothesis $\lambda \in \mathrm{Den}$ were inserted into the above statement, our mathematician Y would then accept it gladly, whereas he would not agree to it at all in its present form. One can therefore distinguish between axioms of choice of different cardinalities by putting restrictions on the cardinality of λ. Specifically, if we write

ND for $\hat{\lambda}((\alpha){:}\alpha \epsilon \lambda.\supset.\alpha \neq \Lambda{:}.(\alpha,\beta){:}\alpha,\beta \epsilon \lambda.\alpha \neq \beta.\supset.\alpha \cap \beta = \Lambda)$,

then we can express the axiom of choice of cardinality n by

$$\text{AxC}(n) \quad \text{for} \quad (\lambda){:}.\text{Nc}(\lambda) \leq n.\lambda \epsilon \text{ND}{:}\supset$$
$$:(\text{E}\gamma)(\alpha){:}\alpha \epsilon \lambda.\supset.(\text{E}_1x).x \epsilon \alpha \cap \gamma.$$

The unrestricted axiom of choice would be

$$\text{AxC} \quad \text{for} \quad \text{AxC}(\text{Nc}(\text{V})).$$

In ND, the N stands for "nonnull" to indicate that no member of λ is Λ, and the D for "disjoint" to indicate that the members of λ are disjoint, or nonoverlapping.

There are a large number of useful statements which are equivalent to the general axiom of choice. We shall state several of these and prove the equivalences. Actually, each one of these statements can be classified as to cardinality, and with suitable relations between the various cardinalities, various implications can be proved between them.

We shall denote these various statements by $Z_1(n)$, $Z_2(n)$, etc., when they have restricted cardinality, and by Z_1, Z_2, etc., when they have unrestricted cardinality.

We take $Z_1(n)$ to be:

"If α is a partially ordered set, of cardinality less than or equal to n, such that every simply ordered subset has a supremum in α, then there is a maximal element of α."

We are to understand this as follows. α is a partially ordered set if $(\text{E}R).\alpha = \text{AV}(R).R \epsilon \text{Pord}$. If $\alpha = \text{AV}(R).R \epsilon \text{Pord}$, then β is a simply ordered subset if $\beta \subseteq \alpha$ and $(\beta \upharpoonleft R \upharpoonright \beta) \epsilon \text{Sord}$; an upper bound of a subset β is an element x of α which follows all members of β, that is, $x \epsilon \text{AV}(R){:}(y){:}y \epsilon \beta.\supset.yRx$; a supremum of a subset β is a least upper bound of β, that is, x is a supremum of β if $x \epsilon \text{AV}(R){:}(y){:}y \epsilon \beta.\supset.yRx{::}(z){:}.z \epsilon \text{AV}(P){:}(y){:}y \epsilon \beta.\supset.yRz{:}\supset{:}xRz$; and a maximal element of α is an x such that $x \max_R \alpha$. We define:

$$\text{Ub}(\beta,R) \quad \text{for} \quad \hat{x}(x \epsilon \text{AV}(R){:}(y){:}y \epsilon \beta.\supset.yRx),$$
$$\text{Sup}(\beta,R) \quad \text{for} \quad \hat{x}(x \epsilon \text{Ub}(\beta,R){:}(z){:}z \epsilon \text{Ub}(\beta,R).\supset.xRz),$$
$$\text{Max}(\beta,R) \quad \text{for} \quad \hat{x}(x \max_R \beta).$$

Then $\text{Ub}(\beta,R)$ is the set of upper bounds of β with respect to R, $\text{Sup}(\beta,R)$ is the set of least upper bounds or suprema of β with respect to R, and $\text{Max}(\beta,R)$ is the set of maximal elements of β with respect to R. Finally, we write:

$$Z_1(n) \quad \text{for} \quad (\alpha,R){::}\text{Nc}(\alpha) \leq n.\alpha = \text{AV}(R).R \epsilon \text{Pord}{:}.(\beta){:}\beta \subseteq \alpha.$$
$$(\beta \upharpoonleft R \upharpoonright \beta) \epsilon \text{Sord}.\supset.\text{Sup}(\beta,R) \neq \Lambda.{:}\supset{:}.\text{Max}(\alpha,R) \neq \Lambda.$$
$$Z_1 \quad \text{for} \quad Z_1(\text{Nc}(\text{V})).$$

We take $Z_2(n)$ to be:
"Any set of cardinality less than or equal to n can be well ordered."
That is, we put:

$$\begin{array}{lll} Z_2(n) & \text{for} & (\alpha){:}\mathrm{Nc}(\alpha) \leq n. \supset .(\mathrm{E}P).P \in \mathrm{Word}.\alpha = \mathrm{AV}(P). \\ Z_2 & \text{for} & Z_2(\mathrm{Nc}(\mathrm{V})). \end{array}$$

We take $Z_3(n)$ to be:
"If λ, of cardinality less than or equal to n, is a set of nonempty sets, then there is a function f such that for any α in λ, $f(\alpha)$ is a member of α."

In order to preserve stratification, we have to make a slight variation, namely, that $f(\alpha)$ is the unit class of a member of α. This in no way diminishes the effectiveness of the result. Then we put:

$$\begin{array}{lll} Z_3(n) & \text{for} & (\lambda){::}\mathrm{Nc}(\lambda) \leq n{:}.(\alpha){:}\alpha \in \lambda. \supset .\alpha \neq \Lambda.{:} \supset {:}.(\mathrm{E}R){:} \\ & & R \in \mathrm{Funct}.\mathrm{Arg}(R) = \lambda.\mathrm{Val}(R) \subseteq 1{:}(\alpha){:}\alpha \in \lambda. \supset .R(\alpha) \subseteq \alpha. \\ Z_3 & \text{for} & Z_3(\mathrm{Nc}(\mathrm{V})). \end{array}$$

We take $Z_4(n)$ to be:
"Let λ, of cardinality less than or equal to n, be a set of sets which is partially ordered by inclusion. If the sum of each simply ordered subset of λ is in λ, then there is a maximal element of λ."

We define:

$$\begin{array}{lll} \subseteq & \text{for} & \hat{\alpha}\hat{\beta}(\alpha \subseteq \beta), \\ Z_4(n) & \text{for} & (\lambda){::}\mathrm{Nc}(\lambda) \leq n{:}.(\mu){:}\mu \subseteq \lambda.(\mu\rceil \subseteq \lceil\mu) \in \mathrm{Sord}. \supset . \\ & & \bigcup\mu \in \lambda.{:} \supset {:}.\mathrm{Max}(\lambda,\subseteq) \neq \Lambda. \\ Z_4 & \text{for} & Z_4(\mathrm{Nc}(\mathrm{V})). \end{array}$$

We take $Z_5(n)$ to be:
"Given a set, of cardinality less than or equal to n, and a nonvacuous property of finite character, there exists a maximal subset having the property."

A property of sets is said to be of finite character if a set has the property when and only when all its finite subsets have the property. For instance, one can state the result given in Ex.XI.3.21 as:

"A Hausdorff space is compact if and only if $\alpha \subseteq \mathrm{CS}.\bigcap\alpha \neq \Lambda$ is a property of α of finite character."

We shall define FC so that $\lambda \in \mathrm{FC}$ if and only if $\alpha \in \lambda$ is a property of α of finite character. Thus

$$\mathrm{FC} \quad \text{for} \quad \hat{\lambda}((\alpha){:}\alpha \in \lambda. \equiv .(\mathrm{SC}(\alpha) \cap \mathrm{Fin}) \subseteq \lambda).$$

Then we put

$$\begin{array}{lll} Z_5(n) & \text{for} & (\alpha,\lambda){:}\mathrm{Nc}(\alpha) \leq n.\lambda \neq \Lambda.\lambda \in \mathrm{FC}. \supset . \\ & & \mathrm{Max}(\lambda \cap \mathrm{SC}(\alpha),\subseteq) \neq \Lambda. \\ Z_5 & \text{for} & Z_5(\mathrm{Nc}(\mathrm{V})). \end{array}$$

We take $Z_6(n)$ to be:

"Every partially ordered set of cardinality less than or equal to n contains a maximal simply ordered subset."

That is, we put:

$Z_6(n)$ for $(\alpha,R)::\mathrm{Nc}(\alpha) \leq n.\alpha = \mathrm{AV}(R).R \in \mathrm{Pord}.: \supset :.(\mathrm{E}\beta):. \beta \subseteq \alpha.(\beta \upharpoonleft R \restriction \beta) \in \mathrm{Sord}:(\gamma):\gamma \subseteq \alpha.(\gamma \upharpoonleft R \restriction \gamma) \in \mathrm{Sord}. \supset .\sim(\beta \subset \gamma).$

Z_6 for $Z_6(\mathrm{Nc}(\mathrm{V}))$.

We take $Z_7(n)$ to be:

"If α is a partially ordered set, of cardinality less than or equal to n, such that every simply ordered subset has an upper bound in α, then there is a maximal element of α."

That is, we put:

$Z_7(n)$ for $(\alpha,R)::\mathrm{Nc}(\alpha) \leq n.\alpha = \mathrm{AV}(R).R \in \mathrm{Pord}:.(\beta):\beta \subseteq \alpha. (\beta \upharpoonleft R \restriction \beta) \in \mathrm{Sord}. \supset .\mathrm{Ub}(\beta,R) \neq \Lambda.: \supset :. \mathrm{Max}(\alpha,R) \neq \Lambda.$

Z_7 for $Z_7(\mathrm{Nc}(\mathrm{V}))$.

We shall now prove a series of implications between $\mathrm{AxC}(n)$ and $Z_i(m)$, from which it will follow that AxC and each of Z_1, Z_2, Z_3, Z_4, Z_5, Z_6, and Z_7 are equivalent. Many of our proofs, as well as the statements of many of the Z's, are adapted from a set of notes by G. A. Hedlund.

Our first theorem proves a result needed in the proof of our second theorem.

Theorem XIV.1.1.

(1) $$\alpha = \mathrm{AV}(P),$$

(2) $$P \in \mathrm{Pord},$$

(3) $$(\beta):\beta \subseteq \alpha.(\beta \upharpoonleft P \restriction \beta) \in \mathrm{Sord}. \supset .\mathrm{Sup}(\beta,P) \neq \Lambda,$$

(4) $$R \in \mathrm{Funct},$$

(5) $$\mathrm{Arg}(R) = \alpha,$$

(6) $$(x):x \in \alpha. \supset .xP(R(x))$$

yield

$$(\mathrm{E}z).z \in \alpha.z = R(z).$$

Proof. Assume the hypotheses. Define

(7) $$W = \hat{\gamma}(\gamma \subseteq \alpha:.(y):y \in \gamma. \supset .R(y) \in \gamma:.(\beta):\beta \subseteq \gamma. (\beta \upharpoonleft P \restriction \beta) \in \mathrm{Sord}. \supset .\mathrm{Sup}(\beta,P) \subseteq \gamma),$$

(8) $$M = \bigcap W,$$

(9) $$A = \hat{x}(x \in M:.(y):y \in M.y(P - I)x. \supset .(R(y))Px).$$

Clearly $\alpha \epsilon W$, so that

(10) $$M \subseteq \alpha,$$

(11) $$M \epsilon W,$$

(12) $$A \subseteq M,$$

(13) $$A \subseteq \alpha.$$

Lemma 1. $(x,y){:}x \epsilon A.y \epsilon M. \supset .yPx.\mathbf{v}.(R(x))Py.$

Proof. Assume

(i) $$x \epsilon A$$

and define

(ii) $$B = \hat{y}(y \epsilon M{:}yPx.\mathbf{v}.(R(x))Py).$$

Clearly

(iii) $$B \subseteq M,$$

(iv) $$B \subseteq \alpha.$$

Let $y \epsilon B$. Then $y \epsilon M$, so that $R(y) \epsilon M$ by (11) and (7).

Case 1. $yPx.y \neq x$. Then $(R(y))Px$ by (i) and (9).

Case 2. $yPx.y = x$. Then $R(x) = R(y)$. But $R(x) \epsilon \mathrm{AV}(P)$ by (6), so that $(R(x))P(R(y))$.

Case 3. $(R(x))Py$. We get $yP(R(y))$ by (6), so that $(R(x))P(R(y))$.

Thus $(R(y))Px.\mathbf{v}.(R(x))P(R(y))$, so that $R(y) \epsilon B$. Thus we have

(v) $$(y){:}y \epsilon B. \supset .R(y) \epsilon B.$$

Let $\beta \subseteq B.(\beta 1 R \upharpoonright \beta) \epsilon \mathrm{Sord}$. Then $\mathrm{Sup}(\beta,P) \subseteq M$ by (iii), (11), and (7).

Case 1. $(z){:}z \epsilon \beta. \supset .zPx$. Then $x \epsilon \mathrm{Ub}(\beta,P)$, so that $y \epsilon \mathrm{Sup}(\beta,P). \supset . yPx$. So $\mathrm{Sup}(\beta,P) \subseteq B$ by (ii).

Case 2. $(\mathrm{E}z).z \epsilon \beta.\sim(zPx)$. Then $(R(x))Pz$ by $z \epsilon \beta$, $\beta \subseteq B$, and (ii). But, since $\mathrm{Sup}(\beta,P) \subseteq \mathrm{Ub}(\beta,P)$, and since $z \epsilon \beta$, we have $(y){:}y \epsilon \mathrm{Sup}(\beta,P). \supset .zPy$. But from $(R(x))Pz$ and zPy, we get $(R(x))Py$. So $(y){:}y \epsilon \mathrm{Sup}(\beta,P). \supset .(R(x))Py$. Then $\mathrm{Sup}(\beta,P) \subseteq B$ by (ii).

So $\mathrm{Sup}(\beta,P) \subseteq B$ in either case. Thus

(vi) $$(\beta){:}\beta \subseteq B.(\beta 1 P \upharpoonright \beta) \epsilon \mathrm{Sord}. \supset .\mathrm{Sup}(\beta,P) \subseteq B.$$

Now by (iv), (v), (vi), and (7), $B \epsilon W$. Then $M \subseteq B$ by (8) and Thm. IX.5.5, Part I. Then by (iii), $B = M$. Then by (ii), $(y){:}y \epsilon M. \supset .yPx.\mathbf{v}. (R(x))Py$, and our lemma follows.

Lemma 2. $(x,y){:}x \epsilon A.y \epsilon M. \supset .yPx.\mathbf{v}.xPy.$

Proof. If $(R(x))Py$, then xPy, since $xP(R(x))$ by (6).

Lemma 3. $(x){:}x \in A. \supset .R(x) \in A.$

Proof. Assume

(i) $$x \in A.$$

Then $x \in M$ by (12), so that

(ii) $$R(x) \in M$$

by (11) and (7).

Assume $y \in M.y(P - I)(R(x))$. By (i) and Lemma 1, $yPx.\mathbf{v}.(R(x))Py$. However, $(R(x))Py$ is impossible by $y(P - I)(R(x))$. So yPx.

Case 1. $x \neq y$. Then $y(P - I)x$. Then by (i) and (9), $(R(y))Px$. But $xP(R(x))$ by (6), so that $(R(y))P(R(x))$.

Case 2. $x = y$. Then $R(x) = R(y)$, so that $(R(y))P(R(x))$.

So in either case, $(R(y))P(R(x))$, and we have shown

(iii) $$(y){:}y \in M.y(P - I)(R(x)). \supset .(R(y))P(R(x)).$$

Then by (ii), (iii), and (9), $R(x) \in A$.

Lemma 4. $(\beta){:}\beta \subseteq A.(\beta 1 P \upharpoonright \beta) \in \text{Sord}. \supset .\text{Sup}(\beta,P) \subseteq A.$

Proof. Assume

(i) $$\beta \subseteq A.(\beta 1 P \upharpoonright \beta) \in \text{Sord}.$$

Then $\beta \subseteq M$ so that by (11) and (7),

(ii) $$\text{Sup}(\beta,P) \subseteq M.$$

Now assume

(iii) $$x \in \text{Sup}(\beta,P),$$

(iv) $$y \in M.y(P - I)x.$$

If now $(z){:}z \in \beta. \supset .zPy$, then $y \in \text{Ub}(\beta,P)$, so that xPy, which would contradict (iv). So there is a z with

(v) $$z \in \beta,$$

(vi) $$\sim(zPy).$$

By (v) and (i), $z \in A$, so that by (iv) and Lemma 2, $zPy.\mathbf{v}.yPz$. Thus yPz by (vi). Also $y \neq z$ by (vi), so that $y(P - I)z$. But $z \in A$, so that by (9) and (iv), $(R(y))Pz$. But by (v) and (iii), zPx. So $(R(y))Px$. Thus we have

(vii) $$(x,y){:}x \in \text{Sup}(\beta,P).y \in M.y(P - I)x. \supset .(R(y))Px.$$

If we use (ii) and (vii) with (9), we can infer $\text{Sup}(\beta,P) \subseteq A$, and our lemma is proved.

Finally, by (13), Lemma 3, Lemma 4, and (7), $A \epsilon W$. Then by (8), $M \subseteq A$, so that by (12), $A = M$. Then Lemma 2 gives $(x,y):x,y \epsilon M. \supset . yPx.\vee.xPy$. So

(14) $$(M \upharpoonleft P \upharpoonright M) \epsilon \text{Sord}.$$

Now by (11), $M \epsilon W$, and certainly $M \subseteq M$. Thus by (7),

(15) $$\text{Sup}(M,P) \subseteq M,$$

and by (3),

(16) $$\text{Sup}(M,P) \neq \Lambda.$$

Then by (16), there is a $z \epsilon \text{Sup}(M,P)$. Then by (15), $z \epsilon M$. So $R(z) \epsilon M$ by (11) and (7). Thus $(R(z))Pz$, since $z \epsilon \text{Sup}(M,P)$. However, $zP(R(z))$ by (6) since $z \epsilon \alpha$ by (10). So $z = R(z)$.

Theorem XIV.1.2. $\vdash (\delta):\text{AxC}(\text{Nc}(\text{USC}(\delta))). \supset .Z_1(\text{Nc}(\delta))$.

Proof. Proof by reductio ad absurdum. Assume

(1) $$\text{AxC}(\text{Nc}(\text{USC}(\delta))),$$

(2) $$\text{Nc}(\alpha) \leq \text{Nc}(\delta),$$

(3) $$\alpha = \text{AV}(P),$$

(4) $$P \epsilon \text{Pord},$$

(5) $$(\beta):\beta \subseteq \alpha.(\beta \upharpoonleft P \upharpoonright \beta) \epsilon \text{Sord}. \supset .\text{Sup}(\beta,P) \neq \Lambda,$$

(6) $$\text{Max}(\alpha,P) = \Lambda.$$

Define

(7) $$\lambda = \hat{\beta}(\text{E}x).x \epsilon \alpha.\beta = \hat{y}\hat{z}(y = x.x(P - I)z).$$

Clearly $\beta,\gamma \epsilon \lambda.\beta \cap \gamma \neq \Lambda. \supset .\beta = \gamma$, so that

(8) $$(\beta,\gamma):\beta,\gamma \epsilon \lambda.\beta \neq \gamma. \supset .\beta \cap \gamma = \Lambda.$$

Further, let $\beta \epsilon \lambda$. Then $x \epsilon \alpha.\beta = \hat{y}\hat{z}(y = x.x(P - I)z)$. Then $\beta = \Lambda. \supset .(z).\sim(x(P - I)z)$, so that, if $\beta = \Lambda$, then $x \epsilon \text{Max}(\alpha,P)$. So by (6), $\beta \neq \Lambda$. Thus

$$(\beta):\beta \epsilon \lambda. \supset .\beta \neq \Lambda,$$

so that by (8)

(9) $$\lambda \epsilon \text{ND}.$$

Also, clearly λ sm $\text{USC}(\alpha)$, so that by (2), $\text{Nc}(\lambda) \leq \text{Nc}(\text{USC}(\delta))$. Then by (9) and (1), there is an S with

(10) $$(\beta):\beta \epsilon \lambda. \supset .(\text{E}_1 w).w \epsilon \beta \cap S.$$

From this we infer by (7), and putting $R = S \cap (P - I)$,

(11) $$R \epsilon \text{Funct},$$

(12) $$\text{Arg}(R) = \alpha.$$

Also,

(13) $$(x):x \epsilon \alpha . \supset .x(P - I)(R(x)).$$

Then by Thm.XIV.1.1 and (3), (4), (5), (11), (12), and (13), we infer that there is a z with $z \epsilon \alpha . z = R(z)$. This contradicts (13).

Corollary. $\vdash \text{AxC} \supset Z_1$.

Theorem XIV.1.3. $\vdash (n):n,n^0 \epsilon \text{NC}.\text{AxC}(n). \supset .Z_1(n)$.

Proof. If $n,n^0 \epsilon$ NC, then by Thm.XI.2.48, Cor. 2, there is a δ with $n = \text{Nc}(\text{USC}(\delta))$. If now $\text{Nc}(\alpha) \leq n$, $\alpha = \text{AV}(P)$, etc., then α is similar to a subset β of USC(δ), and then $\beta = \text{USC}(\gamma)$ where γ is a subset of δ. Now P induces on γ a partial ordering Q with properties analogous to those assumed for P. Then we can put γ and Q for α and P in Thm.XIV.1.2 to infer that γ has a maximal element relative to Q. Then the corresponding element of α is maximal with respect to P.

Theorem XIV.1.4. $\vdash (\delta):Z_1(\text{Nc}(\text{SC}(\delta \times \delta))). \supset .Z_2(\text{Nc}(\delta))$.

Proof. Assume

(1) $$Z_1(\text{Nc}(\text{SC}(\delta \times \delta))),$$

(2) $$\text{Nc}(\alpha) \leq \text{Nc}(\delta).$$

Then

(3) $$\text{Nc}(\text{SC}(\alpha \times \alpha)) \leq \text{Nc}(\text{SC}(\delta \times \delta)).$$

Define

(4) $$A = \hat{P}(P \epsilon \text{Word}.\text{AV}(P) \subseteq \alpha).$$

(5) $$W = \hat{P}\hat{Q}(P,Q \epsilon A:P = Q.\mathbf{v}.(\text{E}x).x \epsilon \text{AV}(Q).P = \text{seg}_x Q).$$

Clearly

(6) $$A = \text{AV}(W).$$

(7) $$W \epsilon \text{Ref}.$$

By Thm.X.6.13, corollary,

(8) $$W \epsilon \text{Trans}.$$

Clearly $PWQ. \supset .\text{No}(P) \leq \text{No}(Q)$. So if PWQ and QWP, then $\text{No}(P) = \text{No}(Q)$ by Thm.XII.3.7. Then P smor Q, so that by Thm. XII.2.1, $\sim(\text{E}x).x \epsilon \text{AV}(Q).P = \text{seg}_x Q$. Then from PWQ, we get $P = Q$. So

(9) $$W \epsilon \text{Antisym}.$$

Lemma 1. $(\beta){:}\beta \subseteq A.(\beta\rceil W\lceil\beta) \in \text{Sord}. \supset .\text{AV}(\bigcup\beta) \subseteq \alpha.\bigcup\beta \in \text{Sord}.$

Proof. Assume

(i) $$\beta \subseteq A,$$

(ii) $$(\beta\rceil W\lceil\beta) \in \text{Sord},$$

and put

(iii) $$B = \bigcup\beta.$$

Let $x \in \text{AV}(B)$.

Case 1. $x \in \text{Arg}(B)$. Then $\langle x,y\rangle \in B$. So by (iii), there is a $P \in \beta$ with $\langle x,y\rangle \in P$. Then $x \in \text{AV}(P)$, so that $x \in \alpha$ and $\langle x,x\rangle \in P$ by (i) and (4). Then $\langle x,x\rangle \in B$ by (iii). Thus xBx.

Case 2. $x \in \text{Val}(B)$. Proceed similarly.

Thus

(iv) $$\text{AV}(B) \subseteq \alpha,$$

(v) $$B \in \text{Ref}.$$

Let xBy and yBz. Then there are P and Q with $P \in \beta.xPy$ and $Q \in \beta.yQz$. By (ii), $PWQ.\mathbf{v}.QWP$.

Case 1. PWQ. Then by (5), $P \subseteq Q$. So xQy, and hence xQz, since $Q \in \text{Trans}$ by (4). Then xBz.

Case 2. QWP. Proceed similarly.

Thus

(vi) $$B \in \text{Trans}.$$

Similarly, we get

(vii) $$B \in \text{Antisym}.$$

Let $x,y \in \text{AV}(B)$. Then xBx and yBy by (v). Then $P \in \beta.xPx$ and $Q \in \beta.yQy$. By (ii), $PWQ.\mathbf{v}.QWP$.

Case 1. PWQ. Then $P \subseteq Q$ by (5). So xQx. Thus $x,y \in \text{AV}(Q)$. Thus $xQy.\mathbf{v}.yQx$, since $Q \in \text{Connex}$ by (4). Then $xBy.\mathbf{v}.yBx$.

Case 2. QWP. Proceed similarly.

Thus

(viii) $$B \in \text{Connex}.$$

Lemma 2. $(\beta,x,y){:}\beta \subseteq A.(\beta\rceil W\lceil\beta) \in \text{Sord}.P \in \beta.y \in \text{AV}(P).x(\bigcup\beta)y. \supset .xPy.$

Proof. Assume the hypothesis. Since $x(\bigcup\beta)y$, there is a Q with $Q \in \beta. xQy$. Then $PWQ.\mathbf{v}.QWP$.

Case 1. $PWQ.P = Q$. Then xPy.

Case 2. $PWQ.P \neq Q$. Then by (5), $w \in \mathrm{AV}(Q).P = \mathrm{seg}_w Q$. By $y \in \mathrm{AV}(P)$, we have $y(Q - I)w$. Then by xQy, we get $x(Q - I)w$. So by the definition of $\mathrm{seg}_w Q$, we get $x(\mathrm{seg}_w Q)y$. That is, xPy.

Case 3. QWP. Then by (5), $Q \subseteq P$. Then xPy.

Lemma 3. $(\beta):\beta \subseteq A.(\beta 1 W \upharpoonright \beta) \in \mathrm{Sord}. \supset .\bigcup\beta \in A$.

Proof. Assume the hypothesis. By (4) and Lemma 1, it suffices to prove $\bigcup\beta \in \mathrm{Word}$. Let

(i) $$B = \bigcup\beta.$$

If now $\gamma \cap \mathrm{AV}(B) \neq \Lambda$, then there is an $x \in \gamma \cap \mathrm{AV}(B)$. So xBx. Then $P \in \beta.xPx$. So $\gamma \cap \mathrm{AV}(P) \neq \Lambda$. Thus there is a y with $y \min_P \gamma$. Then $y \in \gamma \cap \mathrm{AV}(B)$. Also $y \min_B \gamma$, for if $z \in \gamma \cap \mathrm{AV}(B).z(B - I)y$, then $z(P - I)y$ by Lemma 2, contradicting $y \min_P \gamma$.

Lemma 4. $(\beta):\beta \subseteq A.(\beta 1 W \upharpoonright \beta) \in \mathrm{Sord}. \supset .\bigcup\beta \in \mathrm{Ub}(\beta,W)$.

Proof. Assume the hypothesis and put $B = \bigcup\beta$. By (6) and Lemma 3, $B \in \mathrm{AV}(W)$.

Let $P \in \beta$. Then $P \subseteq B$.

Case 1. $P = B$. Then PWB by (5) and Lemma 3.

Case 2. $P \neq B$. Then there is a w in $B - P$ by Thm.IX.4.21. Then $w = \langle x,y \rangle$. So $xBy.\sim(xPy)$. Then by Lemma 2, $\sim y \in \mathrm{AV}(P)$. Then $\mathrm{AV}(B) - \mathrm{AV}(P) \neq \Lambda$. Let z be the least member of $\mathrm{AV}(B) - \mathrm{AV}(P)$ with respect to B, which is a well-ordering relation by Lemma 3. So

(i) $$z \in \mathrm{AV}(B) - \mathrm{AV}(P),$$

(ii) $$(w):w(B - I)z. \supset .w \in \mathrm{AV}(P).$$

If now $v(\mathrm{seg}_z B)w$, then by (ii), $v,w \in \mathrm{AV}(P)$. As vBw, we get vPw by Lemma 2. So

(iii) $$\mathrm{seg}_z B \subseteq P.$$

Conversely, let xPy. Then xBy, since $P \subseteq B$. If zBy, then zPy by Lemma 2. But zPy gives $z \in \mathrm{AV}(P)$, contrary to (i). So $\sim(zBy)$. Then $y(B - I)z$. Thus also $x(B - I)z$, so that $x(\mathrm{seg}_z B)y$. Thus

(iv) $$P \subseteq \mathrm{seg}_z B.$$

Then by (i), (iii), (iv), and (5), PWB.

Lemma 5. $(\beta):\beta \subseteq A.(\beta 1 W \upharpoonright \beta) \in \mathrm{Sord}. \supset .\mathrm{Sup}(\beta,W) \neq \Lambda$.

Proof. Assume the hypothesis and put $B = \bigcup\beta$. Then $B \in \mathrm{Ub}(\beta,W)$ by Lemma 4. Now suppose $P \in \mathrm{Ub}(\beta,W)$. Then

(i) $$P \in A$$

by (6) and

(ii) $$(Q):Q \in \beta. \supset .QWP.$$

Then by (5), $(Q):Q \epsilon \beta . \supset .Q \subseteq P$. Then

(iii) $$B \subseteq P$$

by Thm.IX.5.8, Part II.

Suppose $y \epsilon \text{AV}(B).xPy$. Then yBy, so that there is a $Q \epsilon \beta$ with yQy. Then by (ii), QWP.

Case 1. $Q = P$. Then xQy, so that xBy.

Case 2. $w \epsilon \text{AV}(P).Q = \text{seg}_w P$. Then, since $y \epsilon \text{AV}(Q)$, we have $y(P - I)w$. Then, by xPy, we have also $x(P - I)w$. So $x(\text{seg}_w P)y$. Thus xQy, so that xBy.

So in any case xBy. Thus

(iv) $$(x,y).y \epsilon \text{AV}(B).xPy. \supset .xBy.$$

Now we can proceed as in the proof of Lemma 4, using (iv) instead of Lemma 2, and we deduce finally BWP.

Thus, $B \epsilon \text{Sup}(\beta,W)$.

Lemma 6. $\text{Max}(A,W) \neq \Lambda$.

Proof. By (1), (6), (7), (8), (9), and Lemma 5, we need only prove $\text{Nc}(A) \leq \text{Nc}(\text{SC}(\delta \times \delta))$. However, clearly $A \subseteq \text{SC}(\alpha \times \alpha)$, by (4), so that we get the desired inequality by (3).

Lemma 7. $(P):P \epsilon \text{Max}(A,W). \supset .\text{AV}(P) = \alpha$.

Proof. Let $P \epsilon \text{Max}(A,W)$ and $\text{AV}(P) \neq \alpha$. Then by (4), there is an $x \epsilon \alpha$ with $\sim x \epsilon \text{AV}(P)$. In the notation of Ex.XII.1.5, put $Q = P +_s \{\langle x,x\rangle\}$. By $P \epsilon \text{Max}(A,W)$, we have $P \epsilon A$, so that $P \epsilon$ Word. Then by Ex.XII.1.5(e), we get $Q \epsilon$ Word. Also, clearly $\text{AV}(Q) \subseteq \alpha$. So $Q \epsilon A$. By Ex.XII.1.5(g), $P = \text{seg}_x Q$. So by (5), PWQ. Also, clearly $P \neq Q$, since $x \epsilon \text{AV}(Q). \sim x \epsilon \text{AV}(P)$. Then $P(W - I)Q$, contradicting $P \epsilon \text{Max}(A,W)$, and our lemma is proved.

By Lemma 6, there is a $P \epsilon \text{Max}(A,W)$. So $P \epsilon A$, so that $P \epsilon$ Word by (4). By Lemma 7, $\text{AV}(P) = \alpha$, and our theorem is proved.

Corollary. $\vdash Z_1 \supset Z_2$.

Theorem XIV.1.5. $\vdash (n):n,n^0 \epsilon \text{NC}.Z_1(2^{n\times n}). \supset .Z_2(n)$.

Proof. If $n,n^0 \epsilon \text{NC}$ and $n = \text{Nc}(\delta)$, then $n \times n = \text{Nc}(\delta \times \delta)$, and $\text{Nc}(\text{SC}(\delta \times \delta)) = 2^{n\times n}$.

We now derive $Z_3(m)$ from $Z_2(n)$, but unfortunately there seems to be little relationship between m and n. Indeed one can have m anywhere between 0 and 2^n apparently.

Theorem XIV.1.6. $\vdash (n)(Z_2(n):: \supset ::(\lambda)::\text{Nc}(\bigcup\lambda) \leq n:.(\alpha):\alpha \epsilon \lambda. \supset . \alpha \neq \Lambda.: \supset :.(\text{E}R):R \epsilon \text{Funct}.\text{Arg}(R) = \lambda.\text{Val}(R) \subseteq 1:(\alpha):\alpha \epsilon \lambda. \supset . R(\alpha) \subseteq \alpha)$.

Proof. Assume

(1) $$Z_2(n),$$

(2) $$\mathrm{Nc}(\bigcup\lambda) \leq n,$$

(3) $$(\alpha):\alpha \in \lambda. \supset .\alpha \neq \Lambda.$$

Then by (2) and (1), there is a P with

(4) $$P \in \mathrm{Word},$$

(5) $$\bigcup\lambda = \mathrm{AV}(P).$$

Define

(6) $$R = \hat{\alpha}\hat{\beta}(\alpha \in \lambda:(\mathrm{E}x).x \text{ least}_P\ \alpha.\beta = \{x\}).$$

Clearly by (4) and Thm.X.6.14, Part III,

(7) $$R \in \mathrm{Funct}.$$

Also by (3), (4), and Thm.X.6.14, Part II,

(8) $$\mathrm{Arg}(R) = \lambda.$$

Clearly

(9) $$\mathrm{Val}(R) \subseteq 1,$$

(10) $$(\alpha):\alpha \in \lambda. \supset .R(\alpha) \subseteq \alpha.$$

Corollary. $\vdash Z_2 \supset Z_3$.

Theorem XIV.1.7. $\vdash (n):Z_3(n). \supset .\mathrm{AxC}(n)$.

Proof. Assume

(1) $$Z_3(n),$$

(2) $$\mathrm{Nc}(\lambda) \leq n,$$

(3) $$\lambda \in \mathrm{ND}.$$

By (3) we have

(4) $$(\alpha):\alpha \in \lambda. \supset .\alpha \neq \Lambda,$$

(5) $$(\alpha,\beta):\alpha,\beta \in \lambda.\alpha \neq \beta. \supset .\alpha \cap \beta = \Lambda.$$

By (1), (2), and (4), there is an R with

(6) $$R \in \mathrm{Funct},$$

(7) $$\mathrm{Arg}(R) = \lambda,$$

(8) $$\mathrm{Val}(R) \subseteq 1,$$

(9) $$(\alpha):\alpha \in \lambda. \supset .R(\alpha) \subseteq \alpha.$$

Now put

$$(10) \qquad \gamma = \bigcup(\text{Val}(R)).$$

If now $\alpha \epsilon \lambda$, then $R(\alpha) \subseteq \gamma$ by (10), $R(\alpha) \neq \Lambda$ by (8), and $\alpha \cap R(\alpha) = R(\alpha)$ by (9). So $\alpha \cap \gamma \neq \Lambda$. Thus

$$(11) \qquad (\text{E}x).x \epsilon \alpha \cap \gamma.$$

Now let $y,z \epsilon \alpha \cap \gamma$. Then $y \epsilon u.u \epsilon \text{Val}(R)$ and $z \epsilon v.v \epsilon \text{Val}(R)$. Then $u = R(\beta)$ and $v = R(\gamma)$. So $y \epsilon R(\beta)$ and $z \epsilon R(\gamma)$. By (9), $y \epsilon \beta$ and $z \epsilon \gamma$. But $y,z \epsilon \alpha$. So $\alpha \cap \beta \neq \Lambda$ and $\alpha \cap \gamma \neq \Lambda$. So by (5), $\alpha = \beta$ and $\alpha = \gamma$. So $y,z \epsilon R(\alpha)$. However, by (8), $R(\alpha) = \{w\}$. So $y = w = z$, and thus $y = z$. So by (11),

$$(\text{E}_1x).x \epsilon \alpha \cap \gamma.$$

Corollary. $\vdash Z_3 \supset \text{AxC}$.

We have now proved

$$\vdash \text{AxC} \equiv Z_1 \equiv Z_2 \equiv Z_3.$$

Theorem XIV.1.8. $\vdash (n){:}Z_1(n). \supset .Z_4(n)$.

Proof. If we take R to be $\lambda\rceil \subseteq \lceil\lambda$, then clearly

$$(1) \qquad \lambda = \text{AV}(R),$$

$$(2) \qquad R \epsilon \text{Pord}.$$

Also if $\mu \subseteq \lambda.\bigcup\mu \epsilon \lambda$, then $\{\bigcup\mu\} = \text{Sup}(\mu,R)$. So we get our theorem by taking α to be λ in $Z_1(n)$.

Corollary. $\vdash Z_1 \supset Z_4$.

Theorem XIV.1.9. $\vdash (\delta){:}Z_4(\text{Nc}(\text{SC}(\delta))). \supset .Z_5(\text{Nc}(\delta))$.

Proof. Assume

$$(1) \qquad Z_4(\text{Nc}(\text{SC}(\delta))),$$

$$(2) \qquad \text{Nc}(\alpha) \leq \text{Nc}(\delta),$$

$$(3) \qquad \lambda \neq \Lambda,$$

$$(4) \qquad \lambda \epsilon \text{FC}.$$

Then by (4),

$$(5) \qquad (\beta){:}\beta \epsilon \lambda. \equiv .(\text{SC}(\beta) \cap \text{Fin}) \subseteq \lambda.$$

By (2),

$$(6) \qquad \text{Nc}(\lambda \cap \text{SC}(\alpha)) \leq \text{Nc}(\text{SC}(\delta)).$$

By (3), there is a $\beta \epsilon \lambda$. Now $\Lambda \epsilon (\text{SC}(\beta) \cap \text{Fin})$. So by (5),

$$(7) \qquad \Lambda \epsilon \lambda.$$

Lemma. $(\mu):\mu \subseteq (\lambda \cap \mathrm{SC}(\alpha)).(\mu\rceil \subseteq \lceil\mu) \epsilon \mathrm{Sord}. \supset .\bigcup\mu \epsilon (\lambda \cap \mathrm{SC}(\alpha))$.
Proof. Assume

(i) $$\mu \subseteq (\lambda \cap \mathrm{SC}(\alpha)),$$

(ii) $$(\mu\rceil \subseteq \lceil\mu) \epsilon \mathrm{Sord}.$$

Then by Thm.IX.5.8, Part II,

(iii) $$\bigcup\mu \epsilon \mathrm{SC}(\alpha).$$

We prove by weak induction on n that

(iv) $$(n,\beta):.n \epsilon \mathrm{Nn}.\beta \epsilon n.\beta \subseteq \bigcup\mu: \supset :(\mathrm{E}R):R \epsilon \mathrm{Funct}:\mathrm{Arg}(R) = \mathrm{USC}(\beta): \mathrm{Val}(R) \subseteq \mu:(x):x \epsilon \beta. \supset .x \epsilon R(\{x\}).$$

Now let $\beta \epsilon (\mathrm{SC}(\bigcup\mu) \cap \mathrm{Fin})$. Then by (iv) there is an R with

(v) $$R \epsilon \mathrm{Funct},$$

(vi) $$\mathrm{Arg}(R) = \mathrm{USC}(\beta),$$

(vii) $$\mathrm{Val}(R) \subseteq \mu,$$

(viii) $$(x):x \epsilon \beta. \supset .x \epsilon R(\{x\}).$$

Now we prove by weak induction on n that

(ix) $$(n,R):n \epsilon \mathrm{Nn}.R \epsilon \mathrm{Funct}.\mathrm{Arg}(R) \epsilon n. \supset .\mathrm{Val}(R) \epsilon \mathrm{Fin}.$$

Since $\beta \epsilon \mathrm{Fin}$, one gets $\mathrm{Val}(R) \epsilon \mathrm{Fin}$ by (v), (vi), and (ix).
Case 1. $\beta = \Lambda$. Then $\beta \epsilon \lambda$ by (7).
Case 2. $\beta \neq \Lambda$. Then $\mathrm{Val}(R) \neq \Lambda$. So by (ii) and Thm.XI.3.44, Cor. 3, there is a γ such that

(x) $$\gamma \text{ greatest}_S \mathrm{Val}(R),$$

where we write S for $\mu\rceil \subseteq \lceil\mu$. So $(y):y \epsilon \mathrm{Val}(R). \supset .y \subseteq \gamma$. Then by (viii), $(x):x \epsilon \beta. \supset .x \epsilon \gamma$. Thus $\beta \subseteq \gamma$. Then $\beta \epsilon (\mathrm{SC}(\gamma) \cap \mathrm{Fin})$. However, $\gamma \epsilon \lambda$ by (i) and (vii). So $(\mathrm{SC}(\gamma) \cap \mathrm{Fin}) \subseteq \lambda$ by (5). Thus $\beta \epsilon \lambda$.
Thus in each case $\beta \epsilon \lambda$. So we have shown

$$\beta \epsilon (\mathrm{SC}(\bigcup\mu) \cap \mathrm{Fin}). \supset .\beta \epsilon \lambda.$$

So $(\mathrm{SC}(\bigcup\mu) \cap \mathrm{Fin}) \subseteq \lambda$. Then by (5),

(xi) $$\bigcup\mu \epsilon \lambda.$$

Then by (iii), we conclude our lemma.
Then by (6) and our lemma, we can take λ to be **$\lambda \cap \mathrm{SC}(\alpha)$ in $Z_4(n)$**. Then we infer $\mathrm{Max}(\lambda \cap \mathrm{SC}(\alpha),\subseteq) \neq \Lambda$, as desired.
Corollary. $\vdash Z_4 \supset Z_5$.

Theorem XIV.1.10. $\vdash (n){:}n,n^0 \in \mathrm{NC}.Z_4(2^n).\supset .Z_5(n).$

Theorem XIV.1.11. $\vdash (n){:}Z_5(n).\supset .Z_6(n).$

Proof. Assume

(1) $$Z_5(n),$$

(2) $$\mathrm{Nc}(\alpha) \leq n,$$

(3) $$\alpha = \mathrm{AV}(R),$$

(4) $$R \in \mathrm{Pord}.$$

Take

(5) $$\lambda = \hat{\beta}(\beta \subseteq \alpha.(\beta \upharpoonleft R \upharpoonright \beta) \in \mathrm{Sord}).$$

Clearly $\Lambda \subseteq \alpha.(\Lambda \upharpoonleft R \upharpoonright \Lambda) \in \mathrm{Sord}$. So $\Lambda \in \lambda$. Thus

(6) $$\lambda \neq \Lambda.$$

Also, it is clear from (5) that

(7) $$(\beta){:}\beta \in \lambda.\supset .(\mathrm{SC}(\beta) \cap \mathrm{Fin}) \subseteq \lambda.$$

Let $(\mathrm{SC}(\beta) \cap \mathrm{Fin}) \subseteq \lambda$. If $x \in \beta$, then $\{x\} \in (\mathrm{SC}(\beta) \cap \mathrm{Fin})$. So $\{x\} \in \lambda$. So by (5), $\{x\} \subseteq \alpha$. Then $x \in \alpha$. So

(8) $$(\beta){:}(\mathrm{SC}(\beta) \cap \mathrm{Fin}) \subseteq \lambda.\supset .\beta \subseteq \alpha.$$

Let $(\mathrm{SC}(\beta) \cap \mathrm{Fin}) \subseteq \lambda$ and $x,y \in \mathrm{AV}(\beta \upharpoonleft R \upharpoonright \beta)$. Then $x,y \in \beta \cap \mathrm{AV}(R)$. So $\{x,y\} \in (\mathrm{SC}(\beta) \cap \mathrm{Fin})$. Then $\{x,y\} \in \lambda$. Thus $Q \in \mathrm{Sord}$ if we write Q for $(\{x,y\} \upharpoonleft R \upharpoonright \{x,y\})$. But by Thm.X.6.1, Part VII, $\mathrm{AV}(Q) = \{x,y\}$. Then $xQy.\mathbf{v}.yQx$. So $x(\beta \upharpoonleft R \upharpoonright \beta)y.\mathbf{v}.y(\beta \upharpoonleft R \upharpoonright \beta)x$. Thus $(\beta \upharpoonleft R \upharpoonright \beta) \in \mathrm{Connex}$. So by (8),

$$(\beta){:}(\mathrm{SC}(\beta) \cap \mathrm{Fin}) \subseteq \lambda.\supset .\beta \in \lambda.$$

Then by this and (7), $\lambda \in \mathrm{FC}$. So by (1), (2), and (6),

$$\mathrm{Max}(\lambda \cap \mathrm{SC}(\alpha),\subseteq) \neq \Lambda.$$

But by (5), this is just the conclusion desired.

Corollary. $\vdash Z_5 \supset Z_6.$

Theorem XIV.1.12. $\vdash (n){:}Z_6(n).\supset .Z_7(n).$

Proof. Assume

(1) $$Z_6(n),$$

(2) $$\mathrm{Nc}(\alpha) \leq n,$$

(3) $$\alpha = \mathrm{AV}(R),$$

(4) $$R \in \mathrm{Pord},$$

(5) $$(\beta){:}\beta \subseteq \alpha.(\beta \upharpoonleft R \upharpoonright \beta) \in \mathrm{Sord}.\supset .\mathrm{Ub}(\beta,R) \neq \Lambda.$$

By (1), (2), (3), and (4), we infer that there is a β such that

(6) $$\beta \subseteq \alpha . (\beta \upharpoonleft R \upharpoonright \beta) \in \text{Sord},$$

(7) $$(\gamma) : \gamma \subseteq \alpha . (\gamma \upharpoonleft R \upharpoonright \gamma) \in \text{Sord}. \supset . \sim(\beta \subset \gamma).$$

By (5) and (6), $\text{Ub}(\beta,R) \neq \Lambda$. Take $x \in \text{Ub}(\beta,R)$. Then $x \in \text{Max}(\alpha,R)$. For if not then there is a y with $x(R - I)y$. Then $(z):z \in \beta. \supset .z(R - I)y$. So if we take $\gamma = \beta \cup \{y\}$, then $\gamma \subseteq \alpha.\ (\gamma \upharpoonleft R \upharpoonright \gamma) \in \text{Sord}$, and $\beta \subset \gamma$, contradicting (7). Then $\text{Max}(\alpha,R) \neq \Lambda$.

Corollary. $\vdash Z_6 \supset Z_7$.

Theorem XIV.1.13. $\vdash (n):Z_7(n) \supset Z_1(n)$.

Proof. Since $\text{Sup}(\beta,R) \subseteq \text{Ub}(\beta,R)$, the theorem follows immediately.

Corollary. $\vdash Z_7 \supset Z_1$.

By Thms.XIV.1.8 to XIV.1.13, we have

$$\vdash Z_1 \equiv Z_4 \equiv Z_5 \equiv Z_6 \equiv Z_7.$$

The three statements AxC, Z_2, and Z_3 were considered by Zermelo and proved mutually equivalent (see Zermelo, 1904; and Zermelo, 1908, first paper). The various names "axiom of choice," "Zermelo's axiom," "Zermelo's theorem," and "well-ordering theorem" are to be found attached to various of AxC, Z_2, and Z_3, in a manner that is far from uniform. Actually, since the three statements are equivalent, the choice of names is not logically significant, although it may be important on historical or esthetic grounds.

Since 1935, when Zorn called attention to the considerable usefulness of Z_4 (see Zorn, 1935), the statements Z_1, Z_4, Z_5, Z_6, and Z_7 have come into great favor as alternatives to the axiom of choice. Although Zorn made no claim to priority, and stated only Z_4, each of Z_1, Z_4, Z_5, Z_6, and Z_7 is now known by the name of "Zorn's lemma." Actually Z_6 was stated by Hausdorff (see Hausdorff, 1914, page 140). A dual form of Z_4 was stated by R. L. Moore (see Moore, 1932, page 84), and apparently Z_4 was known to Kuratowski even earlier. Apparently Z_5 is due independently to Teichmüller (see Teichmüller, 1939) and Tukey (see Tukey, 1940, page 7).

Actually Z_1, Z_4, Z_5, Z_6, and Z_7 are not all the statements which bear the title of Zorn's lemma. Most of them have duals, which bear the same name (see Ex.XIV.1.1), and we list others in the exercises below. Others are still being proposed from time to time (see Wallace, 1944, for example).

Besides the three statements originally proposed by Zermelo, and the set of statements known as Zorn's lemmas, there are many other equivalent statements. Typical of such statements is

(A) $$(m,n):m,n \in \text{NC}. \supset .m < n . \mathbf{v} . m = n . \mathbf{v} . m > n$$

(see Ex.XII.4.9 and Ex.XII.4.11). A considerable number of statements of an analogous sort are given by Tarski (see Tajtelbaum-Tarski, 1924). The motive for proving that such statements as (A) are equivalent to the axiom of choice is not to increase the already extensive list of equivalent statements. Rather, it is somewhat as follows. The statement (A) is highly desirable in the arithmetic of transfinite cardinals. Thus mathematicians who are not sympathetic to the axiom of choice would like to derive (A) without the axiom of choice. By proving that (A) is equivalent to the axiom of choice, one shows that this is not possible, so that those mathematicians who wish to use (A) must endorse the axiom of choice, however reluctant they may be to do so. A recent addition to the list of statements of this sort, and in quite a different domain, is Tychonoff's theorem (see Lefschetz, 1942, page 19). A proof of its equivalence with the axiom of choice has been given in Kelley, 1950.

The statement Z_2, if assumed, apparently makes it possible to make choices in any conceivable fashion. For if we assume Z_2, then we can well order the universe V. Then given any nonempty set, we can always specify that the "least" element of it be taken. Thus there is a completely determinate member of each nonempty subset, and all aspects of arbitrariness or choosing are removed. Indeed, in terms of the relation P, which well orders V, one can write an actual formula specifying a unique member for each nonempty set. Then a definition involving any sort of choices can be expressed by an explicit term of the formal logic.

Thus it appears that, by assuming the axiom of choice, one has formal machinery to duplicate any known intuitive procedure involving choices.

Some attention has been given to versions of the axiom of choice for a set λ of nonempty disjoint sets in which the restriction is put not on the cardinality of λ but on the maximum cardinality of members of λ. In this connection, see Mostowski, 1945, and Szmielew, 1947. Also, van Vleck makes a note of the fact that his construction of a nonmeasurable set depends only on choices from a λ whose member sets all have two elements (see van Vleck, 1908).

We mentioned earlier that there are c analytic functions at each point z_0 and c points, so that there is a temptation to conclude that there are $c \times c$ analytic functions. However, in the proposed correspondence we are counting each function many times, because it gets counted at least once at each point where it is analytic, and if it is many-valued it gets counted more than once at each point where it is analytic. Indeed, our count of c analytic functions at a single point counted different branches of a given function as distinct functions. That is, each point and convergent power series defines a branch of an analytic function, and hence an analytic function, so that we can construct a function whose arguments are pairs $\langle z,S\rangle$, where z is a point and S is a series, and whose values are analytic functions. We then merely appeal to the principle that

$$(R){:}R \in \text{Funct.} \supset .\text{Nc}(\text{Val}(R)) \leq \text{Nc}(\text{Arg}(R)).$$

However, no proof of this is known that does not use the axiom of choice. (For a proof using the axiom of choice, use Ex.XIV.1.8, below.)

EXERCISES

XIV.1.1. We mean by an infimum of a set β with respect to R merely the supremum of β with respect to $\breve{R}$. We mean by the dual of $Z_1(n)$ the statement:

"If α is a partially ordered set, of cardinal number less than or equal to n, such that every simply ordered subset has an infimum in α, then there is a minimal element of α."

Indicate why the dual of $Z_1(n)$ is obviously equivalent to $Z_1(n)$. List those of $Z_1(n)$, $Z_4(n)$, $Z_5(n)$, $Z_6(n)$, and $Z_7(n)$ which have duals, state the duals, and indicate why each statement is obviously equivalent to its dual.

XIV.1.2. Take $Z_8(n)$ to be:

"Let λ, of cardinality less than or equal to n, be a set of sets which is partially ordered by inclusion. If the sum of each simply ordered subset of λ is included in some member of λ, then there is a maximal element of λ."

State $Z_8(n)$ symbolically, and prove:

(a) $\vdash (n){:}Z_7(n). \supset .Z_8(n).$
(b) $\vdash (n){:}Z_8(n). \supset .Z_4(n).$
(c) $\vdash Z_8(\text{Nc}(V)) \equiv \text{AxC}.$

XIV.1.3. Take $Z_9(n)$ to be:

"Given a set α, of cardinality less than or equal to n, a property λ of finite character, and a subset β of α with the property λ, then there is a maximal subset of α containing β and having the property λ."

Prove $\vdash (n){:}Z_5(n). \equiv .Z_9(n).$

(*Hint.* To go from left to right, take

$$A = \hat{x}(\text{E}\gamma).\gamma \subseteq \alpha.\gamma \cup \beta \in \lambda.x \in \gamma.$$

If $\beta \subseteq \alpha.\beta \in \lambda$, then clearly $\beta \subseteq A$, so that $(\gamma){:}\gamma \subseteq A. \supset .\gamma \cup \beta \subseteq A.$ Now take α to be A in Z_5. If $\gamma \in \text{Max}(\lambda \cap \text{SC}(A), \subseteq)$, then $\gamma \cup \beta \subseteq A$, so that $\beta \subseteq \gamma$, since γ is maximal in A. Now γ is maximal in α, for if $\gamma \subseteq \delta$ and $\delta \in (\lambda \cap \text{SC}(\alpha))$, then $\delta \subseteq A$ because $\beta \subseteq \delta$. To go from right to left, take β to be Λ.)

XIV.1.4. Define a $Z_{10}(n)$ which generalizes $Z_6(n)$ in the same way that $Z_9(n)$ generalizes $Z_5(n)$ and prove $\vdash (n){:}Z_{10}(n). \equiv .Z_6(n).$ (*Hint.* Take $Z_{10}(n)$ to be (AC1) as stated on page 42 of Birkhoff, 1948.)

XIV.1.5. Define $Z_{11}(n)$ and $Z_{12}(n)$ to be variants of $Z_6(n)$ and $Z_7(n)$ such as given on page 7 of Tukey, 1940. Find the numerical relations between pairs of m, n, and p that are needed as hypotheses for implications between corresponding pairs of $Z_5(m)$, $Z_{11}(n)$, and $Z_{12}(p)$. (*Hint.* Use the proofs indicated on page 8 of Tukey, 1940.)

XIV.1.6. Prove that AxC(n) and $Z_i(n)$ all hold for finite n, indicating in which cases the additional hypothesis $n \neq 0$ is required. (*Hint.* Prove $\vdash (n){:}n \in \text{Nn}. \supset .Z_3(n)$ by weak induction, and derive the other cases from this.)

XIV.1.7. Prove $\vdash \text{AxC}{:} \equiv {:}(R)(\text{E}S).S \in \text{Funct}.\text{Arg}(R) = \text{Arg}(S).S \subseteq R$.

XIV.1.8. Prove $\vdash \text{AxC}{:} \equiv {:}(R){:}R \in \text{Funct}. \supset .(\text{E}S).S \in 1\text{–}1.\text{Val}(R) = \text{Val}(S).S \subseteq R$.

XIV.1.9. Prove $\vdash (\delta){:}\text{AxC}(\text{Nc}(\text{USC}(\delta))). \supset .Z_3(\text{Nc}(\delta))$. (*Hint.* Given λ, define $\mu = \hat{R}(\text{E}\alpha).\alpha \in \lambda.R = \{\alpha\} \times \text{USC}(\alpha)$, and apply AxC(Nc(USC($\delta$))) to μ.)

XIV.1.10. Prove $\vdash (\delta){:}Z_3(\text{Nc}(\text{SC}(\delta))). \supset .Z_2(\text{Nc}(\delta))$. (*Hint.* If $\text{Nc}(\alpha) \leq \text{Nc}(\delta)$, use Z_3 to give an R with $R \in \text{Funct}.\text{Arg}(R) = \text{SC}(\alpha) - 0.\text{Val}(R) \subseteq 1{:}(\beta){:}\beta \subseteq \alpha.\beta \neq \Lambda. \supset .R(\beta) \subseteq \beta$. By Ex.XII.3.6, there is an $A(\phi)$ such that

$$\vdash (\phi){:}\phi \in \text{NO}. \supset .A(\phi) = \iota y\,(\{y\} = R(\alpha - \{A(\theta) \mid \theta < \phi\})).$$

By Ex.XII.3.7, we see that there must be a ϕ such that $\alpha = \{A(\theta) \mid \theta < \phi\}$. Then for θ's less than the least such ϕ, $A(\theta)$ induces a well ordering of α.)

XIV.1.11. Derive Thm.XIV.1.1 by utilizing "definition by transfinite induction." (*Hint.* By Ex.XII.3.8, there is an $A(\phi)$ such that

$$\vdash (\phi){:}.\phi \in \text{NO}.\sim(\text{E}\theta).\theta \in \text{NO}.\phi = \theta +_0 1_0{:} \supset {:}A(\phi) = \iota y\,(y \in \text{Sup}(\{A(\theta) \mid \theta < \phi\},P))$$

$$\vdash (\theta){:}\theta \in \text{NO}. \supset .A(\theta +_0 1_0) = R(A(\theta)).$$

Now use Ex.XII.3.9.)

XIV.1.12. Show how Thm.XII.2.11 can be derived from Thm.XIV.1.1.

2. How Indispensable Is the Axiom of Choice? In topology, the axiom of choice is assumed from the very start, and uses of it or of equivalent statements are frequent, and often tacit. There is little evidence at the present time that any significant portion of topology can be derived without the use of the axiom of choice, or at least of some form of it of restricted cardinality. Moreover, the question of how much topology could be done without the axiom of choice is apparently receiving no attention at all.

In algebra, quite the reverse is true. Some operations in algebra, such as making an infinite number of extensions of a field, are very awkward to perform without the axiom of choice. Certainly, one sacrifices much generality in algebra by not using the axiom of choice. Nevertheless, much can be done without it, and algebraists are inclined to proceed as far as possible without it. For a discussion of this point, see Teichmüller, 1939.

In analysis, one can proceed quite a way without the axiom of choice. If one starts with the theory of nonnegative integers given in Chapter XI, one can proceed as in Landau, 1930, to develop a theory of real and complex numbers without the axiom of choice. One can then proceed through Hardy, 1947, to develop calculus in a rigorous fashion. Hardy does use the axiom of choice at a very few places, in each of which it could be avoided by some device such as making the required choices from among the rational real numbers, which are denumerable, and hence well ordered. Likely Hardy was aware of this, but he does not give any indication. One can then start into Titchmarsh, 1939, which is based on an earlier edition of Hardy, 1947. There are occasional uses of the axiom of choice. Thus on page 13, for each n one takes an x_n at which $s(x) - s_n(x)$ attains its maximum. However, since $s(x) - s_n(x)$ is continuous for each n, one can perfectly well specify x_n uniquely as the leftmost point at which $s(x) - s_n(x)$ attains its maximum, and then x_n is defined as a function value of n, and the axiom of choice is avoided.

One can thus proceed without the axiom of choice through quite considerable portions of the theory of complex variables and other important and useful theories. Indeed, the first apparently unavoidable use in Titchmarsh, 1939, of the axiom of choice occurs in Sec. 10.25 on page 326, in the proof of the first fundamental theorem of Lebesgue measure. Here one picks an open set 0_n for each set E_n of a sequence of measurable sets. There seems no way to specify 0_n uniquely, so that the proof fails unless one is permitted to use the denumerable axiom of choice. We know of no other proof of the theorem which will proceed without the denumerable axiom of choice. That is, to the best of our knowledge, one cannot prove the first fundamental theorem of Lebesgue measure without an appeal to the denumerable axiom of choice.

Two more explicit uses of the denumerable axiom of choice occur in Titchmarsh's development of the theory of Lebesgue measure, namely on page 329 and page 369 of Titchmarsh, 1939. It is thus open to grave doubt that one can develop the theory of Lebesgue measure without use of the denumerable axiom of choice.

Clearly, if one progresses into modern analysis, with its study of Banach and other spaces and its extensive use of topological ideas, it is no longer possible to escape the axiom of choice, because it is so basic in all the topological developments. Even so, in the special spaces of analysis one can sometimes devise special proofs without the axiom of choice for results which require its use in general spaces, and there is a definite amount of interest in this sort of thing (see Barsotti, 1947, for example).

For an illustration near at hand, consider the theorem that, if a Hausdorff space satisfies the second countability axiom, then every countably compact subset is compact. In general, the proof seems to require the denumerable axiom of choice (see the next section). If, however, one takes the real line as the space in question, the theorem specializes to the Heine-Borel theorem, which can be proved without the axiom of choice (see Sec. 6 of Chapter XI).

In subjects, such as the analytic theory of numbers, which use a lot of analysis of the classical sort which is independent of measure theory, it is likely that one can prove all the basic results (including most of the deep results) without the axiom of choice. However, until a very careful scrutiny has been made of all the proofs, this is merely a plausible conjecture.

3. The Denumerable Axiom of Choice. Many mathematicians do not object particularly to the axiom of choice itself but do object to some of its consequences. Thus one can find mathematicians who find arbitrary well ordering repugnant but feel quite sympathetic toward AxC. In view of the fact that $\vdash \text{AxC} \equiv Z_2$, this attitude seems quite silly at first glance. However, if we look at results such as Thm.XIV.1.4 or Ex.XIV.1.10, it begins to appear that the attitude is defensible. Apparently, to prove $Z_2(n)$, one requires $\text{AxC}(m)$ for a much larger m, say m of the order of magnitude of 2^n. For instance, one could apparently assume $\text{AxC}(c)$ without the consequence that the continuum can be well ordered. Actually, one can apparently assume $\text{AxC}(n)$ for quite a large n without entailing well ordering. For instance, one might assume

$$(\alpha,P){:}\alpha = \text{AV}(P).P \in \text{Word}. \supset .\text{AxC}(\text{Nc}(\alpha)).$$

That is, speaking loosely, we would only permit choices to be made in a well-ordered fashion. This assumption would permit making a very large number of choices (at least Nc(NO), for example), but would apparently not enable us to well order any class which we could not well order without the assumption.

A particularly appealing case of this sort is the denumerable axiom of choice, namely, AxC(Den). Many mathematicians find this far less objectionable than any axiom of choice of greater cardinality. Also one can derive a considerable amount of very useful mathematics from the denumerable axiom of choice (notably the theory of Lebesgue measure), whereas a great increase in cardinality seems to be required to get a further considerable increase in the number of provable theorems. Consequently, we shall assume the denumerable axiom of choice as one of our axioms.

Axiom scheme 15. The following statement, and each statement got from it by prefixing some set of universal quantifiers, is an axiom:

$$\text{AxC(Den)}.$$

A more useful form is given in the following theorem, which is just the Principle C enunciated by Teichmüller.

****Theorem XIV.3.1.** $\vdash (\lambda):.\lambda \in \text{Den}:(\alpha):\alpha \in \lambda. \supset .\alpha \neq \Lambda: \supset :(\text{E}R):$ $R \in \text{Funct}.\text{Arg}(R) = \text{Nn}:\text{Val}(R) \subseteq \bigcup\lambda:(\alpha):\alpha \in \lambda. \supset .(\text{E}m).m \in \text{Nn}.R(m) \in \alpha.$

Proof. Assume

(1) $$\text{Nn sm}_S\ \lambda,$$

(2) $$(\alpha):\alpha \in \lambda. \supset .\alpha \neq \Lambda.$$

By Thm.XI.4.12, there is a T such that

(3) $$\text{USC(Nn) sm}_T\ \text{Nn}.$$

Define

(4) $$\mu = \{\{m\} \times S(T(\{m\})) \mid m \in \text{Nn}\}.$$

Clearly

(5) $$(\beta):\beta \in \mu. \supset .\beta \neq \Lambda,$$

(6) $$(\beta,\gamma):\beta,\gamma \in \mu.\beta \neq \gamma. \supset .\beta \cap \gamma = \Lambda.$$

Also clearly USC(Nn) sm μ, so that $\mu \in \text{Den}$. Then by Axiom scheme 15, there is a P such that

(7) $$(\beta):\beta \in \mu. \supset .(\text{E}_1x).x \in \beta \cap P.$$

Taking R to be $P \cap (\bigcup\mu)$, we easily prove that

$$R \in \text{Funct},$$

$$\text{Arg}(R) = \text{Nn},$$

$$\text{Val}(R) \subseteq \bigcup\lambda,$$

$$(\alpha):\alpha \in \lambda. \supset .(\text{E}m).m \in \text{Nn}.R(m) \in \alpha.$$

This theorem is similar to Z_3(Den), but more convenient.

We now prove the well-known result that, if one has a denumerable class of denumerable classes, then the totality of all their elements is likewise denumerable. Let us have a class λ with members $\alpha_0, \alpha_1, \alpha_2, \ldots$, such that each α is denumerable. In general, there is not a unique method of enumerating each α, but there are many enumerations. So for each α_n we must "choose" an ordering, $x_{0,n}, x_{1,n}, x_{2,n}, \ldots$. This is where we require the denumerable axiom of choice unless we can devise some means of specifying a unique ordering for each α. In the proof of Thm.XI.4.18 we specified a unique ordering for each α; indeed $W(n)$ was a function which enumerated α_n. However, in cases where no one knows how to specify a unique ordering for each α, we must appeal to the denumerable axiom of choice.

Theorem XIV.3.2.

**I. $\vdash (\lambda):\lambda \in \text{Den}.\lambda \subseteq \text{Den}. \supset .\bigcup\lambda \in \text{Den}.$

II. $\vdash (\lambda):\lambda \in \text{Den}.\lambda \subseteq \text{Count}. \supset .\bigcup\lambda \in \text{Count}.$

Proof of Part I. Let

(1) $$\lambda \in \text{Den},$$

(2) $$\lambda \subseteq \text{Den}.$$

Put

$$\mu = \{\hat{R}(\text{Nn sm}_R\ \alpha) \mid \alpha \in \lambda\}.$$

By (2),

$$(P).P \in \mu. \supset .P \neq \Lambda.$$

Then by Thm.XIV.3.1, there is an S with

$$S \in \text{Funct},$$

$$\text{Arg}(S) = \text{Nn},$$

$$(m):m \in \text{Nn}. \supset .S(m) \in 1\text{–}1.\text{Arg}(S(m)) = \text{Nn}.\text{Val}(S(m)) \in \lambda,$$

$$(\alpha):\alpha \in \lambda. \supset .(\text{E}m).m \in \text{Nn}.S(m) \in 1\text{–}1.\text{Arg}(S(m)) = \text{Nn}.\text{Val}(S(m)) = \alpha.$$

Then clearly

$$\lambda = \{\text{Val}(S(m)) \mid m \in \text{Nn}\}.$$

Also $\text{Val}(S(0)) \in \text{Den}$. Then by Thm.XI.4.17, Part II, $\bigcup\lambda \in \text{Den}$.

Proof of Part II. Similar, except that we take

$$\mu = \{\hat{R}(\text{E}\beta).\beta \subseteq \text{Nn}.\beta\ \text{sm}_R\ \alpha \mid \alpha \in \lambda\}.$$

Theorem XIV.3.3. $\vdash (\alpha):\alpha \in \text{Infin}. \equiv .\text{Den} \leq \text{Nc}(\alpha)$.

Proof. By Thm.XI.4.6, Cor. 1, we easily go from right to left. Now assume $\alpha \in \text{Infin}$. Put

$$\lambda = \{\text{SC}(\alpha) \cap n \mid n \in \text{Nn}\}.$$

By Ex.XI.3.16, (b), $(\beta):\beta \in \lambda. \supset .\beta \neq \Lambda$. Also, clearly $\lambda \in \text{Den}$. So by Thm.XIV.3.1, there is an R such that

$$R \in \text{Funct},$$

$$\text{Arg}(R) = \text{Nn},$$

(1) $$(m):m \in \text{Nn}. \supset .R(m) \subseteq \alpha.(\text{E}n).R(m) \in n.n \in \text{Nn}.$$

(2) $$(n):n \in \text{Nn}. \supset .(\text{E}m).m \in \text{Nn}.R(m) \in n.$$

Then $\text{Val}(R) \in \text{Den}.\text{Val}(R) \subseteq \text{Count}$. Then $\bigcup\text{Val}(R) \in \text{Count}$ by Thm. XIV.3.2, Part II. Also $\bigcup\text{Val}(R) \in \text{Infin}$ by (2) and Ex.XI.3.16(b). Thus $\bigcup\text{Val}(R) \in \text{Den}$. As $\bigcup\text{Val}(R) \subseteq \alpha$ by (1), we get $\text{Den} \leq \text{Nc}(\alpha)$.

Corollary. $\vdash (\alpha):.\alpha \in \text{Infin}: \equiv :(\text{E}\beta).\beta \subset \alpha.\beta\ \text{sm}\ \alpha$.

Proof. Use Exs.XI.4.14 and XI.4.15.

Thus a class is infinite if and only if it is similar to a proper subset of itself. This is often taken as the definition of an infinite class.

We now prove that any denumerable set of ordinals less than Ω has an upper bound less than Ω.

Theorem XIV.3.4. $\vdash (\alpha)::\alpha \in \text{Den}:(\theta):\theta \in \alpha. \supset .\theta < \Omega.: \supset :.(\text{E}\phi):\phi < \Omega: (\theta):\theta \in \alpha. \supset .\theta < \phi.$

Proof. Assume $\alpha \in$ Den and $(\theta):\theta \in \alpha. \supset .\theta < \Omega.$ Then

$$(1) \qquad \alpha \subseteq \hat{\theta}(\theta < \Omega).$$

By Thm.X.6.14, Part II, there is a least ϕ such that $\alpha \subseteq \hat{\theta}(\theta < \phi)$. Since ϕ is the least such, we certainly get

$$(2) \qquad \bigcup\{\hat{\theta}(\theta \leq \psi) \mid \psi \in \alpha\} = \hat{\theta}(\theta < \phi).$$

Since $\alpha \in$ Den, we get $\{\hat{\theta}(\theta \leq \psi) \mid \psi \in \alpha\} \in$ Den, and by Thm.XII.4.5, Part III, and (1), $\{\hat{\theta}(\theta \leq \psi) \mid \psi \in \alpha\} \subseteq$ Count. So by Thm.XIV.3.2, Part II, $\bigcup\{\hat{\theta}(\theta \leq \psi) \mid \psi \in \alpha\} \in$ Count. Then by (2), $\hat{\theta}(\theta < \phi) \in$ Count. So by Thm.XII.4.5, Part IV, $\phi < \Omega$.

The denumerable axiom of choice suffices for the proof of the well-known properties of Lebesgue measure (see Titchmarsh, 1939, Chapters X, XI, and XII). However, all known proofs of the existence of nonmeasurable sets require the use of an axiom of choice of higher cardinality. Thus one can make an assumption which is strong enough to give the usual properties of measure without entailing the existence of nonmeasurable sets as far as is known. This may be of some comfort to those mathematicians who find nonmeasurable sets distasteful. However, they should not rely too strongly on this, because recently the existence of a nonmeasurable set has been proved from an assumption which could possibly turn out to be weaker than the axiom of choice (see Sierpinski, 1947).

If a Hausdorff space satisfies the second countability axiom, then it is separable. For it has a countable set of neighborhoods, and upon picking a point from each neighborhood (which Thm.XIV.3.1 entitles us to do) we have a denumerable, everywhere dense subset.

We likewise get the theorem that, if a space satisfies the second countability axiom and is countably compact, then it is compact. Let N_0, N_1, N_2, . . . be the countable set of neighborhoods and suppose that every infinite set has a limit point. Then every closed set is compact. For let α be a closed set. Choose N_{α_1} the first N having a point in common with α. Choose $N_{\alpha_{n+1}}$ the first N which has a point in common with $\alpha - (N_{\alpha_1} \cup N_{\alpha_2} \cup \cdots \cup N_{\alpha_n})$. This is merely a definition by strong induction. Then there must be an n such that $\{N_{\alpha_1}, \ldots, N_{\alpha_n}\}$ covers α. For if not, then pick a point x from each of α, $\alpha - N_{\alpha_1}$, $\alpha - (N_{\alpha_1} \cup N_{\alpha_2})$, ... The limit of this set of x's cannot be in any N_{α_i}, and we have a contradiction.

Many times, the axiom of choice is used in a proof when it can be avoided. An example is a proof commonly given of Thm.IX.8.11, that every open set is a sum of neighborhoods, which runs as follows.

"Let α be an open set. Then for each x in α, there is a neighborhood N_x containing x and contained in α. Choose such an N_x for each x in α. Then α is clearly the sum of all such N_x."

Here one must use an axiom of choice of the cardinality of USC(α). However, the axiom of choice is not needed because there is no reason to have a unique N_x for each x. One can just as well take for each x the set of all N_x included in α. As this set is uniquely defined by x, we do not need to appeal to the axiom of choice. In our proof of Thm.IX.8.11, we proceeded in this manner.

As another illustration of a proof with and without the axiom of choice, consider the theorem:

If α is a nonempty closed set in the plane and x is a point, then there is a point of α which is nearest x; that is, a point y in α such that the distance from x to y is less than or equal to the distance from x to any point of α.

Proof with the Axiom of Choice. Take d to be the greatest lower bound of distances from x to points of α, so that for each positive ε there is a point z in α with $|x - z| < d + \varepsilon$. Now choose $z_1, z_2, \ldots$ with

$$| x - z_n | < d + \frac{1}{n} \cdot$$

Then the set $\{z_1, z_2, \ldots\}$ has a limit point, which is the desired y.

Proof without the Axiom of Choice. Take d as above. Define

$$S_n = \hat{z}\left(z \in \alpha . | x - z | \leq d + \frac{1}{n}\right).$$

Then each S_n is closed, and the product of any finite number of S's is nonempty. Then the product of all the S's is nonempty by Ex.XI.3.21, since S_1 is a compact Hausdorff space by the Heine-Borel theorem. Then take y to be any member of the product of all the S's.

In the proof using the axiom of choice, we picked a unique z_n from each S_n. As this was not really necessary in the present case, the proof could just as well be carried out without the axiom of choice.

Clearly it is immaterial in each proof whether x is in α or not. If x is in α, then y turns out to be x itself, of course.

EXERCISES

XIV.3.1. Prove $\vdash (n) : n \in \mathrm{NC}. \supset .n < \mathrm{Den}.\mathbf{v}.n = \mathrm{Den}.\mathbf{v}.n > \mathrm{Den}.$

XIV.3.2. Prove with and without the axiom of choice that, if α and β are two closed nonempty sets in the plane, then there is a point x in α and a point y in β such that the distance between x and y is less than or equal to the distance between any other two points of which one is in α and one is in β.

CHAPTER XV

WE REST OUR CASE

We stated at the beginning that it was our aim to provide a formal symbolic logic which would be adequate for the types of intuitive reasoning used by mathematicians in their mathematical thinking. We disclaim any adequacy for reasoning in nonmathematical fields, but we do claim that we have accomplished our aim as far as mathematical reasoning is concerned. Although divergence of opinion among mathematicians themselves makes it impossible for us to adopt a procedure with respect to the axiom of choice which will satisfy all, we have so arranged matters that different opinions in this respect are readily accommodated within the framework which we have set up. The crucial question is: "Aside from the clearly indicated indeterminancy with regard to the axiom of choice, is our framework sufficient?"

We believe it is, and that a careful and attentive reader will have been convinced by now that it is. We recognize that there cannot be complete assurance that we have indeed listed all essential principles unless we should continue from the foundations we have laid and develop all mathematics. The reasons against our undertaking such a course are too obvious to mention, and we propose instead that we now refer the reader to a succession of carefully written texts which are already in existence and which will carry the reader well into the main stream of mathematics.

Although these texts are carefully written, one will seldom find explicit references in them to logical points. This is right and proper. In the main body of mathematics, a writer should proceed in a logically sound manner, but he should not be preoccupied with logical points. Such a writer should be fully competent in logic and should so phrase his proofs that it is clear that the logical niceties could be supplied if they were called for. However, he should assume similar competence on the part of his readers and should focus attention on the mathematical difficulties and developments. Logical points should be mentioned only in case there is a genuine logical difficulty, and routine logical points should be entirely taken for granted.

In the main, mathematics is written in this fashion. There are to be found cases in which, through ignorance or carelessness, proofs are presented in which it would be difficult to supply the logical details. There are also to be found cases in which an author intrudes quite commonplace logical points into completely mathematical contexts as though he expected them to cause difficulty for his readers. Both extremes should be avoided, and usually are.

We have developed the beginnings of a theory of nonnegative integers. Omitting zero gives the positive integers, from which one can construct in succession the positive rationals, the positive reals, the reals, and finally the complex numbers. Quite adequate details are given in Landau, 1930. Fuller details are given in Kershner and Wilcox, who introduce sets of axioms for each new kind of number and use the Landau constructions only to prove the consistency[1] of their successive sets of axioms. The relative advantages of the alternative modes of development are discussed in Chapter 21 of Kershner and Wilcox.

Landau concerns himself exclusively with mathematical matters. The logic needed for his proofs is assumed and used without comment. Nonetheless, his proofs are set forth with great care (except for one or two inexplicable slips) and it would be merely a routine exercise in logic to justify all his proofs on the basis of our axioms and theorems. Kershner and Wilcox are much more preoccupied with logical matters (in spite of their statement on page 17 that they accept the whole of logic as a fundamental undefined notion) so that their proofs come closer to putting the logical principles in evidence than do Landau's proofs. Doubtless this is helpful to any who try to read their text without having first acquired an adequate logical background, but we do not believe that it makes their proofs any more precise or easy to render into symbolic logic than those of Landau.

The reader may be disturbed to find Kershner and Wilcox using the axiom of choice in the proofs of several of their theorems (including some which do not require its use). However, the theorems for which they have made use of the axiom of choice are not needed for their main developments, and they have apparently been careful always to designate such theorems as depending on the axiom of choice.

If the reader is planning to read either Landau, 1930, or Kershner and Wilcox, we venture to suggest one minor improvement. It is taken for

[1] We have said repeatedly that no proof is known that our symbolic logic is consistent. How then can we prove the consistency of a set of axioms for some branch of mathematics? In an absolute sense, we cannot. Nevertheless, we can prove consistency in a significant fashion. For instance, by taking the I, 1, and σ of Kershner and Wilcox, p. 104, to be $\text{Nn} - \{0\}$, 1, and $\lambda x(x + 1)$, respectively, we can prove *within the symbolic logic* that the Peano axioms (page 104 of Kershner and Wilcox) are consistent. This gives us no positive assurance that these axioms are indeed consistent, since we do not know that the symbolic logic is consistent. However, we have gained significant information, to the effect that the Peano axioms are at least as consistent as our symbolic logic. That is, if our symbolic logic does not contain a contradiction before we add the Peano axioms, then no contradiction will be introduced if we decide to assume the Peano axioms.

granted in both texts that one cannot justify definition by induction until one has some of the properties of $\leq$. This is not so. Given merely Peano's axioms (see Landau, 1930, page 2, or Kershner and Wilcox, page 104), one can prove the special cases of our Thm.XI.3.23 and Thm.XI.3.24 with $m = 1$ by almost precisely the proofs we have given for general m. If this were done, it would simplify the definitions of $+$, $\times$, and $\lessdot$ for Landau (see Landau, 1930, pages 4, 14, and 115) and of $+$ and $\times$ for Kershner and Wilcox (see Kershner and Wilcox, pages 109, 116).

There seems to be a belief that, once one has the real number system, one can proceed into calculus and analysis with no further ado. This is perhaps true of the theory of functions of a single real variable, but for functions of a complex variable some geometric ideas seem indispensable for such results as Cauchy's integral theorem. So perhaps one should proceed next to a careful treatment of geometry. One can "construct" geometry by the Cartesian method, by defining points as ordered triples $\langle x,y,z\rangle$ of real numbers, then lines as sets of points defined by appropriately chosen parametric equations with a single parameter, betweenness on a line by means of the parameter on the line, planes by parametric equations with two parameters, distance and metric properties in the obvious fashion, etc. Then the familiar geometric theorems are forthcoming. Alternatively, one can use the construction indicated above to prove the consistency of some set of axioms for geometry, such as those given in Veblen, 1904, and then base geometry on these axioms. What is most needed perhaps in calculus, complex variable theory, and other branches of analysis is the result that the Cartesian construction indicated above does satisfy the axioms, and hence the theorems, of Euclidean geometry. It also seems necessary to have the Jordan curve theorem, at least for polygons. The proof of the Jordan curve theorem for polygons as sketched on pages 267 to 269 of Courant and Robbins can be carried out rigorously (though much less briefly) in the symbolic logic on the basis either of the Cartesian construction or of some such set of geometric axioms as that given in Veblen, 1904.

Once the real number system and a modicum of geometry are available, one can start on analysis. As a foundation, including a rigorous treatment of calculus, Hardy, 1947, is excellent and fits rather well onto the end of Landau or Kershner and Wilcox. There is not much overlap, and most of the gaps come from Hardy's assumption of simple geometric properties. If one takes pains to supply the necessary geometry, then there are almost no gaps. Typical of the few remaining gaps is the assumption of the binomial theorem on page 142 of Hardy, 1947. This gap is easily filled, for instance by our Ex.XI.3.11(d). For purposes of exposition, Hardy treats some topics out of their logical order, but the logical order is easily restored. A painstaking reader can find (and correct) a few minor slips, but on the whole the book is very carefully written, and the proofs are readily translatable into symbolic logic.

Hardy consistently uses the word "function" in our sense of "function value" and has no word for "function" in our sense. As he deals mainly with particular functions or very special classes of functions, this does not cause him noticeable inconvenience. In many cases in which a careful verbal description would almost certainly require a name for our concept of "function," Hardy instead resorts to the use of formulas involving the familiar notation, $f(x)$. We would not say that Hardy's treatment of functions and function values is inadequate except as far as it succeeds in diverting attention from the important concept of a function (in our sense of the word).

After completing Hardy, 1947, one can turn to Titchmarsh, 1939. This fits perfectly onto the end of Hardy, 1947, because it was deliberately written to fit onto the end of an earlier edition of Hardy, 1947.

In the main, Titchmarsh, 1939, is very carefully written, and the proofs translate readily into symbolic logic. A hiatus comes in the theory of curvilinear integrals of a complex variable. On pages 74 to 79, Titchmarsh gives a proof of the Cauchy integral theorem for a specially limited class of contours for which the Jordan curve theorem is easily proved. His proof does not have an adequate treatment of the question of orientation, in that he does not prove for the irregular regions (see Titchmarsh, 1939, page 76) that traversing them in counterclockwise fashion carries one in the proper direction along the portion of the curve involved in the irregular region. However, the proof is readily supplied, and the real hiatus comes on page 79 where he applies the Cauchy integral theorem to contours more general than those for which he has proved it. To fill this gap it does not suffice merely to prove the Jordan curve theorem in full generality, since two different contours from z_0 to z may cross each other an infinite number of times and in a most unpleasantly complicated manner.

Naturally, the gap can be filled by first going into a full treatment of analysis situs (see Moore, 1932, for instance). However, one would like to avoid this if possible, and we propose the following alternative.

Let us first prove the Jordan curve theorem for polygons (see above). Now, since the polygon is a closed set in the plane, we can use the Heine-Borel theorem to infer that it can be covered by a finite number of interiors of circles with the following properties. Each circle together with its interior touches at most two sides of the polygon and touches two sides only in case the sides have a common vertex which is in the interior of the circle. Using this covering of circles to derive the necessary orientability conditions, one can now prove the Cauchy integral theorem for polygons by the procedure given in Secs. 2.33 and 2.34 of Titchmarsh, 1939. Then by induction on the number of times C intersects itself, one can prove that, if C is a closed curve consisting of a finite number of straight-line segments joined end to end and lies inside a simply connected region in which $f(z)$ is analytic, then

$$\int_C f(z)\, dz = 0.$$

If now, in Sec. 2.36 of Titchmarsh, 1939, we restrict the contours to be curves consisting of a finite number of straight-line segments joined end to end, we nonetheless infer that, if $f(z)$ is analytic in a simply connected region, then there is a single-valued function F defined in the region such that $F'(z) = f(z)$. Next one proves the lemma that, if an arbitrary $g(z)$ is analytic and has a continuous derivative in the region, then for that $g(z)$

$$\int_{z_0}^{z} g'(z)\, dz = g(z) - g(z_0)$$

for any rectifiable path lying in the region and connecting z_0 and z. Letting $g(z)$ be $F(z)$, we infer

$$\int_{z_0}^{z} f(z)\, dz = F(z) - F(z_0)$$

along arbitrary rectifiable paths. This in turn immediately gives the general result that, if C is a closed rectifiable curve lying in the region, then

$$\int_C f(z)\, dz = 0.$$

This amount of generality easily covers most uses which Titchmarsh makes of the Cauchy integral theorem. On pages 100, 120–123, 145, 201–202, and 284*a*, Titchmarsh makes use of much deeper properties of curves, for which one would need an extensive geometrical development. Fortunately, in all these cases, Titchmarsh is deriving isolated results that are not used elsewhere in his text. Thus, for most of Titchmarsh, 1939, one can manage with the very meager geometrical background that we have indicated.

Following Hardy, Titchmarsh undertakes to use "function" in our sense of "function value" and to dispense with any designation for what we call a "function." Throughout most of the text, he succeeds fairly well, but he is exceedingly hampered at a few points, notably in his treatment of analytic continuation. We cannot help but believe that the student would find analytic continuation less incomprehensible if it were explained in terms of f rather than $f(z)$.

We have already commented on the apparently unavoidable use of the denumerable axiom of choice in the theory of Lebesgue measure.

When one has finished Titchmarsh, 1939, one is prepared to read from a wide range of texts. In general, they are written with less painstaking attention to details than is to be found in the texts which we have cited. This is not to be taken as an indication that such texts are not carefully written. Rather, it is that we are getting into a domain where one not only takes logic for granted, but also much of the mathematical theory so meticulously explained by Landau, Kershner and Wilcox, Hardy, and Titchmarsh.

In the usual research papers, even more is taken for granted, so that such papers are commonly unintelligible except to experts in the field. Again, no lack of rigor is necessarily involved. It is merely that in any text it is not worth while supplying details which the readers can readily supply. So, when writing for experts, most details can be suppressed.

How can we be sure that, among all the logical principles implicitly used in such writings, there do not appear some which cannot be derived from our axioms? Naturally, we cannot. To some extent, the lack of any mention of logical principles by the authors is some reassurance, since if they were aware of using some esoteric logical principle, they would doubtless record that fact.

Actually, the question of the adequacy of foundations arises as much for the mathematical foundations as for the logical foundations. With many properties of real numbers being used implicitly, how can we be reassured that they do indeed all follow from some such basis as the axioms given by Kershner and Wilcox? Naturally, we cannot. We have to trust that the care of the author and the scrutiny of his readers suffice to detect any results which do not follow from commonly accepted foundations.

In conclusion, we should like to say that we do not wish to suggest that it is desirable that all mathematical proofs can or should be carried out solely on the logical basis which we have set up. Our symbolic logic is not intended as a model for how mathematicians should think but only as a model of how at the present time they do indeed think. Indeed it is desirable that new and more potent and flexible principles of reasoning be devised and generally accepted, so that distant portions of the mathematical edifice will become more readily accessible. One advantage of a symbolic logic is that it can be made very precise, but an even greater advantage is that it can be changed to fit the circumstances.

BIBLIOGRAPHY

AGNEW, R. P.: "Differential Equations," McGraw-Hill Book Company, Inc., New York, 1942.

ALTSHILLER-COURT, N.: "College Geometry," Johnson Publishing Co., Richmond, 1925. Now published by Barnes & Noble, Inc., New York.

BARSOTTI, I.: A Proof of Two Fundamental Theorems on Linear Transformations in Hilbert Space, without Use of the Axiom of Choice, *Bulletin of the American Mathematical Society,* vol. 53 (1947), pp. 943–949.

BIRKHOFF, G.: "Lattice Theory," American Mathematical Society Colloquium Publications, vol. XXV, rev. ed., New York, 1948.

BIRKHOFF, G., and S. MACLANE: "A Survey of Modern Algebra," The Macmillan Company, New York, 1941.

BOAS, R. P., and H. POLLARD: Properties Equivalent to the Completeness of $\{e^{-t}t^{\lambda_n}\}$, *Bulletin of the American Mathematical Society,* vol. 52 (1946), pp. 348–351.

BÔCHER, M.: "Introduction to Higher Algebra," The Macmillan Company, New York, 1907.

BOČVAR, D. A.: On a Three-valued Calculus and Its Application to the Analysis of Contradictions, *Matématičéskij Sbornik,* New Series, vol. 4 (1939), pp. 287–308. This paper is in Russian, but a review in English, and a correction to this review, appears in the *Journal of Symbolic Logic,* vol. 4 (1939), pp. 98–99, and vol. 5 (1940), p. 119.

BOHNENBLUST, H. F.: "Theory of Functions of Real Variables," Princeton University Lecture Notes, Princeton, 1937.

BOHR, H.: "Almost Periodic Functions," Chelsea Publishing Company, New York, 1947.

BOURBAKI, N.: "Théorie des ensembles," Actualités Scientifiques et Industrielles 846, Hermann & Cie, Paris, 1939.

CHURCH, A.: A Note on the Entscheidungsproblem and Correction to a Note on the Entscheidungsproblem, *Journal of Symbolic Logic,* vol. 1 (1936), pp. 40–41, 101–102.

CHURCH, A.: "The Calculi of Lambda-conversion," Annals of Mathematics Studies, No. 6, Princeton University Press, Princeton, N. J., 1941.

CHURCH, A.: "Introduction to Mathematical Logic, Part I," Annals of Mathematics Studies, No. 13, Princeton University Press, Princeton, N. J., 1944.

Coolidge, J. L.: "A Treatise on Algebraic Plane Curves," Oxford University Press, New York, 1931.

Courant, R., and H. Robbins: "What Is Mathematics?" Oxford University Press, New York, 1941.

Curry, H. B.: The Combinatory Foundations of Mathematical Logic, *Journal of Symbolic Logic*, vol. 7 (1942), pp. 49–64.

Fort, T.: "Infinite Series," Oxford University Press, New York, 1930.

Frege, G.: "Begriffsschrift, eine der arithmetischen nachgebildete Formelsprache des reinen Denkens," Halle, 1879.

Glasgow, R. S.: "Principles of Radio Engineering," 1st ed., McGraw-Hill Book Company, Inc., New York, 1936.

Gödel, K.: Über formal unentscheidbare Sätze der Principia Mathematica und verwandter Systeme I, *Monatshefte für Mathematik und Physik*, vol. 38 (1931), pp. 173–198.

Gödel, K.: "The Consistency of the Continuum Hypothesis," Annals of Mathematics Studies, No. 3, Princeton University Press, Princeton, N. J., 1940.

Halmos, P. R.: "Finite Dimensional Vector Spaces," Annals of Mathematics Studies, No. 7, Princeton University Press, Princeton, N. J., 1942.

Hardy, G. H.: "A Course of Pure Mathematics," 9th ed., The Macmillan Company, New York, 1947.

Hardy, G. H., and E. M. Wright: "An Introduction to the Theory of Numbers," Oxford University Press, New York, 1938.

Hausdorff, F.: "Grundzüge der Mengenlehre," 1st ed., Leipzig, 1914; reprinted by Chelsea Publishing Company, New York, 1949.

Hausdorff, F.: "Mengenlehre," 2d ed., Göschens Lehrbücherei, Gruppe 1, Band 1, Walter De Gruyter & Company, Berlin, 1927; reprinted by Dover Publications, New York, 1944.

Helmer, Olaf: Languages with Expressions of Infinite Length, *Erkenntnis*, vol. 7 (1938), pp. 138–141.

Heyting, A.: "Mathematische Grundlagenforschung, Intuitionismus-Beweistheorie," Ergebnisse der Mathematik und ihrer Grenzgebiete, Springer-Verlag, Berlin, 1934.

Hilbert, D., and W. Ackermann: "Principles of Mathematical Logic," Chelsea Publishing Company, New York, 1950. This is a translation of "Grundzüge der theoretischen Logic," 2d ed.

Hilbert, D., and P. Bernays: "Grundlagen der Mathematik I," 1934; Grundlehren der mathematischen Wissenschaften, vol. XL, "Grundlagen der Mathematik II," 1939; Grundlehren der mathematischen Wissenschaften, vol. L, Springer-Verlag, Berlin.

Kelley, J. L.: "The Tychonoff Product Theorem Implies the Axiom of Choice," *Fundamenta Mathematica*, vol. 37 (1950), pp. 75–76.

KERSHNER, R. B., and L. R. WILCOX: "The Anatomy of Mathematics," The Ronald Press Company, New York, 1950.

KLEENE, S. C., and J. B. ROSSER: The Inconsistency of Certain Formal Logics, *Annals of Mathematics*, Second Series, vol. 36 (1935), pp. 630–636.

LANDAU, E.: "Vorlesungen über Zahlentheorie," vol. 2, S. Hirzel, Leipzig, 1927; reprinted by Chelsea Publishing Company, New York, 1947.

LANDAU, E.: "Grundlagen der Analysis," Akademische Verlagsgesellschaft m. b. H., Leipzig, 1930; reprinted by Chelsea Publishing Company, New York, 1946.

LEFSCHETZ, S.: "Algebraic Topology," American Mathematical Society Colloquium Publications, vol. XXVII, New York, 1942.

MOORE, R. L.: "Foundations of Point Set Theory," American Mathematical Society Colloquium Publications, vol. XIII, New York, 1932.

MOSTOWSKI, A.: "Axiom of Choice for Finite Sets," *Fundamenta Mathematica*, vol. 33 (1945), pp. 137–168.

PEANO, G.: Sul concetto di numero, *Rivista di matematica*, vol. 1 (1891), pp. 87–102, 256–267.

QUINE, W. V.: New Foundations for Mathematical Logic, *American Mathematical Monthly*, vol. 44 (1937), pp. 70–80.

QUINE, W. V.: "Mathematical Logic," First Printing, W. W. Norton & Company, New York, 1940.

QUINE, W. V.: On Ordered Pairs, *The Journal of Symbolic Logic,* vol. 10 (1945), pp. 95–96.

QUINE, W. V.: "Mathematical Logic," rev. ed., Harvard University Press, Cambridge, 1951.

RAMSEY, F. P.: The Foundations of Mathematics, *Proceedings of the London Mathematical Society,* Second Series, vol. 25 (1926), pp. 338–384.

RAMSEY, F. P.: On a Problem of Formal Logic, *Proceedings of the London Mathematical Society,* Second Series, vol. 30 (1930), pp. 264–286.

RANDOLPH, J. F., and M. KAC: "Analytic Geometry and Calculus," The Macmillan Company, New York, 1946.

ROSSER, J. B.: On the Consistency of Quine's "New Foundations for Mathematical Logic," *Journal of Symbolic Logic,* vol. 4 (1939), pp. 15–24.

ROSSER, J. B.: The Burali-Forti Paradox, *Journal of Symbolic Logic,* vol. 7 (1942), pp. 1–17.

SIERPINSKI, W.: "Leçons sur les nombres transfinis," Gauthier-Villars & Cie, Paris, 1928.

SIERPINSKI, W.: Sur une proposition qui entraine l'existence des ensembles non mesurables, *Fundamenta Mathematica,* vol. 34 (1947), pp. 157–162.

SKOLEM, T.: Über einige Grundlagenfragen der Mathematik, *Skrifter utgitt av Det Norske Videnskaps-Akademi i Oslo*, 1929, No. 4.

STONE, J. C., and V. S. MALLORY: "Modern Geometry, Plane and Solid," Benj. H. Sanborn & Co., Chicago, 1930.

STONE, M. H.: "Linear Transformations in Hilbert Space and Their Applications to Analysis," American Mathematical Society Colloquium Publications, vol. XV, New York, 1932.

SZMIELEW, W.: On Choices from Finite Sets, *Fundamenta Mathematica*, vol. 34 (1947), pp. 75–80.

TAJTELBAUM-TARSKI, A.: Sur quelques théorèmes qui équivalent à l'axiome du choix, *Fundamenta Mathematica*, vol. 5 (1924), pp. 147–154.

TEICHMÜLLER, O.: Braucht der Algebraiker das Answahlaxiom? *Deutsche Mathematik*, vol. 4 (1939), pp. 567–577.

TITCHMARSH, E. C.: "The Theory of Functions" 2d ed., Oxford University Press, New York, 1939.

TOWNSEND, E. J.: "Functions of Real Variables," Henry Holt and Company, Inc., New York, 1928.

TUKEY, J. W.: "Convergence and Uniformity in Topology," Annals of Mathematics Studies, No. 2, Princeton University Press, Princeton, N. J., 1940.

VAN VLECK, E. B.: On Non-measurable Sets of Points, with an Example, *Transactions of the American Mathematical Society*, vol. 9 (1908), pp. 237–244.

VEBLEN, O.: A System of Axioms for Geometry, *Transactions of the American Mathematical Society*, vol. 5 (1904), pp. 343–384.

VISSER, C.: On Certain Infinite Sequences, *Proceedings Koninklijke Nederlandsche Akademie van Wetenschappen*, vol. 40 (1937), pp. 358–367.

WALLACE, A. D.: A Substitute for the Axiom of Choice, *Bulletin of the American Mathematical Society*, vol. 50 (1944), p. 278.

WENTWORTH, G., and D. E. SMITH: "Plane and Solid Geometry," Ginn & Company, Boston, 1913.

WHITEHEAD, A. N., and B. RUSSELL: "Principia Mathematica," 2d ed., Cambridge University Press, London, vol. 1, 1925; vol. 2, 1927; vol. 3, 1927.

ZERMELO, E.: Beweis, dass jede Menge wohlgeordnet werden kann, *Mathematische Annalen*, vol. 59 (1904), pp. 514–516.

ZERMELO, E.: Neuer Beweis für die Möglichkeit der Wohlordnung, *Mathematische Annalen*, vol. 65 (1908), pp. 107–128.

ZERMELO, E.: Untersuchungen über die Grundlagen der Mengenlehre I, *Mathematische Annalen*, vol. 65 (1908), pp. 261–281.

ZORN, M.: A Remark on Method in Transfinite Algebra, *Bulletin of the American Mathematical Society*, vol. 41 (1935), pp. 667–670.

INDEX